Merrill
Pre-Calculus
Mathematics

Crosswhite • Hawkinson • Sachs

Charles E. Merrill Publishing Co.
A Bell & Howell Company
Columbus, Ohio

Toronto • London • Sydney

ISBN 0-675-07931-4
Published by
CHARLES E. MERRILL PUBLISHING CO.
A Bell & Howell Company
Columbus, Ohio 43216

Authors

F. Joe Crosswhite is Professor of Mathematics Education at the Ohio State University. He has taught mathematics at every level of high school, at the two-year college level, and at the university level. Dr. Crosswhite obtained his B.S. in Education and M.Ed. from Missouri University and his Ph.D. in mathematics education from the Ohio State University. He took additional graduate work in mathematics at Purdue University and post-doctoral work in educational research at Stanford University. Dr. Crosswhite is active in professional associations and has served on the Board of Directors of the National Council of Teachers of Mathematics. Dr. Crosswhite has published widely in professional journals and has contributed to a number of professional books.

Lawrence D. Hawkinson is Instructional Supervisor of Mathematics at Henry M. Gunn High School in Palo Alto, California. He has taught mathematics at the high school level as well as conducted workshops for teachers. Dr. Hawkinson received his B.A. in mathematics and physics from the University of Texas and his M.A. and Ed.D. in mathematics education from Stanford University. He is a member of several state and national organizations and past president of the California Mathematics Council. He has served on many committees for NCTM and CEEB as a consultant. He has also spoken at NCTM and CMC conferences. He has published several articles for the California Mathematics Council Publications.

Leroy Sachs is a mathematics teacher at Clayton High School and a lecturer in mathematics at Washington University in St. Louis. He has taught mathematics at the junior and senior high school levels and was head of the mathematics department for nine years. Mr. Sachs received his B.A. and M.S. from Washington University with additional graduate work at Cornell University, Southern Illinois University, and St. Louis University. He is past president of the Illinois Council of Teachers of Mathematics and the Missouri Council of Teachers of Mathematics. He has published articles for NEA and NCTM publications. Mr. Sachs has served as a member of the board of directors and the executive committee of the National Council of Teachers of Mathematics.

Reviewers

James W. Deegan
Mathematics Teacher
Nottingham High School
Syracuse, New York

Valarie A. Elswick
Mathematics Teacher
Roy C. Ketcham High School
Wappingers Falls, New York

Virginia T. Gilbert, Ph.D.
Secondary Mathematics Consultant
Clark County School District
Las Vegas, Nevada

Emmett D. Kinkade
Mathematics Department Head
Cleveland High School
Seattle, Washington

Hector Manuel Rios
Chairman of Mathematics Department
Theodore Roosevelt High School
San Antonio, Texas

Dolly Gordon Sturman
Senior Mathematics Teacher
J. M. Atherton High School
Louisville, Kentucky

Staff

Editorial
Project Editor: Cynthia Zengler
Managing Editor: Donald W. Collins
Assistant Editor: Marjorie Seachrist
Associate Production Editor: Susan Opt
Photo Editor: Russ Lappa

Art
Project Artist: Lewis H. Bolen
Art Director: Lester Shumaker
Assistant Artist: Larry Collins
Book Designer: Larry P. Koons

Photo Credits

Preface

Pre-Calculus Mathematics is written to prepare college-bound students for a first course in calculus. The topics presented are prerequisite for calculus. The presentation of these topics develops an intuitive base and some of the working tools for the study of more advanced mathematics.

Many features in Pre-Calculus Mathematics facilitate the teaching and study of mathematics. Students are introduced to the standard concepts and language needed for beginning college mathematics courses. New ideas and techniques are treated in familiar contexts. Reinforcement of important concepts occurs later in using a variety of approaches.

The format and development provide a transition between high school and college texts. Intermediate algebra, analytic geometry, and trigonometry are integrated with other important topics in mathematics by an approach that stresses functions. Separate chapters place special emphases on circular and trigonometric functions, polynomial functions, and transcendental functions. A discussion of rational and irrational numbers provides an early introduction to limits. This concept reappears in sections on graphing functions, upper and lower bounds, and sequences. In the latter part of the book the now familiar concept of limit is treated again using a more formal, precise definition.

Vectors and polar coordinates are treated in separate chapters. A chapter on sequences and series introduces the final three chapters on limits of functions, rates of change, and integrals in which the basic concepts of calculus are considered from an elementary viewpoint.

Pre-Calculus Mathematics employs a reasonable balance of instruction and examples. Completely worked examples serve as models for exercises that follow. Numerous illustrations and diagrams enhance the presentation. The exercise sets provide students with reinforcement of skills and prepare them for topics that will be encountered later.

Chapter end material that includes a summary, review, and test provides an overview of the chapter and a self-check for the student. Student annotations throughout the text supply additional help in understanding the topics presented.

"Excursions in Mathematics" provide supplemental material on history or extend topics presented. "Computers" discuss the history and uses of computers and provide chapter exercises that can be programmed.

An appendix on standardized testing provides information and sample test items. An appendix on matrices includes work on solving systems of equations.

At this level of mathematics many students have access to calculators, therefore, some exercises refer to their use. However, the exercises can be completed with or without their use.

Students will find the style and intuitive approach of Pre-Calculus Mathematics make the text easy to read and understand. Teachers will find that the text develops the basic understandings and manipulative skills that are essential for the study of calculus.

Contents

Chapter 1

Blueprints for a building can be studied as a representation of the structure of the building. The geometry of a line can be studied as a representation of the real number system. To do this, the geometric properties of order and distance must correspond to the related algebraic properties of real numbers.

The Real Number Line

1–1 Points on a Number Line

A ruler, a thermometer, and a coordinate axis are scales based on the principle that *equal distances correspond to equal differences.* Suppose an attempt was made to construct a scale that preserves this principle. The primary goal is to bring the mathematical systems of geometry and algebra together. Therefore, restrict the constructions to those that are valid in geometry. These make use only of a straightedge and compass.

To initiate a scale on a given line, select a point to correspond to the number *zero*. Label it 0. This point is called the **origin.** Then select a second point to correspond to the number *one*. Label it 1. The location of these points is arbitrary.

Two important characteristics of the scale thus are established. The distance between the points labeled 0 and 1 defines a unit of length for the scale. The direction *from 0 to 1* assigns a direction to the line, the **positive direction.** The point labeled 1 is the point one unit distant from the origin in the positive direction.

Using the principle that *equal distances* should *correspond to equal differences,* additional points can be located and labeled on the line. Starting at the origin, construct *unit distances* in both the positive and negative directions. Label the successive points in the positive direction 1, 2, 3, 4, . . . Label those in the negative direction -1, -2, -3, -4, . . . A one-to-one correspondence now is established between the integers and a *subset* of the points on the line.

In this text, when discussing distance or length, the units are implied if not given.

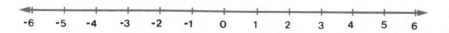

How can this correspondence be extended to include other rational numbers? For example, which point should be labeled $\frac{1}{2}$?

Use the principle that equal distances correspond to equal differences. The point labeled $\frac{1}{2}$ should be equidistant from the points labeled 0 and 1 since $\frac{1}{2} - 0 = 1 - \frac{1}{2}$.

Rational Points on a Number Line

The construction for bisecting a line segment may be used to *↯ review bisecting technique* locate the point for $\frac{1}{2}$.

1. **Locate the point which should be labeled $\frac{3}{5}$.**

   The basic principle requires that the distance between points labeled $\frac{1}{5}, \frac{2}{5}, \frac{3}{5}$, . . . satisfy the following conditions.

   $$\frac{1}{5} - 0 = \frac{2}{5} - \frac{1}{5} = \frac{3}{5} - \frac{2}{5} = \frac{4}{5} - \frac{3}{5} = 1 - \frac{4}{5}$$

   To locate $\frac{3}{5}$, divide the segment from 0 to 1 into five parts of equal length. Use only a straightedge and compass.

   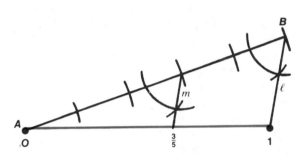

   ↯ It is common to say the point $\frac{3}{5}$ rather than the point labeled $\frac{3}{5}$. The context should enable you to determine whether $\frac{3}{5}$ refers to the point itself or to the number.

   ↯ ? what geometric reasons justify this technique

   Notice that the line m has been constructed parallel to line ℓ and containing the point three-fifths the distance from A to B.

Theoretically, the construction method above locates all points on a given scale which correspond to rational numbers. Practically, of course, it would be almost impossible to actually locate a point such as $\frac{373}{1642}$ by construction. Nevertheless, mathematically a correspondence can be established between the rational numbers and a subset of the points on a line. This procedure generates a scale called the **rational number line**.

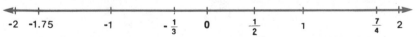

Rational scales are useful in measurement. In fact, only rational scales are required in the physical sciences. However, in the ideal world of mathematics, measures are not always rational.

Construct an isosceles right triangle such that the congruent sides have unit length and one of the congruent sides is the segment of a rational number line defined by the points 0 and 1.

Irrational Points on a Number Line

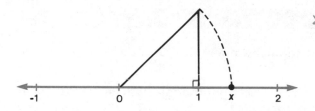

✶ ?..what geometric reasons justify this technique / relates to example 3

Now use a compass to draw an arc with center at 0 and with radius equal to the hypotenuse. This procedure locates the point x on the number line. Would the point x belong to the subset of points with labels which are rational numbers?

Consider a more general case. Suppose right triangle ABC as shown is given.

Solving for h in terms of m and n, it is found that $h = \sqrt{mn}$. In the following examples this relation is used to locate points with labels which are irrational numbers.

What number should be used to label point x?

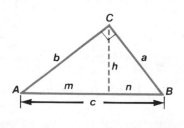

✶ $\dfrac{n}{h} = \dfrac{h}{m}$

$h^2 = mn$

$h = \sqrt{mn}$

? what geometric reasons justify this and the following technique

The measure of the altitude drawn from the right angle to the hypotenuse of a right triangle is the geometric mean between the measure of the two segments of the hypotenuse.

Example

2. **Given a unit length, construct a segment of length $\sqrt{6}$. Let ——— be the unit length.**

   Plan: Construct $h = \sqrt{6} = \sqrt{2 \cdot 3}$ where h is the altitude separating the hypotenuse into segments of length 2 and 3.

   If an angle is inscribed in a semicircle, then the angle is a right angle.

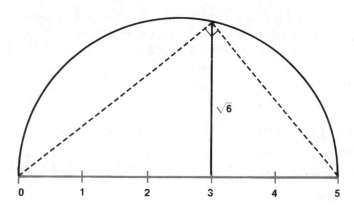

Example

3. **Given a unit length, construct a segment of length $\sqrt{5}$. Let ——— be the unit length.**

   Plan: Since $5 = 4 + 1 = (2)^2 + (1)^2$ construct right triangle with legs 2 and 1 and the hypotenuse will have length $\sqrt{5}$.

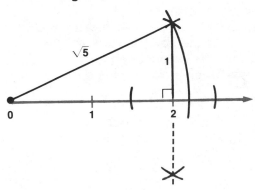

Exercises

Exploratory   Explain how construction can be used to locate the point for each of the following rational numbers.

1. $\frac{2}{5}$ 2. $-\frac{7}{4}$ 3. 1.3   4. -2.85

Explain how to construct segments to locate the points for each of the following.

5. $\sqrt{4}$ 6. $2\sqrt{2}$ 7. $\sqrt{21}$ 8. $\sqrt{35}$

9. Describe two methods for constructing a segment whose length is $\sqrt{12}$ units.

10. Describe all those points that can now be located on a number line using the construction methods in this section. Do you think these points fill the line? Do the numbers identified exhaust the set of real numbers?

Written   Draw a line ℓ and label points for 0 and 1. Draw a second line m through 0. Using 0 as the origin, define a unit of length and positive direction for m. Label the points 1, 2, and 3 on m. Draw a line from 3 on m to 1 on ℓ. Draw lines through 1 and 2 on m parallel to this line.

1. Complete this statement: If three or more parallel lines cut off congruent segments on one transversal, then they ___.

2. Use the theorem in Problem **1** to label the points where the parallel lines intersect line ℓ.

Use construction to locate the point which corresponds to each rational number.

3. $\frac{1}{4}$ 4. $-\frac{5}{2}$ 5. $\frac{3}{8}$ 6. -2

7. Generalize the procedures to locate any point $\frac{m}{n}$, where m and n are integers and $n > 0$.

8. Generalize the procedures to locate any point $\frac{m}{2^n}$, where m and n are integers and $n > 0$.

Given a unit length, construct segments of each given length.

9. $\sqrt{3}$ 10. $\sqrt{5}$ 11. $\sqrt{7}$ 12. $\sqrt{10}$

13. Justify the constructions in Examples **2** and **3**. Prove the constructed segments have the required length.

Challenge   **Suppose** *a* **and** *b* **are any two rational numbers.**

1. Does the midpoint of the segment joining points *a* and *b* always correspond to a rational number?

2. Prove the answer to Problem **1** by writing a formula for the number which corresponds to the midpoint.

3. The rational numbers are dense if and only if between any two different rational numbers there is another rational number. Does the answer to Problem 2 prove that the rational numbers are dense?

4. Prove $\sqrt{3}$ is not a rational number. (Hint: If $\sqrt{3}$ is rational, then it can be represented as the quotient of two relatively prime integers, $\dfrac{a}{b}$. This means that $a^2 = 3b^2$. Can this be true?)

Excursions in Mathematics

Historical Background

Three famous unsolved construction problems remain from ancient Greek geometry. These are (1) **trisecting an angle,** (2) **duplicating a cube,** and (3) **squaring a circle.** These problems were called unsolved because no one was able to do the constructions using only a straightedge and compass. However, mathematicians have used the techniques of modern algebra to prove that these constructions cannot be performed using only straightedge and compass.

A construction can be performed using only straightedge and compass if and only if, when stated algebraically, it gives a certain kind of equation. Trisecting an angle, duplicating a cube, and squaring a circle do not produce the required kind of equation.

Duplicating a cube requires the construction of the edge of a new cube with volume exactly twice that of a given cube. If the original cube has a volume of one cubic unit the equation related to the duplication problem is $x^3 = 2$. This equation does not meet the criteria for constructions. Thus, it is impossible to construct a segment whose length is $\sqrt[3]{2}$ units using only a compass and straightedge.

1–2   The Number Line Postulate

The constructions explored in the previous section can be used to locate all rational points on a number line. They also can be used to find many irrational points. However, there are irrational numbers for which no construction is possible.

We define irrational points to be the points labeled with irrational numbers.

Therefore, the following statement must be accepted as true without being proved. Because it is accepted without proof it is called a postulate and not a theorem.

See excursion.

> There is a one-to-one correspondence between the points on a line and the real numbers. This correspondence is such that, if points *A* and *B* correspond to the real numbers *a* and *b* respectively, then the distance from *A* to *B* is
> 1. *b* − *a* if the direction from *A* to *B* is positive,
> 2. *a* − *b* if the direction from *A* to *B* is negative,
> 3. 0 if *a* = *b*.

The Number Line Postulate (NLP)

✗ see underlined sentence on p.9 to relate this to absolute value

The **NLP** asserts the *existence* of a one-to-one correspondence. Under a one-to-one correspondence, for each real number there is exactly one corresponding point and for each point there is exactly one corresponding real number.

The **NLP** does not specify the correspondence, the origin, the unit of length, or the direction on the line. Once a scale is established on a line as provided in the **NLP**, the number corresponding to a point P is called the **coordinate** of P. The entire scale is called a **coordinate system** on the line. Since the origin, unit of length, and direction are not specified, many coordinate systems can be defined on a line. Keep this in mind as there are times when it is convenient to change the coordinate system on a line. The principle that *equal differences correspond to equal distances* is not guaranteed by the **NLP**. For now, the principle is assumed directly.

Determining distances as specified in the **NLP** introduces unnecessary confusion. Direction must be considered before distance is determined. This happens because distance is usually defined as a nonnegative number. (There are times, such as in working with vectors, when directed distance is important.) The problem is minor when working with specified points and specified numbers. The distance from 5 to 1 or from 1 to 5 is easily seen to be 4. However, when working with variables representing a set of numbers, one cannot always determine direction. Fortunately, mathematicians have devised a convenient symbolism which permits the representation of distance independent of direction.

✳ discuss using a more complex example / $||x|-2|$
Absolute Value
also introduce: "the distance from 2 to x" as opposed to Exploratory statement

The absolute value of x (symbolized |x|) is defined as follows.
1. $|x| = x$ if $x \geq 0$.
2. $|x| = -x$ if $x < 0$.

Examples

1. Find $|-3|$.

   $|-3| = 3$ *Since $x < 0$, $|x| = -x$.*

2. Find $|3 - 7|$ and $|7 - 3|$.

   $|3 - 7| = |-4| = 4$ *Since $x < 0$, $|x| = -x$.*
   $|7 - 3| = |4| = 4$ *Since $x > 0$, $|x| = x$.*

An immediate consequence of the definition of absolute value is that $|a - b| = |b - a|$. Absolute value symbolism can be used to simplify the statement of **NLP**.

Exercises

Exploratory The geometric interpretation of the equation $|x - 3| = 4$ is "the distance from the point x to the point 3 is 4." Give a geometric interpretation for each of the following. *✳ see note above*

1. $|x| = 3$
2. $|x - \frac{3}{4}| = 1$
3. $|x + 3| = 2$
4. $|4 - 2x| = 3$

Use absolute value to explain each of the following.

5. The point x is less than 3 units from the point -2.
6. The point 2 is closer to the point x than it is to the point y.
7. The point x is less than or equal to 5 units from the origin.
8. The point x is greater than 10 units from the origin.

Written Give the geometric interpretation for each of the following.

1. $|x - y| = d$ $(d > 0)$
2. $|x - 2| < 3$
3. $|3 + x| < 1$
4. $|x - y| < d$ $(d \geq 0)$
5. $|x - 2| = |x + 4|$
6. $|2 - x| < |x - 4|$

Use the absolute value to represent each of the following.

7. The point x is at least 3 units from the point 5.
8. The point x is less than or equal to 1 unit from the origin.
9. The point 2d is greater than 4 units from the point -3.
10. The point x is twice as far from the point y as it is from the point z.

Find and graph the values of x that satisfy each open sentence.

11. $|x| = 9$

12. $|x - 2| = 3$

13. $|1 - x^2| = 3$

14. $|2 - x| \leq 4$

15. $|3 + x| > 2$

16. $|x^2 - 5x + 6| = 0$

17. $|x - 2| = |2 - x|$

18. $|x - 3| < |x + 1|$

19. $|2x - 3| < 5$

20. If A has coordinate 3 and B has coordinate 8, what is the directed distance AB? What is the directed distance $-AB$? What is BA?

Challenge Show that each sentence is a theorem, or exhibit values for the variables that make it a false sentence.

1. $|x| + |y| = |x + y|$

2. $|x| - |y| = |x - y|$

3. $|x| \cdot |y| = |xy|$

4. If $y \neq 0$, $\dfrac{|x|}{|y|} = \left|\dfrac{x}{y}\right|$

5. $|a - b| = |b - a|$

Excursions in mathematics

Measurement

The Number Line Postulate asserts the existence of a one-to-one correspondence between the real numbers and the points on a line. Actually many different correspondences may be defined on the same line using different measurement scales. Each scale maps each point on the line into exactly one real number, and conversely. The coordinate system imposed on the line by a given correspondence may be modified by relocating the origin, modifying the unit of length, or changing the direction on the line.

It is possible to transform a given coordinate system by changing the unit of length while keeping the origin and direction unchanged.

If x_E represents a general coordinate in the English system E and x_M represents the corresponding coordinate in the metric system M, how are x_E and x_M related? Express x_M as a function of x_E. $x_M = x_E(2.54)$

Example Find the ratio of the distance $A'B'$ in C' to the distance $A'B'$ in C.

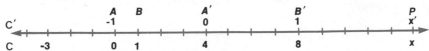

Consider the distance between two points as determined by their coordinates in C' and C.

In C', $A'B' = 1 - 0 = 1$.

$\dfrac{A'B' \text{ in } C'}{A'B' \text{ in } C} = \dfrac{1}{4}$

In C, $A'B' = 8 - 4 = 4$.

Algebraically, $x' \to \frac{1}{4}(x - 4)$.

In general, for any two points Q and R, the ratio of the distance QR in C' to the distance QR in C is $\frac{1}{4}$.

1–3 The Field Properties

The Number Line Postulate assumes a one-to-one correspondence between the points on a line and the real numbers. It can be assumed that equal differences correspond to equal distances. What else is implied by the **NLP?** What undefined terms does it use? Does the **NLP** depend upon even more assumptions?

The undefined terms *point* and *line* are from geometry. Although not stated directly, the usual properties of the relations which apply to points and lines are assumed in the **NLP.** For example, the definition of distance in the postulate is guided by an understanding of the *betweenness relation* and other properties of points on the line.

The **NLP** is introduced to generate a geometric model of the real numbers. In using this model, all the basic properties of real numbers will be used. When the term *real numbers* is used in the **NLP,** a complete mathematical system is imbedded in the postulate. To make full use of the **NLP** in analytic geometry and calculus, the real number system must be understood.

the reason for these introductory sections

A *field* is a mathematical system which consists of a *nonempty set* F with an *equivalence relation* (=) and two *binary operations*, addition (+) and multiplication (·). These operations are defined on F and satisfy the following properties.

Field Properties

A_1:   *Closure*   If a and b are elements of F, then $a + b$ is an element of F.

A_2:   *Associativity*   If a, b, and c are elements of F, then $a + (b + c) = (a + b) + c$.

A_3:   *Additive Identity*   There is an element 0 in F such that for every a in F, $a + 0 = 0 + a = a$.

A_4:   *Additive Inverse*   If a is an element of F, then there is an element $-a$ in F such that $a + (-a) = (-a) + a = 0$.

A_5:   *Commutativity*   If a and b are elements of F, then $a + b = b + a$.

Properties of Addition

M_1:   *Closure*   If a and b are elements of F, then $a \cdot b$ is an element of F.

M_2:   *Associativity*   If a, b, and c are elements of F, then $a \cdot (b \cdot c) = (a \cdot b) \cdot c$.

Properties of Multiplication

M_3: *Multiplicative Identity* There is a nonzero element 1 in F such that for every a in F, $a \cdot 1 = 1 \cdot a = a$.

M_4: *Multiplicative Inverse* If a is an element of F and $a \neq 0$, then there exists an element $\frac{1}{a}$ in F such that $a \cdot \frac{1}{a} = \frac{1}{a} \cdot a = 1$.

M_5: *Commutativity* If a and b are elements of F, then $a \cdot b = b \cdot a$.

D: *Distributive Property* If $a, b,$ and c are elements of F, then $a \cdot (b + c) = (a \cdot b) + (a \cdot c)$.

Property Connecting Addition and Multiplication

The definition of a field includes the existence of an equivalence relation. Therefore, the properties of an equivalence relation, in this case **equality**, are also included among the field properties.

E_1: *Reflexive Property* If a is an element of F, then $a = a$.

E_2: *Symmetric Property* If a and b are elements of F and $a = b$, then $b = a$.

E_3: *Transitive Property* If $a, b,$ and c are elements of F with $a = b$ and $b = c$, then $a = c$.

Properties of an Equivalence Relation

✶ *give examples using* $>, \leq, \neq$

Two binary operations are specified in the field definition. These operations are defined on F. This means that given any two members of F and one of the operations, the result of the operation on these numbers is **unique**. For example, consider the field of real numbers. Given 3 and 4 and the operation $+$, there is only one element of F defined by $3 + 4$. This number is the same regardless of its representation. It may be written as $3 + 4$, 7, or $1 + 6 + 0$, for example. However, only one number is named by $3 + 4$.

The preceding properties are characteristic of all fields. The set of real numbers ($\mathcal{R}$) with the operations of addition and multiplication and the equivalence relation equality is but one example.

Theorems can be proven by using these properties. In proving the theorems, a system of mathematics can be developed.

Uniqueness of an Operation This is an important property of an operation, especially in solving equations. For example, if $x + 4 = 2$, then $(x + 4) + (-4) = 2 + (-4)$ by uniqueness of addition.

Example

1. **Prove each element in F has a unique additive inverse.**

    Suppose $-a$ and A are additive inverses for a in F.
    1. $a + A = 0, a + (-a) = 0$ $\longrightarrow A_4$
    2. $-a + (a + A) = (-a + a) + A$ A_2
    3. $-a + 0 = 0 + A$ Uniqueness of $+$
    4. $-a + 0 = -a, 0 + A = A$ A_3
    5. $-a = A$ E_2, E_3

    Therefore, each element in F has an unique additive inverse.

It is also common to use substitution to justify the uniqueness property.

Exercises

Exploratory   Name the property that is illustrated by each of the following examples.

1. $7 + 4 = 4 + 7$
2. $8(1 + 9) = 8(1) + 8(9)$
3. $(x + 3) + (-3) = 8 + (-3)$
4. $1 \cdot y = y$
5. If $x = y$ then $y = x$.
6. $4(xy) = 4xy$

Give a numerical example illustrating each of the following properties.

7. associativity for addition
8. additive inverse
9. commutativity for multiplication
10. distributive property
11. transitive property of equality
12. symmetric property of equality

13. Explain why the operations of subtraction and division and the properties for these operations are not needed when given addition and multiplication and the properties stated in this section. (Think of how to define subtraction and division in terms of inverse elements.)

Written   Name the property that is illustrated by each of the following examples.

1. $(3 + 1) + [-(3 + 1)] = 0$
2. $(7 + 2) + 9 = 7 + (2 + 9)$
3. $4 \left(\frac{1}{4}\right) = 1$
4. $(7 + 2) + (-3) = 9 + (-3)$
5. $xy + xz = x(y + z)$
6. $4x + 7x = 11x$

Give a numerical example illustrating each of the following properties.

7. multiplicative inverse
8. additive identity
9. reflexive property of equality
10. commutativity for addition
11. multiplicative identity
12. associativity for multiplication

Complete each of the following proofs.

13. The additive identity, 0, is unique
    a. Suppose $0'$ is any additive identity in F.
    b. $0 + 0' = 0'$
    c. $0 + 0' = 0$
    d. $0 = 0 + 0'$
    e. $0 = 0'$

14. If $a, b, c \in F$ and $a + b = a + c$ then $b = c$. *(left cancellation for add. (LCA))*
    a. $a + b = a + c$
    b. $-a \in F$ such that $-a + a = 0$
    c. $-a + (a + b) = -a + (a + c)$
    d. $-a + (a + b) = (-a + a) + b$
       $-a + (a + c) = (-a + a) + c$
    e. $(-a + a) + b = (-a + a) + c$
    f. $0 + b = 0 + c$
    g. $0 + b = b, 0 + c = c$
    h. $b = c$

Prove each of the following.

15. The multiplicative identity, 1, is unique.

16. If $a, b, c \in F$ and $a \neq 0$ and $a \cdot b = a \cdot c$, then $b = c$. *(left cancellation for mult.)*

17. State and prove right cancellation laws for addition and multiplication.

18. The Distributive Property stated in the definition of a field is a *left distributive property*. Show that there is also a *right distributive property*. This is, prove that if a, b, c are in F, then $(a + b) \cdot c = a \cdot c + b \cdot c$.

1-4 Using Field Properties

✱ ? what is the author's objective in presenting the following approach for solving equations? Use "+" to justify uniqueness, addition fact, and substitution.

The field properties can be used to simplify expressions or to solve equations.

Example

1. **Write the solution to $3 + x = 7$.**

$3 + x = 7$	Given
$-3 + (3 + x) = -3 + (3 + 4)$	$+$
$(-3 + 3) + x = (-3 + 3) + 4$	A_2
$0 + x = 0 + 4$	A_4
$x = 4$	A_3

   A theorem such as the Left Cancellation Law for addition **(LCA)**, can also be used to solve $3 + x = 7$.

$3 + x = 7$	Given
$3 + x = 3 + 4$	$+$
$x = 4$	LCA

The following theorem generates a unique solution for every equation of the form $x + a = b$.

> If a and b are elements of F, then there is a unique element $x = b + (-a)$ in F such that $x + a = b$.

Solution Theorem

Proof:

Existence: Consider $x = b + (-a)$.

1. If $a \in F$ then $-a \in F$	A_4
2. $b + (-a) \in F$	A_1
3. $[b + (-a)] + a = b + (-a + a)$	A_2
4. $(-a + a) = 0$	A_4
5. $b + (-a + a) = b + 0$	$+$
6. $b + 0 = b$	A_3
7. $[b + (-a)] + a = b$	E_3
8. $x + a = b$	E_3 and $+$

Uniqueness: Suppose $y + a = b$.

1. $(y + a) + (-a) = b + (-a)$	$+$
2. $y + [a + (-a)] = (y + a) + (-a)$	A_2
3. $a + (-a) = 0$	A_4
4. $y + [a + (-a)] = y + 0 = y$	$+, A_3$
5. $y = b + (-a)$	E_2 and E_3

This theorem can be used to write the solution to equations such as $x + 5 = 7$. If Commutativity is used as well, the solution to equations such as $3 + x = 9$ can be found.

Examples

2.   Write the solution to $x + 5 = 7$.

$$x + 5 = 7$$
$$x = 7 + (-5) \qquad \text{Solution Theorem}$$
$$x = 2 \qquad\qquad +$$

3.   Write the solution to $3 + x = 9$.

$$3 + x = 9$$
$$x + 3 = 9 \qquad\qquad A_5$$
$$x = 9 + (-3) \qquad \text{Solution Theorem}$$
$$x = 6 \qquad\qquad +$$

To solve equations such as $y - 3 = 9$ and $4 - 7(1 - x) = 11$, it is necessary to recall how subtraction is defined in terms of addition.

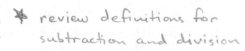 review definitions for subtraction and division

Example

4. **Write the solution for $y - 3 = 9$.**

$$y - 3 = 9$$
$$y - 3 = y + (-3)$$ *Definition of subtraction*
$$y + (-3) = 9$$ E_3
$$y = 9 + 3$$ *Solution Theorem*
$$y = 12$$ $+$

Exercises

Exploratory

1. State a theorem that ensures a unique solution to equations of the type $ax = b, a \neq 0$.

Justify each step by field properties or theorems.

2. $x + 3 = 7$
   $x = 7 + (-3)$

3. $3x = 9$
   $x \cdot 3 = 9$

4. $3(x - 3) = 2$
   $3(x + (-3)) = 2$

5. $5x + 2(x + 3) = 4(x + 7)$
   $5x + 2x + 6 = 4x + 28$

Name the field properties that assert the validity of each algorithm. Assume that denominators are not 0. (Note: Define division as $\dfrac{a}{b} = a \cdot \dfrac{1}{b}$.)

6. $\dfrac{a}{b} + \dfrac{c}{d} = \dfrac{ad + bc}{bd}$

7. $\dfrac{a}{b} \cdot \dfrac{c}{d} = \dfrac{ac}{bd}$

8. $\dfrac{a}{b} - \dfrac{c}{d} = \dfrac{ad - bc}{bd}$

9. $\dfrac{a}{b} \div \dfrac{c}{d} = \dfrac{ad}{bc}$ if $c \neq 0$

Written   Solve each equation. Justify each step by a field property or a theorem.

1. $2 - x = 5$

2. $3x + 14 = 2x - 5$

3. $\dfrac{x + 2}{35} = \dfrac{x - 1}{20}$

4. $12x - 13 = 3(x - 9) + 4$

5. $\dfrac{3}{x - 3} + 2 = \dfrac{6}{2x - 6}, x \neq 3$

6. $8 - \dfrac{7}{x + 5} = 14, x \neq -5$

Prove each of the following.

7. If $xa = b, a \neq 0$ then $x = \dfrac{b}{a}$.
   (This theorem parallels the Solution Theorem.)

8. $-(-a) = a$

9. $-(a + b) = (-a) + (-b)$

10. $a \cdot 0 = 0$ for every real number a

11. To solve the quadratic equation $x^2 - 3x - 4 = 0$, factor $x^2 - 3x - 4$ into $(x - 4)(x + 1)$. Then set each factor equal to zero. What can be used to justify that $a \cdot b = 0$ if and only if $a = 0$ or $b = 0$? Show this is a theorem for fields. (A mathematical system which has this property is said to have no divisors of zero.)

Challenge State and prove some theorems for multiplication of signed numbers, such as $a(-b) = -(ab)$ and $(-a)(-b) = ab$. (Hint: Notice that both $+$ and $-$ are used since the inverses are with respect to addition. When both operations are involved, expect to use the Distributive Property.)

1-5 The Order Properties

The field properties for $+$, $\cdot$, and $=$ are sufficient to solve equations and to work with functions defined on the real numbers. However, to find solution sets for *inequations*, the *order properties* of real numbers are also needed.

Some people use inequality for inequation.

An *order relation* ($<$) defined on a field has the following properties.

0_1: *Trichotomy Property*   If a and b are elements of F, then exactly one of the following is true.
$$a < b, a = b, b < a$$
0_2: *Transitive Property*   If a, b, and c are elements of F with $a < b$ and $b < c$, then $a < c$.
0_3: *Additive Property*   If a, b, and c are elements of F with $a < b$, then $(a + c) < (b + c)$.
0_4: *Multiplicative Property*   If a, b, and c are elements of F with $a < b$ and $0 < c$, then $a \cdot c < b \cdot c$. Also, if $a < b$ and $c < 0$, then $b \cdot c < a \cdot c$.

Properties of an Order Relation

For real numbers, the statement $x > y$ is defined to have the same meaning as $y < x$. The statement $x \leq y$ is defined to mean $x < y$ or $x = y$. Thus, order properties need only be given for the symbol $<$.

A real number a is defined to be positive if $0 < a$. It is defined to be negative if $a < 0$. The trichotomy property implies that 0 is neither positive nor negative, since $0 = 0$. On the other hand, if a real number $a \neq 0$, then a is positive or negative, but not both.

The following theorem is useful for working with real numbers when a number line representation is used.

For $a, b \in \mathcal{R}$, a is less than b (symbolized $a < b$) if and only if there is a positive real number p such that $a + p = b$.

Order Theorem

emphasize that this defines "less than" ($<$)

In general, real number a is less than real number b (symbolized $a < b$) if the direction from the point a to the point b is positive. The relation stated in the above theorem can be visualized on a number line.

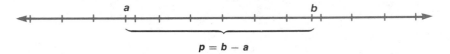

$$p = b - a$$

Proof:

I. Assume $a < b$. In that case $a + (-a) < b + (-a)$ by 0_3, which implies that $0 < b + (-a)$ by A_4. By definition, $b + (-a)$ is a positive number. Also, by the field properties, $a + [b + (-a)] = a + [(-a) + b] = [a + (-a)] + b = 0 + b = b$. The existence of the positive number p is now established, namely $p = b + (-a)$.

II. Assume there is a real number p such that $a + p = b$ and $0 < p$. Then, by 0_3, $a + 0 < a + p$. Since $a + 0 = a$ and $a + p = b$, it follows that $a < b$.

The number p that is associated with a and b when $a < b$ is precisely $|a - b|$ since $|a - b| = b - a$ in this case.

The order properties and the above theorem may be used to find solution sets for inequations. The solution sets of inequations frequently are graphed as **intervals** on a number line. To represent intervals algebraically, the following conventions are adopted.

Recall that $|x|$ is defined to be x if $x > 0$ and $-x$ if $x < 0$.

In graphing intervals, some people use $\bigcirc$ to represent an endpoint of an open interval and $\bullet$ for a closed interval.

$\{x \mid a < x < b\}$ is read the set of x such that a is less than x which is less than b.

✳ *emphasize that this symbolism will be used to write answers*

Definition for Intervals

$\{x \mid a \leq x \leq b\}$ is read the set of x such that a is less than or equal to x which is less than or equal to b.

An **open interval** $\{x \mid a < x < b\}$ is represented as $\langle a, b \rangle$.

A **closed interval** $\{x \mid a \leq x \leq b\}$ is represented as $[a, b]$.

Intervals of *finite length* which contain one but not the other endpoint are represented as $\langle a, b]$ or $[a, b \rangle$. They are interpreted accordingly, on the number line.

Intervals of *indefinite length* are represented as $\langle a, \rightarrow \rangle$, $[a, \rightarrow \rangle$, $\langle \leftarrow, b \rangle$, or $\langle \leftarrow, b]$.

Examples

1. **Solve $|x - 2| \leq 5$.**

   Algebraic Solution

   $x - 2 \leq 5$ when $x - 2 \geq 0$

   $\qquad x - 2 \leq 5, x - 2 \geq 0$

   $\qquad x \leq 7, x \geq 2$

   $\qquad 2 \leq x \leq 7$

   $\qquad x \in [2, 7]$

   $-(x - 2) \leq 5$ when $x - 2 < 0$

   $\qquad -(x - 2) \leq 5, x - 2 < 0$

   $\qquad -x + 2 \leq 5, x - 2 < 0$

   $\qquad -x \leq 3, x < 2$

   $\qquad x \geq -3, x < 2$

   $\qquad -3 \leq x < 2$

   $\qquad x \in [-3, 2\rangle$

   ⚹ other methods possible

   $-5 \leq x - 2 \leq 5$

   $-3 \leq \quad x \quad \leq 7$

   $x \in [-3, 7]$

   Since $|x - 2| \leq 5$ if either situation occurs, the solution set is the union of the two sets $[-3, 2\rangle$ and $[2, 7]$. Thus, $x \in [-3, 7]$ or $-3 \leq x \leq 7$.

   Geometric Interpretation

   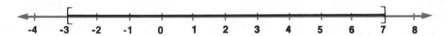

2. **Solve $2x + 3 < x + 5$.**

   Algebraic Solution

   $2x + 3 < x + 5$

   $\quad 2x < x + 2$

   $\quad x < 2$

   $\quad x \in \langle\leftarrow, 2\rangle$

   Geometric Interpretation

Example

3. **Solve $x^2 - 3x - 4 > 0$.** ✳ *use method at bottom of page*

The usual algebraic solution requires an argument by cases.

Algebraic Solution

$$x^2 - 3x - 4 > 0$$
$$(x - 4)(x + 1) > 0$$

$x - 4 > 0$	and	$x + 1 > 0$	(Case 1)	*(Both factors positive.)*
$x - 4 < 0$	and	$x + 1 < 0$	(Case 2)	*(Both factors negative.)*

Case 1 $x - 4 > 0$ and $x + 1 > 0$
$x > 4$ and $x > -1$
$x > 4$

Case 2 $x - 4 < 0$ and $x + 1 < 0$
$x < 4$ and $x < -1$
$x < -1$
$x^2 - 3x - 4 > 0$
$x < -1$ or $x > 4$
$x \in \langle \leftarrow, -1 \rangle$ or $x \in \langle 4, \rightarrow \rangle$

Geometric Interpretation

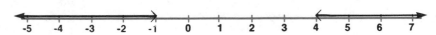

A number line helps to visualize the case argument in Example **3**. First indicate the **critical points** determined by the linear factors. In Example **3**, the critical points are 4 and -1. Then separate the line into all intervals determined by these points.   ✳ *method of critical points*

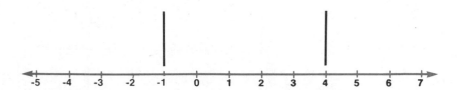

Indicate the sign of each linear *factor* on each interval. Then indicate the sign of the *product* on each interval. All that remains is to determine whether the critical points, or endpoints, do or do not belong to the solution set.

$x - 4$	$-$		$-$	$+$
$x + 1$	$-$		$+$	$+$
$(x - 4)(x + 1)$	$+$		$-$	$+$

-5 -4 -3 -2 -1 0 1 2 3 4 5 6 7

Example

4. **Solve $x^3 - 9x \leq 0$.**

$$x^3 - 9x \leq 0$$
$$x(x + 3)(x - 3) \leq 0$$

The critical points, that is the points at which the linear factors are equal to zero, are 0, -3, and 3.

$$x \leq -3 \text{ or } 0 \leq x \leq 3$$

Geometric Interpretation

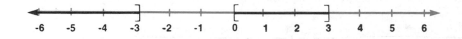

Exercises

Exploratory State each of the following using mathematical symbols. Write each in several different ways.

1. x is a real number greater than y.
2. x is a number less than y.
3. x is a number between 5 and 20, inclusive.
4. x is a number between 5 and 20, exclusive.

Describe each of the following as an interval.

5. $2x > 1$
6. $\frac{1}{2}x \leq 7$
7. $|x - 3| < 5$
8. $|x + 1| \geq 3$
9. $|x| = 4$
10. $|y^2 - 9| \leq 0$

<u>**Written**</u> **Write each sentence using mathematical symbols. Write each in several different ways.**

1. x is a number between -3 and 3, inclusive.

2. x is a number between -3 and 3, exclusive.

3. x is a number less than or equal to 6.

4. 7 is greater than the absolute value of x.

Solve each inequation. Express the solution set in interval notation. Graph each solution set on a number line.

5. $x + 2 \geq 0$

6. $-2x - 3 \geq 5$

7. $-5x - 2 < 4$

8. $3x + 1 \geq 0$

9. $|x + 3| \geq 2$

10. $x^2 - 4 \leq 0$

11. $x^2 > 0$

12. $x^2 - x - 6 < 0$

13. $x^3 - 5x^2 + 6 > 0$

14. $|x| < \dfrac{1}{x}$

15. $|5x - 3| > 1 + 3x$

16. $|x - 2| < \delta$ with $0 < \delta < 1$

17. Show that $|x - a| < b$ is equivalent to $a - b < x < a + b$

Challenge

1. Present a geometric argument to show that $|x - y| \leq |x - z| + |z - y|$.

2. Use the result in the previous problem to show that $|x + y| \leq |x| + |y|$. This is known as the triangle inequality.

3. Use the properties of real numbers to prove that $|x + y| \leq |x| + |y|$.

1–6 The Completeness Property

The *real numbers* and *rational numbers* satisfy the field and order properties and are called **Ordered Fields**. The property that distinguishes the real numbers from the rational numbers, and from all other ordered fields, may be less familiar. This is the property of **completeness**. It suggests that the real numbers fill the number line. The property of completeness provides an intuitive basis for a one-to-one correspondence between real numbers and the points of a line.

It can be shown that $\sqrt{3}$ is not a rational number. Recall the algorithm for finding a *decimal approximation* to $\sqrt{3}$. This can be done accurate to any desired number of decimal places.

Using such a process, it is found that 1.7 is the best lower approximation to one decimal place since $(1.7)^2 = 2.89$ while $(1.8)^2 = 3.24$.

Similarly $(1.73)^2 = 2.9929$ while $(1.74)^2 = 3.0276$. So 1.73 is the best two-place lower approximation. Continuing this process generates a sequence of lower approximations to $\sqrt{3}$.

A computer programmed to generate lower decimal approximation for square roots would supply many more entries for this sequence. Would the process ever terminate before reaching the capacity of the computer? Would a repeating pattern exist beyond some point?

$$S = \{1.7, 1.73, 1.732, 1.7320, \ldots\}$$

Only rational numbers can be represented by terminating or repeating decimals. Since $\sqrt{3}$ is irrational, no number in the sequence ever will be exactly equal to $\sqrt{3}$. Thus, S has infinitely many entries and each represents the *best* lower approximation to some number of decimal places. It should be apparent that S contains a rational number that differs from $\sqrt{3}$ by less than any number one might preassign, however small that number might be.

A comparable set of best *upper approximations* to $\sqrt{3}$ would include:

$$S' = \{1.8, 1.74, 1.733, 1.7321, \ldots\}$$

Notice that $\sqrt{3}$ is always between any two entries of S and S' with the same number of decimal places.

The statement of the completeness property can be expressed equally well in geometric or algebraic terms. <u>The notion of a **nest of closed intervals**</u> is pictured in this way.

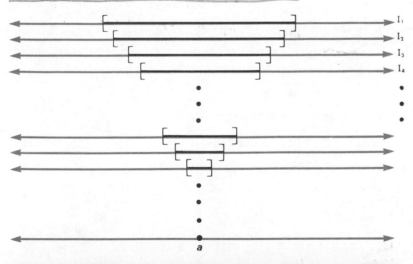

> There is exactly one real number (point) <u>common</u> to all the intervals in an infinite sequence of closed intervals $\{I_n\}$ such that each interval contains its successor and the length of the intervals approaches 0 as n increases without bound (written $\lim\limits_{n \to \infty} I_n = 0$, *where* I_n *is the length of the* nth *interval*).

Using S and S', a sequence of closed intervals can be generated

$$\{I_n\} = \{[1.7, 1.8], [1.73, 1.74], [1.732, 1.733], [1.7320, 1.7321] \ldots\}$$

A computer program using BASIC could be written to illustrate this process.

Completeness Property

✳ discuss limit and its symbolic representation see next page for summary of requirements

The sequence $\{I_n\}$ satisfies the requirements of a nest of closed intervals.

1. Each interval is closed.
2. The sequence is infinite.
3. Each interval contains its successor.
4. $\lim\limits_{n \to \infty} I_n = 0$

To prove the last statement would require some procedures for handling limits. However, these procedures will not be developed at this time. The intuitive notion is that one can find an interval in the sequence whose length, I_n, is less than any preassigned number, however small.

Technically, $\{I_n\}$ may be said to define the real number $\sqrt{3}$. Because of the way the sequences S and S' were found, $\sqrt{3}$ belongs to each of the intervals and is, therefore, the number, or point, guaranteed by the axiom.

Example

1. **Find an approximation for $\sqrt{2}$.**

   $(1.4)^2 = 1.96$ $(1.5)^2 = 2.25$

   $(1.41)^2 = 1.9881$ $(1.42)^2 = 2.0164$

   $(1.414)^2 = 1.999396$ $(1.415)^2 = 2.002225$

   $(1.4142)^2 = 1.9999616$ $(1.4143)^2 = 2.0002445$

   Let $S = \{1.4, 1.41, 1.414, 1.4142, \ldots\}$
   Let $S' = \{1.5, 1.42, 1.415, 1.4143, \ldots\}$

   Then, $\{I_n\} = \{[1.4, 1.5], [1.41, 1.42], [1.414, 1.415], [1.4142, 1.4143], \ldots\}$

Exercises

Written State five decimal upper and lower approximations for each of the following numbers. Represent the first five intervals in a nest of intervals.

1. $\sqrt{5}$ 2. $\sqrt{12}$ 3. $\sqrt{7}$
4. $\sqrt{10}$ 5. $\sqrt{26}$ 6. $\sqrt{18}$
7. Construct a decimal that neither terminates nor is a repeating decimal.

Consider the repeating decimal 3.1$\overline{27}$.

$$3.1\overline{27} = 3 + \frac{1}{10} + \frac{27}{10^3} + \frac{27}{10^5} + \cdots$$

$$= 3 + \frac{1}{10} + \left[\frac{27}{10^3} + \frac{27}{10^3} \cdot \left(\frac{1}{10^2} \right) + \frac{27}{10^3} \cdot \left(\frac{1}{10^2} \right)^2 \cdots \right]$$

The expression within braces is an infinite geometric series. Its sum is $\frac{3}{110}$.

$$\frac{a}{1-r} = \frac{\frac{27}{10^3}}{1 - \left(\frac{1}{10} \right)^2} = \frac{3}{110}$$

Problems 8–11 represent the distinguishing characteristics between rational and irrational numbers.

Therefore, $3.1\overline{27} = 3 + \frac{1}{10} + \frac{3}{110} = \frac{344}{110}$

Use this principle to write each repeating decimal as the quotient of two integers.

8. $0.\overline{6}$ **9.** $1.\overline{36}$ **10.** $-2.2\overline{45}$

11. Prove that every repeating decimal represents a rational number.

Challenge **Solve each of the following.**

1. Is it necessary that the Property of Completeness specify the number it guarantees is unique? Develop an argument that the number is unique, whether the property so specifies or not.

2. Generate successive approximations for π by examining perimeters of inscribed and circumscribed polygons about a circle. Use squares, hexagons, octagons.

Excursions in Mathematics

Alternative Properties of Completeness

Here are two other ways of stating the Completeness Property.

Every bounded nondecreasing sequence of real numbers $\{x_n\}$ such that $x_1 \leq x_2 \leq x_3 \leq \ldots \leq x_{n-1} \leq x_n \leq \ldots$ converges, and its limit is a real number.

Alternative 1: Sequences

Consider the points of a line that correspond to the numbers in the sequence S of

Section 1–6. This sequence has a limit, namely the point corresponding to $\sqrt{3}$. By the **NLP,** which associates differences with distances, this is exactly what would be expected.

Example Determine if $S = \{1.4, 1.41, 1.414, 1.4142, \ldots\}$ has a limit.

$$\{x_n\} = \{1.4, 1.41, 1.414, 1.4142, \ldots\}$$

So, $x_1 = 1.4, x_2 = 1.41, x_3 = 1.414, x_4 = 1.4142, \ldots$ Thus, x_n is nondecreasing and $1.4 \leq x_n \leq 1.42$. Therefore, $\{x_n\}$ has a limit.

The Completeness Property, as formulated in terms of sequences, is related closely to the notion of decimal representation. In fact, the statement that every decimal represents a real number and every real number has a decimal representation is itself an alternative statement of the Completeness Property. *See problems on page 25.*
Another alternative statement of the Completeness Property is called **Dedekind Cuts.** The number defined by this property is called a *cut number.*

Suppose all real numbers are separated into two collections, denoted L and R, such that each of the following is true.

   I. Every number is either in L or in R.
  II. Both L and R are nonempty.
 III. If $a \in L$ and $b \in R$, then $a < b$.

Then, there is a real number c such that all numbers less than c are in L. All numbers greater than c are in R. The number c, the **cut number,** may belong to L or R, but not both.

Alternative 2: Dedekind Cuts

Exercises Suppose R and L are defined such that $R = \{x \mid x^2 \geq 3 \text{ and } x > 0\}$ and $L = \{x \mid x^2 < 3 \text{ or } x < 0\}$.

1. Show that R and L define a Dedekind Cut.
2. What number is defined by this cut?
3. Several Completeness Properties have been stated. Prepare an argument to convince your classmates that these are equivalent. Geometric or algebraic arguments may be used.

Chapter Summary

1. A one-to-one correspondence can be established between the rational numbers and a subset of the points on a line. These points may be established by constructions. (3)

2. **The Number Line Postulate (NLP)**
   There is a one-to-one correspondence between the points on a line and the real numbers. This correspondence is such that if points A and B correspond to the real numbers a and b, then the distance from A to B is $|a - b|$. (8)

3. The absolute value of x, (symbolized $|x|$) is defined as follows. (9)
   1. $|x| = x$ if $x \geq 0$.
   2. $|x| = -x$ if $x < 0$.

4. The set of real numbers with addition, multiplication, and equality form a complete ordered field. (11)

5. For all real numbers a and b, $a < b$ if and only if there exists a positive real number p such that $a + p = b$. (17)

6. The field and order properties may be used to solve equations and inequations. (17)

7. The Completeness Property may be stated as follows. There is exactly one real number (point) common to all the intervals in an infinite sequence of closed intervals $\{I_n\}$. The sequence $\{I_n\}$ is such that each interval contains its successor and $\lim\limits_{n \to \infty} I_n = 0$, where I_n is the length of the nth interval. (23)

Chapter Review

1–1 Explain the use of constructions to locate the point which corresponds to each rational number.

1. $\dfrac{4}{5}$

2. $-\dfrac{5}{4}$

3. -4.47

Explain how to construct a segment to locate the point that should have each label.

4. $\sqrt{15}$

5. $-\sqrt{4.25}$

6. $\sqrt[4]{2}$

1-2 **Write the geometric interpretation of each sentence.**

7. $|x| = 4$

8. $|x - 3| = 5$

9. $|x + y| = d$ $(d \geq 0)$

10. $|2 - x| \leq |x - 4|$

Use absolute values to write each geometric condition.

11. The point x is 5 units distant from the point O.

12. The point 3 is closer to the point x than it is to the point 1.

Find and graph the values of x which satisfy each open sentence.

13. $|x| = 3$

14. $|x - 5| < |x + 3|$

15. $|3x + 1| = 10$

16. $|3 - 2x| \leq 7$

1-3 **Prove each of the following.**

17. Left cancellation law for addition.

18. If $a, b, c \in$ F then $(a + b)(c + d) = ac + ad + bc + bd$.

19. The multiplicative inverse of each nonzero element of $\mathcal{R}$ is unique.

1-4 **Solve each equation. Justify each step by a field property or a theorem proved in this chapter.**

20. $x + 2 = 9$

21. $5x = 35$

22. $1 - x = 5$

23. $2x + 4 = x - 3$

24. $\dfrac{x + 2}{25} = \dfrac{x - 1}{15}$

25. $\dfrac{a}{b} + \dfrac{c}{d} = \dfrac{x}{bd}$

1-5 **Solve each inequation. Write the solution set in interval notation. Graph each solution set on a number line.**

26. $3x > 2$

27. $|x| \leq 3$

28. $|2x + 1| \leq 3x - 1$

29. Use the properties of real numbers to prove that $|x + y| \leq |x| + |y|$.

1-6 **State three decimal lower and upper approximations for each of the following numbers. Represent the first three intervals in a nest of intervals.**

30. $\sqrt{8}$

31. $\sqrt{15}$

32. $\sqrt{27}$

Chapter Test

Explain how to construct a segment to locate the point that corresponds to each number.

1. 1.7

2. $\sqrt{4.25}$

Write the geometric interpretation of each of the following.

3. $|x + 2| \leq 4$

4. $|x - \frac{1}{2}| < 3$

5. $|3x - 1| = 2$

6. $|x - 3| = |x + 5|$

Find and graph the values which satisfy each open sentence.

7. $|x - 2| = 1$

8. $|2 - x| \leq 8$

9. $|x^2 + 5x + 4| = 0$

10. $|2x - 1| \leq 11$

11. State and prove the left cancellation law for multiplication.

Solve each equation. Justify each step by a field property or a theorem proved in this chapter.

12. $3x - 2(x + 1) = \frac{1}{2}(2x + 10)$

13. $\frac{3}{x + 2} + 4 = \frac{2}{4x + 8}$

Solve each inequation. Write the solution set in interval notation. Graph each solution set on a number line.

14. $\frac{1}{3}x < 9$

15. $|x + 1| \geq 4$

16. $5x - 2 \geq 0$

Computers

The Early Years

The modern electronic digital computer has altered the life of us all. It enters into almost all aspects of today's world. Where once such impact was limited to the fields of business, science and the military, it has now spread to education, construction, automobiles, medicine, recreation, travel and even into the home.

The roots of modern computing lie in mankind's needs to be able to calculate easily and accurately. Although much of today's use of the computer involves areas far removed from mere computation, the computer itself grew from such needs. Perhaps the first device used in the aid of computation was the oriental abacus, still used in many cultures today. The earliest mechanical calculating devices date to the early 1600's. All the machines used gears, wheels, cranks, and levers to manage the input of digital data and to solve the problem of "carrying over" in the place-value base ten number system. A number of mechanical aids for computation were developed by Blaise Pascal (1642). Copies of these devices are on display in Turin, Italy and Paris, France. Gottfried Leibnitz's machine (1694) was able to divide and multiply, unfortunately not reliably. It is currently on display at the Leibnitz Institute in Hanover, West Germany.

In 1822, Charles Babbage of England produced a Difference Engine used for calculations of tables of logarithms and other values needed in astronomical work. The designs for a machine he called "The Analytical Engine" were developed in the 1830's. Many of his ideas have made possible the computer as presently known.

In the late 1800's Herman Hollerith of the United States advanced the ideas and techniques of storing data and instructions on punched cards. His device used electricity for power and made possible the storage of cen-

The Difference Engine was developed by Charles Babbage.

sus data. Punched cards and tapes originally were developed for providing instructions to looms and other types of machines.

World War II brought about the design and construction of the first electronic digital computers which are the direct ancestors of those in use today. The ENIAC (1946) and the UNIVAC (1950) were machines that used electronic signals and were controlled by vacuum tubes. By today's standards they were huge, slow, and created a great deal of heat. However, they could interpret data, store data, and store instructions. In addition they could perform thousands of calculations per second, store values, and output relevant results.

The next generation of computers appeared early in the 1960's with the development of solid-state electronics, principally transistors. They allowed for less heat, smaller size, and

ENIAC was built in 1946 and became known as the prototype of later computers.

greater reliability as well as higher speed.

By the late 1960's the process of real miniaturization came about with the invention of integrated circuits. Entire functions of the older computers were now manufactured as unit circuits and speed now reached the staggering level of millions of calculations per second.

Exercises For those students who have access to a computer, suggested exercises will be included in each chapter. In most cases they are included to give experience in writing segments of programs that use the material learned in the course. Many times the computer is much too powerful a machine to use to solve the problem at hand. However, learning to express segments of problems in programming form is valuable in itself.

Write programs for each of the following.

1. Given $X = 32$, $Y = 100$, and $Z = 2$, compute and print the values for $A = XYZ$, $B = \dfrac{X + Y}{Z}$, $C = (X + Y)^2$, $D = \dfrac{X + Y}{-(Y + Z)}$, $E = X^2 + 3Y + Z$, and $F = X \div Y + Y \div Z$.

2. Given a pair of numbers, X and Y, compute and print the arithmetic mean, $A = \dfrac{X + Y}{2}$, the geometric mean, $G = \sqrt{XY}$, and the harmonic mean $H = \dfrac{2 X Y}{X + Y}$.

3. Given a pair of numbers, A and B, find the solution set for $|X - A| < B$. Print the pair of numbers, R and S, which determine the open interval $\langle R, S \rangle$ for the solution set.

4. Given a pair of numbers, A and B, find the solution set for $|X - A| > B$. Print the pair of numbers, R and S, which are the endpoints of the open intervals $\langle \leftarrow, R \rangle$ and $\langle S, \rightarrow \rangle$ for the solution set.

5. Given the values $-5, -4, -3, -2, -1, 0, 1, 2, 3, 4, 5$ for X, compute and print X' for various values of C where $X' = X + C$.

6. Given $X = \sqrt{2}$, compute and print upper and lower approximations rounded to the tenth decimal place.

Chapter 2

Buildings are composed of parts that follow straight lines which are parallel or perpendicular to each other. The relationship of these lines to each other determines the form of the structure. Similarly, the relationship of lines on a plane determines the structure of the coordinate system described on the plane.

The Plane

2-1   The Cartesian Coordinate System

To represent the points of a plane, it is convenient to use the Number Line Postulate (**NLP**). Consider two perpendicular lines. A coordinate system on each line is established by the **NLP**. The point of intersection of the lines is called the **origin**. Each line is called an **axis**. Usually the horizontal line is called the x-axis and the vertical line the y-axis. The origin is the 0-point on each axis. The point corresponding to 1 on the x-axis is to the right of the origin. The point corresponding to 1 on the y-axis is above the origin. The unit of measure need not be the same on each axis. However, unless indicated otherwise, the unit of length on both axes will be the same.

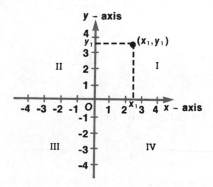

It is necessary to use two real numbers, usually represented by x and y, to name a point in the plane. These numbers are called the **coordinates** of the point and the ordered pair (x, y) is used to locate the point. The x-coordinate of a point is called the **abscissa**. The y-coordinate of the point is called the **ordinate**. Two ordered pairs of real numbers (x_1, y_1) and (x_2, y_2) are equal if and only if $x_1 = x_2$ and $y_1 = y_2$.

A statement in if and only if form can be written as two conditional statements.

1. Find a and b if $(x_1, y_1) = (x_2, y_2)$ and $(x_1, y_1) = (3a - b, 2a + b)$ and $(x_2, y_2) = (1, 4)$.

$$(x_1, y_1) = (3a - b, 2a + b) \qquad (x_2, y_2) = (1, 4)$$
$$\text{Therefore, } 3a - b = 1 \text{ and } 2a + b = 4$$
$$a = 1 \text{ and } b = 2$$

The set of points in the plane and the associated set of ordered pairs of real numbers sometimes are called a **Cartesian coordinate system**. The two axes separate the plane into four regions called **quadrants**. The quadrants are numbered as the figure shows. A point on either axis is not considered to be in any quadrant.

$(-2, 3)$ is in Quadrant II.
$(1, 0)$ is not in any quadrant.
$(2, y)$ is in Quadrant I or Quadrant IV. ✳ if y ≠ 0

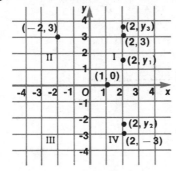

2. **In which quadrant will (x, y) lie given the following conditions?**

   x is positive and y is negative.
   It is in Quadrant IV.

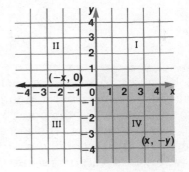

3. **In which quadrant will (x, y) lie given the following conditions?**

   x is negative and y is zero.
   It is in no quadrant.

✳ use Exploratory 1 thru 6 for examples

Let $\mathscr{R}$ be the set of all real numbers. The set of all ordered pairs of real numbers, (x, y), is indicated by $\mathscr{R} \times \mathscr{R}$ (read $\mathscr{R}$ cross $\mathscr{R}$) and is called the **Cartesian product,** or **cross product,** of $\mathscr{R}$ with $\mathscr{R}$.

$$\mathscr{R} \times \mathscr{R} = \{(x, y) \mid x, y \in \mathscr{R}\}$$

✳ emphasize

Cartesian Product

Examples

4. Find $A \times B$ if $A = \{a, b\}$ and $B = \{1, 2, 3\}$.

   $A \times B = \{(a, 1), (a, 2), (a, 3), (b, 1), (b, 2), (b, 3)\}$

5. Plot all the points of $C \times D$ if $C = \{1, 2\}$ and $D = \{2, 3\}$.

   $C \times D = \{(1, 2), (1, 3), (2, 2), (2, 3)\}$

✳ have an example such as B × A

use Written #13 or 14

There is a one-to-one correspondence between the points in the plane and the set of ordered pairs in $\mathscr{R} \times \mathscr{R}$. Thus, all the points of a plane can be represented by ordered pairs of real numbers in a Cartesian coordinate system.

Exercises

Exploratory State the quadrants in which (x, y) can be found given the following conditions. State any points which do not belong to any quadrant.

1. $x = y$
2. $|x| > 0$
3. $|y| > 0$
4. $xy > 0$
5. $xy < 0$
6. $x = -y$

Find $A \times B$ for each of the following.

7. $A = \{1, 2, 3, 4\}$
   $B = \{A, B, C\}$
8. $A = \{Sam, June, Tina\}$
   $B = \{14, 15, 16\}$
9. $A = \{\pi, e, i\}$
   $B = \{-4, -3, 0, 15\}$

Written Find real numbers x and y so that each of the following is true.

1. $(x - 1, y + 2) = (4, 3)$
2. $(x^2 - 4x, y - 4) = (-3, 7)$
3. $(2x + 3, y^2) = (-5, 16)$
4. $(\sqrt{x - 3}, |y|) = (5, 2)$
5. $(\sqrt{x}, 3y + 1) = (2, 10)$
6. $(|x + 1|, |y| - 1) = (4, 0)$

Use a graph to solve each of the following.

7. Rectangle *ABCD* has vertices *A*, *B*, and *C* at $(h, k - 1)$, $(r, k - 1)$, $(r, k + 1)$. What are the coordinates of *D*?

8. Rectangle *ABCD* has vertices *A*, *B*, and *C* at $(-2, 4)$, $(3, 4)$, $(3, -1)$. What are the coordinates of *D*?

9. In isosceles triangle *ABC*, the vertices of the base angles *B* and *C* are at $(0, -4)$ and $(4, -4)$. What are the coordinates of *A* if its ordinate is 5?

10. In isosceles triangle *ABC*, the vertices of base angles *C* and *B* are at $(h, k - 2)$ and $(h, k + 4)$. What is the ordinate of *A*?

Solve each of the following.

11. If $M = \{a, b, c\}$ and $N = \{d\}$, find $M \times N$.

12. If $P = \{2, 5, 8\}$ and $Q = \emptyset$, find $P \times Q$.

13. If $M = \{a, b\}$ and $N = \{a, c\}$, find $M \times N$ and $N \times M$. Is $M \times N = N \times M$?

14. Is the Cartesian product a commutative operation? Explain.

15. If $P = \{x | x \in \mathbb{Z} \text{ and } -1 \le x \le 1\}$ and $Q = \{y | y \in \mathbb{Z} \text{ and } 0 \le y \le 2\}$, find $P \times Q$. Graph $P \times Q$.

16. If $R = \{x | x \in \mathbb{Z} \text{ and } -2 \le x \le 0\}$ and $S = \{y | y \in \mathbb{Z} \text{ and } 0 \le y \le 2\}$, find $R \times S$. Graph $R \times S$.

Suppose $\overline{AB}$ is parallel to the *y*-axis, and its midpoint is on the *x*-axis. What are the coordinates of *A* for each point *B*?

17. $(4, 5)$ 18. (h, k) 19. $(p + 2, q - 3)$ 20. $(-3, -1)$

Suppose $\overline{CD}$ is parallel to the *x*-axis and its midpoint is on the *y*-axis. What are the coordinates of *C* for each point *D*?

21. $(3, -2)$ 22. (h, k) 23. $(p + 2, q - 3)$ 24. $(2, 4)$

25. Draw a straight line through $(0, 0)$ and $(1, 1)$. What angle does the line make with the positive *x*-axis? Write the coordinates of at least three more points on the line.

2-2 Distance

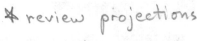

The symbol $P(x, y)$ is used to designate a point *P* with coordinates (x, y). To find the distance between two points $P(x_1, y_1)$ and $Q(x_2, y_2)$ first draw perpendiculars to each axis from *P* and *Q*. The segments, $\overline{AB}$ and $\overline{CD}$, are called the projections of $\overline{PQ}$ on the *x* and *y* axes respectively. Thus, $AB = |x_2 - x_1|$ and $CD = |y_2 - y_1|$. Does $PR = AB$ and $RQ = CD$? The Pythagorean Theorem applies to right triangle *PQR*.

$$PQ^2 = PR^2 + RQ^2$$

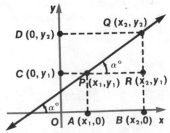

Using the Pythagorean Theorem, the distance between $P(x_1, y_1)$ and $Q(x_2, y_2)$ is as follows.

$$PQ = \sqrt{(x_2 - x_1)^2 + (y_2 - y_1)^2}$$

Distance Formula

Example

1. Show that the triangle with vertices at $A(-3, 4)$, $B(5, 2)$, and $C(-1, -5)$ is isosceles but not equilateral.

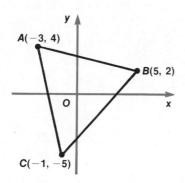

$$AB = \sqrt{(5 + 3)^2 + (2 - 4)^2} = \sqrt{68}$$

$$BC = \sqrt{(-1 - 5)^2 + (-5 - 2)^2} = \sqrt{85}$$

$$AC = \sqrt{(-1 + 3)^2 + (-5 - 4)^2} = \sqrt{85}$$

$\triangle ABC$ is isosceles because $AC = BC$. It is not equilateral because $AC \neq AB$ and $BC \neq AB$.

A method is needed for finding the coordinates of a point P on $\overline{AB}$ such that $AP:AB = k$ (k is a nonnegative constant). Suppose A and B are the points with coordinates (x_1, y_1) and (x_2, y_2) respectively. Draw $\overline{PD}$ and $\overline{AE}$ parallel to the x-axis. Draw $\overline{PC}$ and $\overline{BE}$ parallel to the y-axis.

If k is negative, then (x_1, y_1) is between (x_0, y_0) and (x_2, y_2).

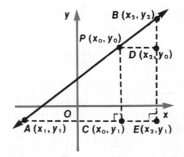

$$\frac{AP}{AB} = \frac{AC}{AE} \quad \text{and} \quad \frac{AP}{AB} = \frac{ED}{EB}$$

$$\frac{AC}{AE} = \frac{x_0 - x_1}{x_2 - x_1} = k \quad \text{and} \quad \frac{ED}{EB} = \frac{y_0 - y_1}{y_2 - y_1} = k$$

$$x_0 - x_1 = k(x_2 - x_1) \quad \text{and} \quad y_0 - y_1 = k(y_2 - y_1)$$

The coordinates of point P are x_0 and y_0.

$$x_0 = x_1 + k(x_2 - x_1) \qquad y_0 = y_1 + k(y_2 - y_1)$$

In the special case where P is the midpoint of $\overline{AB}$, $k = \frac{1}{2}$.

These formulas are important for geometric proof.

$$x_0 = x_1 + \frac{1}{2}(x_2 - x_1) \qquad x_0 = \frac{x_2 + x_1}{2}$$

$$y_0 = y_1 + \frac{1}{2}(y_2 - y_1) \qquad y_0 = \frac{y_2 + y_1}{2}$$

Examples

2. Find the coordinates of point P which is $\frac{2}{5}$ of the way from $A(6, -2)$ to $B(1, 3)$.

   Let P be at (x_0, y_0). Then $\frac{AP}{AB} = \frac{2}{5}$, $x_0 = 6 + \frac{2}{5}(1 - 6) = 4$, and $y_0 = -2 + \frac{2}{5}(3 + 2) =$

   0. Then P has the coordinates $(4, 0)$.

3. Find the coordinates of the midpoint P of $\overline{AB}$ if the coordinates of A and B are $(1, 3)$ and $(-5, 13)$ respectively.

   Let P be at (x_0, y_0). Then, $x_0 = 1 + \frac{1}{2}(-5 - 1) = -2$, and $y_0 = 3 + \frac{1}{2}(13 - 3) = 8$. Thus, P has the coordinates $(-2, 8)$.

Exercises

Exploratory   Find the distance between each pair of points whose coordinates are listed below.

1. $(7, 5), (7, -3)$
2. $(2, 4), (-10, 4)$
3. $(3, -5), (6, 1)$
4. $(4, 0), (0, 4)$
5. $(-3, 1), (4, -2)$
6. $(3, \sqrt{3}), (4, \sqrt{3})$

Find the coordinates of P such that $\dfrac{AP}{AB} = k$.

7. $A(1, 2), B(4, 6), k = \frac{3}{4}$
8. $A(-5, 11), B(2, 2), k = \frac{2}{3}$
9. $A(4, -7), B(-2, -1), k = \frac{1}{4}$
10. $A(-2, 3), B(-8, 0), k = \frac{1}{3}$

Find the coordinates of the midpoint of each segment AB.

11. $A(1, 2), B(4, 6)$
12. $A(-5, 11), B(2, 2)$
13. $A(4, -7), B(-2, -1)$
14. $A(-2, 3), B(-8, 0)$

Written   Find the distance between each pair of points.

1. $(2, a), (5, a)$
2. $(h, k), (1, 1)$
3. $(a, -1), (b, -1)$
4. $(h, k), (h - 2, k + 3)$
5. $(2k, 4k), (3k, 6k)$
6. $(3, k + 1), (2k, k - 1)$

Find the coordinates of P such that $\dfrac{AP}{AB} = k$.

7. $A(h, 0), B(0, m), k = \frac{2}{5}$
8. $A(0, p), B(n, 0), k = \frac{3}{5}$
9. $A(1.7, 8.3), B(-2.3, 8.3), k = \frac{1}{4}$
10. $A(\sqrt{2}, \sqrt{3}), B(-\sqrt{2}, -\sqrt{3}), k = \frac{1}{3}$

11-14.   Find the coordinates of the midpoint of each segment AB in Problems 7-10.

Solve each of the following.

15. Show that the triangle with vertices $A(-4, 5)$, $B(3, 2)$, and $C(6, 9)$ is a right triangle

16. Isosceles triangle ABC has base $\overline{AB}$ joining $A(5, -5)$ and $B(9, 1)$. For what values of x will $(x, 2)$ be the vertex of the triangle?

17. Triangle ABC has vertices $A(-1, 1)$, $B(3, 5)$, and $C(5, 1)$. Show that the segment joining the midpoints of $\overline{AB}$ and $\overline{AC}$ is half as long as $\overline{BC}$.

18. Show that the segments with endpoints $A(-6, 8)$, $B(8, -2)$ and $C(-3, -4)$, $D(5, 10)$ bisect each other.

19. Show that the quadrilateral with vertices $A(1, 1)$, $B(4, -2)$, $C(1, -3)$, and $D(-2, 0)$ is a parallelogram.

20. Show that the quadrilateral with vertices $A(4, 3)$, $B(2, -2)$, $C(-3, -4)$, and $D(-1, 1)$ is a rhombus.

21. Show that $(2, 3)$ is the center of a circle through $(5, 7)$, $(-1, -1)$ and $(-2, 0)$.

22. Find the point on the y-axis which is equidistant from $(1, 1)$ and $(5, -5)$.

23. Two vertices of an equilateral triangle are at $(-3, 6)$ and $(-3, 2)$. Find two possible pairs of coordinates for the third vertex.

24. Which angle has the greatest measure in a triangle with vertices at $A(1, 4)$, $B(3, -1)$, and $C(-5, -5)$?

25. For what values of x is the distance from $A(x, 3)$ to $B(-4, 0)$ equal to 5?

26. Show that the points $A(5, -2)$, $B(2, 3)$, and $C(-4, 13)$ are collinear.

27. Is the point $(2, 5)$ inside, on, or outside, the circle with center $(1, 1)$ and radius 4?

28. Find x such that $(x, 3)$ is on the circle with center $(1, -1)$ and radius 5.

2–3 Slope

Any two points determine a line. The slope of the line is the ratio of the change in the ordinates of the points to the corresponding change in the abscissas. Let (x_1, y_1) and (x_2, y_2) be two points which determine $\overleftrightarrow{AB}$.

The slope m of $\overleftrightarrow{AB}$ is defined as follows.

$$m = \frac{y_2 - y_1}{x_2 - x_1} \qquad (x_2 \neq x_1)$$

Definition of Slope

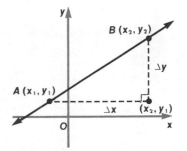

The numerator $y_2 - y_1$ is the **change in y.** Sometimes it is written as Δy, read delta y. It is also called the **rise.** Likewise $x_2 - x_1$, the **change in x,** is written as Δx. It is sometimes called the **run.**

$$m = \frac{\Delta y}{\Delta x} \qquad \text{or} \qquad \frac{\text{rise}}{\text{run}}$$

The slope of any segment of a line is the same as the slope of the line.

Example

1. **Find the slope of the line through $(3, 5)$ and $(6, -2)$.**

$$m = \frac{y_2 - y_1}{x_2 - x_1} = \frac{5 - (-2)}{3 - 6} = -\frac{7}{3}$$

Example

2. **The point $(-1, 3)$ is on a line with slope $\frac{2}{3}$ The abscissa of point P on the line is 2. Find the ordinate of P.**

$$m = \frac{y_2 - y_1}{x_2 - x_1}$$

$$\frac{2}{3} = \frac{y - 3}{2 - (-1)}$$

$$\frac{2}{3} = \frac{y - 3}{3}$$

$$2 = y - 3$$

$$5 = y$$

If $x_2 = x_1$, then the slope of the line is *not* defined, since division by zero is not defined. In this case the line is *vertical*. If $y_2 = y_1$, then the slope is 0 and the line is *horizontal*.

Note carefully the difference between a line with no slope and a line with zero slope.

Examples

3. **Find the slope of the line through $(3, 5)$ and $(3, 2)$.**

$$m = \frac{y_2 - y_1}{x_2 - x_1} = \frac{2 - 5}{3 - 3}$$

Since $3 - 3 = 0$, the slope of the line is undefined. The line is vertical.

4. **Find the slope of the line through $(1, 4)$ and $(5, 4)$.**

$$m = \frac{y_2 - y_1}{x_2 - x_1} = \frac{4 - 4}{5 - 1} = \frac{0}{4}$$

The slope of the line is 0, so the line is horizontal.

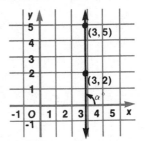

The angle α which a line makes with a positively directed ray on the x-axis is called the **inclination** of the line.

Inclination of a line

Notice that $0° \leq \alpha \leq 180°$. Note that the symbol α represents both the angle α and the measure of angle α. The meaning will be clear from the context.

Right triangle ABC is determined by constructing $\overline{AC}$ parallel to the x-axis and $\overline{BC}$ parallel to the y-axis. Since $\tan \alpha = \dfrac{BC}{AC}$ or $\dfrac{y_2 - y_1}{x_2 - x_1}$, $\tan \alpha = m$. If $m > 0$, then $\alpha < 90°$ and the line rises to the right. If $m < 0$, then $90° < \alpha < 180°$, and the line falls to the right.

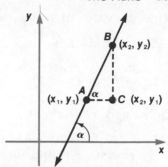

Examples

5. **Find $\tan \alpha$ for the given line through (1, 2) and (2, 3). Determine whether the line rises or falls to the right.**

    $$\tan \alpha = \frac{3 - 2}{2 - 1} = 1$$

    Since $\tan \alpha > 0$, $\alpha < 90°$. The line rises to the right.

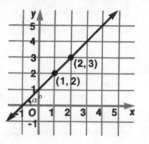

6. **Find $\tan \alpha$ for the given line through (2, 1) and (2, 5). Determine whether the line rises or falls to the right.**

    $$\tan \alpha = \frac{5 - 1}{2 - 2} = \frac{4}{0}$$

    Tan α is not defined. The line neither falls nor rises. In this case, $\alpha = 90°$.

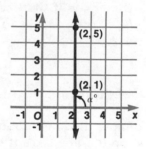

Exercises

Exploratory Find the slope, if it exists, of the line through each pair of points.

1. (3, 4), (1, 1)
2. (−3, 5), (−3, 9)
3. (2, 5), (1, −4)
4. (−1, −2), (5, −2)
5. (6, 3), (−7, 3)
6. (−8, 1), (−5, −8).

Use slope to show that the points in each set are collinear.

7. (8, 1), (2, −5), (−4, −11)
8. (15, 1), (3, −5), (−3, −8)
9. (1, 3), (5, 11), (−3, −5)
10. (1, −4), (4, −1), (8, 3)

Written Find the slope, if it exists, of the line through each pair of points.

1. (2a, b), (−5a, 3b)
2. (2, x + 2), (1, 2)
3. (a, a²), (1, a)
4. (a², 4a − 3)(a + 6, −a²)
5. (5m, 10m), (15, 30)
6. (12x, 6x), (−8x, 3x)

Find the value of k in each set to make the points collinear.

7. $(3, 6), (1, 2), (4, k)$

8. $(2, 3), (6, 9), (k, 6)$

9. $(7, -2), (0, 5), (3, k)$

10. $(9, 2), (k, 3), (-1, 4)$

11. $(4, 0), (4, k), (4, 3)$

12. $(2, 7), (-3, 7), (k, 7)$

Solve each of the following.

13. Find the ordinate of the point with abscissa -8 and which lies on the line through $(4, 3)$ and $(7, -11)$.

14. Find the slope of the line through the midpoints of the congruent sides of the isosceles triangle with vertices $A(-1, 2)$, $B(5, 0)$ and $C(1, 8)$.

15. Find the slope of the median to the base of the isosceles triangle in Problem **14**. Compare it to the slope of the base.

16. Find the slope of each side of the square with vertices $A(-1, 4), B(9, -1), C(4, -11)$, and $D(-6, -6)$. Compare the slopes of two adjacent sides and two opposite sides.

17. Find the slopes of the diagonals $\overline{AC}$ and $\overline{BD}$ of the square in Problem **16**.

18. Find the measure of the angle of inclination of the line through $(0, 0)$ and $(\sqrt{3}, 1)$.

19. Find the tangent of the angle of inclination of the line through $(3, 6)$ and $(5, 4)$.

20. Determine if $D(-1, -2)$ lies on the line segment joining $A(-6, -4)$ and $B(0, \frac{1}{2})$.

21. Determine if the line through $(2, 0)$ and $(0, 4)$ rises or falls to the right. Decide if $\alpha < 90°$ or $90° < \alpha < 180°$.

22. Determine if the line through $(2, 1)$ and $(5, 1)$ rises or falls to the right. Find a value for $\tan \alpha$.

2–4 Equations of a Line

Consider the line through (x_1, y_1) with slope m. For any point (x, y) on this line, except the point (x_1, y_1) itself, the slope may be written as follows.

$$m = \frac{y - y_1}{x - x_1} \qquad (x \neq x_1)$$

Multiply both sides of the equality by $(x - x_1)$. The resulting equation is $y - y_1 = m(x - x_1)$.

✳ emphasize this form

If the point (x_1, y_1) lies on a line having slope m, the point-slope form of the equation of the line is as follows.

$$y - y_1 = m(x - x_1)$$

Point-Slope Form

There are several forms for the equation of a line. Any one can be used, but $y = mx + b$ is the most popular.

The point $(0, b)$, in which a line intersects the y-axis is called the **y-intercept** of the line. Let $(x_1, y_1) = (0, b)$ in the point-slope equation. Thus, $y - b = m(x - 0)$ implies $y = mx + b$.

Suppose the slope of a line is m and its y-intercept is $(0, b)$. The slope-intercept form of the equation of the line is as follows.

$$y = mx + b$$

Does a line with equation $y = mx + b$ have a y-intercept $(0, b)$ and slope m? Since $b = m \cdot 0 + b$, the point $(0, b)$ has coordinates which satisfy the slope-intercept equation. The y-intercept is $(0, b)$. The point $(1, m + b)$ also satisfies the slope-intercept equation since $m + b = m \cdot 1 + b$. Therefore, the point $(1, m + b)$ is on the line. The slope of the line segment joining the two points $(0, b)$ and $(1, m + b)$ is $\frac{m + b - b}{1 - 0}$ or m.

Therefore, $y = mx + b$ is the equation of the line with slope m and y-intercept $(0, b)$.

? what is the author doing / why

Example

1. Find the equation of the line through $(1, 2)$ with slope 3.

$$y - y_1 = m(x - x_1)$$
$$y - 2 = 3(x - 1)$$
$$y = 3x - 1$$

Use point-slope form.
$y_1 = 2$, $m = 3$, $x_1 = 1$

✻ note location of C

The equation $Ax + By + C = 0$, where A and B are not both zero, is called the general form of the equation of the line.

The equation can be rewritten $y = -\frac{A}{B}x - \frac{C}{B}(B \neq 0)$. Thus, the equation can be transformed into the slope-intercept form where $-\frac{A}{B}$ is the slope and $\left(0, -\frac{C}{B}\right)$ is the y-intercept. If $B = 0$ then the line is vertical and has equation $x = -\frac{C}{A}$.

Example

2. Find the slope and y-intercept of the line $3x + 2y - 7 = 0$.
    Notice that $A = 3$, $B = 2$, and $C = -7$.
    $$-\frac{A}{B} = -\frac{3}{2} \quad \text{and} \quad -\frac{C}{B} = \frac{7}{2}$$
    The slope is $-\frac{3}{2}$ and the y-intercept is $\left(0, \frac{7}{2}\right)$.

Linear equations are equations of graphs of straight lines. For convenience, the line with equation $Ax + By + C = 0$ will be referred to as *the line $Ax + By + C = 0$*.

Example

3. **Find the general form of the equation of a line through $(-2, 3)$ and $(4, -1)$.**

$$m = \frac{3 - (-1)}{-2 - 4} = -\frac{4}{6} = -\frac{2}{3}$$

Use the point-slope form of the equation. ✦ *note*

$$y - y_1 = m(x - x_1)$$
$$y - 3 = -\frac{2}{3}(x + 2)$$
$$3y - 9 = -2x - 4$$
$$2x + 3y - 5 = 0$$

$m = -\frac{2}{3}, x_1 = -2, y_1 = 3$

Points in a plane also can be represented by expressing x and y in terms of some third variable t. Suppose $x = 3 - 2t$ and $y = t + 5$. If $t = 2$, then $x = -1$ and $y = 7$. Equations such as $x = 3 - 2t$ and $y = t + 5$ are called **parametric equations** and t is called a **parameter**. If the parameter can be eliminated, then y can be expressed in terms of x.

Example

4. **Let $x = 3 - 2t$ and $y = t + 5$. Write an equivalent equation in terms of x and y.**

$$t = y - 5$$
$$x = 3 - 2t$$
$$x = 3 - 2(y - 5)$$
$$x = 3 - 2y + 10$$
$$x + 2y - 13 = 0$$

✦ *illustrate use of linear combinations*
Substitute $y - 5$ for t.

Thus, $x = 3 - 2t$ and $y = t + 5$ are the parametric equations of the straight line with equation $x + 2y - 13 = 0$.

In general, $x = a + bt$ and $y = c + dt$, are the parametric equations of a line as long as not both b and d are zero.

Parametric Equations

The slope-intercept form of the equation is found in this way.

$$x = a + bt \quad \text{and} \quad y = c + dt$$
$$t = \frac{x - a}{b}$$
$$y = c + d\frac{(x - a)}{b}$$
$$y = \frac{d}{b}x + \frac{bc - ad}{b}$$

Thus $\dfrac{d}{b}$ is the slope and $\dfrac{bc - ad}{b}$ is the ordinate of the y-intercept. What happens in the equations if $b = 0$?

If $b = 0$, then $x = a$ is the equation of the vertical line through $(a, 0)$.

Example

5. **Find a pair of parametric equations for the line through $(-1, 4)$ and $(1, -2)$.**

$$\text{slope} = m = \frac{4 - (-2)}{-1 - 1} = \frac{-3}{1}$$

Since $\dfrac{d}{b} = -\dfrac{3}{1}$, let $d = -3$ and $b = 1$. The values for d and b may vary.

$$x = a + t \qquad \text{and} \qquad y = c - 3t$$

If $t = 0$ then (a, c) is a point on the line. Let $(a, c) = (1, -2)$.

$$x = 1 + t \qquad \text{and} \qquad y = -2 - 3t$$

Notice that in the parametric equations $x = a + bt$ and $y = c + dt$, the point (a, c) is on the line, and $\dfrac{d}{b}$ is the slope, provided $b \neq 0$.

Not all equations of lines are first-degree equations or linear equations. If an equation can be written as the product of linear factors equal to 0, then the equation represents one or more straight lines.

Linear factors are factors that can be written as first-degree expressions.

Examples

6. **Express $x^2 - 2xy + y^2 + 2x - 2y + 1 = 0$ as the product of linear factors.**

$$x^2 - 2xy + y^2 + 2x - 2y + 1 = 0$$
$$(x - y)^2 + 2(x - y) + 1 = 0$$
$$[(x - y) + 1]^2 = 0$$
$$(x - y + 1)^2 = 0$$

7. **Express $x^3 - 2x^2 - xy^2 + 2y^2 = 0$ as the product of linear factors, and then graph the equation.**

$$x^3 - 2x^2 - xy^2 + 2y^2 = 0$$
$$x^2(x - 2) - y^2(x - 2) = 0$$
$$(x^2 - y^2)(x - 2) = 0$$
$$(x - y)(x + y)(x - 2) = 0$$

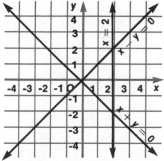

The graph of the equation consists of the graphs of the lines $x - 2 = 0$, $x - y = 0$, and $x + y = 0$.

Exercises

Exploratory   State the point-slope form of the equation of the line through the given point and having the slope given.

1. $(1, 7), m = \dfrac{2}{5}$

2. $(-5, 4), m = -\dfrac{4}{5}$

3. $(10, 4), m = 2$

Find the general form of the equation of the line through each pair of points.

4. $(12, 3), (2, -5)$

5. $(-4, 0), (0, 4)$

6. $(5, 7), (5, -3)$

7. $(8, 4), (8, -1)$

8. $(0, 2), (5, 2)$

9. $(3, -5), (-1, -5)$

Written   Find the general form of the equation of the line through the given point and having the slope given.

1. $(-7, -6), m = -\dfrac{1}{4}$

2. $(p, q), m = \dfrac{1}{2}$

3. $(2, -3), m = \dfrac{r}{2}$

Find the general form of the equation of the line through each pair of points.

4. $(3, -5), (2, -1)$

5. $(5, 2), (7, 9)$

6. $(-7, -1), (4, -2)$

7. $(3, 1), (-2, 4)$

8. $(a, 6), (2a, -1)$

9. $(3, -2b), (-1, b)$

Solve each of the following.

10. Find the equation of the line through $(k, 9)$ and $(4, -1)$. For what values of k is the slope of the line undefined?

11. Find the equation of the line containing the median from A to $\overline{BC}$ in the triangle with vertices $A(13, -7)$, $B(-8, 1)$. and $C(2, -5)$.

12. Find the equations of the lines containing the diagonals $\overline{AC}$ and $\overline{BD}$ of the parallelogram with vertices $A(-5, -1)$, $B(3, 3)$, $C(-1, 7)$, and $D(-9, 3)$. Find the coordinates of the point of intersection.

13. Show that the equation of the line through $(a, 0)$ and $(0, b)$ is $\dfrac{x}{a} + \dfrac{y}{b} = 1$ (a and $b \neq 0$). This equation is called the **double-intercept form.**

Express each of the following as the product of linear factors. Draw the graph of the resulting equation. No graphing.

14. $x^2 - xy + 2x = 0$

15. $x^2 - y^2 + 6y - 9 = 0$

16. $2x^2 + 3xy + y^2 - 5x - 5y = 0$

17. $3x^2 - xy - 7x + 2y + 2 = 0$

Write the general form of the equation of the line for each pair of parametric equations given below.

18. $\begin{cases} x = 3 - t \\ y = 2 + t \end{cases}$

19. $\begin{cases} x = 5 + 7t \\ y = 4 - 4t \end{cases}$

20. $\begin{cases} x = -1 + 2t \\ y = 3 + 4t \end{cases}$

Write a pair of parametric equations for each of the following.

21. $x + 2y = 7$

22. $5x - y = 1$

23. $2x + 3y = 9$

Write a pair of parametric equations for the line through each pair of points.

24. $(4, -1), (0, 3)$

25. $(-5, -11), (2, -4)$

26. $(-3, -2), (1, 4)$

Solve each of the following.

27. Find the slope of the line through $A(2, 3)$ and $B(-3, 1)$. Substitute the slope in the form $y = mx + b$. Since $A(2, 3)$ lies on the line, solve for b using the coordinates of point A. State the equation of the line.

28. Find the point of intersection of the graphs of $2x - y = 5$ and $3x + y = 10$. Show that any line through this point of intersection can be written in the form $(2x - y - 5) + k(3x + y - 10) = 0$, when k is any real number.

2–5 Parallel and Perpendicular Lines

If two parallel lines are cut by a transversal, the corresponding angles are congruent. In other words, two parallel lines have the same inclination.

> **Two distinct nonvertical lines ℓ_1 and ℓ_2 with slopes m_1 and m_2, respectively, are parallel if and only if $m_1 = m_2$.**

Theorem Parallel Lines

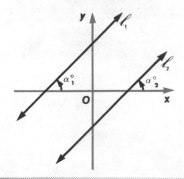

Proof: Suppose ℓ_1 and ℓ_2 are two nonvertical lines with inclinations α_1 and α_2.

I. If $\ell_1 \parallel \ell_2$, $m_1 = \tan \alpha_1$, $m_2 = \tan \alpha_2$, and $\alpha_1 = \alpha_2$, then $\tan \alpha_1 = \tan \alpha_2$, and $m_1 = m_2$.

II. If $m_1 = m_2$, $m_1 = \tan \alpha_1$, and $m_2 = \tan \alpha_2$, then $\tan \alpha_1 = \tan \alpha_2$. Since α_1 and α_2 are both angles with measures between $0°$ and $180°$, $\alpha_1 = \alpha_2$, and $\ell_1 \parallel \ell_2$.

Examples

1. **Write the equation of the line through $(1, 3)$ which is parallel to the line $2x + y - 4 = 0$.**

    The slope of the line $2x + y - 4 = 0$ is $-\dfrac{A}{B} = -\dfrac{2}{1}$ or -2.

    emphasis use of slope–intercept instead of $-\dfrac{A}{B}$

    Using the point-slope form, the equation of the line through $(1, 3)$ with slope -2 is $y - 3 = -2(x - 1)$ or $2x + y - 5 = 0$.

2. **Show that the quadrilateral with vertices $A(3, -1)$, $B(5, 2)$, $C(0, 7)$ and $D(-2, 4)$ is a parallelogram.**

    Slope of $\overline{AB} = \dfrac{2 - (-1)}{5 - 3} = \dfrac{3}{2}$ Slope of $\overline{BC} = \dfrac{2 - 7}{5 - 0} = -1$

    Slope of $\overline{CD} = \dfrac{7 - 4}{0 - (-2)} = \dfrac{3}{2}$ Slope of $\overline{AD} = \dfrac{4 - (-1)}{-2 - 3} = -1$

    Hence, $\overline{AB} \parallel \overline{CD}$.   Hence, $\overline{BC} \parallel \overline{AD}$.

    Therefore, $ABCD$ is a parallelogram.

In order to show lines to be perpendicular, the following theorem can be used.

Two nonvertical lines ℓ_1 and ℓ_2 with slopes m_1 and m_2, respectively, are perpendicular if and only if $m_1 m_2 = -1$.

Theorem Perpendicular Lines

Proof: Define ℓ_1' to be the line given by $y = m_1 x$ and ℓ_2' to be the line given by $y = m_2 x$. Then ℓ_1' is parallel to ℓ_1 and ℓ_2' is parallel to ℓ_2.

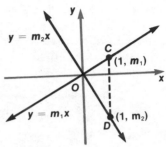

If $\ell_1 \perp \ell_2$ then $\ell_1' \perp \ell_2'$.

$\angle DOC$ is a right angle.
$\triangle DOC$ is a right triangle.
$OC^2 + OD^2 = CD^2$
$(1^2 + m_1^2) + (1^2 + m_2^2) = [(1 - 1)^2 + (m_1 - m_2)^2]$
$2 + m_1^2 + m_2^2 = m_1^2 - 2m_1 m_2 + m_2^2$
$2 = -2\, m_1\, m_2$
$m_1 m_2 = -1$ *The converse can be proved by reversing the steps in the proof.*

Examples

3. **Show that the triangle with vertices $A(1, 2)$, $B(-1, -3)$, $C(-11, 1)$ is a right triangle. Verify this by using the Pythagorean Theorem.**

   Slope of $\overline{AB} = \dfrac{2 - (-3)}{1 - (-1)} = \dfrac{5}{2}$ Slope of $\overline{BC} = \dfrac{-3 - 1}{-1 - (-11)} = -\dfrac{4}{10}$

   Since the product of the slopes is -1, the sides are perpendicular, and the triangle is a right triangle.

   $AB^2 = 5^2 + 2^2 = 29$ $BC^2 = 4^2 + 10^2 = 116$ $AC^2 = 12^2 + 1^2 = 145$

   Hence, $AC^2 = BC^2 + AB^2$.

4. **Write the equation of the line which passes through $(3, 2)$ and is perpendicular to the graph of $x - 3y + 2 = 0$.**

   The slope of $x - 3y + 2 = 0$ is $-\dfrac{A}{B} = \dfrac{1}{3}$

   Since the slope of the required line is -3, the equation is $y - 2 = -3(x - 3)$ or $3x + y - 11 = 0$.

Exercises

Exploratory   State whether the graphs of the following equations are parallel, perpendicular, or neither.

1. $x + y = 5$
    $x + y = 10$

2. $x + y = 5$
    $x - y = 5$

3. $2y + 3x = 5$
    $3y - 2x = 5$

4. $2y + 3x = 5$
    $3y + 3x = 5$

5. $3x - 8y = 11$
    $3x - 6y = 10$

6. $y = 2x$
    $y = 2x - 4$

Written Write the equation of the line which passes through the given point and is parallel to the graph of the equation given.

1. $(-9, 3)$; $3x - 4y = 12$

2. $(6, 11)$; $12y - 5x = 4$

3. (a, b); $ax + by = c$

Write the equation of the line through the given point and perpendicular to the given line.

4. $(6, 0)$; $7x - 3y = 7$

5. $(0, 5)$; $15x - 3y = 10$

6. (a, b); $ax + by = c$

Solve each of the following.

7. For what value of k is the graph of $kx - 7y + 10 = 0$ parallel to the graph of $8x - 14y + 3 = 0$? For what value of k are the graphs perpendicular?

8. For what value of k is the graph of $2x - ky + 5 = 0$ parallel to the graph of $3x + 7y + 15 = 0$? For what value of k are the graphs perpendicular?

Write the equation of the line which is the perpendicular bisector of each segment whose endpoints are given.

9. $A(-5, 5)$, $B(1, 11)$

10. $E(a, b)$, $F(3a, 5b)$

11. $C(6a, 8b)$, $D(4a, 0)$

12. $J(2, k)$, $K(-6, k - 4)$

Solve each of the following.

13. Show that $\overline{AB}$ is the perpendicular bisector of $\overline{CD}$ if the endpoints are $A(-2, 7)$, $B(8, 15)$, $C(-1, 16)$ and $D(7, 6)$.

14. The endpoints of one diagonal of a square are $A(-6, 4)$ and $C(2, 2)$. Find the coordinates of the other vertices.

15. Show that $A(5, -5)$, $B(4, 3)$, $C(-3, 7)$ and $D(-2, -1)$ are the vertices of a rhombus.

16. Parallelogram $PQRS$ has vertices $P(-1, 0)$, $Q(1, 1)$ and $S(-2, 3)$. Find the slope of $\overline{RS}$.

17. Given points $A(4, 2)$, $B(3, -1)$, and $C(0, 3)$, find the equation of a line through A parallel to $\overline{BC}$. Find the equation of a line through B parallel to $\overline{AC}$.

18. Find the coordinates of the fourth vertex of the parallelogram $ABCD$ if $A(-5, -1)$, $B(3, 3)$ and $C(-1, 7)$ are the other three vertices.

19. Show that the triangle with vertices $A(0, 0)$, $B(12, 4)$, and $C(4, 8)$ can be inscribed in a semicircle. What is the length of the diameter?

20. Show that the equation of any line parallel to $4x - 2y = 1$ can be written as $4x - 2y = c$. If the line contains the point $(5, -1)$, find the equation of the line.

Excursions in Mathematics

Nonperpendicular Axes

Normally axes which are perpendicular to each other are used but it is possible to coordinatize the plane using any two intersecting number lines. Suppose that two coordinate axes form an angle of 45°. The unit length on each axis is the same. A point in the plane is indicated by the ordered pair $[x, y]$ of real numbers. Given an ordered number pair $[a, b]$, the corresponding point is a units from the y-axis parallel to the x-axis and b units from the x-axis parallel to the y-axis.

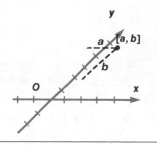

2-6 Distance Between a Point and a Line

Let $y = mx + b$ and $y = mx + c$ represent equations of parallel lines that are neither vertical nor horizontal. The line perpendicular to both these equations and containing $(0, c)$ is represented by $y = -\dfrac{x}{m} + c$.

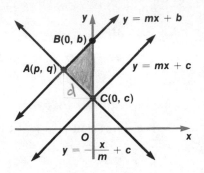

Since the point (p, q) lies on both lines, it can be expressed in several ways.

$$(p, q) = (p, mp + b) = \left(p, \frac{-p}{m} + c\right)$$

The fact that $mp + b = -\dfrac{p}{m} + c$ implies $p = \dfrac{m(c - b)}{m^2 + 1}$.

The distance d between the two parallel lines can be found by using the Pythagorean Theorem.

$$
\begin{aligned}
d^2 &= AC^2 \\
&= BC^2 - AB^2 \\
&= (b - c)^2 - (\sqrt{(p - 0)^2 + (mp + b - b)^2})^2 \\
&= (b - c)^2 - p^2(1 + m^2) \\
&= (b - c)^2 - \left[\frac{m(c - b)}{m^2 + 1}\right]^2 (1 + m^2) \\
&= \frac{(m^2 + 1)(b - c)^2 - m^2(b - c)^2}{m^2 + 1} \\
&= \frac{(b - c)^2}{m^2 + 1} \\
d &= \frac{|b - c|}{\sqrt{m^2 + 1}}
\end{aligned}
$$

A specific example may help in following the derivation of this theorem.

This formula for the distance between nonvertical, nonhorizontal, parallel lines can be used to derive the formula for the distance between a point and a line.

Let $y = mx + b$ represent a line that is neither vertical nor horizontal. Let (p, q) represent a point. The equation of the line parallel to $y = mx + b$ and containing (p, q) is given by $y = mx + (q - mp)$. The distance between the line $y = mx + b$ and the point (p, q) equals the distance between the two parallel lines.

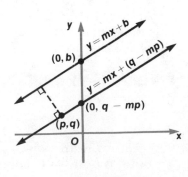

$$d = \frac{|b - q + mp|}{\sqrt{m^2 + 1}}$$

This last formula is usually modified to apply to the form $Ax + By + C = 0$ for a line and (x_0, y_0) for a point. Since only nonvertical and nonhorizontal lines are being considered, $Ax + By + C = 0$ may be written as $y = -\dfrac{A}{B}x - \dfrac{C}{B}$.

In this case, $m = -\dfrac{A}{B}, b = -\dfrac{C}{B}, p = x_0,$ and $q = y_0.$

$$d = \frac{\left|-\dfrac{C}{B} - y_0 - \dfrac{A}{B}x_0\right|}{\sqrt{\left(-\dfrac{A}{B}\right)^2 + 1}}$$

$$= \frac{\dfrac{1}{|B|} \cdot |Ax_0 + By_0 + C|}{\dfrac{1}{|B|}\sqrt{A^2 + B^2}}$$

$$= \frac{|Ax_0 + By_0 + C|}{\sqrt{A^2 + B^2}}$$

The restrictions to nonvertical and nonhorizontal lines were made to avoid the problem of zero denominators. By testing a few cases, observe that this last formula also holds for vertical and horizontal lines.

> The distance, d, between the line $Ax + By + C = 0$ and point (x_0, y_0) is given by
> $$d = \frac{|Ax_0 + By_0 + C|}{\sqrt{A^2 + B^2}}$$
> when at least one of A and B is nonzero.

* discuss formula

Distance from a Point to a Line

* problem solving hint

The distance between two parallel lines is the length of the perpendicular segment from any point on one line to the other line.

This formula may be used to find the distance between ℓ_1 represented by $Ax + By + C = 0$ and ℓ_2 parallel to ℓ_1. Simply use any point (x_0, y_0) on ℓ_2 and apply the formula using $Ax + By + C = 0$ and (x_0, y_0).

Examples

1. Find the distance between the point (2, 3) and the line for $3x + 4y - 5 = 0$.
    For $3x + 4y - 5 = 0, A = 3, B = 4,$ and $C = -5$ and for $(x_1, y_1), x_1 = 2$ and $y_1 = 3$.
    $$d = \frac{|3 \cdot 2 + 4 \cdot 3 - 5|}{\sqrt{(3)^2 + (4)^2}} = \frac{13}{5}$$

2. Find the distance between the parallel lines $9x - 5y = 8$ and $9x - 5y = -1$.
    The point (2, 2) is on the line $9x - 5y = 8$. The distance from (2, 2) to the line is the same as the distance between the lines. In the equation $9x - 5y = -1$, $A = 9, B = -5,$ and $C = 1$.
    $$d = \frac{|9(2) - 5(2) + 1|}{\sqrt{9^2 + (-5)^2}} = \frac{9}{\sqrt{106}} = \frac{9\sqrt{106}}{106}$$

Example

3. In triangle ABC with A $(8, -2)$, B $(6, 4)$, and C $(-2, 0)$, find the length of the altitude h from A to $\overline{BC}$.

Slope of $\overline{BC}$ = $\dfrac{4 - 0}{6 - (-2)} = \dfrac{1}{2}$

The equation of the line containing $\overline{BC}$ is $y = \frac{1}{2}(x + 2)$ or $x - 2y + 2 = 0$.

Thus, $h = \dfrac{|1(8) + (-2)(-2) + 2|}{\sqrt{(1)^2 + (-2)^2}} = \dfrac{14}{\sqrt{5}} = \dfrac{14\sqrt{5}}{5}$.

Exercises

Exploratory Find A, B, C, and $\sqrt{A^2 + B^2}$.

1. $x + y - 5 = 0$
2. $y - 2x = 0$
3. $3y - 2x - 5 = 0$
4. $3x + 4y + 5 = 0$
5. $x - y = 7$
6. $5x - 12y = 8$
7. $15x + 8y = 34$
8. $2y + 3x = 15$
9. $12x - 5y = 20$

Written Find the distance between the line for each equation and the point given.

1. $x - 3y + 7 = 0$; $(1, 4)$
2. $12x - 5y + 2 = 0$; $(2, 2)$
3. $x + 3y - 10 = 0$; $(-8, -2)$
4. $8x + 6y = 11$; $(0, 6)$
5. $3x + 4y - 12 = 0$; $(4, 0)$
6. $3x - y = 7$; $(-1, 2)$

Find the length of the altitude from A to $\overline{BC}$ in each triangle. Then find the area of the triangle.

7. $A(5, 5)$, $B(3, 0)$, $C(-1, 2)$
8. $A(12, 4)$, $B(1, 1)$, $C(0, 8)$

Find the distance between the sides $\overline{AB}$ and $\overline{CD}$ in each parallelogram $ABCD$. Then find the area of the parallelogram.

9. $A(-9, -5)$, $B(-3, -8)$, $C(0, 0)$, $D(-6, 3)$
10. $A(0, 6)$, $B(5, 10)$, $C(3, 2)$, $D(-2, -2)$

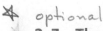

2-7 Theorems from Geometry

Using coordinate methods and some basic theorems from geometry, it is possible to prove some other theorems from geometry. Some of these theorems are much simpler to prove by coordinate methods than by Euclidean methods.

The image of any translation, rotation, or reflection of a geometric figure is congruent to the original figure. Therefore, it is possible to relocate the figure to simplify computation.

Coordinate methods are also referred to as analytic methods.

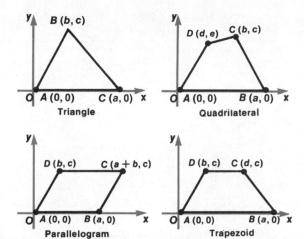

Triangle | Quadrilateral | Parallelogram | Trapezoid

The selection of a coordinate system sometimes emphasizes different properties of figures.

Examples

1. **Prove: A line segment joining the midpoints of two sides of a triangle is parallel to and equal in length to one-half the third side.**

   In the figure $P\left(\dfrac{b}{2}, \dfrac{c}{2}\right)$ and $Q\left(\dfrac{a+b}{2}, \dfrac{c}{2}\right)$ are the midpoints of $\overline{AB}$ and $\overline{BC}$ respectively.

   $$PQ = \sqrt{\left(\frac{a+b}{2} - \frac{b}{2}\right)^2 + \left(\frac{c}{2} - \frac{c}{2}\right)^2} = \sqrt{\frac{a^2}{4}} = \frac{|a|}{2}$$

   Since $AC = |a|$, $PQ = \frac{1}{2}AC$. The slope of $\overline{PQ}$ is $\dfrac{\dfrac{c}{2} - \dfrac{c}{2}}{\dfrac{a+b}{2} - \dfrac{b}{2}}$ or 0.

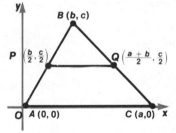

   The slope of $\overline{AC}$ is $\dfrac{0-0}{a-0}$ or 0. Therefore, $\overline{PQ} \parallel \overline{AC}$.

2. **Prove: The diagonals of a parallelogram bisect each other.**

   Let $MNPQ$ be a parallelogram with vertices $M(0, 0)$, $N(x_1, 0)$, $P(x_1 + x_2, x_3)$ and $Q(x_2, x_3)$.

   $$\text{Midpoint of } \overline{QN} = \left(\frac{x_1 + x_2}{2}, \frac{x_3}{2}\right)$$

   $$\text{Midpoint of } \overline{MP} = \left(\frac{x_1 + x_2}{2}, \frac{x_3}{2}\right)$$

   Therefore, the segments $\overline{MP}$ and $\overline{QN}$ bisect each other.

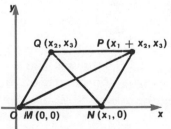

Exercises

Exploratory Name the midpoint of the segment which has the given endpoints.

1. $(8, 0), (-6, 0)$
2. $(24, 0), (0, -18)$
3. $(11, 7), (5, 11)$
4. $(-3, -2) (8, 4)$
5. $(0, 0), (a, b)$
6. $(a, b), (c, d)$

Written Prove each of the following analytically.

1. The diagonals of a square are perpendicular.

2. The diagonals of a rectangle are equal in length.

3. The segments joining the midpoints of a quadrilateral, taken in order, form a parallelogram.

4. Every point on the perpendicular bisector of a segment is equidistant from the endpoints of the segment.

5. The medians to the congruent sides of an isosceles triangle are equal in length.

6. The segments joining the midpoints of a rectangle, taken in order, form a rhombus.

Challenge Prove each of the following analytically.

1. In any triangle, the sum of the squares of the lengths of the medians is equal to three fourths of the sum of the squares of the lengths of the three sides.

2. In $\square\,ABCD$, P and Q are points of trisection of the diagonal $\overline{DB}$. Prove $APCQ$ is a parallelogram.

optional

2–8 Loci

A **locus** is the set of all points, and only those points, which satisfy a given set of conditions. For example, the locus of points equidistant from a given point in a plane is a circle. It is possible to express the given conditions algebraically. Then an equation for the locus relative to some coordinate system is found.

Examples

1. Find the equation of the locus of points (x, y) such that the slope of the line joining (x, y) and $(4, 0)$ is twice the slope of the line joining (x, y) and $(-1, -5)$.

$$\frac{y - 0}{x - 4} = \frac{2(y + 5)}{x + 1}$$
$$xy + y = 2xy + 10x - 8y - 40$$
$$0 = xy + 10x - 9y - 40$$

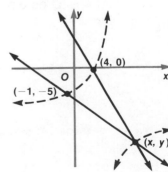

If $x \neq 4$ and $x \neq -1$, then this equation is true for the coordinates of any point which satisfies the condition. By reversing the steps with the same restrictions, it is possible to show that any point with coordinates which satisfy $xy + 10x - 9y - 40 = 0$ is a point in the locus.

Thus, the locus is $\{(x, y)\,|\,xy + 10x - 9y - 40 = 0\}$.

2. **Find the equation of the locus of points equidistant from the *y*-axis and the point *P*(4, 0).**

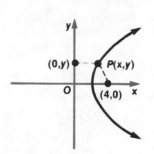

*|x| is chosen so the distance will
always be positive.*

$$\sqrt{(x-4)^2 + y^2} = |x|$$
$$(x-4)^2 + y^2 = x^2$$
$$x^2 - 8x + 16 + y^2 = x^2$$
$$y^2 - 8x + 16 = 0$$

Any point which is equidistant from (4, 0) and the *y*-axis must have coordinates which satisfy $y^2 - 8x + 16 = 0$. The locus is $\{(x, y) | y^2 - 8x + 16 = 0\}$. The graph is called a **parabola**.

3. **Find the locus of points whose coordinates satisfy the in-equality $y \geq 2x - 1$.**

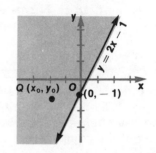

Any point on the line $y = 2x - 1$ belongs to the set. The rest of the points in the plane must be points whose coordinates satisfy either $y > 2x - 1$ or $y < 2x - 1$. The origin (0, 0) is above the line. It is reasonable to think that every point on the same side of the line as the origin must be in the locus. To prove this, think of a point $Q(x_0, y_0)$ on the same side of the line as the origin such that $y_0 < 2x_0 - 1$. There would exist at least one point between *Q* and the origin with coordinates such that $y_0 = 2x_0 - 1$. All such points lie on the line shown as the boundary. Therefore, *Q* would have to be on the other side of the line $y = 2x - 1$. This contradicts the assumption about *Q*.

Thus those points not on the line which satisfy the condition must have coordinates which are greater than those on the line $y = 2x - 1$. The rest of the points must lie above the line.

Exercises

Exploratory   Describe the locus for each of the following.

1. All points at a given distance from a given point.

2. All the midpoints of the radii of a circle with radius measuring 8 inches.

3. All points in a plane that are equidistant from two given points.

4. All the points in space that are a given distance from a given line.

Written   Find the equation of the locus of points equidistant from each pair of points.

1. $A(-7, 1), B(3, -5)$
2. $M(8, 3), N(2, -1)$
3. $J(3, 0), K(-7, 0)$
4. $C(5, -2), D(5, -8)$
5. $P(1, 0), Q(p + 1, 0)$
6. $R(3, q), S(3, q - 2)$

Solve each of the following.

7. Find the equation of the locus of points equidistant from (6, 0) and the *y*-axis.

8. Find the equation of the locus of points equidistant from (5, −7) and the *x*-axis.

9. Find the equation of the locus of points (x, y) such that the slope of the line through (x, y) and $(-1, 7)$ is one-half of the slope of the line through (x, y) and $(3, 5)$.

10. Find the equation of the locus of points such that the slope of the line through (x, y) and $(4, 0)$ is the negative reciprocal of the slope of the line through (x, y) and $(-4, 0)$. What kind of curve is this locus?

Sketch the graph of each locus.

11. $\{(x, y)|y \geq 2x + 1\}$

12. $\{(x, y)|y > 3x - 5\}$ (a broken line)

13. $\{(x, y)|2x + 5y \geq 10\}$

14. $\{(x, y)|7x - 3y < 6\}$

15. $\{(x, y)|6 \leq 2x + 3y \leq 15\}$

16. $\{(x, y)|x - 2 \leq y \leq x + 2\}$

do after 6-6 p.183

2–9 Complex Numbers and the Plane

Complex numbers provide solutions to certain equations such as $x^2 + 2x + 2 = 0$ which have no solution in the set of real numbers. A **complex number** is written in the form $a + bi$, where a and b are real numbers. The symbol i is defined so that $i^2 = -1$. Since any real number a can be written as $a + 0i$, the real numbers are a subset of the complex numbers. The **real part** of the complex number $a + bi$ is a. The **imaginary part** is b. Any number which can be written in the form $0 + bi$ is called a **pure imaginary** number.

The following statements define operations with complex numbers.

The word imaginary is used only because historically it has been used in this manner.

Equality: $a + bi = c + di$ if and only if $a = c$ and $b = d$.
Addition: $(a + bi) + (c + di) = (a + c) + (b + d)i$.
Multiplication: $(a + bi)(c + di) = (ac - bd) + (ad + bc)i$

Operations for Complex Numbers

The field properties of addition and multiplication apply. However, the usual properties of order do not apply.

Examples

1. Show $5 + 2i = 2(i + 2.5)$.

   $2(i + 2.5) = 2i + 2(2.5) = 2i + 5$
   Since $a = 5, b = 2, c = 5$, and $d = 2$, the real parts are equal and the imaginary parts are equal. Thus, the complex numbers are equal.

2. Multiply $(2 + 5i)$ and $(4 - 3i)$

   $(2 + 5i)(4 - 3i) = (2(4) - (5)(-3)) + (2(-3) + 5(4))i$
   $= (8 + 15) + (-6 + 20)i$
   $= 23 + 14i$

Complex numbers can be represented graphically. Since the real numbers use up all the points on the line, complex numbers which are not real have to be placed elsewhere. In the Cartesian coordinate system there is a one-to-one correspondence between the points in the plane and the ordered number pairs (a, b). There also is a one-to-one correspondence between the ordered number pairs (a, b) and the complex numbers $a + bi$. It is $(a, b) \leftrightarrow (a + bi)$. Hence, there is a one-to-one correspondence between the set of complex numbers and the points in the plane.

If *arrows* are drawn from the origin to each point (a, b), then there is also a one-to-one correspondence between the arrows and the complex numbers. These arrows will be the *geometric interpretation* of complex numbers. The arrow often is called a **position vector.**

The length of the arrow, called the **magnitude** of the arrow, is $\sqrt{a^2 + b^2}$. The *slope* of the arrow is $\frac{b}{a}$.

Let the vector $\overline{OP}$ represent $a + bi$, and the vector $\overline{OQ}$ represent $c + di$. By definition, the sum is $(a + c) + (b + d)i$. The real part of the sum is $a + c$. This can be represented by $\overline{OS}$. Construct $\overline{ST} \perp \overline{OS}$, $\overline{QV} \perp \overline{ST}$. Make $VT = b$. Then $\overline{ST}$ represents the imaginary part $(b + d)$. Arrows have been chosen in the first quadrant for convenience. Similar results are obtained in the other quadrants. In the study of vectors the sum, represented by $\overline{OT}$, is the *resultant* of $\overline{OP}$ and $\overline{OQ}$. It is also the diagonal of the parallelogram $OQTP$.

Two arrows which are in opposite directions and have the same length are **additive inverses** of each other. Their sum is $0 + 0i$. The number $0 + 0i$, called the **additive identity,** is the only complex number which is *not* represented by an arrow. It is represented by a point.

Subtraction can be defined so that $(a + bi) - (c + di) = (a + bi) + (-c - di)$. Thus $(c + di)$ and $(-c - di)$ are additive inverses. Graphically, the difference of two complex numbers is the sum of the first number and the additive inverse of the other number.

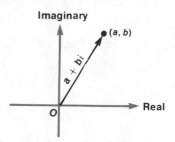

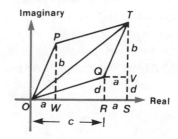

The geometric arrows are analogous to force diagrams in physics.

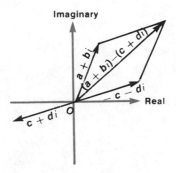

Example

3. **Find the additive inverse of $5 - 2i$.**

$(5 - 2i) + (-5 + 2i) = 0 + 0i$

Therefore, $-5 + 2i$ is the additive inverse of $5 - 2i$.

Examples

4. Subtract $2 + 6i$ from $3 - 7i$.

   $(3 - 7i) - (2 + 6i) = (3 - 2) + (-7 - 6)i = 1 - 13i$

5. Prove that addition of complex numbers is commutative.

   Show that $(a + bi) + (c + di) = (c + di) + (a + bi)$

$(a + bi) + (c + di) = (a + c) + (b + d)i$	*Definition of addition*
$= (c + a) + (d + b)i$	*A_3 for real numbers*
$= (c + di) + (a + bi)$	*Definition of addition*

   Therefore, addition of complex numbers is commutative.

Exercises

Exploratory Write each of the following in the form $a + bi$.

1. $(6 + 3i) + (7 - 2i)$

2. $(-1 - i) + (-3 - 5i)$

3. $(1 + i)(1 - i)$

4. $(8 - 2i)(4 - i)$

5. $(3i^2 - 4)$

6. $1 + i^2 + i^3 + i^4$

Written Write each of the following in the form $a + bi$.

1. i^{47}

2. $(-i)^{23}$

3. $3i^{30}$

4. $(2 + i)(4 - 2i + i^2)$

5. $(1 - 3i)(1 + 3i + 9i^2)$

6. $\dfrac{10 - i}{2 + 3i} \times \dfrac{(2 - 3i)}{(2 - 3i)}$

7. $\dfrac{4}{6 - 5i}$

8. $\dfrac{7}{i^2 - 1}$

9. $\dfrac{12 - i}{5 + 2i}$

10. $\dfrac{5 + 4i}{1 - 2i}$

11. $\dfrac{4 - 3i}{2 + i}$

12. $\dfrac{(1 - i)^2}{(1 + i)^2}$

Solve for x and y.

13. $(x + y) + (3x - y)i = 3 + 5i$

14. $(2x - y) + (3x - 2y)i = -15 + 4i$

Represent each complex number sum graphically.

15. $(5 + i) + (1 - 4i)$

16. $(5 - 2i) + (9 - 2i) + (-12 + 3i)$

17. $(3 + 4i) + (7 - 2i) + (-1 + 3i)$

18. $(5 - 2i) - (2 - 3i)$

19. $(-7 + 8i) + (-1 + 2i)$

20. $(6 - i) + (2 - 3i) - (3 + i)$

Find the magnitude and slope of the corresponding arrow for each complex number.

21. $3 - 5i$

22. $5 + 12i$

23. $4 - i$

24. $1 + i$

Prove each of the following.

25. Addition of complex numbers is associative.

26. The additive inverse of $a + bi$ is $-a - bi$.

27. The set of complex numbers is closed under addition.

28. Multiplication of complex numbers is commutative.

29. Multiplication of complex numbers is associative.

30. The multiplicative inverse of $a + bi$ is $\dfrac{a}{a^2 + b^2} - \dfrac{b}{a^2 + b^2}i$.

31. The set of complex numbers is closed under multiplication.

32. The set of complex numbers $\mathcal{C}$ with $+$, $\cdot$, and $=$ is a field. Use previous problems.

Chapter Summary

1. Two ordered pairs (x_1, y_1) and (x_2, y_2) are equal if and only if $x_1 = x_2$ and $y_1 = y_2$ (33)

2. A Cartesian coordinate system contains the set of points in the plane and the associated set of ordered pairs of real numbers. (34)

3. The set of all ordered pairs of real numbers, (x, y), is indicated by $\mathcal{R} \times \mathcal{R}$ and is called the Cartesian product, or a cross product. (35)

4. The formula for the distance between two points $P(x_1, y_1)$ and $Q(x_2, y_2)$ is $PQ = \sqrt{(x_2 - x_1)^2 + (y_2 - y_1)^2}$. (36)

5. A point $P(x_0, y_0)$ on a line segment AB with $A(x_1, y_1)$, $B(x_2, y_2)$, and $\dfrac{AP}{AB} = k$ has coordinates $x_0 = x_1 + k(x_2 - x_1)$ and $y_0 = y_1 + k(y_2 - y_1)$. (37)

6. The coordinates of the midpoint of a line segment AB with $A(x_1, y_1)$ and $B(x_2, y_2)$ are $\left(\dfrac{x_1 + x_2}{2}, \dfrac{y_1 + y_2}{2}\right)$. (37)

7. The slope m of $\overleftrightarrow{AB}$ through the points (x_1, y_1) and (x_2, y_2) is $m = \dfrac{y_2 - y_1}{x_2 - x_1}$. The slope is sometimes written as $\dfrac{\text{rise}}{\text{run}}$. (39)

8. If the slope of a line is positive, then the line rises to the right. If the slope of a line is negative, then the line falls to the right. (41)

9. The point-slope form of the equation of a line with slope m and through a point (x_1, y_1) is $y - y_1 = m(x - x_1)$. (42)

10. The slope intercept form of the equation of a line with slope m and y-intercept $(0, b)$ is $y = mx + b$. (43)

11. The equation $Ax + By + C = 0$ is called the general form of the equation of a line. (43)

12. The parametric equations of a line are $x = a + bt$ and $y = c + dt$. (44)

13. Two distinct nonvertical lines are parallel if and only if they have the same slope. (47)

14. Two nonvertical lines with slopes m_1 and m_2 are perpendicular if and only if $m_1 m_2 = -1$. (48)

15. The distance between a point $P(x_0, y_0)$ and a line with equation $Ax + By + C = 0$ is $d = \dfrac{|Ax_0 + By_0 + C|}{\sqrt{A^2 + B^2}}$. (51)

16. A complex number is written in the form $a + bi$, where a and b are real numbers. The real part is a. The imaginary part is b. (56)

Chapter Review

2-1 **Find real numbers x and y so that each of the following is true.**

  1. $(14 - x, y - 7) = (21, -13)$
  2. $(\sqrt{x + 1}, \sqrt{2y + 5}) = (2, 3)$

Find $M \times N$.

  3. $M = \{3, 5\}, N = \{1, 2, 3\}$
  4. $M = \{a, b, c\}, N = \{c\}$

2-2 **Find the coordinates of P such that $\dfrac{AP}{AB} = K$.**

  5. $A(7, 1), B(-3, 3), K = \frac{2}{3}$
  6. $A(2, 8), B(0, 0), K = 3$

2-3 **Find the value of K in each set to make the points collinear.**

  7. $(8, K), (K, 4), (2, 3)$
  8. $(7, -1), (K, 2), (1, 5)$

  9. Determine if the line through $(5, 3)$ and $(2, 7)$ rises or falls to the right. Let slope $m = \tan \alpha$. Decide whether $\alpha < 90°$ or $90° < \alpha < 180°$.

2-4 **Write the general form of the equation of each line described.**

  10. Passes through $(4, 1)$ and $(1, 7)$
  11. Passes through $(1, 2)$ and has slope $\frac{4}{3}$.
  12. Has parametric equation $x = 1 - 3t$ and $y = -2 + t$.

2-5 **Write the equation of each line described below.**

  13. Parallel to $3x - 5y = 11$ and passes through $(4, 7)$
  14. Perpendicular to $8x - y = 4$ and passes through $\left(1, \frac{5}{16}\right)$

2-6 **Find each distance given the following conditions.**

  15. From $(4, -7)$ to the line $3x - 4y - 5 = 0$
  16. Between the lines $4x + 5y - 7 = 0$ and $4x + 5y + 2 = 0$

2-7 **Prove each of the following.**

  17. The median of an isosceles trapezoid is parallel to the bases.
  18. If a parallelogram has one right angle, then it is a rectangle.

2-8 **Find the equation of the locus of points satisfying each of the following conditions.**

  19. All points three units from $(2, -5)$.
  20. Points equidistant from $(2, 4)$ and $(4, 4)$.

2-9 **Write each of the following in the form $a + bi$.**

  21. $(4 + 5i) + (2 - 7i)$
  22. $\dfrac{2 - i}{1 + i} + \dfrac{4}{1 - i}$

  23. Find the magnitude and slope of $12 - 5i$.

Chapter Test

Find R X S.

1. $R = \{-2, 0, 1\}, S = \{4, 8, 12\}$

2. $R = \{1, 2, 3\}, S = \{10, 9, 8\}$

Find the distance between each pair of points. Then, write a pair of parametric equations for each line.

3. $A(2, 3), B(-1, 5)$

4. $A(1, 4), B(3, -1)$

Find the slope of the line through the given points.

5. $(3, 2), (4, 6)$

6. $(0, 0), (-2, 3)$

Write the general form of the equation of each line described.

7. Passes through $(0, -3)$ with slope $\frac{3}{5}$

8. Passes through $(-1, -3)$ and $(4, -3)$

9. Perpendicular to $y = \frac{2}{3}x + 5$ and passes through $(0, 7)$

10. Parallel to $y = -4x + 5$ and passes through $(1, 3)$

Find each distance given the following conditions.

11. From $(2, 3)$ to the line $3x - 4y = 0$

12. Between the lines $2x + 3y = 1$ and $2x + 3y = 4$

Prove each of the following.

13. The diagonals of a rhombus are perpendicular.

14. The diagonals of an isosceles trapezoid are congruent.

Sketch the graph of each locus.

15. All points 4 units from $(1, 2)$

16. $\{(x, y)|y \leq 2x + 1\}$

Find the magnitude and slope of the corresponding arrow for each complex number.

17. $2 + 2i$

18. $6 - 8i$

19. $7 + 5i$

20. $5 + 6i$

Computers

Now and In the Future

The evolution of the computer and its use has been so rapid that it staggers the imagination. A story commonly heard in the industry compares the development of the automobile and the computer. Had the auto progressed as rapidly as the computer, we would now be driving cars that would get 1500 miles to the gallon and would cost only $7.50.

Each new generation of computer has increased speed of computation and reliability tenfold or more, memory capacity twenty fold, and has decreased component costs. Lately only approximately six years have lapsed for each new generation to take place. The second generation of computers occurred in the early 1960's. This generation developed solid-state electronics. Transistors replaced vacuum tubes. The third generation of computers used integrated circuits which were tiny chemically treated circuits instead of individually wired components. By the mid-1970's, the fourth generation of computers was established. Microprocessors, which are entire sub-systems with multiple functions through wafers of various integrated circuits, replaced circuits made by connecting smaller integrated circuits.

The latter is sometimes referred to as a "computer on a chip." It has allowed large computer installations to be smaller, faster and cheaper. But it has also made it possible for powerful but more elementary machines to be produced so that they are affordable even in small businesses, schools, and homes. Today a computer can be so small as to be held in the hand. Some companies have calculator size computers capable of complex functions.

A microcomputer chip contains thousands of individual transistors.

Robots are computers of the future. These machines will be walking computers capable of performing tasks that involve some decision making such as routine household chores. They will also be used to perform tasks such as assembly line jobs and dangerous jobs.

Although it is likely that certain upper limits on speed and capacity will be determined by physical laws concerning the speed of electrical impulses, molecular size, and the like, new breakthroughs continue to be made in all areas of computer manufacturing. Fiber optics, laser impulses, advances in input and output devices, and continued refinement of the solid-state art are expected to develop computers so fast and so reliable that they will be beyond anything imaginable today.

This computer has the power of a computer that twenty years ago would have weighed a ton.

Exercises **Write programs for each of the following.**

1. Given the coordinates of the endpoints of a line segment (x_1, y_1) and (x_2, y_2), compute and output the midpoint P and the slope M. Account for the case of a vertical line segment.

2. Given the coordinates of three points, determine if they are collinear. Output the coordinates of the points and a statement of collinearity.

3. Given the length of the legs of a right triangle, compute the length of the hypotenuse. Print out the perimeter and area of the right triangle.

4. Given a straight line in the form $Ax + By = C$, read in the values of A, B, and C. Compute and print out the values of the slope of the line (M = $-$A $\div$ B), the vertical intercept (V = C $\div$ B), and the horizontal intercept (H = C $\div$ A). Print out the values M, V, and H.

Given the three pairs of coordinates of vertices of a triangle, write programs to test for the following. Note: In comparing distances, it is better to compare their squares because of truncating errors involved. Even so it is possible that special methods may be necessary when testing for equality of distance.

5. The triangle does not exist.

6. The triangle is isosceles but not equilateral.

7. The triangle is equilateral.

8. The triangle is right but not isosceles.

9. The triangle is right and isosceles.

10. The triangle is scalene.

Given two sets of coordinates of points, test and output the results for each of the following.

11. They lie on the same line.

12. They lie on parallel lines.

13. Given the coordinates of the center and the radius of a circle, input coordinates of various points. Determine if the points are inside, outside, or on the circle. Output the results.

14. Given the coordinate of the four vertices of a quadrilateral, determine if they form a parallelogram, rectangle, square, or a rhombus. Output the results.

Chapter 3

For some people, the choice of the day's activities depends on the weather forecast. Mathematics also uses dependent relationships. These generally involve the pairing of elements through formulas or rules, listings or rosters, or graphs.

3-1 Relations

A pairing of elements of a set with elements of the same or a second set is called a mathematical relation. The following set is a relation.

$$\{(2, 5), (2, 6), (7, 10), (6, 18)\}$$

> **A relation R is a <u>set</u> of ordered pairs. The domain, D(R), of the relation is the <u>set</u> of all first elements. The range, R(R), is the <u>set</u> of all second elements.**

✳ emphasize word "set"

Definition of Relation, Domain, and Range

If M and N are two sets, the Cartesian product $M \times N$ can be formed. This is the set of all possible ordered pairs for which the first element is selected from M and the second from N.

$$M \times N = \{(x, y) \mid x \in M \text{ and } y \in N\}$$

If a relation R is a specific subset of $M \times N$, it is referred to as a relation from M to N.

Example

1. Let $M = \{1, 2, 3\}$ and $N = \{5, 9\}$. Name four relations in $M \times N$.

    $R_1 = \{(1, 5), (2, 5), (3, 5)\}$
    $R_2 = \{(1, 5), (2, 9)\}$
    $R_3 = \{(1, 9), (3, 5), (3, 9)\}$
    $R_4 = \{(1, 5), (1, 9), (2, 5), (2, 9), (3, 5), (3, 9)\}$

    The relation R_4 is $M \times N$ itself.

Two relations are *equal* if and only if they contain the same ordered pairs. Most relations studied in this book are subsets of the Cartesian product of the real number system with itself, $\mathcal{R} \times \mathcal{R}$. The domain or range of a relation may be restricted to subsets of the real numbers.

Examples

2. **Name the domain and range of** $\{(x, x^2)|x \in \mathcal{R}\}$.

    The domain is the set of real numbers.
    The range is the set of nonnegative real numbers.

    ✱ emphasize the importance of answering these questions

3. **Name the domain and range of** $\left\{(x, y)|y = \dfrac{1}{x - 1}\right\}$.

    The domain is the set of real numbers excluding 1.
    The range is the set of real numbers excluding 0.

The graph of a relation is the graph of all its ordered pairs.

Example

4. **Graph the following relation.**

    $T = \{(x, y)|y = 2x\}$

    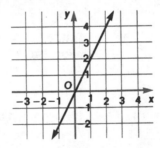

    Only a portion of the entire graph can be drawn.

A mathematical relation makes a correspondence between the elements of its domain and range. This relationship is called a **mapping**. Thus, $-1 \rightarrow -2$ is read -1 *maps into* -2 or -1 *corresponds with* -2. The relation T in Example **4** can be written $T:x \rightarrow 2x$. It can be said that x maps into y where $y = 2x$.

Suppose each element of the domain corresponds to exactly one element of the range and each element of the range corresponds to exactly one element of the domain. Then the relation is called **one-to-one**, abbreviated 1–1. Thus S is 1–1 but V and W are not.

✱ note importance for future material (3-2)

$$S = \{(1, 2), (3, 4), (2, 5)\} \quad yes$$
$$V = \{(1, 2), (1, 3), (4, 1)\} \quad no$$
$$W = \{(1, 2), (2, 3), (3, 2)\} \quad no$$

No two ordered pairs have the same first element or the same second element for a 1–1 function.

If the range of a relation in $M \times N$ is the entire set N, then the relation is **onto** N. The relation $T = \{(x, y) | y = 2x, x \in Z\}$ is defined **into** $\mathcal{R}$ but **onto** the set of even integers. This relation is also 1–1.

✱ *note importance for future material*

Exercises

Exploratory Let $M = \{1, 2\}$ and $N = \{a, b, c\}$.

1. List $M \times N$.
2. List $N \times M$.
3. Is $(1, c) \in M \times N$?
4. Is the relation $S = \{(1, a), (2, b), (1, c)\}$ in $M \times N$?
5. Find a relation in $M \times N$ that is 1–1.

Assume that each relation is defined in $\mathcal{R} \times \mathcal{R}$. Name the domain and range of each relation.

6. $\{(x, y) | y = x^2\}$
7. $\{(x, y) | y = \sqrt{x}\}$
8. $\left\{(x, y) | y = \dfrac{2}{x}\right\}$

Written Assume that each relation is defined in $\mathcal{R} \times \mathcal{R}$. **Name the domain and range of each relation.**

1. $\{(x, y) | y^3 = x\}$
2. $\left\{(x, y) | y = \dfrac{2x}{x - 1}\right\}$
   (Solve for x in terms of y.)
3. $\{(x, y) | y = x^2 - x\}$
   (Use the quadratic formula.)
4. $\{(x, y) | x + y = 2 \text{ and } x < 3\}$
5. $\{(x, y) | x^2 + y^2 = 4\}$
6. $\{(x, y) | y^2 = x^2\}$

Draw the graph of each relation.

7. $S = \{(x, y) | x^2 + y^2 = 4, -1 \le x \le 1\}$
8. $T = \{(x, y) | x^2 + y^2 = 4, -2 \le x \le -1, 1 \le x \le 2\}$
9. $S \cup T$
10. $S \cap T$
11. $\{(x, y) | x, y \in \mathcal{R}\} \cap S$

Write the relation for each graph.

12.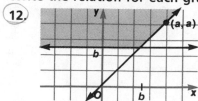

13.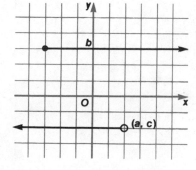

Challenge Find the domain and range of the relation U.

$$U = \left\{(x, y) \mid y = \sqrt{\frac{x + 1}{x - 2}}\right\}$$

(Hint: Consider two separate cases which will ensure that the radicand is nonnegative. Case **1:** $x + 1 \geq 0$ and $x - 2 > 0$. Case **2:** $x + 1 \leq 0$ and $x - 2 < 0$.)

3-2 Functions

There are special relations called **functions.** Many useful and mathematically interesting relations are functions.

✻ emphasize "relation"

A function is a relation such that for each first element there corresponds a *unique* second element.

Definition of Function

A function need not be 1–1 as the function listed below demonstrates. *It may be "many to one" but never "one to many."*

$$\{(a_1, b_1), (a_2, b_2), (a_3, b_2)\}$$

On the other hand, if a relation is 1–1 then it is a function.

$$\{(a_1, b_1), (a_2, b_2), (a_3, b_3)\}$$

By considering the graphs of relations, it will be clear how to distinguish those which are functions. Figures **a** and **b** are relations which are *not* functions. Figures **c** and **d** are relations which are functions.

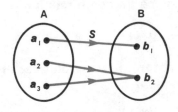

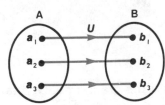

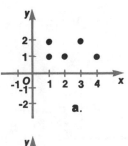

a.

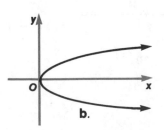

b.

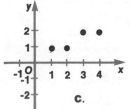

c.

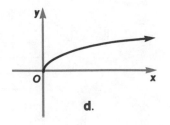

d.

For a relation to be a function, no vertical line can be drawn that will intersect the graph of the relation in more than one point of the graph.

✳ review vertical and horizontal line test/ inverse relations

A relation S is a function if and only if $(a, b) \in S$ and $(a, c) \in S$ Implies $b = c$.

Alternate Definition of Function.

Examples

1. **Given the relation $T = \{(x, y)|y = 3x\}$, show that T is a function.**

   $(a, b) \in T$ means $b = 3a$. $(a, c) \in T$ means $c = 3a$.   *Note: Show if $(a, b) \in T$ and $(a, c) \in T$, then $b = c$.*

   Since $b = 3a$ and $c = 3a$, then $b = c$. Therefore, T is a function.

2. **Given the relation $U = \{(x, y)|y^2 = 3x\}$, determine if it is a function.**

   $(a, b) \in U$ means $b^2 = 3a$. $(a, c) \in U$ means $c^2 = 3a$.   *Note: $(3, -3)$ and $(3, 3)$ both belong to U.*

   Since $b^2 = 3a$ and $c^2 = 3a$, $b^2 = c^2$. However, $b^2 = c^2$ does not imply $b = c$, only that $|b| = |c|$. Therefore, U is not a function.

The ordered pair (a, b) of the function f can be represented by $b = f(a)$. The value of $f(a)$ is the **value** of the function f at a. The element $f(a)$ is not the function itself. The function f contains all the ordered pairs. The element $f(a)$ is the element of the range which corresponds to element a of the domain.

The ordered pair $(\pi, 3)$ of the function f also can be named by $(\pi, f(\pi))$ or by $f{:}\pi \rightarrow 3$. In general, the complete function is described by the notation $y = f(x)$, especially when plotting in an xy-coordinate system. The ordered pairs are given the general form (x, y) or $(x, f(x))$.

Note: $b = f(a)$ is read b equals f of a.

✳ review function notation /

Example

3. **Draw the graph of the function f defined by $f = \{(x, y)|y = x^2 - 1$ for $x \in \langle 0, 2]$ and $y = -x$ for $x \in [-2, 0]\}$.**

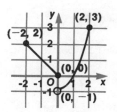

Often the notation $f(x) = \begin{cases} x^2 - 1, x \in \langle 0, 2] \\ -x, x \in [-2, 0] \end{cases}$ is used to define functions similar to the one given in the example. It is impossible to draw the graph of f without lifting the pencil from the paper. A function of this type is called a _discontinuous_ _function_. With a _discontinuous function_, it is often necessary to specify the intervals in which it is defined.

✳ introduce

Example

4. **Find the domain and range of the function $g\!:\!y = \dfrac{1}{2x^2 - 2}$**

The domain of g, symbolized $D(g)$, is the set of all real numbers for which $2x^2 - 2 \neq 0$.

$$2x^2 - 2 \neq 0$$
$$x^2 \neq 1$$
$$x \neq 1 \quad \text{and} \quad x \neq -1$$

The domain is the set of all real numbers except 1 and -1. To find the range, $R(g)$, solve for x in terms of y.

$$y = \frac{1}{2x^2 - 2}$$
$$2x^2 - 2 = \frac{1}{y}$$
$$x^2 = \frac{1}{2y} + 1$$
$$x = \pm \sqrt{\frac{1}{2y} + 1}$$

This means y must be such that $\dfrac{1}{2y} + 1 \geq 0$ if x is to be real. Since y cannot be 0, two cases remain.

If $y > 0$, then $\dfrac{1}{2y} \geq -1$.

$$\frac{1}{2} \geq -y$$
$$-\frac{1}{2} \leq y \qquad \textit{Multiply by } -1.$$

Since $y > 0$, and $-\dfrac{1}{2} \leq y, y > 0$.

If $y < 0$, then $\dfrac{1}{2y} \geq -1$.

$$\frac{1}{2} \leq -y \qquad \textit{y is negative.}$$
$$-\frac{1}{2} \geq y \qquad \textit{Multiply by } -1.$$

Since $y < 0$ and $-\dfrac{1}{2} \geq y, -\dfrac{1}{2} \geq y$.

The complete range contains all real numbers for which $y \in \langle 0, \to \rangle$ or $y \in \left\langle \leftarrow, -\dfrac{1}{2} \right]$. The range of f contains all real numbers <u>except</u> those in the interval $\left\langle -\dfrac{1}{2}, 0 \right]$.

✳ note

Exercises

Exploratory Given that $f:x \to \dfrac{24}{x} - 2$, find each image. ✻ discuss

1. $f(3)$
2. $f(-3)$
3. $-f(3)$
4. $f(0)$

5. $f(6)$
6. $f(\pi)$
7. $f(x^2)$
8. $f\left(\dfrac{24}{x+2}\right)$

9. What is the relationship between the number of elements in the domain and range of a function which is $1 - 1$?

10. If a relation is $1-1$, is it necessarily a function? Explain fully.

Written Consider the function f described by the table of values.

x	-3	-2	-1	0	1	2	3
$f(x)$	0	1	-1	1	-2	-3	0

Find each of the following.

1. $f(1)$
2. $f(-3)$
3. a for which $f(a) = 1$
4. a for which $f(a) = a$
5. a for which $f(a) = 0$.

6. If $f(x) = x^3 - x^2 - 6x + 4$, find $f(0)$, $f(3)$ and $f(-2)$. Notice that the three values are identical. Explain this result by appropriate grouping and factoring of f.

7. Given $f:x \to x - 1$ and $g:x \to \dfrac{x^2 - 1}{x + 1}$, determine the domain and range of each. Draw their graphs. Describe in words the difference and similarity of f and g.

Given the following graph of the function f. Find each of the following.

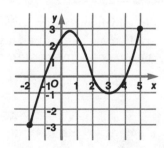

8. $D(f)$
9. $R(f)$
10. All zeros of f ✻ discuss
11. The value of x for which $f(x)$ is a maximum.
12. The value of x for which $f(x)$ is a minimum.
13. The maximum value for $f(x)$.
14. The minimum value for $f(x)$.
15. The maximum value for $f(x)$, if f is defined on $[0, 4]$.
16. The minimum value for $f(x)$, if f is defined on $[0, 4]$.

If $f(x) = 3x - 1$ and $g(x) = x^2 + 1$, find each image.

17. $f(x + h)$ **18.** $g(x + h)$ **19.** $f(x) + g(x)$

Graph each relation. Determine if it is a function.

20. $f(x) = \begin{cases} x, x \geq 0 \\ -x, x < 0 \end{cases}$ **21.** $f(x) = \begin{cases} x^2, x \geq 0 \\ -x^2, x < 0 \end{cases}$ **22.** $f(x) = \begin{cases} x, x \in [-1, 4] \\ -x, x < 0 \end{cases}$

23. $f: \begin{cases} y^2 = x, x \geq 0 \\ y = 0, x < 0 \end{cases}$ **24.** $f: \begin{cases} y = \sqrt{1 - x^2}, x \in [0, 1] \\ y = -\sqrt{1 - (x - 2)^2}, x \in \langle 1, 3] \end{cases}$

25. $f(x) = \begin{cases} 1, x \text{ an even integer} \\ 0, x \text{ an odd integer} \end{cases}$

Challenge   Consider the implication if (a, b) and (a, c) are both elements of the given relations.

1. Show that $f: y = \dfrac{3}{x - 2}, x \neq 2$ is a function.   **2.** Show that $g: x^2 - y^2 = 1$ is not a function.

3. Determine the domain and range of the function $g: x \to \dfrac{1}{3x^2 + 3}$.

3–3   Special Functions

   Some functions are fundamental enough to warrant particular attention. Many more complicated functions are made up of variations on these functions.

A constant function is a function which assigns the same real number to every element of the domain.

Constant Function

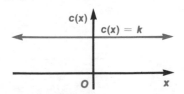

   A constant function, c, is a function in which the range contains a single element. The function itself may be defined as $c(x) = k$ for every $x \in D(c)$. Graphically a horizontal line contains every point in the graph of c.

A constant function may be discontinuous.

The identity function maps each element of the domain into itself. This function is denoted I.

Identity Function

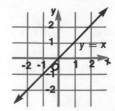

   Thus, $I(x) = x$ for every element in $D(I)$. The graph of the function is the line $y = x$ when the domain is the set of all real numbers.

A **linear function** is a function of the form $f(x) = mx + b$ for $m, b \in \mathcal{R}$ and $x \in D(f)$.

Linear Function

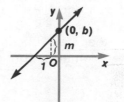

The graph of f is determined by its slope m and its y-intercept $(0, b)$.

A constant function, whose graph is a horizontal line with slope 0, is a linear function. The equation can be written $y = 0x + b$ or $y = b$. A vertical line is *not* a linear function for two reasons. Its slope is *not defined*, and it is a relation which is *not* a *function*.

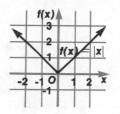

The **absolute value function** can be defined as follows.

$$f(x) = |x| = \begin{cases} x, x \geq 0 \\ -x, x < 0 \end{cases}$$

Absolute Value Function

A **step function** is a discontinuous function which "jumps" from one level to another.

Step Function

A step function often is compared with a postage stamp function or a taxicab function. The charge for stamps or taxi rides is always a multiple of some basic jump in cost, never an "in-between" amount. Another step function is the **greatest integer function**.

✳ note that ⟦x⟧ will be used instead of [x]

The **greatest integer function** is a step function f such that $f(x) = [x]$, where $[x]$ is the greatest integer *not greater than* x.

Greatest Integer Function

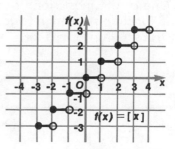

✳ working definition: what was the last integer you passed in moving from left to right on the number line?
$$⟦2\tfrac{3}{4}⟧ \neq -2 \text{ but } = -3$$

By studying the graph, it is clear that if *a* is an integer and *a* ≤ *x* < *a* + 1, then [*x*] = *a*. Notice the designation of the endpoints of the intervals. This function does not merely truncate the decimal part of numbers which are nonintegers. If it did, then *f*(1.7) would be 1 and *f*(−1.7) would be −1. Instead, [1.7] = 1, but [−1.7] = −2.

There are other step functions besides those whose graphs are horizontal segments. Consider the function in the figure.

The greatest integer function assigns an integer to each real number. It assigns the integer immediately left of the point on the number line unless the number itself is an integer.

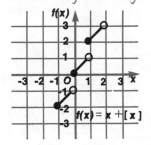

$f(x) = x + [x]$

A **periodic function** is a function such that $f(x + p) = f(x)$ for some *p* and all *x* ∈ *D*(*f*).

Periodic Function

The least positive value for *p* for which $f(x + p) = f(x)$ is true is called the *fundamental period*. Further multiplies of *p* will create other periods. The figure shows a periodic function.

The graph repeats itself in regular intervals.

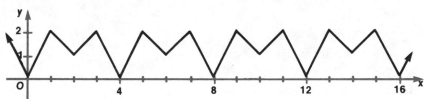

If the graph of this function continued indefinitely, a period might be 4, 8, 12, 16, . . . units long. It is clear that 4 is the fundamental period. Thus, the following is true.

$$f(5) = f(1 + 4) = f(1) = 2$$
$$f(9.7) = f(5.7 + 4) = f(5.7) = f(1.7 + 4) = f(1.7)$$

One of the most significant of the periodic functions is the sine function studied in trigonometry. The fundamental period of the sine function is 2π. Thus, $\sin (x + 2\pi) = \sin x$.

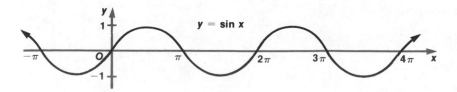

$y = \sin x$

Example

1. Graph $f: x \rightarrow 3.75$. Identify the function.

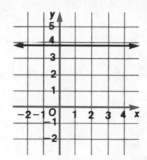

Constant function

Exercises

Exploratory Identify each function as a constant (C), identity(*I*), linear (L), or none of these (N).

1. $\{(3, 3), (5, 5), (-2, -2) (a, a)\}$

2. $\{(x, y)|y = \pi\}$

3. $\{(3, 3), (5, 3), (-2, 3) (-3, 3)\}$

4. $\{(x, y)|y = 3x - 7\}$

5. $\{(x, y)|2y = 4 - 5x\}$

6. $\{(x, y)|y = -5x + x^2\}$

7. $\{(3, 5), (4, 6), (5, 7), (6, 8)\}$

8. $\{(x, y)|y - x = 0\}$

9. $\{(x, y)|y = \begin{cases} -x, x < 0 \\ x, x \geq 0 \end{cases}\}$

10. $\{(x, y)|y = \begin{cases} -|x|, x \geq 0 \\ |x|, x < 0 \end{cases}\}$

Written Sketch each graph. Unless noted, use $x \in \mathcal{R}$.

1. $y = -|x|, x \in \{-3, -2, -1, 0, 1, 2, 3\}$

2. $y = |x| + 1$

3. $y = |x + 1|$

4. $y = 1 - |x|$

5. $y = 2|x|$

6. $y = \dfrac{|x|}{x}$

7. $|xy| = 0, y \in \mathcal{R}$

8. $|x| + |y| = 4$

9. $y = [x + 1]$

Find $f(x)$ for $x \in \{-2, -1, 0, 1, 2\}$

10. $f(x) = [x] - x + |x|$

11. $f(x) = x - x^2 + |x|$

Solve each of the following.

12. Find a linear function f whose slope is -3 and for which $f(-1) = -2$.

13. Find the slope of the linear function g if $g(4) = -2$ and $g(-1) = 2$. ✶ relate to C2

14. If h is a constant function such that $h(-2) = 5$, find $h(3)$.

Find the values of x for which each sentence is true.

15. $|x + 2| = x + 2$

16. $|x - 2| = 2 - x$

17. $|3x - 2| = 8$

18. $|5x + 4| = -2$

19. $-|x + 2| = -1$

20. $|2x - 5| > 7$

Challenge Solve each of the following.

1. For the linear function f, $f(x) = 3x + 2$. Show that the point $P(s - 1, 3s - 1)$ lies on the graph of f, where s is any real number.

2. Consider the periodic function f where $f(x + p) = f(x)$. Show that $f(x + 3p) = f(x)$.

3. If f, has a period of 2π, give the smallest three positive values of x such that $f(-\pi) = f(x)$.

3-4 The Algebra of Functions

＊emphasize

It often is possible as well as desirable to perform certain algebraic operations with functions if their domains and ranges are compatible.

> If f and g are functions, then $f + g$ and $f \cdot g$ are functions such that
>
> $$(f + g)(x) = f(x) + g(x)$$
> $$(f \cdot g)(x) = f(x) \cdot g(x)$$
>
> where $D(f + g) = D(f \cdot g) = D(f) \cap D(g)$. ✻

Adding and Multiplying Functions

＊note / also contrast multiplication with composition (3-5)

The domain of $f + g$ and $f \cdot g$ is the intersection of the domains of f and g. It makes no sense to add or multiply functions for values of x for which one of the functions is not defined.

Example

1. Given $f = \{(0, 1), (2, 3), (4, 1)\}$ and $g = \{(1, 2), (0, 3), (2, -1), (-2, 5)\}$, find $f + g$ and $f \cdot g$.

   $$f + g = \{(0, 4), (2, 2)\}$$
   $$f \cdot g = \{(0, 3), (2, -3)\}$$

   Notice that
   $$D(f) \cap D(g) = \{0, 2\}.$$

To add two or more functions, add the values of each function for each x in the intersection of their domains.

To find points on $f + g$, use the edge of a piece of paper to mark x and $f(x)$. Slide the paper along the vertical line between $(x, 0)$ and $(x, f(x))$ until x is superimposed on $g(x)$. The ordinate of $f + g$ is the ordinate of the point corresponding to $f(x)$ on the piece of paper.

Let f and g be functions such that $D(f) \cap D(g) \neq \emptyset$. Then the

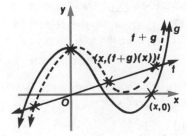

＊ discuss this technique

functions $-f, f - g, \frac{1}{f}$ and $\frac{1}{g}$ are defined in the following way.

1. $-f = -1f$ or $-(f(x)) = -1 \cdot f(x)$
2. $f - g = f + (-g)$ or $(f - g)(x) = f(x) - g(x)$
3. $\left(\frac{1}{f}\right)(x) = \frac{1}{f(x)}$ if $f(x) \neq 0$
4. $\left(\frac{f}{g}\right)(x) = \left(f \cdot \frac{1}{g}\right)(x) = \frac{f(x)}{g(x)}$ if $g(x) \neq 0$

Operations with Functions

Notice that the functions $-f$ and $\frac{1}{f}$ have the following important properties.

$(a, -b) \in -f$ if and only if $(a, b) \in f$

$\left(a, \frac{1}{b}\right) \in \frac{1}{f}$ if and only if $(a, b) \in f$ and $b \neq 0$.

Properties of Functions

Example

2. Given $f = \{(0, 3), (1, 4), (2, 0), (3, 2)\}$ and $g = \{(0, -1), (1, 4), (2, 1), (4, 2)\}$, find $f - g, \frac{g}{f}$, and $\frac{f}{g}$.

$$f - g = \{(0, 4), (1, 0), (2, -1)\}$$
$$\frac{g}{f} = \left\{\left(0, -\frac{1}{3}\right), (1, 1)\right\}$$
$$\frac{f}{g} = \{(0, -3), (1, 1), (2, 0)\}$$

Notice that $2 \notin D\left(\frac{g}{f}\right)$.

Exercises

Exploratory Given $f = \{(1, -1), (2, 3), (-3, 0)\}$ and $g = \{(0, 3), (1, 1), (2, -4), (3, 5)\}$, find each function.

1. $f + g$
2. $g + f$
3. $f \cdot g$
4. $g \cdot f$
5. $f - g$
6. $g - f$
7. $\frac{f}{g}$
8. $\frac{g}{f}$

Written Given that $f(x) = 3x + 1$ and $g(x) = 2x - 3$, find each function.

1. $f + g$
2. $g + f$
3. $f \cdot g$
4. $g \cdot f$

5. $f - g$ 6. $g - f$ 7. $\dfrac{f}{g}$ 8. $\dfrac{g}{f}$

Given that f is the identity function, $f(x) = x$, and g is the reciprocal function, $g(x) = \dfrac{1}{x}$, find each function.

9. $f + g$ 10. $g + f$ 11. $f \cdot g$ 12. $g \cdot f$

13. $f - g$ 14. $g - f$ 15. $\dfrac{f}{g}$ 16. $\dfrac{g}{f}$

Sketch each function.

17. $y = x + |x|$ 18. $y = x \cdot |x|$ 19. $y = |x - 1| + x$

20. $y = \dfrac{x}{|x|}$ 21. $y = \dfrac{1}{x + |x|}$ 22. $y = [-x]$

23. $y = -[x]$ 24. $y = x - [x]$ 25. $y = |x| + [x]$

Find a linear function f whose graph has the following conditions.

26. parallel to the graph of $3x + y = 6$; $f(4) = 5$ 27. perpendicular to the graph of $2x - 3y = 7$; $f(6) = \dfrac{1}{2}$

Challenge If **O** represents the **zero function**, $\{(x, y) | y = 0$ for all $x \in D(f)\}$, show that $f + (-f) = 0$.

3–5 Composition of Functions

An algebraic operation unique to functions is the **composition of functions.**

> If f and g denote functions, then their **composition,** denoted $f \circ g$, is the function such that $(f \circ g)(x) = f(g(x))$. Its domain is $D(f \circ g) = \{x | x \in D(g)$ and $g(x) \in D(f)\}$.

The figure illustrates the definition

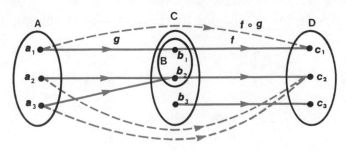

[Margin notes:]
* emphasize difference between $f \circ g$ and $f \circ g$ / and the order

Composition of Function

* save discussion of this statement until examples have been discussed

* try to side step explaining this diagram

$$D(g) = A = \{a_1, a_2, a_3\}$$
$$R(g) = B = \{b_1, b_2\}$$
$$D(f) = C = \{b_1, b_2, b_3\}$$
$$R(f) = D = \{c_1, c_2, c_3\}$$

$$g = \{(a_1, b_1), (a_2, b_2), (a_3, b_2)\}$$
$$f = \{(b_1, c_1), (b_2, c_2), (b_3, c_3)\}$$
$$f \circ g = \{(a_1, c_1), (a_2, c_2), (a_3, c_2)\}$$
$$D\,(f \circ g) = \{a_1, a_2, a_3\} = D(g)$$
$$R\,(g) = \{b_1, b_2\} \subseteq D(f)$$
$$R\,(f \circ g) = \{c_1, c_2\} \subseteq R(f)$$

✷ do example 2 before 1

Examples

1. **Let $f = \{(0, 1), (1, 2), (3, 5), (4, 1)\}$ and $g = \{(0, 2), (1, 3), (5, 4)\}$. Find $f \circ g$ and $g \circ f$.**

$$f \circ g = \{(1, 5), (5, 1)\}$$
$$g \circ f = \{(0, 3), (3, 4), (4, 3)\}$$

   Notice $D\,(f \circ g) = \{1, 5\} \subseteq D(g)$
   $R(f \circ g) = \{5, 1\} \subseteq R(f)$
   $D(g \circ f) = \{0, 3, 4\} \subseteq D(f)$
   $R(g \circ f) = \{3, 4\} \subseteq R(g)$

   It should be clear that every element in the domain of $f \circ g$ is in the domain of g, and every element in the range of $f \circ g$ is in the range of f.

2. **Let f and g be functions such that $f : x \rightarrow \sqrt{x}$ and $g : x \rightarrow 2x + 1$. Find $f \circ g$.**

   Since $D(f) = [0, \rightarrow)$, and $(f \circ g)(x) = f(g(x))$, only nonnegative values of $g(x)$ can be used.

$$g(x) \geq 0$$
$$2x + 1 \geq 0$$
$$2x \geq -1$$
$$x \geq -\frac{1}{2}$$

   Therefore, $D(f \circ g) = \left[-\dfrac{1}{2}, \rightarrow\right) \subseteq D(g)$ and $R\,(f \circ g) = R(f)$.

   $(f \circ g)(x) = f(g(x)) = f(2x + 1) = \sqrt{2x + 1}$ for $x \geq -\dfrac{1}{2}$.

In general, the composition of functions is not commutative. That is, $f \circ g$ is not always the same function as $g \circ f$. However, some special cases do exist where commutativity holds.

Example

3.   Let $f(x) = x^2$ and $g(x) = \dfrac{1}{x}$. Find $f \circ g$ and $g \circ f$.

$$(f \circ g)\,(x) = f(g(x)) = f\!\left(\frac{1}{x}\right) = \left(\frac{1}{x}\right)^2 = \frac{1}{x^2}$$

$$(g \circ f)\,(x) = g(f(x)) = g(x^2) = \frac{1}{x^2}$$

Here $f \circ g = g \circ f$. The range of $f \circ g$ is all positive real numbers, although $R(f)$ includes 0. The domain of $g \circ f$ is all real numbers except 0, while $D(f)$ includes 0.

The composition of more than two functions is possible. If f, g, and h are functions, then $(f \circ g \circ h)(x) = (f \circ g)\,(h(x)) = f(g(h(x)))$. The domains and ranges of the individual functions must be properly limited.

Exercises

Exploratory   For each of the given pairs of functions, find $f \circ g$ and $g \circ f$.

1. $f = \{(1, -1), (2, 3), (-3, 0)\}$
     $g = \{(0, 3), (1, 1), (2, -4), (3, 5)\}$

2. $f(x) = 3x + 1$
     $g(x) = 2x - 3$

3. $f(x) = x$ (identity function)
     $g(x) = \dfrac{1}{x}$ (reciprocal function)

4. $f(x) = \dfrac{1}{x^2 - 1}$
     $g(x) = \dfrac{1}{x}$

5. $f(x) = \sqrt{x}$
     $g = \{(1, -1), (2, 4), (3, 0), (-2, 5)\}$

If $f(x) = x^2 + 1$ and $g(x) = x - 1$, find each of the following.

6. $(f \circ g)\,(-1)$

7. $(g \circ f)\,(-1)$

8. $(f \circ g)\,(0)$

9. $(g \circ f)\,(0)$

Written   Find $f \circ g \circ h$ for each of the following.

1. $f(x) = 2x$
     $g(x) = x^2$
     $h(x) = x + 1$

2. $f(x) = x^3$
     $g(x) = \dfrac{1}{x}$
     $h(x) = \dfrac{3}{x + 2}$

3. $f(t) = t^2$
     $g(t) = 3t$
     $h(t) = \sqrt{t^2 - 1}$

4. $f = \{(0, -3), (2, 5), (-1, 1), (4, 2)\};\ g = \{(-1, 2), (4, 2), (0, -1)\};\ h = \{(4, 2), (1, 0), (3, -1)\}$

Find $f \circ g$ and $g \circ f$ for each of the following. Specify the domain and range of each.

5. $f(x) = \sqrt{x}$
     $g(x) = x^3$

6. $f(x) = \sqrt{x}$
     $g(x) = x^2$

7. $f(u) = \sqrt[3]{u}$
     $g(u) = u^3$

8. $f(q) = \sqrt{q}$
$g(q) = 2q^2 - 1$

9. $f(t) = \sqrt{t}$
$g(t) = 1 - 3t^2$

Find separate functions to express each function as the composition of two or more functions.

10. $m: x \rightarrow \sqrt{x^2}$

11. $n: r \rightarrow \sqrt{r^2 - 1}$

12. $p: x \rightarrow (2x^6 - 4x)^{25}$

13. $q: x \rightarrow \left(\dfrac{x + 1}{x - 1}\right)^2$

Use more than two functions.

14. $r: z \rightarrow \dfrac{3}{2 + \dfrac{1}{\sqrt{z}}}$

Use four functions.

15. $s: x \rightarrow \dfrac{3(x + 1)^2}{2(x + 2)}$

(Hint: First express $x + 2$ as $(x + 1)$ + 1.)

16. If $f(t) = t + \dfrac{1}{t}$, $g(s) = \sqrt{s^2 - 1}$ and $h(r) = r + 1$, find $f \circ g \circ h$.

Challenge   Sketch the following functions. Describe what happens to the graph of g whenever the graph of $f \circ g$ is such that $f(x) = |x|$.

1. $f \circ g$ where $f(x) = |x|$ and $g(x) = [x]$

2. $f \circ g$ where $f(x) = |x|$ and
$$g(x) = \begin{cases} x, x \in \langle -4, -2] \\ -2, x \in \langle -2, 2] \\ x - 4, x \in [2, \rightarrow) \end{cases}$$

3. Consider two linear functions $f(x) = ax + b$ and $g(x) = cx + d$. Prove that $f \circ g$ and $g \circ f$ are both linear functions and that they have the same slope.

4. Given $f(x) = \sqrt{4 - x^2}$ and $g(x) = \sqrt{3x}$, find $D(f + g)$. By adding ordinates, draw the graph of $f + g$ and estimate $R(f + g)$.

3–6   Inverse Functions

Some rules have associated rules such that, whatever one accomplishes, the other performs in just the opposite manner. Many parlor games which start *Think of a number*, *double it*, *add ten*, . . . , *and tell me your result* are examples of this *doing* followed by *undoing* process.

Example

1.   Compare $f \circ g$ and $g \circ f$. Let f and g be functions such that $f: x \rightarrow \dfrac{\sqrt{x}}{2 + \sqrt{x}}$

and $g: x \rightarrow \left(\dfrac{2x}{1 - x}\right)^2$.

The functions f and g can be described by the chart.

f	f	g	g
Think of a number.	x	x	Think of a number.
Take its square root.	$\sqrt{x}$	$\dfrac{1}{x}$	Take its reciprocal.
Take the reciprocal.	$\dfrac{1}{\sqrt{x}}$	$\dfrac{1}{x} - 1$	Subtract 1.
Multiply by 2.	$\dfrac{2}{\sqrt{x}}$	$\dfrac{1 - x}{2x}$	Divide by 2.
Add 1.	$\dfrac{2}{\sqrt{x}} + 1$	$\dfrac{2x}{1 - x}$	Take the reciprocal.
Take the reciprocal.	$\dfrac{\sqrt{x}}{2 + \sqrt{x}}$	$\left(\dfrac{2x}{1 - x}\right)^2$	Square.

$$f \circ g : x \rightarrow \frac{\sqrt{g(x)}}{2 + \sqrt{g(x)}} = \frac{\sqrt{\left(\dfrac{2x}{1 - x}\right)^2}}{2 + \sqrt{\left(\dfrac{2x}{1 - .x}\right)^2}}$$

Trace the steps of $(f \circ g)(x)$ and $(g \circ f)(x)$ carefully. Note the reversal of operations performed.

$$= \frac{\dfrac{2x}{1 - x}}{2 + \dfrac{2x}{1 - x}}$$

$$= \frac{\dfrac{2x}{1 - x}}{\dfrac{2 - 2x + 2x}{1 - x}}$$

$$= \frac{2x}{2} = x$$

$$g \circ f : x \rightarrow \left(\frac{2 \cdot f(x)}{1 - f(x)}\right)^2 = \left(\frac{2 \cdot \dfrac{\sqrt{x}}{2 + \sqrt{x}}}{1 - \dfrac{\sqrt{x}}{2 + \sqrt{x}}}\right)^2$$

$$= \left(\frac{2\sqrt{x}}{2 + \sqrt{x} - \sqrt{x}}\right)^2$$

$$= \left(\frac{2\sqrt{x}}{2}\right)^2$$

$$= x$$

The functions *f* and *g* are a pair of **inverse functions.** Each function reverses the process of the other.

✳ note relationship to composition of functions / note domains

Inverse Function

> The functions *f* and *g* are **inverse functions** if $f(g(x)) = x$ for every $x \in D(g)$ and $g(f(y)) = y$ for every $y \in D(f)$.

The inverse of the function *f* is written f^{-1}. In this case, f^{-1} does *not* mean $\frac{1}{f}$.

✳ note symbolism

A pair of functions which are inverses are shown in the figure. Notice that $B = D(f^{-1}) = R(f)$ and $A = R(f^{-1}) = D(f)$.

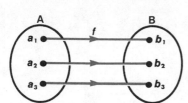

f

$(a_1, b_1), (a_2, b_2), (a_3, b_3)$

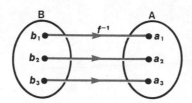

f^{-1}

$(b_1, a_1), (b_2, a_2), (b_3, a_3)$

It should be clear what happens when the compositions are taken.

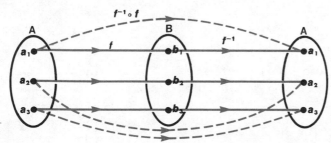

A similar diagram can be drawn for the function $f \circ f^{-1}$ which maps the set B into itself.

If the function *f* is not 1−1 as in the figure, its inverse is not a function. The function f^{-1} must map the elements of set *B* back into *A*. Such a mapping is possible, but it is a relation which is not a function.

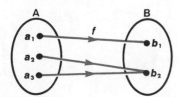

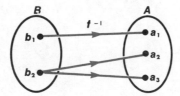

For a function to have an inverse which is a function, it must be 1–1. The inverse of a function f has the point (b, a) on its graph whenever the graph of the function contains the point (a, b), since for every $b = f(a)$ it is true that $a = f^{-1}(b)$. Thus, the graph of f^{-1} is the *reflection* of the graph of f in the line $y = x$.

If $(a, f(a)) \in f$ and $(f(a), a) \in g$ and conversely, then g is the inverse of f.

Examples

2. **Find the inverse of $f{:}x \rightarrow 3x - 2$.**

$$y = f(x)$$
$$y = 3x - 2$$
$$y + 2 = 3x$$
$$\frac{y + 2}{3} = x$$
$$f^{-1}(y) = x$$
$$f^{-1}(y) = \frac{y + 2}{3}$$

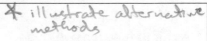

Note that $y = f(x)$ and $x = f^{-1}(y)$ name the same function. Only after interchanging x and y is a new function f^{-1} formed.

Since f^{-1} will be plotted in the usual Cartesian coordinate plane, and the domain of a function *usually* is plotted along the x-axis, the x and y are interchanged. The function f^{-1} is expressed as a function of x.

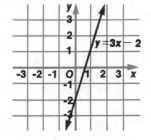

$$y = f^{-1}(x) = \frac{x + 2}{3}$$

Since f is $1 - 1$, so is f^{-1}. Also $D(f^{-1}) = R(f)$ and $R(f^{-1}) = D(f)$. Finally, check to see that f^{-1} satisfies the definition of an inverse function.

$$(f \circ f^{-1})(x) = f(f^{-1}(x)) = f\left(\frac{x + 2}{3}\right) = 3\left(\frac{x + 2}{3}\right) - 2 = x$$

$$(f^{-1} \circ f)(x) = f^{-1}(f(x)) = f^{-1}(3x - 2) = \frac{3x - 2 + 2}{3} = x$$

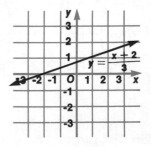

3. **Find the inverse of $f{:}x \rightarrow \dfrac{3}{x^2 - 1}$**

$$y = f(x)$$
$$y = \frac{3}{x^2 - 1}$$
$$x^2 - 1 = \frac{3}{y}$$

$$x^2 = \frac{3}{y} + 1$$

$$x = \pm \sqrt{\frac{3}{y} + 1}$$

Interchange x and y.

$$y = \pm \sqrt{\frac{3 + x}{x}}$$

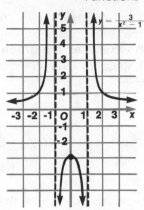

This does not define a function, but either $y = +\sqrt{\frac{3 + x}{x}}$ or $y = -\sqrt{\frac{3 + x}{x}}$ defines a function. If $g(x) = \sqrt{\frac{3 + x}{x}}$ is chosen, then $D(g) = \langle \leftarrow, 3] \cup \langle 0, \rightarrow \rangle = R(f)$ and $R(g) = [0, \rightarrow)$. Restrict f and g so that $D(f) = R(g)$. Then $g = f^{-1}$:

$$x \rightarrow \sqrt{\frac{3 + x}{x}}, x \neq 0, 1.$$ Check that $(f \circ f^{-1})(x) = x$ for $x \in \langle \leftarrow, -3] \cup \langle 0, \rightarrow \rangle$ and $(f^{-1} \circ f)(x) = x$ for $x \in \langle 0, 1 \rangle \cup \langle 1, \rightarrow \rangle$.

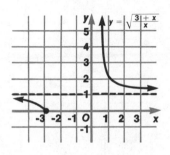

Before looking for the inverse of a function f, restrict D(f) so that f is 1 − 1. After finding f^{-1}, check that $(f \circ f^{-1})(x) = x$ for $x \in D(f^{-1})$ and $(f^{-1} \circ f)(x) = x$ for $x \in D(f)$.

The graphs of f(x) and $f^{-1}(x)$ are reflections of each other through the line y = x.

By equating inverses of both sides of functional equations, certain properties of functions may be uncovered. For example, if $f(ab) = f(a) + f(b)$, then ab can be found by equating inverses.

$$f^{-1}(f(ab)) = f^{-1}(f(a) + f(b))$$
$$ab = f^{-1}(f(a) + f(b))$$

✳ how mathematicians keep themselves busy

Now let $f(a) = x$ and $f(b) = y$. That is, $a = f^{-1}(x)$ and $b = f^{-1}(y)$.

$$f^{-1}(x) \cdot f^{-1}(y) = f^{-1}(x + y)$$

Exercises

Exploratory **Determine the inverse of each function.**

1. $f(x) = \frac{2x + 5}{3}$

2. $f = \left\{ (2, 3), (5, -1), (3, 0), \left(\frac{1}{2}, -\frac{1}{2} \right) \right\}$

3. $g(x) = x^3 - 6$

4. $f(x) = \dfrac{1}{x - 1}$ **5.** $h = \{(7, 1), (2, 3), (-3, -1)\}$ **6.** $j(x) = x^2 - 2$

Written Find the inverse for each function. ~~Restrict the domain as needed to ensure a 1 — 1 function.~~

1. $y = \dfrac{x - 1}{x + 1}$ **2.** $y = \dfrac{x + 1}{x}$ **3.** $y = x^2 + 2$

4. $f(x) = x^2 - 1$ **5.** $g(t) = \sqrt{1 - t^2}$ **6.** $h(u) = \sqrt{1 + u^2}$

7. $j(x) = \dfrac{1}{x^2 + 1}$ **8.** $k(v) = |v|$ **9.** $m(x) = \sqrt{x} + 5$

Restrict the domain of the function so that it is $1 - 1$. Draw the graph of the inverse of this restricted function.

10.
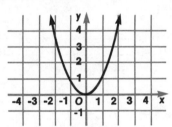

11.
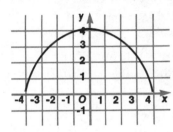

12.
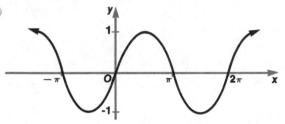

Draw the graph of f and construct f^{-1} from it.

13. $f(x) = 3x - 2$ **14.** $f(x) = x^2 + 2, x \geq 0$ **15.** $f(x) = \sqrt{1 - x^2}, x \leq 0$

16. $f(x) = x + [x]$ **17.** $f(x) = |x| + 2x$ **18.** $f(x) = \dfrac{1}{x}$

Find f^{-1} for each of the following.

19. $f(x) = x^2 - 2x$ **20.** $f(x) = x^2 + 4x$ **21.** $f(x) = \sqrt{x - 4}$
 $x \in [1, \rightarrow)$ $x \in [-2, \rightarrow)$ $x \in [4, \rightarrow)$

Determine if f and g are inverse functions. Explain.

22. $f(x) = \dfrac{1}{1 - x}$ **23.** $f(x) = \dfrac{1}{1 - x}$ **24.** $f(x) = \dfrac{x - 1}{x}$

 $g(x) = \dfrac{x}{x - 1}$ $g(x) = \dfrac{x - 1}{x}$ $g(x) = \dfrac{x}{x - 1}$

25. Suppose $f = g^{-1}$ and $h \circ f \circ g = g$. What can be said about any necessary relationships among the functions?

26. Show that for $f(x) = 2x + 2$ and $g(x) = x + 3$, $(f \circ g)^{-1} = g^{-1} \circ f^{-1}$.

Challenge Prove each of the following.

1. The inverse of a $1 - 1$ function is also $1 - 1$.

2. $(f^{-1})^{-1} = f$

3. The inverse of a linear function is a linear function. Compare the slopes and y-intercepts of a linear function and its inverse.

4. By equating inverses in the expression $(f(a))^n = f(na)$, derive the following $f^{-1}(x^n) = n\, f^{-1}(x)$.

3-7 Increasing and Decreasing Functions

The function $f(x) = x^3$ has the property that if $x_1 < x_2$ then $f(x_1) < f(x_2)$. This means that the graph rises as it is traced from left to right. Functions with this property are called **increasing functions**.

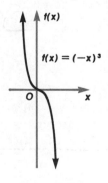

$f(x) = x^3$

Increasing Function

> A function f is **increasing** if whenever $x_1, x_2 \in D(f)$ and $x_1 < x_2$, $f(x_1) < f(x_2)$.

Decreasing functions are defined in a similar way.

> A function is **decreasing** if whenever $x_1, x_2 \in D(f)$ and $x_1 < x_2$, then $f(x_1) > f(x_2)$.

Decreasing Function

The graph of a decreasing function falls as it is traced from left to right. The function $f(x) = (-x)^3$ is a decreasing function.

$f(x) = (-x)^3$

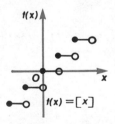

$f(x) = [x]$

The greatest integer function is not an increasing function. But its graph rises in steps as it is traced from left to right. The function has the property that if $x_1 < x_2$, then $f(x_1) \leq f(x_2)$. Functions with this property are called **nondecreasing functions**.

> A function f is **nondecreasing** if whenever $x_1, x_2 \in D(f)$ and $x_1 < x_2$, then $f(x_1) \leq f(x_2)$
>
> A function f is **nonincreasing** if whenever $x_1, x_2 \in D(f)$ and $x_1 < x_2$, then $f(x_1) \geq f(x_2)$

Nondecreasing

Nonincreasing

Nondecreasing functions have graphs that remain constant or rise as they are traced from left to right. Nonincreasing functions have graphs that remain constant or fall as they are traced from left to right.

note the possibility of satisfying two definitions

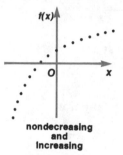

nondecreasing
and
increasing

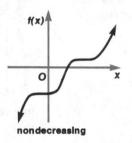

nondecreasing

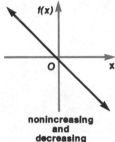

nonincreasing
and
decreasing

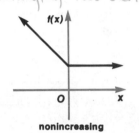

nonincreasing

If a function is increasing it is also nondecreasing. But, a nondecreasing function *may or may not* be increasing. Similarly, a function that is decreasing is nonincreasing, but a function that is nonincreasing *may or may not* be decreasing.

A constant function is the only function which is *both* nondecreasing and nonincreasing.

note this situation

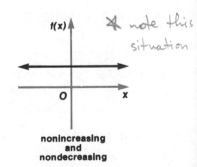

nonincreasing
and
nondecreasing

Functions which are *either* nondecreasing or nonincreasing are called **monotonic**. A monotonic function is **strictly monotonic** if it is either increasing or decreasing.

Sometimes a function is monotonic on a part of its domain. Consider the function defined by $f(x) = (x - 2)^2$. If it is restricted to the domain $\{x | x \geq 2\}$, then the restricted function is increasing. The function f is said to be *increasing on the interval* $[2, \rightarrow)$.

There is an unlimited number of intervals over which f is increasing. The interval $[2, \rightarrow)$ is the largest such interval.

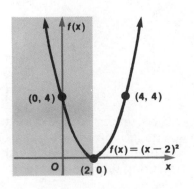

(0, 4)   (4, 4)

$f(x) = (x - 2)^2$

O   (2, 0)

Example

1. Show that $y = (x - 2)^2$ is decreasing on $\langle \leftarrow, 2 \rangle$.

   Choose $a < b < 2$ and show $f(a) > f(b)$.
   Suppose $f(a) > f(b)$.

   $$f(a) > f(b) \text{ if and only if } f(a) - f(b) > 0$$

   Therefore,

   $$(a - 2)^2 - (b - 2)^2 > 0$$
   $$a^2 - 4a + 4 - b^2 + 4b - 4 > 0$$
   $$a^2 - b^2 - 4(a - b) > 0$$
   $$(a + b)(a - b) - 4(a - b) > 0$$
   $$(a + b - 4)(a - b) > 0$$

   Since $a < b < 2$, $a - b < 0$. Also, since $a + b < 2 + 2 = 4$, $a + b - 4 < 0$.
   Therefore, $(a + b - 4)(a - b)$ is positive and $f(a) - f(b) > 0$. So, $f(a) > f(b)$.

The following theorems describe some useful properties of ✗ *not discussed* ↓
monotonic functions.

If a function f is monotonic over a closed interval $[a, b]$, then f reaches its maximum and minimum values at its endpoints.

Theorem for Monotonic Functions

Proof:

Let f be nondecreasing over $[a, b]$. For every $x \in [a, b]$, if $x_1 < x_2$, then $f(x_1) \leq f(x_2)$ by definition. Since $a \in [a, b]$ and $a \leq x$ for all $x \in [a, b]$, the definition states that $f(a) \leq f(x)$ for all $x \in [a, b]$. Since $b \in [a, b]$ and $x \leq b$ for all $x \in [a, b]$, the definition states that $f(x) \leq f(b)$, for all $x \in [a, b]$. Thus, f reaches its maximum value at b and its minimum value at a.

A similar argument holds for nonincreasing functions.

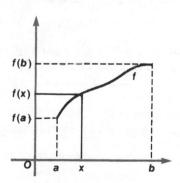

If a function f is strictly monotonic on $[a, b]$ then f is 1–1 on $[a, b]$.

Theorem for Strictly Monotonic Functions

Proof:

Let f be increasing on $[a, b]$. Suppose $x_1, x_2 \in [a, b]$ such that $x_1 \neq x_2$. If $x_1 < x_2$ then $f(x_1) < f(x_2)$. So, $f(x_1) \neq f(x_2)$. Similarly, $x_1 > x_2$ implies $f(x_1) > f(x_2)$. In either case, $x_1 \neq x_2$ implies $f(x_1) \neq f(x_2)$ and f must be 1–1.

A similar argument holds for decreasing functions.

From this theorem, it can be concluded that a strictly monotonic function must have an inverse function.

Exercises

Exploratory   Identify each function as nondecreasing, increasing, nonincreasing, decreasing, or a combination.

1. $y = x^2, x \leq 0$
2. $y = |x|$
3. $y = k, k \in \mathcal{R}$
4. $y = -2x + 5$
5. $y = [x]$
6. $y = x + [x]$

Written   Identify each function as nondecreasing, increasing, nondecreasing, decreasing, or a combination.

1. $y = x + |x|$
2. $y = \sqrt{1 - x^2}$
3. $y = (x + 1)^2$
4. $y = \begin{cases} -2, x \in \langle \leftarrow, -1] \\ x, x \in \langle -1, 1] \\ 2, x \in \langle 1, \rightarrow \rangle \end{cases}$
5. $y = \begin{cases} x + 1, x \in \langle \leftarrow, 1] \\ x^2 + 1, x \in \langle 1, \rightarrow \rangle \end{cases}$
6. $y = \begin{cases} x + 1, x \in \langle \leftarrow, 1] \\ x^2 - 1, x \in \langle 1, \rightarrow \rangle \end{cases}$

Given $f(x) = (x - 1)^2$, solve each of the following.

7. Determine the largest intervals upon which f is increasing, or decreasing.

8. Find the maximum and the minimum values of f on the interval $[0, 1]$.

9. If $|h| < 1$ and $k = 1$, determine the relationship between $f(k + h)$ and $f(k)$. (Is $f(h + k)$ greater than, less than, or equal to $f(k)$?)

10. If $|h| < 1$ and $k = 2$, determine the relationship between $f(h + k)$ and $f(k)$.

11. If $|h| < \frac{1}{10}$ and $k = 1$, determine the relationship between $f(h + k)$ and $f(k)$.

12. If $|h| < 10^{-6}$ and $k = 1$, determine the relationship between $f(h + k)$ and $f(k)$.

Show algebraically each of the following.

13. For $x \leq 0$, $y = x^2$ is decreasing.
14. The function $f(x) = 5x + 2$ is increasing.
15. The function $f(x) = x^3$ is increasing.
16. For $x \in [0, 1]$, $y = \sqrt{1 - x^2}$ is decreasing.
17. Show by a counterexample that the product of two nondecreasing functions is not necessarily a nondecreasing function.

Challenge   Solve each of the following.

1. Prove that if functions f and g are nondecreasing on an interval, then $f + g$ is nondecreasing on the interval.

2. Prove or disprove the following statement. If a function f is increasing, then its inverse also is increasing.

3. Prove that a strictly monotonic function has an inverse function.

4. Prove algebraically that any linear function with slope $m < 0$ is decreasing.

Chapter Summary

1. A relation S is a set of ordered pairs. The domain $D(S)$ of a relation is the set of all first elements. The range $R(S)$ is

the set of all second elements. Given two sets M and N, a relation from M to N is a subset of the Cartesian product $M \times N$. (65)

2. Two relations are equal if and only if they contain the same ordered pairs. (66)

3. If a relation S has the property that each element of $D(S)$ is paired with exactly one element of $R(S)$ and each element of $R(S)$ is paired with exactly one element of $D(S)$, then S is one-to-one, 1–1. If S is a relation in $M \times N$ and $R(S) = N$, then S is onto. Otherwise, S is into. (66)

4. A function is a relation such that for each first element there corresponds a unique second element. (68)

5. A relation S is a function if $(a, b) \in S$ and $(a, c) \in S$ then $b = c$. (69)

6. The domain of a function f is the set of all real numbers for which the function is defined. (69)

7. If f and g are functions, then for every $x \in D(f) \cap D(g)$, $(f + g)(x) = f(x) + g(x)$, $(f \cdot g)(x) = f(x) \cdot g(x)$, $-(f(x)) = -f(x)$, $(f - g)(x) = f(x) - g(x)$ and $\left(\dfrac{f}{g}\right)(x) = \dfrac{f(x)}{g(x)}$ for $g(x) \neq 0$. (76)

8. The composition of two functions f and g, denoted $f \circ g$, is the function such that $(f \circ g)(x) = f(g(x))$. Its domain is $D(f \circ g) = \{x \mid x \in D(g) \text{ and } g(x) \in D(f)\}$. (78)

9. The functions f and g are inverse functions if $f(g(x)) = x$ for every $x \in D(g) = R(f)$ and $g(f(y)) = y$ for every $y \in D(f) = R(g)$. (83)

10. a. A function f is increasing if whenever $x_1, x_2 \in D(f)$ and $x_1 < x_2$, then $f(x_1) < f(x_2)$. (87)

    b. A function f is decreasing if whenever $x_1, x_2 \in D(f)$ and $x_1 < x_2$, then $f(x_1) > f(x_2)$. (87)

    c. A function f is nondecreasing if whenever $x_1, x_2 \in D(f)$ and $x_1 < x_2$, then $f(x_1) \leq f(x_2)$. (88)

    d. A function f is nonincreasing if whenever $x_1, x_2 \in D(f)$ and $x_1 < x_2$, then $f(x_1) \geq f(x_2)$. (88)

    e. A function is monotonic if it is either nondecreasing or nonincreasing. A monotonic function is strictly monotonic if it is either increasing or decreasing. (88)

11. If a function is monotonic over a closed interval, then it reaches its maximum and minimum values at the endpoints of the interval. (89)

12. If a function is strictly monotonic on an interval $[a, b]$, then it is 1–1 on that interval. (89)

13. A strictly monotonic function must have an inverse function. (89)

Chapter Review

3–1 Assume that the relation $S = \{(x, y) \mid y = x^2 + 4\}$ is defined in $\mathcal{R} \times \mathcal{R}$.

   1. Graph S.   **2.** Find $D(S)$.   **3.** Find $R(S)$.

3–2 Given that $f : x \to \dfrac{4}{x^2 - 1}$, find each of the following.

   4. $f(2)$ **5.** $f(-2)$ **6.** $-f(2)$

   7. $f(1)$ **8.** $f(-1)$ **9.** $f(0)$

   10. $f\left(\dfrac{1}{2}\right)$ **11.** $f\left(\dfrac{1}{8}\right)$ **12.** $D(f)$

   13. $R(f)$ **14.** All $x \in D(f)$ for which $f(x) = 0$

   15. $x \in \langle 1, 2]$ for which f reaches its maximum value

   16. $x \in \langle 1, 2]$ for which f reaches its minimum value.

3–3 Identify each function as constant (C), identity (I), linear (L), or none of these (N).

   17. $\{(2, 1), (1, 3), (-1, 2)\}$ **18.** $\{(x, y) \mid y = [x - 1]\}$

   19. $\{(x, y) \mid y = |x| - |-x|\}$ **20.** $y = 4x + 5$

   21. Sketch the graph of $y = \dfrac{x}{|x|}$. Use $x \in \mathcal{R}$.

3–4 Given that $f = \{(0, 2), (-1, 2), (2, 0)\}$ and $g = \{(0, 0), (-1, 3), (2, -1), (3, 2)\}$, find each of the following.

   22. $f + g$ **23.** $f \cdot g$

   24. $f - g$ **25.** $g - f$

   26. $\dfrac{f}{g}$ **27.** $\dfrac{g}{f}$

   28. Find a linear function f whose graph is parallel to the graph $y = 4x + 6$ and $f(4) = 26$.

3–5 Solve each of the following.

   29. Given $f = \{(0, 2), (1, -1), (3, 2)\}$ and $g = \{(2, 1), (-1, 3), (1, 0), (0, 0), (-2, 2)\}$, find $f \circ g$ and $g \circ f$. State the domain and range of each.

   30. Given $f(x) = x + 2$ and $g(x) = 3x - 1$, find $f \circ g$ and $g \circ f$. State the domain and range of each. Compare with the domain and range of each of f and g.

3–6 Find the inverse of each function. Restrict the domain as needed to ensure a 1–1 function. Check to make sure the inverse has been found.

   31. $\{(1, 2), (-1, 3), (2, 3), (0, 1)\}$ **32.** $f(x) = x$

3–7 Identify each function as nondecreasing, increasing, nonincreasing, decreasing, or a combination.

   33. $y = x^3$ **34.** $y = 1 - x$

   35. Let $f : x \to x^2 - 3x + 2$. Determine the intervals upon which f is increasing or decreasing. Find the maximum and minimum values of f on the interval $[0, 0.5]$.

Chapter Test

Let $M = \{1, 2\}$ and $N = \{a, b\}$.

1. List $M \times N$.

2. Find all the relations of M into N.

3. Which of these relations are onto?

4. Which are 1–1?

Given that $f: x \rightarrow x^2 - x$, find each of the following.

5. $f(0.01)$

6. $f(0)$

7. $f(1)$

8. $D(f)$

9. $R(f)$

10. All $x \in D(f)$ for which $f(x) = 6$

11. $x \in [1, 2]$ for which f reaches its maximum value.

12. $x \in [1, 2]$ for which f reaches its minimum value.

13. Graph the relation $f(x) = \begin{cases} x + 2, x \in [-2, 0] \\ 2 - x, x \in [0, 2] \end{cases}$. Is f a function? Is it 1–1?

Identify each function as constant (C), identity (I), linear (L), or none of these (N).

14. $\{(x, y) | y = x^2 + 2\}$

15. $\{(x, y) | y = 3x - 7\}$

16. $\{(x, y) | y = \begin{cases} |x|, x \geq 0 \\ -|x|, x < 0 \end{cases} \}$

Given that $f(x) = 2x - 1$ and $g(x) = x + 3$, find each of the following.

17. $f + g$

18. $g \cdot f$

19. $f - g$

20. $g - f$

21. Given $f(x) = \dfrac{1}{x^2 - 4}$ and $g(x) = \dfrac{1}{2x}$, find $f \circ g$ and $g \circ f$. State the domain and range of each.

22. Write $f: x \rightarrow \dfrac{x^2 + 2}{x - 1}$ as the composition of two or more functions.

Find the inverse of each function. Restrict the domain as needed to ensure a 1–1 function. Check to be sure that the inverse has been found.

23. $h(x) = x^2 - 1$

24. $k(x) = |x|$

25. Sketch f and f^{-1} for $f: y = x^2 - x - 6$. State the domain and range of each of f and f^{-1}.

Identify each function as nondecreasing, increasing, nonincreasing, decreasing, or a combination.

26. $y = [x]$

27. $y = \begin{cases} 1 - x^2, x \in \langle \leftarrow, 0] \\ x^2 + 1, x \in [0, \rightarrow\rangle \end{cases}$

28. Show algebraically that $y = x^3$ is increasing for $x \geq 1$. (Hint: $a^3 - b^3 = (a - b)(a^2 + ab + b^2)$)

Computers

Business Computers

Initial development of computers required very large financial commitments, especially for research and development. For example, the first electronic digital computer, the ENIAC, was developed to produce tables used in artillery problems. It covered approximately 1500 square feet, had 18,000 vacuum tubes, required 130,000 watts of power, and weighed 30 tons. Other machines were designed and built for special uses and customers such as Bell Telephone, General Electric, Princeton University Institute for Advanced Studies, Los Alamos Atomic Energy Installation, the Census Bureau, and various military centers. These machines performed computations very quickly and thus could compile massive volumes of data.

Even though the size of the computers was greatly reduced, by 1970 there were only about 60,000 computers worldwide. Most installations beyond the specialized areas mentioned above were still in large corporate offices, industrial sites, universities, and banking institutions. Installation required special environments, large memory devices, special staff and training facilities, and large commitment to maintenance and updating of equipment. The cost of all of these special needs made it extremely difficult for smaller companies to own a computer.

As technology progressed and the demand for computers increased, two things happened. First, computer costs fell so that smaller businesses and institutions were able to have computer installations.

No longer were computers large, bulky machines but smaller machines able to fit in a

This is a medium-scale computer system.

This is a small business system.

small room with one or two operators. Companies did not need a large department of computer personnel but rather several trained people. The reduced maintenance cost of computers made them available to even very small businesses. Second, remote access to large computer complexes became possible through time-shared equipment. Large scale collection and processing of data has now progressed to the state where whole computer networks may be connected, thus providing enormous computer power. If a company felt a

limited need for computers, they could "buy" time on large computers.

These developments have helped large capacity computers to become available to all companies at a more reasonable rate.

Today most companies use computers to some extent. Some companies limit the use to only payroll calculations while others use computers to design new products, to control the quality of goods, and to maintain records.

Exercises Graphic capabilities of individual computers vary greatly. Using available manuals, research the capabilities of the computer to be used. Then write programs to output the graphs of each of the following relations.

1. $y = \frac{1}{2}x^2$

2. $y = x^3$

3. $y = \begin{cases} x, x \geq 0 \\ -x, x < 0 \end{cases}$

4. $y = \begin{cases} x^2, x \geq 0 \\ -x^2, x < 0 \end{cases}$

5. $y = \begin{cases} \sqrt{x}, x \geq 0 \\ 0, x < 0 \end{cases}$

6. $|x| + |y| = 4$

7. $y = x + |x|$

8. $y = \dfrac{1}{x + |x|}$

9. $y = [x] - x + |x|$ ([x] in BASIC is INT(X) and |x| is ABS(X).)

Chapter 4

Symmetry, reflection, rotation, and translation are typical properties of relations which simplify the problem of graphing. These properties also help provide artistic structures.

Graphing Techniques

4–1 Symmetry

Knowledge of the properties of relations helps when drawing their graphs. An accurate graph may be needed for a particular application, but a sketch usually is enough. A sketch should emphasize the most significant features of the relation. If a graph has symmetry, only part of the graph needs to be plotted. Then, the rest of the graph may be sketched.

> Two distinct points P and P' are symmetric with respect to a line ℓ if it is the perpendicular bisector of $\overleftrightarrow{PP'}$. If $P = P'$, the point is symmetric with respect to ℓ if P is on ℓ.

Symmetry

A set of points is symmetric with respect to a line ℓ if, for every point P in the set, there is another point P' in the set such that P and P' are symmetric with respect to ℓ. In that case, the graph of the set is said to be symmetric about ℓ.

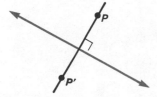   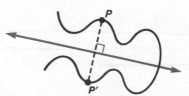

> The graph of a relation S is symmetric with respect to the y-axis if $(-a, b) \in S$ whenever $(a, b) \in S$.

Symmetry with respect to the y-axis.

In general, the graph of a function f is symmetric with respect
to the y-axis if $f(-x) = f(x)$.

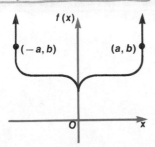 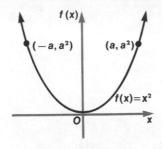

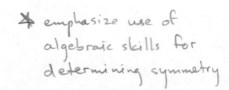

*emphasize use of
algebraic skills for
determining symmetry*

1. Determine if the graph of $f(x) = x^4 + 3x^2 + 2$ is symmetric with respect to the
    y-axis.

$$f(-x) = (-x)^4 + 3(-x)^2 + 2$$
$$= x^4 + 3x^2 + 2 = f(x)$$

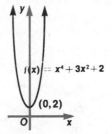

The graph of $f(x) = x^4 + 3x^2 + 2$ is symmetric with respect to the y-axis.

The graph of a relation S is symmetric with respect to the
x-axis if $(a, -b) \in S$ whenever $(a, b) \in S$.

**Symmetry with respect to
x-axis**

2. Determine if the graph of the relation S defined by $\dfrac{x^2}{4} - \dfrac{y^2}{9} = 1$ for $x \in$
    $\langle\leftarrow, -2] \cup [2, \rightarrow\rangle$ is symmetric with respect to the x-axis.

    Let $y = 3$. $\dfrac{x^2}{4} - \dfrac{(3)^2}{9} = 1$

                            $\dfrac{x^2}{4} = 2$

*note this example
is confusing because
of its symmetry with
respect to y-axis
also*

$$x^2 = 8$$
$$x = \pm \sqrt{8}$$

Let $y = -3$. $\dfrac{x^2}{4} - \dfrac{(-3)^2}{9} = 1$

$$\dfrac{x^2}{4} = 2$$
$$x^2 = 8$$
$$x = \pm \sqrt{8}$$

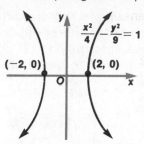

In general, $\dfrac{a^2}{4} - \dfrac{b^2}{9} = \dfrac{a^2}{4} - \dfrac{(-b)^2}{9}$, so if $(a, b) \in S$ then $(a, -b) \in S$. Therefore, the graph of the relation is symmetric with respect to the x-axis.   ✳ note

✳

The graph of a relation S is symmetric with respect to the line $y = x$ if $(b, a) \in S$ whenever $(a, b) \in S$.

Symmetry with respect to the line $y = x$.

Example

3. Determine if the graph of $T = \{(x, y) \mid xy = 1\}$ is symmetric with respect to the line $y = x$.

If $(a, b) \in S$ then $ab = 1$.
If $ab = 1$ then $ba = 1$.
So, $(b, a) \in S$.

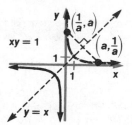

Thus, the graph of $T = \{(x, y) \mid xy = 1\}$ is symmetric with respect to the line $y = x$.

✳ discuss

Two distinct points P and P' are symmetric with respect to a point Q, or P' is the reflection of P in Q, if Q is the midpoint of $\overline{PP'}$. Point Q is symmetric with respect to itself.

Reflection

A set of points is symmetric with respect to a point Q if, for every point P in the set, there is another point P' in the set such that P and P' are symmetric with respect to Q. In that case, the graph of the set is said to be symmetric about Q.

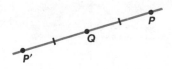

In graphing, pairs of points often are tested for symmetry with respect to the origin. In Figure **a**, the graph is symmetric with respect to the point (1, 0). The graph in Figure **b** is symmetric with respect to the origin.

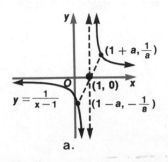

a.

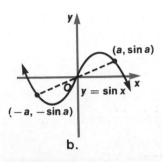

b.

✱ use trigonometric examples

The graph of a relation S is symmetric with respect to the origin if (−a, −b) ∈ S whenever (a, b) ∈ S.

Symmetry with respect to the origin

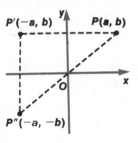

In general, the graph of a function f is symmetric with respect to the origin if $f(-x) = -f(x)$ for all $x \in D(f)$.

To locate the reflection of a point (a, b) in the origin, first reflect in the y-axis. Then reflect this new point in the x-axis.

Example

4. **Reflect the point (−2, 3) in the origin.**

(−2, 3) reflected in the y-axis yields (2, 3).
(2, 3) reflected in the x-axis yields (2, −3).

Therefore, (−2, 3) reflected in the origin yields (2, −3).

Relations whose graphs are symmetric with respect to the y-axis are called **even relations**. Polynomial functions whose terms are all of even degree are even functions.

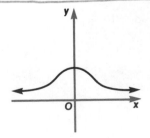

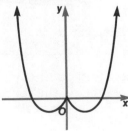

Relations whose graphs are symmetric with respect to the origin are called **odd relations**. Polynomial functions whose terms are all of odd degrees are odd functions.

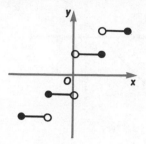 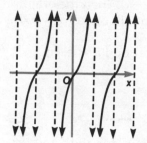

Some functions are neither even nor odd.

✗ note

Examples

5. **Determine if the polynomial function $y = x^8 - 3x^4 + 2x^2 + 1$ is odd, even, or neither.**

    All the terms have even degrees. So $f(x) = f(-x)$.
    The graph is symmetric with respect to the y-axis.

    Therefore, $y = x^8 - 3x^4 + 2x^2 + 1$ is an even function.

    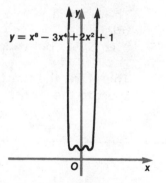

6. **Determine if the polynomial function $y = 3x^9 + 4x^7 - x^3 + 2x$ is odd, even, or neither.**

    Since all the terms have odd degrees, $f(x) = -f(-x)$.
    So the graph is symmetric with respect to the origin.

    Therefore, $y = 3x^9 + 4x^7 - x^3 + 2x$ is an odd function.

    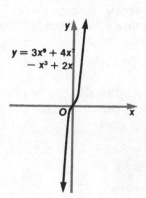

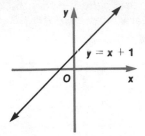

✱ reminder a specifi
example disproves

7. **Determine if the function $y = x + 1$ is odd, even, or neither.**

$F(1) = 2$ $F(-1) = 0$

So $f(x) \neq -f(-x)$ and $f(x) \neq f(\ x)$. Then the graph is not symmetric either to the origin or to the y-axis.

Therefore, $y = x + 1$ is neither odd nor even.

In order for a function f to be symmetric with respect to either the y-axis or the origin, its domain must be symmetric about the origin. That is, if $a \in D(f)$, then $-a \in D(f)$.

✱ note

Example

8. **Determine if the function $f:x \rightarrow x^2 + 1$ where $x \in [-1, 2]$ is symmetric with respect to the y-axis.**

The domain $[-1, 2]$ is not symmetric about the origin.
   $(2, 5) \in f$ but $(-2, 5) \notin f$.

Therefore, the function f is not symmetric with respect to the y-axis.

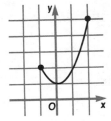

Exercises

Exploratory   Locate the reflection of each point in (a) the x-axis, (b) the y-axis, (c) the origin, (d) the line $y = x$, and (e) the point $(3, -2)$.

1. $(0, 0)$ 2. $(1, 1)$ 3. $(-2, 5)$
4. $(-3, -7)$ 5. $(2, 0)$ 6. $(2, -1)$

Written   Classify the graph of each relation as symmetric with respect to (a) the x-axis, (b) the y-axis, (c) the origin, (d) the line $y = x$, and (e) none of these symmetries.

1. $y = 5x$ 2. $y = 5x + 2$
3. $y = 3x^2 + 4x + 3$ 4. $y = -x$
5. $y = |x + 1|$ 6. $y = x^3 + 7x$
7. $y = -x^4 - 2$ 8. $y = 2x^4 + 6x^2 - 3$

9. $y = [x]$

10. $|x| + |y| = 1$

11. $x = 3y^2$

12. $x = 2y^3$

13. $x^2 + y^2 = 16$

14. $y = 2x^3 + x^2 + 4$

15. $y = (2x^3 - 3)^2$

16. $y = \pm\sqrt{x - 4}$

17. $y = (2x^2 - 3)^3$

18. $y = \dfrac{x^2}{x + 1}$

19. $y = x|x|$

20. $y = |x| \, (x^2 + 4)$

21. Identify the relations which are even or odd in Problems **1–20**.

22. Reflect the point $(-3, 2)$ in the y-axis. Then reflect that point successively in the lines $x = 2$, $x = 4$, $x = 6$, $x = 8$. What are the coordinates of the final image?

23. Reflect the Figure F in the y-axis and the x-axis. Then repeat, reflecting first in the x-axis and then in the y-axis. Repeat the reflection. This time reflect in the origin only. What conclusion can be made?

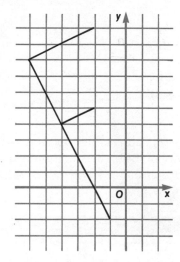

Challenge **Show by example each of the following.**

1. Even though the domain of a function is symmetric with respect to the y-axis, the function itself need not exhibit any symmetries.

2. An even function need not be 1–1.

4–2 Intercepts and Excluded Regions

The graph of a relation is easier to draw when the intercepts, extent, and excluded regions are known.

A **y-intercept** of a relation is a point $(0, b)$ on its graph. An **x-intercept** is a point $(a, 0)$ on its graph. It is possible that there are no x- or y-intercepts.

⚹ emphasize the ordered pair

Example

1. Find the *x*- and *y*-intercepts of the function $y = 3(x - 2)^2 + 4$.

(0, *b*) is the *y*-intercept
$$b = 3(0 - 2)^2 + 4$$
$$b = 16$$

(*a*, 0) is the *x*-intercept
$$0 = 3(a - 2)^2 + 4$$
$$-4 = 3(a - 2)^2$$
no solution ✗ ? *why did he stop*

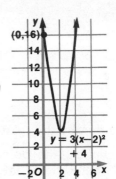

(0,16)

The *y*-intercept is (0, 8). Since the equation on the right above had no solution, there is no *x*-intercept.

Many relations have graphs which extend without bound in the *x*- or *y*- direction or both. Other relations are limited in extent in one or more directions by their domain or range.

✗ *use of domain and range to limit graphing regions*

Example

2. Determine the extent of the graph of $f(x) = \sqrt{3 - x^2} + 2$

$x \in D(f)$
$$3 - x^2 \geq 0$$
$$3 \geq x^2$$
$$-\sqrt{3} \leq x \leq \sqrt{3}$$

Note: $3 - x^2 \geq 0$ so that $\sqrt{3 - x^2}$ is defined in the set of real numbers.

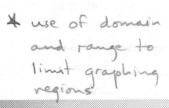

Therefore, $D(f) = [-\sqrt{3}, \sqrt{3}]$

To find the range of $y = \sqrt{3 - x^2} + 2$, notice that $\sqrt{3 - x^2} = 0$ when $|x| = \sqrt{3}$ and $\sqrt{3 - x^2} = \sqrt{3}$ when $x = 0$.
So, $0 + 2 \leq \sqrt{3 - x^2} + 2 \leq \sqrt{3} + 2$.
$$2 \leq y \leq \sqrt{3} + 2$$

Therefore, $y \in [2, 2 + \sqrt{3}]$. The lower and upper bounds of the range are 2 and $2 + \sqrt{3}$, respectively.

Polynomial functions are not limited in extent. Within intervals of their domains they may have certain **excluded regions** which do not contain any part of the graph.

Example

3. Determine excluded regions for $f(x) = x(x + 3)(x - 4)$.

In the interval	$f(x)$ is	Excluded
$\langle 4, \rightarrow\rangle$	> 0	$y < 0$
$\langle 0, 4\rangle$	< 0	$y > 0$
$\langle -3, 0\rangle$	> 0	$y < 0$
$\langle \leftarrow, -3\rangle$	< 0	$y > 0$

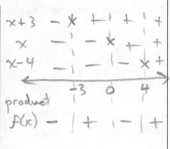

The function f exists only in the nonshaded regions.

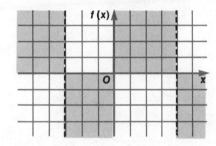

Exercises

Exploratory Determine whether each relation is symmetric with respect to the x-axis, the y-axis, the origin, or the line $y = x$. Then, find the intercepts. Next, determine the excluded regions.

1. $y = \pm\sqrt{x^2 - 1}$ 2. $y = x(x^2 - 9)$

3. $y = \dfrac{2x + 1}{x - 1}$ 4. $y = (x + 2)(1 - x)(x - 3)$ graph

Written Shade the excluded regions and sketch the curve.

1. $y = \pm\sqrt{x^2 - 1}$ 2. $y = x(x^2 - 9)$

3. $y = \dfrac{2x + 1}{x - 1}$ 4. $y = (x + 2)(1 - x)(x - 3)$

Find the x- and y-intercepts, if any.

5. $y = 2(x + 1)^2 - 3$ 6. $y = 3(1 - x)^3 + 2$ 7. $y = 4(x - 3)^2 + 3$

Determine the extent for each relation.

8. $y = \sqrt{4 - x^2} + 3$ **9.** $y = \pm \dfrac{x}{\sqrt{x^2 - 16}}$ **10.** $y = 5 + \sqrt{(x - 3)^3}$

Shade the excluded regions.

11. $y = (x - 2)(x + 3)$ **12.** $y = (x - 2)^2(x + 3)$ **13.** $y = (x^2 - 1)(x - 3)^2$

4-3   Asymptotes

Knowing asymptotes helps further in the graphing of a relation.

> An **asymptote** is a straight line toward which a graph tends as x approaches some specific value, or as x increases or decreases without bound.

Asymptotes

Asymptotes fall into three categories. These are *vertical*, *horizontal*, and *slant*.

✸ discuss meaning
✸ of symbolism

> The line for $x = a$ is a **vertical asymptote** for a function $y = f(x)$ if $f(x) \to \infty$ or $f(x) \to -\infty$ as $x \to a$ either from the left or from the right.

Vertical Asymptote

Example

1. Determine the vertical asymptote for $f(x) = \dfrac{x}{x + 1}$.

   ✸ note for future use
   The symbol ϵ, epsilon, designates a small positive number.

   If $x = -1$, then $x + 1 = 0$. Therefore, $f(-1)$ does not exist.
   But, $f(-1 + \epsilon)$ and $f(-1 - \epsilon)$ exist for every number $\epsilon > 0$, no matter how small ϵ is.

	x	$f(x)$	x	$f(x)$
ϵ	$-1 + \epsilon$	$f(-1 + \epsilon)$	$-1 - \epsilon$	$f(-1 - \epsilon)$
0.1	-0.9	-9	-1.1	11
0.01	-0.99	-99	-1.01	101
0.001	-0.999	-999	-1.001	1001
0.000001	-0.999999	-999999	-1.000001	1000001

   ✸ note symbolism

   Let $x \to a^+$ symbolize "x gets close to a from the right or positive side" and $x \to a^-$ mean "x gets close to a from the left or negative side."

As x approaches -1 from the right, $f(x)$ decreases without bound. Written, $f(x) \to -\infty$ as $x \to -1^+$. If $x \to -1^-$, then $f(x) \to \infty$.

Therefore, the line with the equation $x = -1$ is a vertical asymptote for f.

Sometimes a curve has more than one vertical asymptote.

Example

2. **Determine the vertical asymptotes of the function $f(x) = \dfrac{x}{x^2 - 1}$.**

$f(1)$ and $f(-1)$ are not defined.
The lines $x = -1$ and $x = 1$ are both asymptotes.
As $x \to -1^+$, $f(x) \to \infty$.
As $x \to -1^-$, $f(x) \to -\infty$.

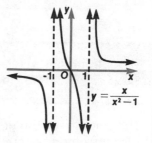

Similarly, $f(x) \to -\infty$ as $x \to 1^-$, and $f(x) \to \infty$ as $x \to 1^+$.

> The line for $y = b$ is a horizontal asymptote for a function $y = f(x)$ if $f(x)$ approaches the constant value b as x increases or decreases without bound.

✳ note change in which one approaches too

Horizontal Asymptote

Example

3. **Determine the horizontal asymptotes for $f : y = \dfrac{x}{x + 1}$.**

✳ introduce concept of limit and this fraction making technique

If $x \neq -1$, and $x \neq 0$, then $f(x) = \dfrac{x}{x + 1} = \dfrac{1}{1 + \dfrac{1}{x}}$.

As $x \to \pm\infty$, $\dfrac{1}{x} \to 0$ and $\dfrac{1}{1 + \dfrac{1}{x}} \to 1$. As $x \to \infty$, $y \to 1^-$. As $x \to -\infty$ $y \to 1^+$.

x	-1000	-100	-10	0	10	100	1000
$f(x)$	$\dfrac{1000}{999}$	$\dfrac{100}{99}$	$\dfrac{10}{9}$	$\dfrac{0}{1}$	$\dfrac{10}{11}$	$\dfrac{100}{101}$	$\dfrac{1000}{1001}$

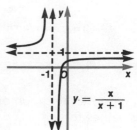

Therefore, $y = 1$ is a horizontal asymptote.

Another method for finding the horizontal asymptote is to solve for x in terms of y.

$$y = \frac{x}{x+1}$$
$$y(x+1) = x$$
$$xy - x = -y$$
$$x(1-y) = y$$
$$x = \frac{y}{1-y}$$

✳ note limit technique will be faster

Solving for x in terms of y shows that $y = 1$ is a horizontal asymptote.

note which one approaches
✗ ±∞

The oblique line ℓ is a slant asymptote for a function $y = f(x)$ if the graph of f approaches ℓ as $x \to \infty$ or $x \to -\infty$.

Slant Asymptote

The distance of the graph from the asymptote approaches 0. If ℓ is the line $y = mx + b$, then $f(x) \to mx + b$ or $[f(x) - (mx + b)] \to 0$ as $x \to \infty$ or $x \to -\infty$.

Example

4. **Determine the slant asymptote for the function** $f(x) = \dfrac{x^2 - 2x + 1}{x}$.

$$f(x) = \frac{x^2 - 2x + 1}{x}$$

note technique

$$f(x) = x - 2 + \frac{1}{x}$$

As $x \to \pm\infty$, $\dfrac{1}{x} \to 0$ and $f(x) \to x - 2$.

As $x \to \infty$, $[f(x) - (x-2)] \to 0^+$.

As $x \to -\infty$, $[f(x) - (x-2)] \to 0^-$.

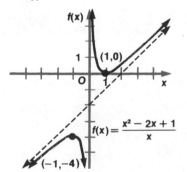

Therefore, the line $y = x - 2$ is a slant asymptote for f.

Note: The line $x = 0$ is a vertical asymptote with $y \to \infty$ as $x \to 0^+$ and $y \to -\infty$ as $x \to 0^-$.

Suppose the graph of $f(x)$ is a curve which crosses the y-axis. As values for x are chosen closer to zero, the variable terms of lower degree in $f(x)$ dominate over those of higher degree. For example, if $f(x) = x^5 + 2x$, then $f\left(\dfrac{1}{10}\right) = \dfrac{1}{100000} + \dfrac{2}{10}$. The term x^5 contributes relatively little to the value for $f\left(\dfrac{1}{10}\right)$ compared to the term $2x$. Sometimes this idea may be used to determine the approximate shape and slope of such a curve near the y-axis.

Examples

5. **Determine the shape of the graph near the origin for $f : y = x^3 - 5x$.**

   The graph of f is close to the line $y = -5x$, since x^3 contributes very little to the value of $f(x)$ when $x \to 0$.

   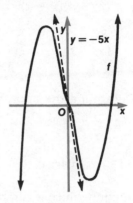

6. **Determine the shape of the graph near the origin for $g : y = x^3 - 5x^2$.**

   The graph of g is close to the curve $y = -5x^2$, since x^3 contributes very little to the value of $f(x)$ when $x \to 0$.

   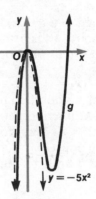

Exercises

Exploratory   Determine any horizontal or vertical asymptotes for the following.

1. $y = \dfrac{x}{(x-1)(x+2)}$

2. $y = \dfrac{x+2}{x^2+4}$

3. $y = \dfrac{(x - 3)(x + 1)}{(2x + 1)(x + 2)}$

Determine any slant asymptotes.

4. $y = \dfrac{x^2 + 3x - 4}{x}$

5. $y = \dfrac{3x^3 - 2x + 1}{2x^2}$

Determine the approximate shape of the curve near the origin for the following.

6. $y = 3x^3 - 7x^2 + 2x$

7. $y = 2x^3 + 3x^2$

Written Sketch the curve of the relation. Check for symmetry, intercepts, excluded regions, asymptotes, and the shape of the curve near the origin.

1. $y = (x^2 - 4)(x + 2)^2$

2. $y = \sqrt{x}(x^2 - 9)$

3. $y = -\dfrac{2}{x}$

4. $y = \dfrac{3x - 1}{x + 1}$

5. $y = \dfrac{x - 1}{x^2 - 4}$

6. $y = \dfrac{x - 1}{x^2 + 4}$

7. $y = x^{-2}$

8. $y = \pm\sqrt{x^3}$

9. $y = \sqrt{4 - x^2} + 3$

10. Determine the approximate shape of the curve near the origin for $y = \dfrac{3x}{4x^2 + 2}$

4-4 Translations

A function which is complicated to graph may be related by a translation to an equation which is easier to graph.

> If a function $y = f(x)$ has the variable x replaced by $(x - h)$, then the result is a translation $|h|$ units to the right if $h > 0$ or $|h|$ units to the left is $h < 0$.

※ discourage use of specific techniques from this section

※ note the use of subtraction

Translation

If (a, b) is a point on the original function f, then $f(a) = b$. If g_1 is the new function, $g_1(x) = f(x - h)$, then $g_1(a + h) = f(a + h - h) = f(a) = b$. Therefore, every point (a, b) on f has a corresponding point $(a + h, b)$ on g_1 which has the same ordinate but is shifted h units to the right or left of (a, b).

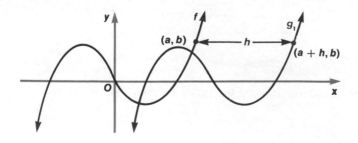

If g_2 is a new function, $g_2(x) = f(x) - k = y - k$, then $g_2(a) = f(a) - k = b - k$. Therefore, every point (a, b) on f has a corresponding point $(a, b - k)$ on g_2 which has the same abscissa but is shifted k units up or down from (a, b).

Often it is convenient to draw new axes over the graph of the old function. To do this shift the origin from $(0, 0)$ to the point $(h, 0)$ if only a *horizontal shift* is desired. Shift the origin from $(0, 0)$ to point $(0, k)$ if only a *vertical shift* is desired. The origin is shifted to (h, k) if both a horizontal and a vertical shift are desired.

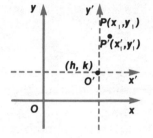

✳ note this is the technique that has been discussed previously

Consider $P(x_1, y_1)$ in the xy-plane and $P'(x_1', y_1')$ in the $x'y'$-plane. Since these are the same point, $x_1' = x_1 - h$ and $y_1' = y_1 - k$. The coordinates of P are changed by the amount of shift of the origin. This is true even if the point P is not in the first quadrant.

The transformation can be described by the **equations of translation**.

$$\begin{cases} x' = x - h \\ y' = y - k \end{cases}$$

If the shift of the origin involves a move to the left or down or both, the same equations of translation may be used. This is because h or k or both may be negative.

A shift of a curve h units to the right is the same as a shift of the vertical axis h units to the left. The new origin is located at the point $(-h, 0)$. The equations of translation are $x' = x - (-h)$ and $y' = y - 0$.

$$\begin{cases} x' = x + h \\ y' = y \end{cases}$$

The point (a, b) on the original curve has coordinates $(a + h, b)$ in the $x'y'$-system.

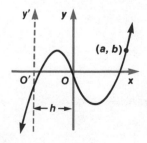
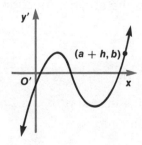

Examples

1. **Draw the graph of the function $f: y = (2x - 3)^2$.**

   Change the form of f so that $x - h$ occurs in place of x.

   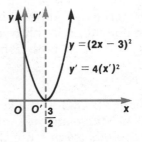

   $y = (2x - 3)^2$ transforms to $y = 4\left(x - \dfrac{3}{2}\right)^2$

   Since $x' = x - \dfrac{3}{2}$, the new equation is $y = 4(x')^2$.

   The new origin must be located at the point $\left(\dfrac{3}{2}, 0\right)$.

2. **Draw the graph of $g: y = 3x^2 + 4x + 4$. Consider both horizontal and vertical shifts of the axes.**

   Since $3x^2 + 4x + 4$ is not factorable into the form $a(x - h)^2$, it must be changed in form by completing the square.

   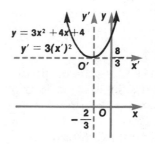

   $$y = 3x^2 + 4x + 4$$
   $$y = 3\left(x^2 + \frac{4}{3}x + \frac{4}{9}\right) + 4 - 3\left(\frac{4}{9}\right)$$
   $$y = 3\left(x + \frac{2}{3}\right)^2 + \frac{8}{3}$$
   $$y - \frac{8}{3} = 3\left(x + \frac{2}{3}\right)^2 \qquad \textit{Equations of translation}$$
   $$y' = 3(x')^2 \qquad \begin{cases} y' = y - \frac{8}{3} \\ x' = x - \left(-\frac{2}{3}\right) \end{cases}$$

   The new origin O' is a point on the graph of g. Substitute the coordinates of O' into the original expression for g.

   $$g(x) = 3x^2 + 4x + 4$$
   $$g\left(-\frac{2}{3}\right) = 3\left(-\frac{2}{3}\right)^2 + 4\left(-\frac{2}{3}\right) + 4 = \frac{4}{3} - \frac{8}{3} + 4 = \frac{8}{3}$$

   Thus, $O'\left(-\dfrac{2}{3}, \dfrac{8}{3}\right)$ is a point on the original function g.

Exercises

Exploratory Apply the equations of translation to the points given. Determine their coordinates in the $x'y'$-plane.

1. $P(-2, 3), Q(1, 1)$; $\begin{cases} x' = x - 5 \\ y' = y + 2 \end{cases}$

2. $P(a, b), Q(c, d)$; $\begin{cases} x' = x - 3 \\ y' = y - 4 \end{cases}$

3. $P(a, b), Q(c, d);$ $\begin{cases} x' = x - h \\ y' = y - k \end{cases}$

4. $P(a, b), Q(c, d);$ $\begin{cases} x' = x \\ y' = y + 1 \end{cases}$

5. $P(0, 0), Q(a, a);$ $\begin{cases} x' = x - h \\ y' = y - k \end{cases}$

6. $P(a, b), Q(b, a);$ $\begin{cases} x = x' + h \\ y = y' + k \end{cases}$

Find new coordinates for P and Q. The origin is moved to a new point O' as indicated. Write the equations of translation.

7. $P(1, 3), Q(2, -3), O'(4, 2)$

8. $P(6, -2), Q(0, 5), O'(-3, 5)$

9. $P(-1, -1), Q(0, 0), O'(1, -2)$

10. $P(a, b), Q(0, 0), O'(h, k)$

Written   Graph each function or relation by considering shifts of axes.

1. $y = 3(x - 2)^2$

2. $y = 4(x + 3)^2$

3. $y = (3x + 1)^2$

4. $y = x^2 - 5x + \dfrac{25}{4}$

5. $y = 4x^2 - 12x + 9$

6. $y = 9x^2 - 30x + 20$

7. $y = 3x^2 + 5x - 2$

8. $y = |x + 2|$ *(Hint: Complete the square.)*

9. $y = |2x - 3|$

10. $y = |4x + 2| - 3$

11. $y = [x + 3]$

12. $f\!:\!x^2 + y^2 - 6x + 4y + 9 = 0$
    (Hint: Complete the square in both x and y.)

13. $f\!:\!x^2 - y^2 + 8x + 6y - 34 = 0$

14. $f\!:\!4x^2 + 9y^2 - 16x + 54y + 61 = 0$

Solve each of the following.

15. Write the equations of translation which change the right triangle formed by the points $A(1, 8)$, $B(5, 10)$ and $C(11, -2)$ so that its right-angle vertex is located at the origin of the new system.

16. Find the equation of the curve $x^2 + y^2 = 1$ if it is translated by the equations A and then by equations B.

    $A\!:\begin{cases} x' = x - 2 \\ y' = y + 3 \end{cases}$ $B\!:\begin{cases} x'' = x' + 1 \\ y'' = y' - 2 \end{cases}$

    Write a single set of translation equations which make the shift in one step.

4–5 Rotations   ✳ not done

Rotations are transformations which also are useful in graphing functions. Graphing the relation $S\!:\!x^2 + 2xy + \sqrt{2}x - \sqrt{2}y + y^2 = 0$ is difficult in the xy-coordinate plane. The complicated equation can be transformed to the form $y' = (x')^2$. This parabola is easy to draw in the $x'y'$-plane. For the present, only transformation of points under rotation of the axes will be studied.

Suppose the original axes are to be rotated in a counter-clockwise direction through the angle θ. If the *radius vector* to the point $P(x, y)$ which is $P'(x', y')$ is inclined an angle ϕ, phi,

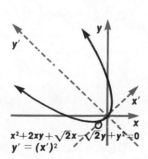

$x^2 + 2xy + \sqrt{2}x - \sqrt{2}y + y^2 = 0$
$y' = (x')^2$

to the x'-axis, then it is inclined an angle $(\theta + \phi)$ to the x-axis.

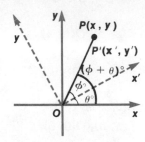

If the length of the radius vector is ρ, rho, then $\sin \phi = \dfrac{y'}{\rho}$ or

$y' = \rho \sin \phi$, and $\cos \phi = \dfrac{x'}{\rho}$ or $x' = \rho \cos \phi$. Likewise $y = \rho \sin (\theta + \phi)$ and $x = \rho \cos (\theta + \phi)$.

$$\begin{cases} x = \rho \cos (\theta + \phi) \\ y = \rho \sin (\theta + \phi) \end{cases}$$
$$\begin{cases} x = \rho \cos \theta \cos \phi - \rho \sin \theta \sin \phi \\ y = \rho \sin \theta \cos \phi + \rho \cos \theta \sin \phi \end{cases}$$
$$\begin{cases} x = x' \cos \theta - y' \sin \theta \\ y = x' \sin \theta + y' \cos \theta \end{cases}$$
$$\begin{cases} x' = x \cos \theta + y \sin \theta \\ y' = -x \sin \theta + y \cos \theta \end{cases}$$

Refer to Challenge problem on page 115.

These two sets of transformational equations are called the **equations of rotation.** They give the relationships between the coordinates of a given point in the xy-plane and the $x'y'$-plane under a rotation through an angle θ. A rotation of θ in the xy-plane is a function which maps $(x, y) \rightarrow (x', y')$. A rotation of $-\theta$ in the xy-plane maps $(x', y') \rightarrow (x, y)$.

Examples

1. **Find the coordinates of $P(-3, 5)$ after a rotation of the axes through 30°.**

    For 30°, $\sin \theta = \dfrac{1}{2}$, $\cos \theta = \dfrac{\sqrt{3}}{2}$. The point P is transformed to the point $P'(x', y')$ by the following equations of rotation.

    $$\begin{cases} x' = x \cos \theta + y \sin \theta \\ y' = -x \sin \theta + y \cos \theta \end{cases}$$
    $$\begin{cases} x' = -3 \cdot \dfrac{\sqrt{3}}{2} + 5 \cdot \dfrac{1}{2} = \dfrac{5 - 3\sqrt{3}}{2} \\ y' = 3 \cdot \dfrac{1}{2} + 5 \cdot \dfrac{\sqrt{3}}{2} = \dfrac{3 + 5\sqrt{3}}{2} \end{cases}$$

    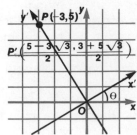

    Thus P' is the point $\left(\dfrac{5 - 3\sqrt{3}}{2}, \dfrac{3 + 5\sqrt{3}}{2} \right)$.

2. Find the coordinates of $P(10, -2)$ after a rotation of the axes through the angle θ when $\tan \theta = \dfrac{3}{4}$.

Here $\sin \theta = \dfrac{3}{5}$, $\cos \theta = \dfrac{4}{5}$ if $0° \le m \angle \theta \le 180°$. (Why?) Apply the equations of rotation.

$$\begin{cases} x' = x \cos \theta + y \sin \theta \\ y' = -x \sin \theta + y \cos \theta \end{cases}$$

$$\begin{cases} x' = 10 \cdot \dfrac{4}{5} + (-2) \cdot \dfrac{3}{5} = 8 - \dfrac{6}{5} = \dfrac{34}{5} \\ y' = -10 \cdot \dfrac{3}{5} + (-2) \cdot \dfrac{4}{5} = -6 - \dfrac{8}{5} = -\dfrac{38}{5} \end{cases}$$

Thus, P' is the point $\left(\dfrac{34}{5}, -\dfrac{38}{5} \right)$.

Exercises

Exploratory Find the coordinates of each point after rotation through the given angle.

1. $P(5, 2)$, $m \angle \theta = 60°$ 2. $P(-3, 0)$, $m \angle \theta = 45°$ 3. $P(-2, -1)$, $m \angle \theta = 30°$

Written Write the coordinates of each point after rotation through the given angle.

1. $P(2, -5)$, $m \angle \theta = 60°$
2. $P(4, 4)$, $m \angle \theta = 45°$
3. $P(5, 12)$, $m \angle \theta = 30°$
4. $P(1, 1)$, $\sin \theta = 1$, $0 < \theta \le 90$
5. $P(2, -4)$, $\cos \theta = 0$, $0 < \theta \le 90$
6. $P(0, 3)$, $\tan \theta = 0$, $90 < \theta \le 180$
7. $P(-2, -3)$, $\tan \theta = 1$
8. $P(5, -5)$, $\tan \theta = \dfrac{\sqrt{3}}{3}$
9. $P(3, 5)$, $\tan \theta = \sqrt{3}$

A square has vertices at $(0, 0)$, $(5, 0)$, $(5, 5)$, and $(0, 5)$. Give the coordinates of the square after the indicated rotation of the axes is completed.

10. counterclockwise, $m \angle \theta = 45°$ 11. clockwise, $m \angle \theta = 45°$
12. counterclockwise, $m \angle \theta = 30°$
13. A right triangle has vertices at $A(0, 0)$, $B(-8, 6)$ and $C(-5, 10)$. What are the coordinates of the vertices of $\triangle A'B'C'$ after the axes have been rotated through an angle θ, where $\tan \theta = \dfrac{4}{3}$? Sketch the two triangles. Does the transformation preserve the size and shape of triangle ABC?

Challenge Use the rotational equations $\begin{cases} x = x' \cos \theta - y' \sin \theta \\ y = x' \sin \theta + y' \cos \theta \end{cases}$ to derive the formulas for x' and y'. (Hint: Remember $\sin^2 \theta + \cos^2 \theta = 1$. Use this fact to arrange terms so that x' or y' can be isolated.

4–6 Other Transformations

Sometimes a reflection of a graph produces one which is more familiar.

Reflection of a function f in the x-axis is the transformation defined by $g(x) = -f(x)$. The ordinates of g are the additive inverses of the ordinates of f.

✳ note similiarity to a scalar multiplier of −1

Reflection in the x-axis

Example

1. Draw the graph of $f(x) = -|x - 2| - 3$.

    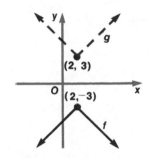

    Rewrite f as $f(x) = -(|x - 2| + 3)$. Draw the graph of $g(x) = |x - 2| + 3$. Reflect the function g in the x-axis for the graph of f.

Reflection of a function f in the y-axis is the transformation defined by $g(x) = f(-x)$.

Reflection in the y-axis

Example

2. Draw the graph of $f{:}y = \sqrt{-2x}$.

    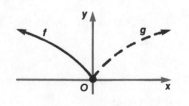

    Let $g(x) = f(-x)$. This means $g(x) = \sqrt{2x}$. Draw the graph of $g(x) = \sqrt{2x}$. Reflect the curve in the y-axis to get the graph of f.

Reflection of a function f in the line $y = x$ is the transformation defined by $g = \{(y, x)|(x, y) \in f\}$. Equations of reflection:

$$\begin{cases} x' = y \\ y' = x \end{cases}$$

note seldom used except when x and y are exchanged

Reflection in the line $y = x$

Example

3. **Draw the graph of $f{:}x = |y - 3| + 1$ by a reflection in the line $y = x$.**

    By interchanging x and y, $g{:}y = |x - 3| + 1$. The desired graph is found by reflecting the graph of g in $y = x$.

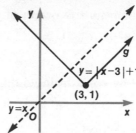
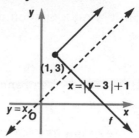

Dilation is a transformation brought about by scalar multiplication. If the scalar k is such that $k > 1$, then *stretching* occurs. If k is such that $0 < k < 1$, then *shrinking* occurs. If $k < 0$, then a combination of dilation and reflection in the x-axis takes place.

effects of scalar multiplication

Scalar multiplication kf of a function produces a multiplication of the ordinates of f; $(kf)(x) = k \cdot f(x)$.

Scalar Multiplication

Example

4. **Draw the graph of $f{:}y = 2|x - 1| + 3$ by considering a dilation.**

    note alternative techniques

    $$f{:}y = 2|x - 1| + 3 = 2\left(|x - 1| + \frac{3}{2}\right)$$

    Let $g = \frac{1}{2}f$ or $2g = f$.

    Then $g{:}y = |x - 1| + \frac{3}{2}$ and $y - \frac{3}{2} = |x - 1|$.

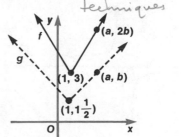

Exercises

Exploratory The graphs of f and kf are shown. Determine the limits of k.

1.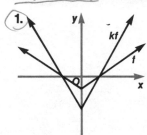

2.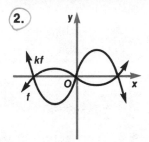

By considering a dilation discuss how the graph of g is related to that of f, if $g = k \cdot f$.

3. $k = 1$ **4.** $k = -1$ **5.** $0 < k < 1$

6. $-1 < k < 0$ **7.** $k < -1$ **8.** $k > 1$

Written Draw the graph of f by considering a dilation of a familiar curve.

1. $y = 3|x + 1| - 6$ **2.** $y = -2x^2 + 4x + 2$ **3.** $y = 0.5(x - 1)^2 + 2$

Draw the graph of each of the following.

4. $y = -|x - 3| - 4$ by reflection in the x-axis.

5. $y = \sqrt{-x - 4}$ by a reflection in the y-axis.

6. $x = |2y - 1| + 2$ by a reflection in the line $y = x$

Challenge Solve each of the following.

1. Given the linear function $f{:}y = mx + b$ discuss the effect on f of the dilation kf.

2. Prove: If the graphs of f and kf intersect on the y-axis and $k \neq 1$, then $f(0) = 0$.

4–7 Continuity

Continuity was introduced as a property of a curve which may be drawn completely without lifting one's pencil. Some curves do not possess this property. They have at least one of three characteristics.

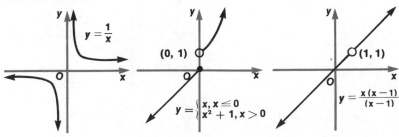

Infinite Discontinuity Jump Discontinuity Point Discontinuity

A curve is continuous at a point $(a, f(a))$ if it does not have any of the three discontinuities at $x = a$. A combination of criteria must be used to describe continuity.

A function $y = f(x)$ is continuous at a if the following are true.

a. As $x \to a^-$, $f(x)$ approaches a finite value b.
b. As $x \to a^+$, $f(x)$ approaches the same finite value b.
c. The value $b = f(a)$.

The three parts of the continuity definition take care of precisely the same three cases of discontinuity already discussed.

> A function is continuous on an interval if it is continuous at all interior points of that interval.

Continuous Function

Therefore, a function which is continuous on an interval cannot contain a point of discontinuity for any x in the interval.

Examples

1. **Determine if $f(x) = \dfrac{|x|}{x}$ is continuous.**

    a) As $x \to 0^-$, $f(x) \to -1$
    b) As $x \to 0^+$, $f(x) \to 1$

    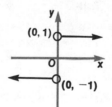

    Therefore, the function $f(x) = \dfrac{|x|}{x}$ has a jump discontinuity at $x = 0$.

2. **Determine if $x^2y = 1$ is continuous.**

    a) As $x \to 0^-$, $y \to \infty$
    b) As $x \to 0^+$, $y \to \infty$

    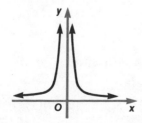

    Therefore, the function $x^2y = 1$ has an infinite discontinuity at $x = 0$.

3. Determine if $f(x) = \dfrac{x^2 - 4}{x - 2}$ is continuous.

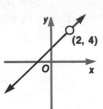

$$f(2) = \frac{(2)^2 - 4}{2 - 2}$$

Therefore, $f(2)$ is not defined

Thus, the function $y = \dfrac{x^2 - 4}{x - 2}$ is discontinuous at $x = 2$.

Exercises

Exploratory   Determine which functions are continuous and which are discontinuous. Identify each discontinuity as an infinite, jump, or point discontinuity.

1. $y = \dfrac{1}{x}$

2. $y = x^2 + 2$

3. $y = \begin{cases} x, x < 0 \\ 0, x = 0 \\ x, x > 0 \end{cases}$

4. $y = \dfrac{x^2 - 1}{x + 1}$

5. $y = |x - 1|$

6. $y = \begin{cases} 1, x \text{ rational} \\ 0, x \text{ irrational} \end{cases}$

Consider the functions f, g, h and j with a an interior point in the interval of definition. Explain each answer fully.

7. Suppose that as $x \to a^+$, $f(x) \to b$ and as $x \to a^-$, $f(x) \to c$, where $b \neq c$. Is f continuous at a?

8. Suppose that as $x \to a^+$, $h(x) \to b$ and $h(a) = c$, where $b \neq c$. Is h continuous?

9. Suppose that as $x \to a^+$, $g(x) \to b$ and as $x \to a^-$, $g(x) \to b$ also. Is g continuous?

10. Suppose that as $x \to a^+$, $j(x) \to b$ and $j(a) = b$. Is j continuous?

Written   Determine which functions are continuous and which are discontinuous. Identify each discontinuity as an infinite, jump, or point discontinuity.

1. $y = \begin{cases} x, x > 0 \\ -x, x < 0 \end{cases}$

2. $y = -x, |x| < 1$

3. $f(x) = \dfrac{x^2 - 1}{x - 1}$

4. $f(x) = \begin{cases} \dfrac{x^2 - 1}{x - 1}, x \neq 1 \\ 1, x = 1 \end{cases}$

5. $f(x) = \begin{cases} \dfrac{x^2 - 1}{x - 1}, x \neq 1 \\ 2, x = 1 \end{cases}$

6. $g(x) = x + \dfrac{1}{x}$

7. $y = x + [x]$

8. $y = x + |x|$

9. $y = \begin{cases} x + 1, x \leq 0 \\ x^2 + 1, x > 0 \end{cases}$

It is possible to assign values to $f(x)$ that remove some discontinuities. Find this value for $f(x)$ for each of the following.

10. $f(x) = \dfrac{x^2 - 5x + 6}{x - 2}$

11. $g(x) = \dfrac{x^2 - 5}{x + \sqrt{5}}$

12. $h(x) = \dfrac{x^3 + 8}{x + 2}$

13. $j(x) = \begin{cases} x^2, x < 3 \\ 12 - x, x > 3 \end{cases}$

14. $k(x) = \dfrac{x^2 - x}{\sqrt{x} - 1}$ *Hint: Rationalize the denominator.*

Chapter Summary

1. The graph of a relation S is symmetric with respect to the y-axis if $(-a, b) \in S$ whenever $(a, b) \in S$. (97)
2. The graph of a relation S is symmetric with respect to the x-axis if $(a, -b) \in S$ whenever $(a, b) \in S$. (98)
3. The graph of a relation S is symmetric with respect to the line $y = x$ if $(b, a) \in S$ whenever $(a, b) \in S$ (99)
4. The graph of a relation S is symmetric with respect to the origin if $(-a, -b) \in S$ whenever $(a, b) \in S$. (100)
5. The line $x = a$ is a vertical asymptote for a function $y = f(x)$ if $f(x) \to \infty$ or $f(x) \to -\infty$ as $x \to a^+$ or $x \to a^-$. (106)
6. The line $y = b$ is a horizontal asymptote for a function $y = f(x)$ if $f(x)$ approaches the constant value b as $x \to \infty$ or $x \to -\infty$. (107)
7. The oblique line ℓ is a slant asymptote for a function $y = f(x)$ if the graph of f approaches ℓ as $x \to \infty$ or $x \to -\infty$. (108)
8. If a function $y = f(x)$ has the variable x replaced by $(x - h)$, then there is a translation $|h|$ units to the right if $h > 0$ or $|h|$ units to the left if $h < 0$. (110)
   Equations of translation:
   $$\begin{cases} x' = x - h \\ y' = y - k \end{cases} \quad \text{where } (h, k) \text{ is the new origin}$$
9. *Equations of rotation*: (114)
   $$\begin{cases} x' = x \cos \theta + y \sin \theta \\ y' = -x \sin \theta + y \cos \theta \end{cases}$$
10. The reflection of a function f in the x-axis is the transformation defined by $g(x) = -f(x)$. (116)
11. The reflection of a function f in the y-axis is the transformation defined by $g(x) = f(-x)$. (116)
12. The reflection of a function f in the line $y = x$ is the transformation defined by $g = \{(y, x) | (x, y) \in f\}$. (117)
13. The scalar multiplication kf of a function f is a multiplication of the ordinates of f defined by $(kf)(x) = k \cdot f(x)$. (117)
14. For a function $y = f(x)$ to be continuous at $x = a$, the following must be true. (119)
    a. As $x \to a^-$, $f(x) \to b$ where b is some finite value.
    b. As $x \to a^+$, $f(x) \to b$ also.
    c. The value $b = f(a)$.
15. A function is continuous on an interval if it is continuous at all values in that interval. (119)

Chapter Review

4-1 Classify the graph of each relation with respect to each symmetry.

    a. the x-axis   **b.** the y-axis   **c.** the origin
    d. the line $y = x$ **e.** none of these

    1. $y = x^2 - 2$ **2.** $xy = 4$ **3.** $3x^2 - 2y^2 = 6$

    4. Identify each relation in Problems **1–3** as even (E) or odd (O).

4-2 Determine whether each relation is symmetric with respect to the x-axis, the y-axis, the
4-3 origin, or the line $y = x$. Then, find the intercepts and asymptotes if they exist. Next, determine the extent and excluded regions. Shade these regions and sketch the curve.

    5. $y = \dfrac{x + 1}{x - 1}$ **6.** $y = 2(x - 1)^2 - 1$

    7. $y = x^2 + 1$ **8.** $y = \dfrac{x^3 - 2x^2 + 1}{x - 1}$

    9. $y = 3x^3 - 5x^2 - 2x$ **10.** $y = \dfrac{(x + 2)(x + 1)}{(3x - 1)(x + 3)}$

4-4 Apply the equations of translation to the points given to determine their coordinates in the $x'y'$-plane.

    11. $P(-1, 3)$, $Q(2, -5)$; $\begin{cases} x' = x + 5 \\ y' = y - 7 \end{cases}$ **12.** $P(a, b)$, $Q(c, d)$; $\begin{cases} x' = x + h \\ y' = y + k \end{cases}$

Find new coordinates for P and Q if the origin is moved to a new point O' as indicated. Write the equations of transformation.

    13. $P(3, 1)$, $Q(2, -3)$, $O'(5, -7)$ **14.** $P(a, 0)$, $Q(0, b)$, $O'(h, k)$

Graph each function or relation by considering shifts of axes.

    15. $y = (x + 2)^2 - 1$ **16.** $y = |x - 3|$

4-5 **17.** Write the coordinates of the point $(-2, 4)$ after rotation through the angle $\theta = 45°$.

4-6 Draw the graph of f by considering a dilation of a familiar curve.

    18. $y = 2|x - 1| - 3$ **19.** $y = 2[x]$

4-7 Determine which functions are continuous. Then determine which are discontinuous. Identify each discontinuity as an infinite, jump, or point discontinuity.

    20. $f(x) = \dfrac{-x}{(x - 1)^2}$ **21.** $y = \begin{cases} x + 1, x < 0 \\ 1 - x, x \geq 0 \end{cases}$

    22. $y = -x$ **23.** $y = \begin{cases} \dfrac{|x|}{x}, x \neq 0 \\ 1, x = 0 \end{cases}$

    24. If any function in Problems **20–23** has a point discontinuity, assign a value to $f(x)$ to remove the discontinuity.

Chapter Test

Classify the graph of each relation with respect to each symmetry.

    a. the x-axis   **b.** the y-axis   **c.** the origin

    d. the line $y = x$ **e.** none of these

1. $3x^4 + x^3 - 2x^2 = y$ **2.** $y = [x] + x$

3. $x^3 - x^2y - y + 2x = 0$ **4.** $x^3y^2 - x^2y^3 = 0$

5. Identify each relation in Problems **1–4** as even (E) or odd (O).

Determine whether each relation is symmetric with respect to the x-axis, the y-axis, the origin, or the line $y = x$. Then, find the intercepts and asymptotes if they exist. Next, determine the extent and excluded regions. Shade these regions and sketch the curve.

6. $y = \dfrac{x}{x^2 - 4}$ **7.** $y = \dfrac{(x + 1)^2}{(x - 1)^3}$

8. Apply the equations of translation $\begin{cases} x' = x - a \\ y' = y - a \end{cases}$ to the points $P(0, 0)$ and $Q(b, b)$.

Graph each function or relation by considering shifts of axes.

9. $(x - 2)^2 + (y + 3)^2 = 4$ **10.** $y = 3x^2 + 5x - 2$

11. Draw the graph of $f{:}y = 2|x - 1| + 3$ by considering one or more transformations.

Determine which functions are continuous. Then determine which are discontinuous. Identify each discontinuity as an infinite, jump, or point discontinuity.

12. $y = \dfrac{x - 2}{x^3 - 8}$ **13.** $y = \begin{cases} \dfrac{[x]}{x}, & x \neq 0 \\ 1, & x = 0 \end{cases}$

14. If the function in either Problem **12** or **13** has a point discontinuity assign a value to $f(x)$ to remove the discontinuity.

Computers

Home Computers

The first use of home computers involved the playing of computer games, often attached to the family television set. Recently, however, with the development of the microprocessor, true home computing is now available. Often costing less than $1000, home computers can do many daily functions needed by a family. Computers can be programmed to do the family budget and balancing the checkbook. They also can plan the weekly menu and shopping, keeping an up to date inventory of the family pantry. Various homework skills for the students in the household can be practiced with the aid of specially designed programs. The computer can be programmed to switch the heat on and off in certain rooms at various times of the day to conserve energy. They can also be used to switch different electrical appliances on and off. Recreation activities, such as learning how to play chess, can also be accomplished through a home computer. Even small business management can be helped by using the small home computer.

Using CRT (Cathode Ray Tube) monitors, often in color, graphic displays can be designed. The addition of a small printer gives the capability of printing computer output. Word processing programs provide the capability of composition of letters and manuscripts. Some installations even have musical scale production through audible electronic tones.

In some communities, closed circuit TV networks have been built allowing for home and business access to data banks and special means of communicating "computer to computer." It is possible to make a purchase from a department store by communicating with the store's computer. Interactive games on TV

Systems such as this one can alert the people of the house to existing danger and call for help.

where the contestants are the home audience are possible and may become the TV of the future with the help of the computer. The home of the future will certainly be computer oriented.

Many companies have developed video games that use small computer systems.

Exercises Write programs for each of the following.

1. Given $f(x) = \dfrac{3x - 1}{x + 1}$. Choose inputs of x closer and closer to -1 from the right, that is as $x \to -1^+$. Output a table of values for y. Determine the value the function approaches.

2. Given $f(x) = \dfrac{3x - 1}{x + 1}$. Choose inputs of x such that $x \to -1^-$. Output a table of values for y. Determine the value the function approaches.

3. Given $f(x) = \dfrac{x - 1}{x^2 - 4}$. Input x such that $x \to 2^+$. Output a table of values for y. Determine the value the function approaches.

4. Given $f(x) = \dfrac{x + 1}{x^2 - 4}$. Input x such that $x \to 2^-$. Output a table of values for y. Determine the values the function approaches.

5. By using the equation of rotation

$$x' = x \cos \theta + y \sin \theta$$
$$y' = -x \sin \theta + y \cos \theta$$

output ordered pairs (x', y') for each (x, y) and corresponding θ.

6. Output the graph for $y = 2\,|x - 1| + 3$.

Many structures involve a common property known as periodicity. Circular functions are important because they are periodic functions.

Circular Functions

+ discuss the non-arbitrariness of the placement of the integers

5-1   Wrapping Functions

Several functions can be generated by mapping the points of a line onto the points of a circle. Consider a circle with center at the origin and a radius of 1 unit. This circle is called a **unit circle**. The equation of this circle is $x^2 + y^2 = 1$.

Suppose a line ℓ is tangent to the circle at (1, 0). This line is perpendicular to the *x*-axis. Match the real numbers with the points on ℓ. Use the same scale as on the axes with zero at (1, 0).

Now imagine that ℓ is a flexible tape measure which has no thickness. Wrap the tape measure around the circle in both the clockwise and counterclockwise directions. Then each real number point on the tape measure falls on a point of the circle. The mapping of the points of ℓ onto the points of the circle is called a *wrapping function*.

Notice that each point of ℓ maps onto only one point of the circle. Each point of the circle will be the image of many points of ℓ. Therefore, the wrapping function is not a 1-1 mapping.

Since the radius of the circle is 1 unit, the circumference $C = 2\pi$ units.

$$\frac{\pi}{2} \rightarrow (0, 1)$$

$$\pi \rightarrow (-1, 0)$$

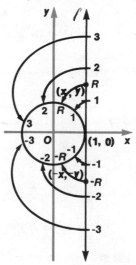

Since $\frac{\pi}{2}$ is between 1 and 2 on the unit circle, $\frac{\pi}{2}$ maps onto a point on the unit circle between 1 and 2.

A function *f* such that $f(x) = f(x + p)$ is a **periodic function**. If *p* is the *least* positive *constant* for which the equality is true, then *p* is called the **period** of the function.

Periodic Function

When $R > 0$, the tape measure is wrapped counterclockwise around the circle. If $R < 0$, then the wrapping is clockwise.

Examples

1. **Find the image of $-R$ and $R + \pi$ if $R \to (x, y)$.**

   Since R and $-R$ are symmetric with respect
   to the x-axis, $-R \to (x, -y)$.

   Since $\pi = \frac{1}{2}C$, $R + \pi \to (-x, -y)$.

   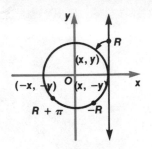

2. **Find the image of $R - \pi$ and $\frac{\pi}{2} - R$ if $R \to (x, y)$.**

   Since $\pi = \frac{1}{2}C$, $R - \pi \to (-x, -y)$.

   To find the image of $\frac{\pi}{2} - R$, reflect the figure

   in the line $y = x$.

   Thus, $\frac{\pi}{2} - R \to (y, x)$.

   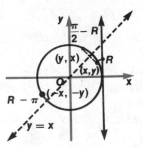

Exercises

Exploratory **Complete the following mappings.**

1. $\frac{3\pi}{2} \to (\underline{\quad}, \underline{\quad})$

2. $2\pi \to (\underline{\quad}, \underline{\quad})$

3. $-\frac{\pi}{2} \to (\underline{\quad}, \underline{\quad})$

4. $-\pi \to (\underline{\quad}, \underline{\quad})$

5. If $R \to (-1, 0)$, what are
   at least two different
   values for R?

6. If $R \to (x, y)$, then $R + 2\pi \to$
   $(\underline{\quad}, \underline{\quad})$ and $R + 4\pi \to$
   $(\underline{\quad}, \underline{\quad})$.

For each value for R, find the quadrant in which (x, y) is located if $R \to (x, y)$.

7. $\frac{\pi}{4}$

8. $\frac{5\pi}{6}$

9. $\frac{7\pi}{4}$

10. $\frac{6\pi}{5}$

11. $-\frac{3\pi}{4}$

12. $-\frac{8\pi}{5}$

Written **For each value for R, write the quadrant in which (x, y) is located if $R \to (x, y)$.**

1. $\frac{\pi}{6}$

2. $\frac{\pi}{3}$

3. $\frac{16\pi}{3}$

④ $-\dfrac{52\pi}{11}$ ⑤ 2   ⑥ -5

Complete the following mappings.

7. If $\dfrac{\pi}{6} \to (x, y)$, then $-\dfrac{\pi}{6} \to ($ ___ , ___ $)$.   ⑧ If $\dfrac{\pi}{6} \to (x, y)$, then $\dfrac{5\pi}{6} \to ($ ___ , ___ $)$.

⑨ If $\dfrac{\pi}{4} \to (x, y)$, then $\dfrac{3\pi}{4} \to ($ ___ , ___ $)$.   10. If $\dfrac{\pi}{4} \to (x, y)$, then $-\dfrac{\pi}{4} \to ($ ___ , ___ $)$.

⑪ If $\dfrac{\pi}{6} \to (x, y)$, then $\dfrac{\pi}{3} \to ($ ___ , ___ $)$.   12. If $\dfrac{\pi}{8} \to (x, y)$, then $\dfrac{3\pi}{8} \to ($ ___ , ___ $)$.

$\left(\text{Hint: } \dfrac{\pi}{2} - \dfrac{\pi}{6} = \dfrac{\pi}{3}\right)$ $\left(\text{Hint: } \dfrac{\pi}{2} - \dfrac{\pi}{8} = \dfrac{3\pi}{8}\right)$

13. If $\pi \to (-1, 0)$, show that   14. If $\pi \to (-1, 0)$, show that
$\dfrac{\pi}{4} \to \left(\dfrac{\sqrt{2}}{2}, \dfrac{\sqrt{2}}{2}\right)$. $-\dfrac{\pi}{4} \to \left(\dfrac{\sqrt{2}}{2}, \dfrac{-\sqrt{2}}{2}\right)$.

15. If f and g both are periodic functions with period k, show that $(f + g)$ has period k.

and $\dfrac{\pi}{4} \to ($, $)$

5-2 The Circular Functions

By assigning one of the coordinates of the point (x, y) on the unit circle to each real number r, two functions may be defined. These functions are called the **cosine** and **sine functions**. They are symbolized by *cos* and *sin* respectively.

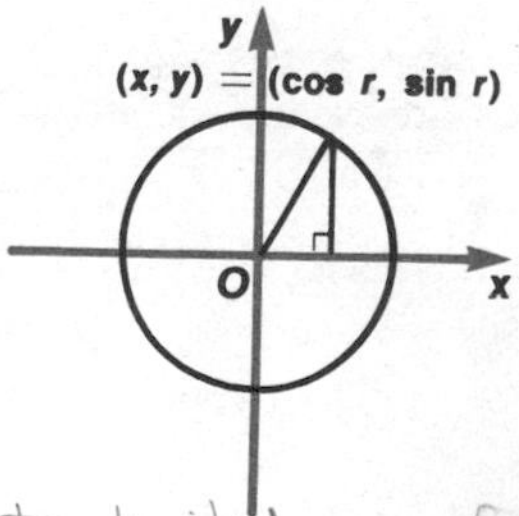

$(x, y) = (\cos r, \sin r)$

✱ note limited use of this form

Cosine and Sine Functions

The *cosine* function is defined as follows.
    cosine $= \{(r, x) | r \to (x, y)$ by the wrapping function$\}$
The *sine* function is defined as follows.
    sine $= \{(r, y) | r \to (x, y)$ by the wrapping function$\}$

It is customary to write $x = \cos r$ when $(r, x) \in$ cosine and $y = \sin r$ when $(r, y) \in$ sine. Since (x, y) is a point on the unit circle $\cos^2 r + \sin^2 r = x^2 + y^2 = 1$.
    Another function, the **tangent function**, (symbolized *tan*), can be defined in terms of the *cosine* and *sine* functions.

✱ note more common form and relationships
To avoid confusion with $\sin(r^2)$ which is written $\sin r^2$, $(\sin r)^2$ is written $\sin^2 r$.

✱

Tangent Function

The *tangent* function is defined as follows.
tangent $= \left\{\left(r, \dfrac{y}{x}\right) | r \to (x, y)$ by the wrapping function, $x \neq 0\right\}$

In general, $\tan r = \dfrac{\sin r}{\cos r}$. Since the three functions, *sine*, *cosine*, and *tangent*, are all related to a circle, <u>they are called **circular functions**</u>.

Since the wrapping function is not a 1–1 mapping, the *cosine* and *sine* functions are not 1–1 mappings. If $r \rightarrow (x, y)$ and $(r + 2\pi) \rightarrow (x, y)$, then $\cos r \rightarrow x$ and $\cos (r + 2\pi) \rightarrow x$. Also, $\sin r \rightarrow y$ and $\sin (r + 2\pi) \rightarrow y$.

Since the circumference of the unit circle is 2π, the value of the *sine* and *cosine* functions at the boundaries of the quadrants are given below.

The cos r is the abscissa and the sin r is the ordinate.

	0	$\dfrac{\pi}{2}$	π	$\dfrac{3\pi}{2}$
sin	0	1	0	-1
cos	1	0	-1	0
tan	0	undefined	0	undefined

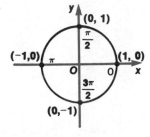

The values of the *cosine* and *sine* functions at these points are called the **quadrantal values**. The *tangent* function can be evaluated at 0 and π, but not at $\dfrac{\pi}{2}$ and $\dfrac{3\pi}{2}$.

These are quadrantal values because they occur at the boundaries of the quadrants.

Examples

1. Find $\sin \dfrac{\pi}{3}$, $\cos \dfrac{\pi}{3}$, and $\tan \dfrac{\pi}{3}$.

   Since $\overarc{AB} = \dfrac{\pi}{3}$, $m\,\overarc{AB} = \dfrac{1}{6} \cdot$ (circumference of the circle). Therefore, $\overarc{AB}$ has the same length as the radius, which is 1. The distance formula can be used.

   $$\left(\cos \frac{\pi}{3} - 1\right)^2 + \sin^2 \frac{\pi}{3} = 1$$

   $$\cos^2 \frac{\pi}{3} - 2\cos \frac{\pi}{3} + 1 + \sin^2 \frac{\pi}{3} = 1$$

   $$-2\cos \frac{\pi}{3} + 1 + \left(\sin^2 \frac{\pi}{3} + \cos^2 \frac{\pi}{3}\right) = 1$$

   $$-2\cos \frac{\pi}{3} + 2 = 1$$

   $$-2\cos \frac{\pi}{3} = -1$$

   $$\cos \frac{\pi}{3} = \frac{1}{2}$$

   By substitution, $\sin^2 \dfrac{\pi}{3} + \left(\dfrac{1}{2}\right)^2 = 1$

   $$\sin \frac{\pi}{3} = \pm \frac{\sqrt{3}}{2}$$

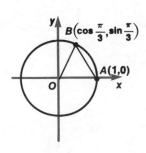

Thus, $\sin^2 \dfrac{\pi}{3} = \dfrac{3}{4}$.

Since $\frac{\pi}{3}$ is in the first quadrant, the positive value for $\sin \frac{\pi}{3}$ is chosen.

$$\tan \frac{\pi}{3} = \frac{\sin \frac{\pi}{3}}{\cos \frac{\pi}{3}} = \frac{\frac{\sqrt{3}}{2}}{\frac{1}{2}} = \sqrt{3}$$

2. Find $\sin \left(-\frac{\pi}{3}\right)$, $\cos \left(-\frac{\pi}{3}\right)$, and $\tan \left(-\frac{\pi}{3}\right)$.

The functions of $-r$ also may be found by a reflection of the circle about the x-axis. Since $r \rightarrow (x, y)$, $-r \rightarrow (x, -y)$.

$$\sin \left(-\frac{\pi}{3}\right) = -\left(\sin \frac{\pi}{3}\right) = -\frac{\sqrt{3}}{2}$$

$$\cos \left(-\frac{\pi}{3}\right) = \left(\cos \frac{\pi}{3}\right) = \frac{1}{2}$$

$$\tan \left(-\frac{\pi}{3}\right) = -\left(\tan \frac{\pi}{3}\right) = -\sqrt{3}$$

In general, ✳ note
$$\sin (-r) = -\sin r$$
$$\cos (-r) = \cos r$$
$$\tan (-r) = -\tan r$$

3. Find $\sin \frac{2\pi}{3}$, $\cos \frac{2\pi}{3}$, and $\tan \frac{2\pi}{3}$.

Use a reflection about the y-axis, $(\pi - r) \rightarrow (-x, y)$.

$$\sin \frac{2\pi}{3} = \frac{\sqrt{3}}{2} \qquad \cos \frac{2\pi}{3} = -\frac{1}{2} \qquad \tan \frac{2\pi}{3} = -\sqrt{3}$$

Exercises

Exploratory Find $\sin r$ for each of the following.

1. $r = 2\pi$
2. $r = 0$
3. $r = \frac{1}{2}\pi$

Find $\cos r$ for each of the following.

4. $r = 0$
5. $r = \frac{3}{2}\pi$
6. $r = 2\pi$

Find $\tan r$ for each of the following.

7. $\sin r = \frac{4}{5}$, r in quadrant I
8. $\cos r = \frac{8}{17}$, r in quadrant I

Written Find $\sin r$.

1. $\cos r = \frac{3}{4}$, r in quadrant I
2. $\cos r = \frac{5}{12}$, r in quadrant IV

Find $\cos r$.

3. $\sin r = \frac{1}{2}$, r in quadrant II
4. $\sin r = \frac{\sqrt{2}}{2}$, r in quadrant I
5. $\sin r = \frac{-5}{13}$, r in quadrant III
6. $\tan r = \sqrt{3}$, r in quadrant III

Find $\tan r$.

7. $\sin r = \frac{3}{4}$, r in quadrant I
8. $\cos r = \frac{8}{17}$, r in quadrant IV

9. $r = 0$
10. $r = \frac{\pi}{3}$

11. Find $\sin \frac{\pi}{6}$, $\cos \frac{\pi}{6}$, and $\tan \frac{\pi}{6}$. (Hint: Reflect the circle in $y = x$.)

Find each of the following. Use the results of Problem 11.

12. $\sin \left(-\frac{\pi}{6} \right)$ 13. $\cos \left(-\frac{\pi}{6} \right)$ 14. $\sin \frac{5\pi}{6}$

15. Since $\frac{\pi}{4}$ is $\frac{1}{8}$ of the circle, $\frac{\pi}{4} \rightarrow (x, x)$, and $\cos \frac{\pi}{4} = \sin \frac{\pi}{4}$. Find $\cos \frac{\pi}{4}$, $\sin \frac{\pi}{4}$, and $\tan \frac{\pi}{4}$.

Find each of the following. Use the results of Problem 15.

16. $\sin \left(-\frac{\pi}{4} \right)$ 17. $\sin \frac{3\pi}{4}$ 18. $\tan \frac{3\pi}{4}$

Find the value of each of the following.

19. $\sin \frac{7\pi}{6}$ 20. $\cos \left(-\frac{5\pi}{4} \right)$ 21. $\tan \left(-\frac{15\pi}{4} \right)$

22. Show that $|\sin r| \leq 1$.
23. Show that $|\cos r| \leq 1$.
24. Copy the figure at the right and indicate the coordinates of each point shown. Keep it for future reference.

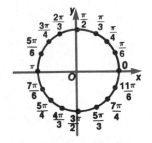

5-3 Graphs of Circular Functions

Since both $x = \cos r$ and $y = \sin r$ define functions in $\mathcal{R} \times \mathcal{R}$, they may be graphed in a coordinate plane. Using variables x and y in the traditional way for constructing graphs, the functions to be graphed are $y = \cos x$ and $y = \sin x$. Both of these functions may be graphed by taking pairs of directed lengths from the figure used to define the wrapping function.

this change of variables is difficult for some students

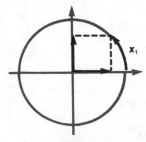

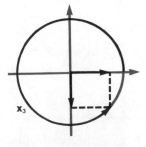

x_1 = length of arc
$\cos x_1$ = directed length indicated on the horizontal axis
$\sin x_1$ = directed length indicated on the vertical axis

$-x_2$ = length of arc
$\cos x_2$ = directed length indicated on the horizontal axis
$\sin x_2$ = directed length indicated on the vertical axis

x_3 = length of arc
$\cos x_3$ = directed length indicated on the horizontal axis
$\sin x_3$ = directed length indicated on the vertical axis

By generating sets of ordered pairs of the form $(x, \cos x)$ and $(x, \sin x)$ in this way, the following graphs may be drawn.

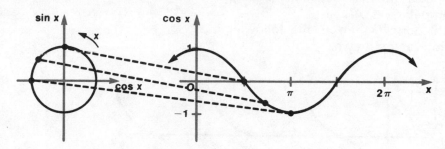

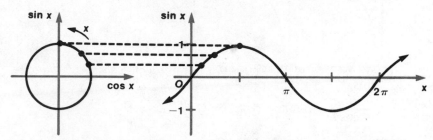

Several properties of these functions can be read from the graphs. The domains of the *sine* and *cosine* functions are $\mathcal{R}$. The range of each function is $\{y \mid -1 \le y \le 1, y \in \mathcal{R}\}$. The period of each function is 2π. The portion of the function included in one period is called a **cycle**.

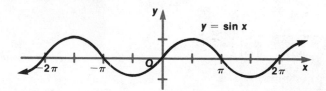

＊ note

The *sine* function is symmetric with respect to the origin, therefore, it is an *odd function*.

 ＊ note

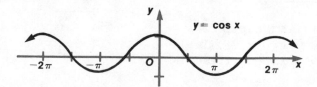

The *cosine* function is symmetric with respect to the y-axis, thus, it is an *even function*.

If a periodic function has a maximum M and a minimum m, the **amplitude** is defined as $A = \left| \dfrac{M - m}{2} \right|$. The maximum value for both the *sine* and *cosine* function is 1. The minimum value is -1. Therefore, for $y = \sin r$ and $y = \cos r$, the amplitude is 1. For $y = A \sin r$ and $y = A \cos r$, the maximum and minimum values are A and $-A$. The amplitude is $|A|$.

Informally, amplitude can be defined as the distance from the middle of the curve to the top or bottom.

Using ordered pairs of the form $(x, \tan x)$, the following graph of the *tangent* function can be drawn.

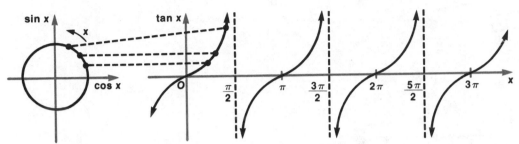

The period of the function is π. In the wrapping function, if $r \to (x, y)$, then $(r + \pi) \to (-x, -y)$. Thus,

$$\tan (r + \pi) = \frac{\sin (r + \pi)}{\cos (r + \pi)} = \frac{-\sin r}{-\cos r} = \tan r.$$

Tan r was defined as $\frac{y}{x}$ thus,

since $\frac{-y}{-x} = \frac{y}{x}$,

$\tan r = \tan (r + \pi)$.

As x approaches $\frac{\pi}{2}, \frac{3\pi}{2}, \frac{5\pi}{2}$, or any $\frac{(2n + 1)\pi}{2}$, where n is an integer, $\cos x$ approaches 0, and the *tangent* function becomes very large in absolute value. The function is *undefined* when x reaches these values. Thus, the *tangent* function has no amplitude.

The functions vary in sign as x varies from 0 to 2π. The chart below indicates the change.

Function \ Quadrant	I	II	III	IV
sin x	+	+	−	−
cos x	+	−	−	+
tan x	+	−	+	−

Another device for remembering the positive signs is $\frac{S|A}{T|C}$.
All Students Take Calculus

The graph of $y = \sin 2x$ is not the same as the graph of $y = \sin x$. As x varies from 0 to π, $2x$ varies from 0 to 2π. On the interval $[0, \pi]$, $\sin 2x$ assumes all values of the sine function. The period of $y = \sin 2x$ is π.

$$y = \sin 2(x + \pi)$$
$$y = \sin (2x + 2\pi)$$
$$y = \sin 2x$$

In general, the period of $y = \sin nx, n \in Z$, is $\frac{2\pi}{n}$. The function

✳ relate to Chapter 4

reciprocal effect on the original period

$y = \cos nx$ also has period $\dfrac{2\pi}{n}$. The period for $\tan nx$ is $\dfrac{\pi}{n}$.

Examples

1. **Sketch the graph of $y = 2 \sin 3x$. Find the amplitude and period.**

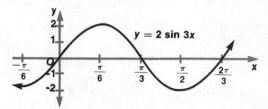

The amplitude is $|2|$ or 2.

The period is $\dfrac{2\pi}{3}$.

2. **Sketch the graph of $y = -5 \cos 4x$.**

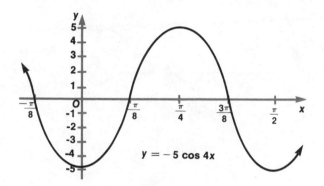

The amplitude is $|-5|$ or 5.

The period is $\dfrac{2\pi}{4}$ or $\dfrac{\pi}{2}$.

The negative coefficient has the effect of *reflecting* the graph of $5 \cos 4x$ about the x-axis.

3. **Sketch the graph of $y = \sin\left(2x - \dfrac{\pi}{3}\right)$.**

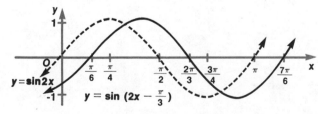

Solving the inequalities $0 \le 2x - \dfrac{\pi}{3} \le 2\pi$, the interval for x becomes $\left[\dfrac{\pi}{6}, \dfrac{7\pi}{6}\right]$. The period is the same as for $y = \sin 2x$.

The graph of $y = \sin\left(2x - \dfrac{\pi}{3}\right)$ is the same as that of $y = \sin 2x$ shifted $\dfrac{\pi}{6}$ units to the right. This difference is called a **phase shift**. The graph of $y = \sin\left(2x + \dfrac{\pi}{3}\right)$ has a phase shift of $\dfrac{\pi}{6}$ units but to the left.

Phase shift is sometimes called displacement.

Translations can be used to show displacement.

✳ note have students rewrite $y = \sin\left(2x + \frac{\pi}{3}\right)$

to $y = \sin 2\left(x + \frac{\pi}{6}\right)$

The graphs of $y = A \sin (nx + \alpha)$ and $y = A \cos (nx + \alpha)$ have amplitudes of $|A|$, periods of $\frac{2\pi}{n}$ and phase shifts of $\frac{\alpha}{n}$ relative to $A \sin nx$ and $A \cos nx$. The phase shift is to the left, if $\frac{\alpha}{n} > 0$. The phase shift is to the right if $\frac{\alpha}{n} < 0$. The graph of $y = A \tan (nx + \alpha)$ has period $\frac{\pi}{n}$ and phase shift $\frac{\alpha}{n}$.

Graphs of Sine and Cosine Functions

Examples

4. **Sketch the graph of $y = 3 \sin 2x + 2 \sin 3x$.**

   The graph of the function may be drawn by sketching $y = 3 \sin 2x$ and $y = 2 \sin 3x$ and adding the ordinates. The period of the sum is 2π. The amplitude of the sum is less than or equal to 5.

   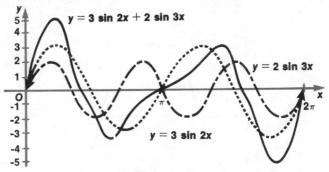

5. **Sketch the graph of $y = x \sin x$.**

   The graph of the function may be drawn by sketching $y = x$ and $y = \sin x$ and multiplying ordinates.

   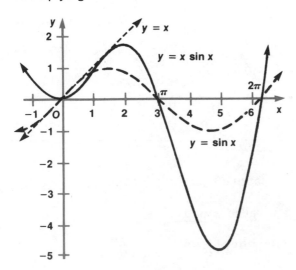

   This function has neither a period nor an amplitude.

Exercises

Exploratory   Write an equation of the *sine* function with each given amplitude and period.

1. amplitude = 3, period = 4

2. amplitude = $\frac{2}{3}$, period = π

Write an equation of the *cosine* function with each given amplitude and period.

3. amplitude = $\frac{1}{3}$, period = π

4. amplitude = 4, period = 2π

Write an equation of a *tangent* function with each given period.

5. period = 2π

6. period = $\frac{\pi}{2}$

Written   Find the amplitude (if applicable) and period of each function. Sketch the graph.

1. $y = 2 \cos x$

2. $y = -\sin 2x$

3. $y = 4 \tan \frac{\pi}{3}x$

4. $y = -\frac{2}{3} \sin \frac{\pi}{6}x$

5. What are the maximum and minimum values of $y = 2 + 3 \cos 2x$? Sketch the graph.

6. What are the maximum and minimum values of $y = 5 - 2 \sin 4x$? Sketch the graph.

Find the period, phase shift, and amplitude (if applicable) for each function. Sketch the graph.

7. $y = -\frac{1}{4} \cos \left(2x + \frac{\pi}{3} \right)$

8. $y = 3 \sin \left(\frac{\pi}{3}x - \frac{\pi}{6} \right)$

9. $y = \frac{1}{2} \tan \left(\frac{\pi}{6}x + \frac{\pi}{3} \right)$

10. $y = \frac{2}{3} \sin (2x - 1)$

Sketch the graph of each function.

11. $y = \sin x + \sin 2x$

12. $y = \cos 2x + \cos 3x$

13. $y = x \cos x$

14. $y = \sin^2 x$

5–4   Other Circular Functions

The reciprocals of the *sine*, *cosine*, and *tangent* functions also are functions.

The *secant* function is defined as follows.
$$\text{secant} = \left\{ (x, y) \mid y = \sec x = \frac{1}{\cos x} \right\}$$
The *cosecant* function is defined as follows.
$$\text{cosecant} = \left\{ (x, y) \mid y = \csc x = \frac{1}{\sin x} \right\}$$
The *cotangent* function is defined as follows.
$$\text{cotangent} = \left\{ (x, y) \mid y = \cot x = \frac{1}{\tan x} = \frac{\cos x}{\sin x} \right\}$$

Reciprocal Functions

Appropriate restrictions must be placed on the domain of each function. For example, $\sec \frac{\pi}{2}$ is undefined since $\cos \frac{\pi}{2} = 0$.

The graph of each circular function and its reciprocal are shown. Notice that as a function *increases*, its reciprocal *decreases*. Both a function and its reciprocal have the same sign. If a function is less than 1 in absolute value, its reciprocal is greater than 1 in absolute value. The period of a function is the same as the period of its reciprocal.

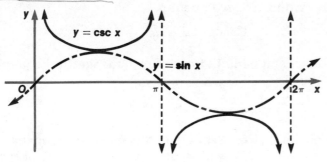

☆ discuss use of reciprocal graphs to produce these graphs

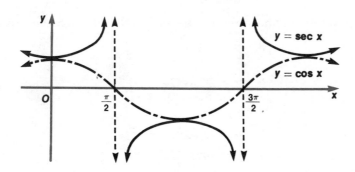

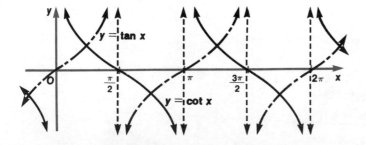

Example

1. Find the period and phase shift of $y = 2 \sec \left(\frac{2\pi}{3}x + \frac{\pi}{6} \right)$. Find the values of the function for which it is undefined. Sketch the graph.

$$\text{Period} = \frac{2\pi}{n} = \frac{2\pi}{\frac{2\pi}{3}} = 3$$

Refer to phase shift for sine and cosine on page 136.

$$\text{Phase shift} = \frac{\alpha}{n} = \frac{\frac{\pi}{6}}{\frac{2\pi}{3}} = \frac{1}{4}$$

The function is undefined when $\cos\left(\frac{2\pi}{3}x + \frac{\pi}{6}\right) = 0.$ $\sec x = \frac{1}{\cos x}$

But, $\cos(2k + 1)\frac{\pi}{2} = 0$ for all $k \in Z.$

Therefore, $\frac{2\pi}{3}x + \frac{\pi}{6} = (2k + 1)\frac{\pi}{2}$

$$\frac{2\pi}{3}x = (2k + 1)\frac{\pi}{2} - \frac{\pi}{6}$$

$$x = (2k + 1)\frac{3}{4} - \frac{1}{4}$$

$$x = \frac{1}{4}[3(2k + 1) - 1]$$

$$x = \frac{1}{2}(3k + 1)$$

Therefore, when $x = \frac{1}{2}(3k + 1)$ the function is undefined.

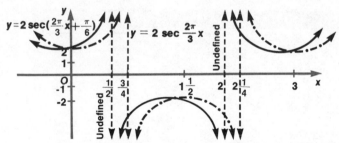

Exercises

Exploratory For what values of x is each function undefined?

1. $\sec x$
2. $\csc x$
3. $\cot x$

4. $\tan x$
5. $3 \sec 2x$
6. $\frac{2}{3}\csc \frac{\pi}{2}x$

7. $\cot\left(\frac{1}{2}x + \pi\right)$
8. $\tan\left(x - \frac{\pi}{2}\right)$
9. $\sec\left(x + \frac{\pi}{2}\right)$

Name the quadrant described by each set of conditions.

10. $\sec x > 0, \tan x < 0$
11. $\cos x < 0, \csc x < 0$
12. $\cot x > 0, \sin x > 0$
13. $\sec x < 0, \csc x > 0$

Written **Graph the equations.**

1. $y = 2 \csc \left(\dfrac{\pi}{6}x - \dfrac{\pi}{2} \right)$

2. $y = \dfrac{1}{2} \cot \left(2x - \dfrac{\pi}{6} \right)$

3. $y = -\sec \left(\dfrac{\pi}{3}x + \dfrac{\pi}{6} \right)$

4. $y = -2 \tan \left(x + \dfrac{\pi}{4} \right)$

Prove each statement.

5. $|\sin x| \leq |\csc x|$

6. $|\sec x| \geq |\tan x|$

Use the Pythagorean Identity, $\sin^2 x + \cos^2 x = 1$, to prove the following.

7. $1 + \cot^2 x = \csc^2 x$

8. $\tan^2 x + 1 = \sec^2 x$

5–5 Identities

An **identity** is an equation which is true for all permissible values of the variables. To prove that an equation is an identity, assume the expressions on each side of the equal sign are equivalent. Then use algebraic properties to write equivalent equations until there is a statement which is an easily recognized identity. An alternate method is to convert one member of the equation into the other by appropriate substitution.

When working with these identities, any values for which the denominator is zero must be excluded.
Equivalent equations are those which are true in both directions. They express "if and only if" relationships.

Examples

1. **Prove that $\tan^2 x + 1 = \sec^2 x$ is an identity.**

$$\tan^2 x + 1 = \sec^2 x$$

$$\frac{\sin^2 x}{\cos^2 x} + 1 = \sec^2 x$$

$$\frac{\sin^2 x + \cos^2 x}{\cos^2 x} = \sec^2 x$$

$$\frac{1}{\cos^2 x} = \sec^2 x$$

$$\sec^2 x = \sec^2 x$$

Thus, $\tan^2 x + 1 = \sec^2 x$.

$\sin^2 x + \cos^2 x = 1$
$\dfrac{1}{\cos x} = \sec x$

2. **Prove that $\sec x + \tan x = \dfrac{\cos x}{1 - \sin x}$.**

$$\sec x + \tan x = \frac{\cos x}{1 - \sin x}$$

$$\frac{1}{\cos x} + \frac{\sin x}{\cos x} = \frac{\cos x}{1 - \sin x}$$

$$\frac{1 + \sin x}{\cos x} = \frac{\cos x}{1 - \sin x}$$

Since $\sin x \neq 1$, the value of $x \neq (2n + 1)\,\pi/2$ where $n \geq 0$.

$\sec x = \dfrac{1}{\cos x}$

$$\frac{(1 + \sin x)\cos x}{\cos^2 x} = \frac{\cos x}{1 - \sin x}$$

$$\frac{(1 + \sin x)\cos x}{1 - \sin^2 x} = \frac{\cos x}{1 - \sin x}$$

$$\frac{(1 + \sin x)\cos x}{(1 - \sin x)(1 + \sin x)} = \frac{\cos x}{1 - \sin x}$$

$$\frac{\cos x}{1 - \sin x} = \frac{\cos x}{1 - \sin x}$$

$\cos^2 x = 1 - \sin^2 x$

Since $\sin x \neq -1$, the value of $x \neq (2n + 1)\frac{\pi}{2}$ where $n \geq 0$.

Therefore, $\sec x + \tan x = \dfrac{\cos x}{1 - \sin x}$ for $x \neq (2n + 1)\dfrac{\pi}{2}$.

3. **Define csc x in terms of cot x.**

$$\csc x = \frac{1}{\sin x}$$

$$\csc^2 x = \frac{1}{\sin^2 x}$$

$$\csc^2 x = 1 + \frac{\cos^2 x}{\sin^2 x}$$

$$\csc^2 x = 1 + \cot^2 x$$

$$\csc x = \pm\sqrt{1 + \cot^2 x}$$

Since $\sin^2 x + \cos^2 x = 1$,
$1 + \dfrac{\cos^2 x}{\sin^2 x} = \dfrac{1}{\sin^2 x}$

$\cot x = \dfrac{\cos x}{\sin x}$

4. **Simplify the expression $\dfrac{1}{1 + \sin x} + \dfrac{1}{1 - \sin x}$.**

$$\frac{1}{1 + \sin x} + \frac{1}{1 - \sin x} = \frac{1 - \sin x + 1 + \sin x}{(1 + \sin x)(1 - \sin x)}$$

$$\frac{1}{1 + \sin x} + \frac{1}{1 - \sin x} = \frac{2}{1 - \sin^2 x}$$

$$\frac{1}{1 + \sin x} + \frac{1}{1 - \sin x} = \frac{2}{\cos^2 x}$$

$$\frac{1}{1 + \sin x} + \frac{1}{1 - \sin x} = 2\sec^2 x$$

$1 - \sin^2 x = \cos^2 x$

$\dfrac{1}{\cos x} = \sec x$

Exercises

Exploratory Simplify each expression.

1. $\tan n \cot n$
2. $\sec^2 A - 1$
3. $\sin x + \cos x \tan x$
4. $\csc x \cos x \tan x$
5. $2(\csc^2 m - \cot^2 m)$
6. $\dfrac{\tan^2 A - \sin^2 A}{\tan^2 A \sin^2 A}$

Write an expression for each of the following.

7. $\sin x$ in terms of $\cos x$
8. $\sec x$ in terms of $\tan x$

9. cot x in terms of csc x

10. tan x in terms of sin x

Written Prove each identity.

1. $\sin x \sec x = \tan x$

2. $\cos^2 r - \sin^2 r = 2\cos^2 r - 1$

3. $\cos^2 r - \sin^2 r = 1 - 2\sin^2 r$

4. $\sec a - \cos a = \sin a \tan a$

5. $\cos^4 x - \sin^4 x = \cos^2 x - \sin^2 x$

6. $\tan A \sin A + \cos A = \sec A$

7. $\tan B + \cot B = \sec B \csc B$

8. $\sin r \sec r - \sin r \csc r = \tan r - 1$

9. $\dfrac{\sec x}{\cos x} - \dfrac{\tan x}{\cot x} = 1$

10. $\dfrac{1 - \tan^2 y}{1 - \cot^2 y} = \dfrac{\cos^2 y - 1}{\cos^2 y}$

11. $\dfrac{1 + \tan x}{1 - \tan x} = \dfrac{\cot x + 1}{\cot x - 1}$

12. $\dfrac{1}{\sqrt{1 - \sin x}} = |\sec x| \sqrt{1 + \sin x}$

13. $\dfrac{\cos r}{\cos r - \sin r} = \dfrac{1}{1 - \tan r}$

14. $\sqrt{\dfrac{1 - \cos x}{1 + \cos x}} = \dfrac{1 - \cos x}{|\sin x|}$

15. $\dfrac{\sin A - \cos A}{\cos A} + \dfrac{\sin A + \cos A}{\sin A} = \sec A \csc A$

5-6 Sum and Difference Formulas

To determine if a statement is true may be difficult. It is easier to prove a statement to be false than to prove one to be true. One counterexample is sufficient to prove a statement is false.

Example

1. Determine if $\cos(r_1 + r_2) = \cos r_1 + \cos r_2$.

   Let $r_1 = \dfrac{\pi}{3}$ and $r_2 = \dfrac{\pi}{6}$.

   $\cos\left(\dfrac{\pi}{3} + \dfrac{\pi}{6}\right) = \cos\left(\dfrac{\pi}{2}\right) = 0$

   $\cos\dfrac{\pi}{3} + \cos\dfrac{\pi}{6} = \dfrac{1}{2} + \dfrac{\sqrt{3}}{2} = \dfrac{1 + \sqrt{3}}{2}$

   Therefore, $\cos(r_1 + r_2) \neq \cos r_1 + \cos r_2$.

note importance of this example

To find a formula for $\cos(r_1 + r_2)$, let $m\ \widehat{AP} = r_1$ and $m\ \widehat{PQ} = r_2$. Then $m\ \widehat{AQ} = r_1 + r_2$. Let $-r_2 \rightarrow R$. Then $m\ \widehat{AR} = |-r_2| = r_2$ and $m\ \widehat{RP} = r_1 + r_2$. Therefore, $AQ = RP$.

Use the distance formula to state that $AQ = RP$.

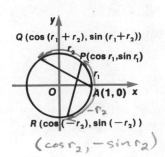
$(\cos r_2, -\sin r_2)$

$$\sqrt{[\cos(r_1 + r_2) - 1]^2 + \sin^2(r_1 + r_2)} = \sqrt{[\cos r_1 - \cos(-r_2)]^2 + (\sin r_1 + \sin r_2)^2}$$

$$[\cos(r_1 + r_2) - 1]^2 + \sin^2(r_1 + r_2) = [\cos r_1 - \cos(-r_2)]^2 + (\sin r_1 + \sin r_2)^2$$

$$\cos^2(r_1 + r_2) - 2\cos(r_1 + r_2) + 1 + \sin^2(r_1 + r_2) =$$

$$\cos^2 r_1 - 2\cos r_1 \cos r_2 + \cos^2 r_2 + \sin^2 r_1 + 2\sin r_1 \sin r_2 + \sin^2 r_2$$

✳ note changes

$$2 - 2\cos(r_1 + r_2) = 2 - 2\cos r_1 \cos r_2 + 2\sin r_1 \sin r_2$$

$$\cos(r_1 + r_2) = \cos r_1 \cos r_2 - \sin r_1 \sin r_2$$

Using the above form, a formula for $\cos(r_1 - r_2)$ can be derived. Rewrite $\cos(r_1 - r_2)$ as $\cos(r_1 + (-r_2))$.

$$\cos(r_1 + (-r_2)) = \cos r_1 \cos(-r_2) - \sin r_1 \sin(-r_2)$$

Thus, $\cos(r_1 - r_2) = \cos r_1 \cos r_2 + \sin r_1 \sin r_2$

$\cos(-r) = \cos r$ *✳ reminder*
$\sin(-r) = -\sin r$

✳ note

The sum and difference formulas for the cosine function are as follows.

$$\cos(r_1 + r_2) = \cos r_1 \cos r_2 - \sin r_1 \sin r_2$$
$$\cos(r_1 - r_2) = \cos r_1 \cos r_2 + \sin r_1 \sin r_2$$

Sum and Difference Formulas for Cosine Function

Examples

2. **Show that** $\cos\left(\dfrac{\pi}{2} - r_2\right) = \sin r_2.$

$$\cos\left(\frac{\pi}{2} - r_2\right) = \cos\frac{\pi}{2}\cos r_2 + \sin\frac{\pi}{2}\sin r_2$$

$$\cos\left(\frac{\pi}{2} - r_2\right) = 0 \cdot \cos r_2 + 1 \cdot \sin r_2$$

$$\cos\left(\frac{\pi}{2} - r_2\right) = \sin r_2$$

3. **Show that** $\sin\left(\dfrac{\pi}{2} - r_2\right) = \cos r_2.$

Let $r_2 = \dfrac{\pi}{2} - x$. Then, $\cos r_2 = \cos\left(\dfrac{\pi}{2} - x\right) = \sin x.$ *Use Example 2.*

Since $x = \dfrac{\pi}{2} - r_2$, $\cos r_2 = \sin\left(\dfrac{\pi}{2} - r_2\right)$.

The formulas for $\sin(r_1 + r_2)$ and $\sin(r_1 - r_2)$ can be derived using the results from Examples **2** and **3**.

$$\sin(r_1 + r_2) = \cos\left[\frac{\pi}{2} - (r_1 + r_2)\right]$$

$$\sin(r_1 + r_2) = \cos\left[\left(\frac{\pi}{2} - r_1\right) - r_2\right]$$

$$\sin(r_1 + r_2) = \cos\left(\frac{\pi}{2} - r_1\right)\cos r_2 + \sin\left(\frac{\pi}{2} - r_1\right)\sin r_2$$

$$\sin(r_1 + r_2) = \sin r_1 \cos r_2 + \cos r_1 \sin r_2$$

Similarly, $\sin [r_1 + (-r_2)] = \sin r_1 \cos (-r_2) + \cos r_1 \sin (-r_2)$
$\qquad\qquad \sin [r_1 + (-r_2)] = \sin r_1 \cos r_2 - \cos r_1 \sin r_2$

✻ note

The sum and difference formulas for the sine function are as follows.

$$\sin (r_1 + r_2) = \sin r_1 \cos r_2 + \cos r_1 \sin r_2$$
$$\sin (r_1 - r_2) = \sin r_1 \cos r_2 - \cos r_1 \sin r_2$$

Sum and Difference Formulas for Sine Function

The sine and cosine formulas can be used to find the formulas for $\tan(r_1 + r_2)$ and $\tan(r_1 - r_2)$. As in all identities exclude the values for which the denominator is zero.

✻ note exclusions

$$\tan (r_1 + r_2) = \frac{\sin (r_1 + r_2)}{\cos (r_1 + r_2)}$$

$$\tan (r_1 + r_2) = \frac{\sin r_1 \cos r_2 + \cos r_1 \sin r_2}{\cos r_1 \cos r_2 - \sin r_1 \sin r_2}$$

$$\tan (r_1 + r_2) = \frac{\dfrac{\sin r_1 \cos r_2}{\cos r_1 \cos r_2} + \dfrac{\cos r_1 \sin r_2}{\cos r_1 \cos r_2}}{1 - \dfrac{\sin r_1 \sin r_2}{\cos r_1 \cos r_2}}$$

Divide by $\cos r_1 \cos r_2$.

$$\tan (r_1 + r_2) = \frac{\tan r_1 + \tan r_2}{1 - \tan r_1 \tan r_2}$$

Similarly, $\tan [r_1 + (-r_2)] = \dfrac{\tan r_1 + \tan (-r_2)}{1 - \tan r_1 \tan (-r_2)}$

$\cos (-r) = \cos r$
$\sin (-r) = -\sin r$

$$\tan (r_1 - r_2) = \frac{\tan r_1 - \tan r_2}{1 + \tan r_1 \tan r_2}$$

✻ note

The sum and difference formulas for the *tangent* function are as follows.

$$\tan (r_1 + r_2) = \frac{\tan r_1 + \tan r_2}{1 - \tan r_1 \tan r_2} \left.\vphantom{\frac{\tan r_1}{1}}\right\}$$

$$\tan (r_1 - r_2) = \frac{\tan r_1 - \tan r_2}{1 + \tan r_1 \tan r_2} \quad \text{If } r_1, r_2$$
$$\neq (2k + 1) \cdot \frac{\pi}{2}, k \in Z.$$

$$\tan (r_1 \pm r_2) = \frac{\sin (r_1 \pm r_2)}{\cos (r_1 \pm r_2)} \quad \text{If } r_1 \text{ or } r_2 \text{ is}$$
$$(2k + 1) \cdot \frac{\pi}{2}, k \in Z.$$

Sum and Difference Formulas for Tangent Function

It is assumed that $1 - \tan r_1 \tan r_2 \neq 0$ and $1 + \tan r_1 \tan r_2 \neq 0$.

Example

4. Simplify $\tan\left(\dfrac{\pi}{2} + x\right)$.

$$\tan\left(\frac{\pi}{2} + x\right) = \frac{\sin\left(\dfrac{\pi}{2} + x\right)}{\cos\left(\dfrac{\pi}{2} + x\right)}$$

or $\tan\left(\dfrac{\pi}{2}+x\right) = \dfrac{\tan\frac{\pi}{2} + \tan x}{1 - \tan\frac{\pi}{2}\tan x}$

undefined

$=$

$$\tan\left(\frac{\pi}{2} + x\right) = \frac{\sin\dfrac{\pi}{2}\cos x + \sin x \cos\dfrac{\pi}{2}}{\cos\dfrac{\pi}{2}\cos x - \sin\dfrac{\pi}{2}\sin x}$$

$$\tan\left(\frac{\pi}{2} + x\right) = -\frac{\cos x}{\sin x}$$

$\dfrac{\cos x}{\sin x} = \cot x$

$$\tan\left(\frac{\pi}{2} + x\right) = -\cot x$$

The sum and difference formulas can be used to prove important identities. The table shows patterns that can be found.

Function \ α	$\dfrac{\pi}{2} - x$	$\dfrac{\pi}{2} + x$	$\dfrac{3\pi}{2} - x$	$\dfrac{3\pi}{2} + x$	$\pi - x$	$\pi + x$	$2\pi - x$	$2\pi + x$
sin α	cos x	cos x	−cos x	−cos x	sin x	−sin x	−sin x	sin x
cos α	sin x	−sin x	−sin x	sin x	−cos x	−cos x	cos x	cos x
tan α	cot x	−cot x	cot x	−cot x	−tan x	tan x	−tan x	tan x

All the identities to the right of the second bold line have the same function named on both sides of the identity. The identities to the left of the bold line have a function on one side and the "co"*function* on the other. For example, cos α when α has a value $\dfrac{\pi}{2} \pm x$ or $\dfrac{3\pi}{2} \pm x$ is always $\pm \sin x$.

Since the table represents identities, there is no loss of generality in assuming $0 < x < \dfrac{\pi}{2}$. The correct sign of a function can be determined by noting the quadrant in which $n \cdot \dfrac{\pi}{2} + x$ lies. For example, $\dfrac{\pi}{2} + x$ is in the second quadrant. Therefore, $\sin\left(\dfrac{\pi}{2} + x\right) > 0$, $\cos\left(\dfrac{\pi}{2} + x\right) < 0$, and $\tan\left(\dfrac{\pi}{2} + x\right) < 0$. Remember that the *secant*, *cosecant*, and *cotangent* functions have the same signs as their reciprocals.

Examples

5. **Write $\sin\left(\dfrac{5\pi}{2} + x\right)$ as a function of x for $0 < x < \dfrac{\pi}{2}$.**

   Since $\dfrac{5\pi}{2}$ is an odd multiple of $\dfrac{\pi}{2}$, the *cosine* function is used. When $0 < x < \dfrac{\pi}{2}$, $\dfrac{5\pi}{2} + x$ is in the second quadrant, and the *sine* function is positive. Therefore, $\sin\left(\dfrac{5\pi}{2} + x\right) = \cos x$.

6. **Write $\sec(3\pi - x)$ as a function of x for $0 < x < \dfrac{\pi}{2}$.**

   Since 3π is an even multiple of $\dfrac{\pi}{2}$, the *secant* function is used. When $0 < x < \dfrac{\pi}{2}$, $3\pi - x$ is in the second quadrant.
   Therefore, $\sec(3\pi - x) = -\sec x$.

7. **Find $\tan \dfrac{5\pi}{6}$.**

   $$\tan \frac{5\pi}{6} = \tan\left(\pi - \frac{\pi}{6}\right) = -\tan \frac{\pi}{6} = -\frac{1}{\sqrt{3}} = \frac{-\sqrt{3}}{3}$$

8. **Find $\sin \dfrac{7\pi}{4}$.**

   $$\sin \frac{7\pi}{4} = \sin\left(2\pi - \frac{\pi}{4}\right) = -\sin \frac{\pi}{4} = -\frac{1}{\sqrt{2}} = \frac{-\sqrt{2}}{2}$$

9. **Write $a \sin nx + b \cos nx$ using just one function.**

   $$a \sin nx + b \cos nx = \sqrt{a^2 + b^2}\left[\frac{a}{\sqrt{a^2 + b^2}} \sin nx + \frac{b}{\sqrt{a^2 + b^2}} \cos nx\right]$$

   Let $r \in \mathcal{R}$ such that $\cos r = \dfrac{a}{\sqrt{a^2 + b^2}}$ and $\sin r = \dfrac{b}{\sqrt{a^2 + b^2}}$.

   Thus, $a \sin nx + b \cos nx = \sqrt{a^2 + b^2} \sin(nx + r)$.

Exercises

Exploratory Find the value of each function.

1. $\cos \dfrac{7\pi}{12}$

2. $\sin \dfrac{\pi}{12}$

3. $\tan \dfrac{2\pi}{3}$

4. $\sec \dfrac{5\pi}{6}$

5. $\csc \dfrac{3\pi}{4}$

6. $\sin \dfrac{5\pi}{12}$

7. $\cos \dfrac{5\pi}{3}$

8. $\tan \dfrac{7\pi}{6}$

9. $\cos \dfrac{\pi}{12}$

Written Write each of the following as a function of x.

1. $\sin\left(\dfrac{\pi}{2} - x\right)$
2. $\sec(3\pi + x)$
3. $\cot\left(\dfrac{3\pi}{2} - x\right)$

4. $\cos\left(\dfrac{5\pi}{2} + x\right)$
5. $\tan(2\pi - x)$
6. $\csc(5\pi + x)$

Find the value of each function, given $0 < x < \dfrac{\pi}{2}$, $0 < y < \dfrac{\pi}{2}$, $\sin x = \dfrac{4}{5}$ and $\cos y = \dfrac{3}{5}$.

7. $\sin(x + y)$
8. $\cos(x - y)$
9. $\tan(x + y)$
10. $\sin(x - y)$

Prove each identity.

11. $\sin(x + y) + \sin(x - y) = 2\sin x \cos y$
12. $\sin^2 x - \sin^2 y = \sin(x + y)\sin(x - y)$

13. $\dfrac{\cos(x + y)}{\cos(x - y)} = \dfrac{1 - \tan x \tan y}{1 + \tan x \tan y}$
14. $\tan\left(\dfrac{\pi}{4} + x\right) = \dfrac{1 + \tan x}{1 - \tan x}$

15. $\sin\left(\dfrac{\pi}{6} + x\right) = \cos\left(\dfrac{\pi}{3} - x\right)$
16. $\sin\left(\dfrac{\pi}{3} + x\right) - \cos\left(\dfrac{\pi}{6} + x\right) = \sin x$

Write each of the following using just one function. Sketch the graph.

17. $\sqrt{3}\sin 3x + \cos 3x$
18. $\sin\dfrac{1}{2}x + \cos\dfrac{1}{2}x$

5–7 Double and Half Number Formulas

Values of the circular functions of $2r$ can be found by using the addition formulas.

$\cos 2r = \cos(r + r)$
$\cos 2r = \cos r \cos r - \sin r \sin r$
$\cos 2r = \cos^2 r - \sin^2 r$

Since $\cos^2 r + \sin^2 r = 1$, there are two alternate forms for $\cos 2r$.

Double-number formulas for the *cosine* function are as follows.

$$\cos 2r = \cos^2 r - \sin^2 r$$
$$\cos 2r = 1 - 2\sin^2 r$$
$$\cos 2r = 2\cos^2 r - 1$$

Double-number Formulas for Cosine Function

The formulas for $\sin(r + r)$ and $\tan(r + r)$ can be used to derive the formulas for $\sin 2r$ and $\tan 2r$.

Double-number formulas for the *sine* function and the *tangent* function are as follows.

$$\sin 2r = 2\sin r \cos r$$
$$\tan 2r = \dfrac{2\tan r}{1 - \tan^2 r}$$

Double-number Formulas for Sine and Tangent Functions

Example

1. Find the sine, cosine, and tangent values of $\frac{\pi}{3}$ from those of $\frac{\pi}{6}$ using the double-number formulas.

$$\sin \frac{\pi}{3} = 2 \sin \frac{\pi}{6} \cos \frac{\pi}{6} = 2 \left(\frac{1}{2}\right)\left(\frac{\sqrt{3}}{2}\right) = \frac{\sqrt{3}}{2} \qquad \sin\frac{\pi}{3} = \sin\frac{2\pi}{6}$$

$$\cos \frac{\pi}{3} = 2 \cos^2 \frac{\pi}{6} - 1 = 2 \left(\frac{\sqrt{3}}{2}\right)^2 - 1 = 2 \left(\frac{3}{4}\right) - 1 = \frac{1}{2}$$

$$\tan \frac{\pi}{3} = \frac{2 \tan \frac{\pi}{6}}{1 - \tan^2 \frac{\pi}{6}} = \frac{2\left(\frac{1}{\sqrt{3}}\right)}{1 - \left(\frac{1}{\sqrt{3}}\right)^2} = \frac{\frac{2}{\sqrt{3}}}{\frac{2}{3}} = \frac{3}{\sqrt{3}} = \sqrt{3}$$

The **half-number formulas** can be derived from the **double-number formulas.**

$$\cos 2r = 2 \cos^2 r - 1$$

Let $2r = x$. Then $r = \frac{x}{2}$.

$$\cos x = 2 \cos^2 \frac{x}{2} - 1$$

$$\frac{1 + \cos x}{2} = \cos^2 \frac{x}{2}$$

$$\pm\sqrt{\frac{1 + \cos x}{2}} = \cos \frac{x}{2}$$

The choice of sign depends on the quadrant in which $\frac{x}{2}$ is located. The development of the half-number formulas for the *sine* and *tangent* functions is similar to that for $\cos \frac{x}{2}$.

The half-number formulas for the *sine*, *cosine*, and *tangent* functions are as follows.

$$\sin \frac{x}{2} = \pm\sqrt{\frac{1 - \cos x}{2}}$$

$$\cos \frac{x}{2} = \pm\sqrt{\frac{1 + \cos x}{2}}$$

$$\tan \frac{x}{2} = \pm\sqrt{\frac{1 - \cos x}{1 + \cos x}}$$

Half-number Formulas

Examples

2. Find $\cos \dfrac{\pi}{12}$.

$$\cos \frac{\pi}{12} = \sqrt{\frac{1 + \cos \dfrac{\pi}{6}}{2}} = \sqrt{\frac{1 + \dfrac{\sqrt{3}}{2}}{2}} = \frac{1}{2}\sqrt{2 + \sqrt{3}}$$

The positive root is chosen because $\dfrac{\pi}{12}$ is in the first quadrant.

3. Find $\tan \dfrac{5\pi}{8}$.

If $\dfrac{x}{2} = \dfrac{5\pi}{8}$, then $x = \dfrac{5\pi}{4}$.

$$\tan \frac{5\pi}{8} = -\sqrt{\frac{1 - \cos \dfrac{5\pi}{4}}{1 + \cos \dfrac{5\pi}{4}}} = -\sqrt{\frac{1 - \left(\dfrac{-1}{\sqrt{2}}\right)}{1 + \left(\dfrac{-1}{\sqrt{2}}\right)}}$$

$$= -\sqrt{\frac{\sqrt{2} + 1}{\sqrt{2} - 1}} = -\left(\frac{\sqrt{2} + 1}{1}\right) = -1 - \sqrt{2}$$

The negative root is chosen because $\dfrac{5\pi}{8}$ is in the second quadrant.

Exercises

Exploratory   Find the value of each function.

1. $\sin \dfrac{\pi}{8}$

2. $\cos \dfrac{\pi}{8}$

3. $\tan \dfrac{\pi}{8}$

4. $\sin \dfrac{7\pi}{12}$

5. $\cos \dfrac{7\pi}{12}$

6. $\tan \dfrac{7\pi}{12}$

7. $\sin \dfrac{3\pi}{8}$

8. $\cos \dfrac{3\pi}{8}$

9. $\tan \dfrac{3\pi}{8}$

Written   Find the value of each function, given $0 < \theta < \dfrac{\pi}{2}$ and $\tan \theta = \dfrac{3}{4}$.

1. $\sin 2\theta$

2. $\cos 2\theta$

3. $\tan 2\theta$

4. $\sin \dfrac{1}{2}\theta$

5. $\cos \dfrac{1}{2}\theta$

6. $\tan \dfrac{1}{2}\theta$

Prove each identity.

7. $\sec 2\theta = \dfrac{\sec^2 \theta}{2 - \sec^2 \theta}$

8. $\csc 2\theta = \dfrac{1}{2}\sec \theta \csc \theta$

9. $\cot 2\theta = \dfrac{\cot^2 \theta - 1}{2 \cot \theta}$

10. $\sin 2\theta = \dfrac{2 \tan \theta}{1 + \tan^2 \theta}$

11. $\tan \frac{1}{2}\theta = \frac{1 - \cos \theta}{\sin \theta}$

12. $\tan \frac{1}{2}\theta = \frac{\sin \theta}{1 + \cos \theta}$

13. $\dfrac{1 - \tan^2 \frac{1}{2}\theta}{1 + \tan^2 \frac{1}{2}\theta} = \cos \theta$

14. $2 \cos \theta \csc 2\theta = \csc \theta$

Derive the following formulas with the given conditions.

15. For $\sin \frac{x}{2}$, using $\cos 2r = 1 - 2 \sin^2 r$

16. For $\sin 3x$ in terms of $\sin x$

17. For $\cos 3x$, in terms of $\cos x$

18. For $\tan 3x$ in terms of $\tan x$

19. Sketch the graph of $y = \cos^2 x$.

(Hint: $\cos 2x = 2 \cos^2 x - 1$ or
$\cos^2 x = \frac{1}{2} + \frac{1}{2} \cos 2x.)$

5–8 Equating Products and Sums

Sometimes it is necessary to convert sums into products of functions. To find a suitable product for $\sin A + \sin B$, the formulas for $\sin (x + y)$ and $\sin (x - y)$ can be used.

$$\sin (x + y) = \sin x \cos y + \cos x \sin y$$
$$+ \sin (x - y) = \sin x \cos y - \cos x \sin y$$
$$\overline{\sin (x + y) + \sin (x - y) = 2 \sin x \cos y}$$

Let $x + y = A$ and $x - y = B$. Then $2x = A + B$.

$$x = \frac{A + B}{2} \qquad y = \frac{A - B}{2}$$

$$\sin A + \sin B = 2 \sin \frac{A + B}{2} \cos \frac{A - B}{2}$$

The formulas for $\sin (x + y)$ and $\sin (x - y)$ are used to derive the formula for $\sin A - \sin B$. The formulas for $\cos (x + y)$ and $\cos (x - y)$ are used to find $\cos A + \cos B$ and $\cos A - \cos B$.

The formulas for identities involving sums or products for *cosine* and *sine* functions are as follows.

$$\sin A + \sin B = 2 \sin \frac{A + B}{2} \cos \frac{A - B}{2}$$

$$\sin A - \sin B = 2 \cos \frac{A + B}{2} \sin \frac{A - B}{2}$$

$$\cos A + \cos B = 2 \cos \frac{A + B}{2} \cos \frac{A - B}{2}$$

$$\cos A - \cos B = -2 \sin \frac{A + B}{2} \sin \frac{A - B}{2}$$

Identities Involving
Sum or Product

Examples

1. Write cos 8t − cos 2t as a product.

$$\cos 8t - \cos 2t = -2 \sin \frac{8t + 2t}{2} \sin \frac{8t - 2t}{2}$$

$$\cos 8t - \cos 2t = -2 \sin \frac{10t}{2} \sin \frac{6t}{2}$$

$$\cos 8t - \cos 2t = -2 \sin 5t \sin 3t$$

2. Write $\sin \frac{3\pi}{4} \cos \frac{\pi}{4}$ as a sum.

$$\sin \frac{3\pi}{4} \cos \frac{\pi}{4} = \frac{1}{2} \left[2 \cos \frac{1}{2}\left(\frac{3\pi}{2}\right) \cos \frac{1}{2}\left(\frac{\pi}{2}\right) \right]$$

Let $\frac{3\pi}{2} = A + B$ and $\frac{\pi}{2} = A - B$. Then $A = \pi$ and $B = \frac{\pi}{2}$.

Therefore, $\sin \frac{3\pi}{4} \cos \frac{\pi}{4} = \frac{1}{2} \left[2 \sin \frac{1}{2}\left(\pi + \frac{\pi}{2}\right) \cos \frac{1}{2}\left(\pi - \frac{\pi}{2}\right) \right]$

$$\sin \frac{3\pi}{4} \cos \frac{\pi}{4} = \frac{1}{2}\left(\sin \pi + \sin \frac{\pi}{2}\right)$$

Exercises

Exploratory Solve each problem.

1. If $A + B = \frac{\pi}{3}$ and $A - B = \frac{\pi}{6}$, find A and B.

2. If $A + B = \frac{5\pi}{4}$ and $A - B = \frac{3\pi}{4}$, find A and B.

3. Find a product for the expression $\sin \frac{\pi}{4} + \sin \frac{5\pi}{4}$.

4. Find a product for the expression $\cos \frac{\pi}{3} - \cos \frac{2\pi}{3}$.

Written Write each sum as a product.

1. $\sin 2x + \sin 4x$

2. $\cos 3x - \cos x$

3. $\sin \frac{\pi}{3} - \sin \frac{\pi}{6}$

4. $\cos 5 + \cos 3$

5. $\sin 4x - \sin 3x$

6. $\cos 9x - \cos 6x$

Write each product as a sum or difference.

7. $2 \sin 4x \cos 2x$

8. $-2 \sin 6x \sin 3x$

9. $\cos 5x \sin 3x$

10. $\cos 11x \cos 7x$

11. $\cos \left(\frac{\pi}{3} + x\right) \sin \left(\frac{\pi}{6} - x\right)$

12. $\sin \left(\frac{\pi}{4} - x\right) \cos \left(\frac{\pi}{4} + x\right)$

13. $\cos \left(\frac{\pi}{2} - x\right) \cos \left(\frac{\pi}{2} + x\right)$

14. $\cos \left(\frac{3\pi}{2} - x\right) \sin \left(\frac{3\pi}{2} + x\right)$

Prove each identity.

15. $\dfrac{\cos 5x + \cos 3x}{\sin 5x - \sin 3x} = \cot x$

16. $\dfrac{\cos 8x - \cos 6x}{\sin 8x + \sin 6x} = -\tan x$

17. $\sin \dfrac{\pi}{5} + \sin \dfrac{2\pi}{15} = \cos \dfrac{\pi}{30}$

18. $\cos \dfrac{8\pi}{9} + \cos \dfrac{2\pi}{9} = \cos \dfrac{5\pi}{9}$

19. $\dfrac{\sin 3x + \sin x}{\sin 3x - \sin x} = \dfrac{2}{1 - \tan^2 x}$

20. $\sin \left(x + \dfrac{\pi}{3} \right) + \sin \left(x - \dfrac{\pi}{3} \right) = \sin x$

21. $\dfrac{1 + \cos x + \cos 2x}{\sin x + \sin 2x} = \cot x$

22. $\dfrac{\sin x + \sin 3x + \sin 5x}{\cos x + \cos 3x + \cos 5x} = \tan 3x$

5–9 Inverse Relations

Suppose $\sin x = \dfrac{1}{2}$. Then x might be $\dfrac{\pi}{6}, \dfrac{5\pi}{6},$ or $-\dfrac{7\pi}{6}$. In general x is $\dfrac{\pi}{6} + 2\pi n$ or $\dfrac{5\pi}{6} + 2\pi n$, where n is any integer. For $y = \sin x$ there is an unlimited number of values of x for each y value. This means that the inverse relation is not a function. If $y = \sin x$, then $x = \sin y$ is the **inverse relation.**

To express the inverse relation as y, in terms of x, it is necessary to invent a designation for the expression "y *is the number whose sine is* x." The designation for this relation is **arcsine.** The inverse relation for cosine and tangent are designated **arccosine** and **arctangent.**

Remember the difference between function and relation.

The arcsine is to be read "number whose sine is" or "arc whose sine is."

> The inverse relation for sine, cosine, and cotangent are defined as follows.
> $$\text{arcsine} = \{(x, y) \,|\, x = \sin y\}$$
> $$\text{arccosine} = \{(x, y) \,|\, x = \cos y\}$$
> $$\text{arctangent} = \{(x, y) \,|\, x = \tan y\}$$

Inverse Relations

The value of y is measured along the *arc of the unit circle.* Then x is the sine, cosine, or tangent of the measure of the arc.

The inverse relations are formed by interchanging the variables x and y. Thus the graphs of the inverse relations can be found by reflecting the graphs of $y = \sin x$, $y = \cos x$, and $y = \tan x$ in the line $y = x$.

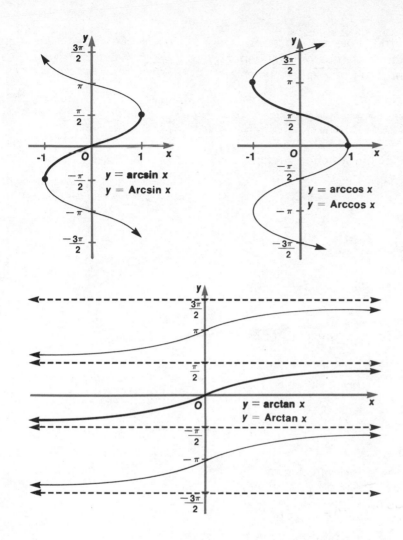

$y = \textbf{arcsin } x$
$y = \textbf{Arcsin } x$

$y = \textbf{arccos } x$
$y = \textbf{Arccos } x$

$y = \textbf{arctan } x$
$y = \textbf{Arctan } x$

The ranges of the inverse relations are often restricted so that they are functions.

> **The inverse functions for sine, cosine, and tangent are as follows.**
>
> $$\text{Arcsine} = \left\{ (x,y) \,\middle|\, y = \text{arcsine } x, \, -\frac{\pi}{2} \le y \le \frac{\pi}{2} \right\}$$
>
> $$\text{Arccosine} = \{ (x,y) \,|\, y = \text{arccos } x, \, 0 \le y \le \pi \}$$
>
> $$\text{Arctangent} = \left\{ (x,y) \,\middle|\, y = \text{arctan } x, \, -\frac{\pi}{2} < y < \frac{\pi}{2} \right\}$$

Inverse Functions

Notice that the names of the inverse *functions* are capitalized. This is done to distinguish them from the general relations. These restricted domains result in *y* values which are called **principal values**.

Some sources use Sin⁻¹ instead of Arcsin. Both expressions represent the inverse function.

Examples

1. **Find the principal value for the function Arctan 1.**

$$y = \arctan 1$$
$$\tan y = 1$$
$$\frac{\sin y}{\cos y} = 1$$
$$\sin y = \cos y$$

Since sin y = cos y, the general values for the relation arctan 1 are $\frac{\pi}{4} + \pi n$ where $n \in Z$.

The function Arctan 1 has the principal value of $\frac{\pi}{4}$.

2. **Find the principal values for the function Arccos $\left(-\frac{\sqrt{3}}{2}\right)$.**

$$y = \arccos\left(-\frac{\sqrt{3}}{2}\right)$$
$$\cos y = -\frac{\sqrt{3}}{2}$$

Since cos y = $-\frac{\sqrt{3}}{2}$, the general values for the relation arccos $\left(-\frac{\sqrt{3}}{2}\right)$ are $\frac{5\pi}{6} + 2n\pi$ and $\frac{7\pi}{6} + 2n\pi$.

The Arccos $\left(-\frac{\sqrt{3}}{2}\right)$ has the principal value of $\frac{5\pi}{6}$.

3. **Evaluate sin (arctan $\sqrt{3}$).**

Since the tangent is positive, all solutions lie in the first or third quadrants.

$$\sin(\arctan \sqrt{3}) = \sin\left(\frac{\pi}{3} + \pi n\right) = \pm\frac{\sqrt{3}}{2}$$

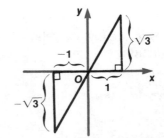

4. **Show that Arcsin $\frac{3}{5}$ + Arcsin $\frac{4}{5}$ = $\frac{\pi}{2}$.**

Let Arcsin $\frac{3}{5}$ = y_1 and Arcsin $\frac{4}{5}$ = y_2.

Both y_1 and y_2 are in the first quadrant.

$$\sin y_1 = \frac{3}{5} \qquad \sin y_2 = \frac{4}{5}$$

$$\cos y_1 = \frac{4}{5} \qquad \cos y_2 = \frac{3}{5}$$

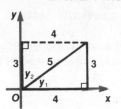

$$\text{Arcsin } \frac{3}{5} + \text{Arcsin } \frac{4}{5} = y_1 + y_2$$

$$\sin (y_1 + y_2) = \sin y_1 \cos y_2 + \cos y_1 \sin y_2$$

$$\sin (y_1 + y_2) = \frac{3}{5} \cdot \frac{3}{5} + \frac{4}{5} \cdot \frac{4}{5}$$

$$\sin (y_1 + y_2) = \frac{9}{25} + \frac{16}{25} = 1$$

Therefore, $y_1 + y_2 = \frac{\pi}{2}$ and $\text{Arcsin } \frac{3}{5} + \text{Arcsin } \frac{4}{5} = \frac{\pi}{2}$.

There are also principal values for arcsec x, arccsc x, and arccot x. They are seldom used, and there is some disagreement about what the principal values should be.

Exercises

Exploratory Find each general or principal value.

1. $\arcsin \dfrac{\sqrt{3}}{2}$

2. $\text{Arctan } 0$

3. $\text{Arcsin } \dfrac{1}{\sqrt{2}}$

4. $\arccos \left(-\dfrac{1}{2}\right)$

5. $\text{Arccos } (-1)$

6. $\text{Arctan } (-1)$

Written Find each general or principal value.

1. $\arctan \sqrt{3}$

2. $\arctan \left(-\dfrac{1}{\sqrt{3}}\right)$

3. $\arccos \dfrac{\sqrt{3}}{2}$

4. $\arcsin \left(-\dfrac{1}{2}\right)$

5. $\arccos \dfrac{1}{3}$ $\left(\textit{Hint: Express in terms of Arccos } \dfrac{1}{3}.\right)$

6. $\text{Arcsin } (-1)$

7. $\text{Arccos } \left(-\dfrac{\sqrt{3}}{2}\right)$

Evaluate each expression.

8. $\sin \left(\text{Arctan } \dfrac{1}{\sqrt{3}}\right)$

9. $\cos \left(\text{Arcsin } \dfrac{3}{5}\right)$

10. $\tan \left(\arcsin \dfrac{5}{12}\right)$

11. $\sec \left[\arcsin \left(-\dfrac{1}{2}\right)\right]$

12. $\sin \left(\arcsin \dfrac{2}{3}\right)$

13. $\cos \left(\arccos \dfrac{3}{5}\right)$

14. $\tan (\text{Arctan } 3)$

15. $\sin \left(\text{Arcsin } \dfrac{1}{5}\right)$

16. Show $\text{Arcsin } \dfrac{4}{5} + \text{Arcsin } \dfrac{5}{13} = \text{Arccos } \dfrac{16}{65}$.

17. Show $\text{Arctan } \dfrac{1}{2} + \text{Arctan } \dfrac{1}{3} = \dfrac{\pi}{4}$.

5–10 Equations with Circular Functions

Equations which contain circular functions often can be solved by the same methods that have been used to solve other equations.

Examples

1. **Solve for A if $2 \sin A + 1 = 2$.**

    $$2 \sin A + 1 = 2$$
    $$2 \sin A = 1$$
    $$\sin A = \frac{1}{2}$$

    Thus, $A = \frac{\pi}{6} + 2n\pi$ or $\frac{5\pi}{6} + 2n\pi$.

2. **Solve for the principal values of θ if $2 \cos^2\theta - \cos \theta - 3 = 0$.**

    $$2 \cos^2\theta - \cos \theta - 3 = 0$$
    $$(2 \cos \theta - 3)(\cos \theta + 1) = 0$$

    $2 \cos \theta - 3 = 0 \qquad$ or $\qquad \cos \theta + 1 = 0$

    $\cos \theta = \dfrac{3}{2} \qquad$ or $\qquad \cos \theta = -1$

    Since $|\cos \theta| \leq 1$, there is no solution for $\cos \theta = \dfrac{3}{2}$. For $\cos \theta = -1$, $\theta = \pi$.

3. **Find all solutions for $1 + \sin x = 3 \cos^2x$ such that $0 \leq x < 2\pi$.**

    $$1 + \sin x = 3 \cos^2x$$
    $$1 + \sin x = 3(1 - \sin^2x)$$
    $$1 + \sin x = 3 - 3 \sin^2x$$
    $$3 \sin^2x + \sin x - 2 = 0$$
    $$(3 \sin x - 2)(\sin x + 1) = 0$$

    If an equation contains more than one circular function, it usually is best to express all functions in terms of one function, if possible.

    $3 \sin x - 2 = 0 \qquad$ or $\qquad \sin x + 1 = 0$

    $\sin x = \dfrac{2}{3} \qquad$ or $\qquad \sin x = -1$

    $\text{Arcsin} (-1) = x \qquad\qquad Arcsin\ (-1) = -\dfrac{\pi}{2}$

    Thus, $x = \text{Arcsin } \dfrac{2}{3}$, $\pi - \text{Arcsin } \dfrac{2}{3}$, or $\arcsin (-1) = \dfrac{3\pi}{2} + 2\pi n$.

Example

4. **Find all solutions for $\cos x = \sin 2x$ such that $0 \le x < 2\pi$.**

$$\cos x = \sin 2x$$
$$\cos x = 2 \sin x \cos x$$
$$\cos x - 2 \sin x \cos x = 0$$
$$\cos x (1 - 2 \sin x) = 0$$

If $\cos x$ is used as a divisor, then the resulting equation is not equivalent to the original equation.

$$\cos x = 0 \quad \text{or} \quad 1 - 2 \sin x = 0$$
$$\cos x = 0 \quad \text{or} \quad \sin x = \frac{1}{2}$$

Thus, $x = \dfrac{\pi}{2}, \dfrac{3\pi}{2}$ or $x = \dfrac{\pi}{6}, \dfrac{5\pi}{6}$.

Exercises

Exploratory   Solve such that $0 \le x \le 2\pi$.

1. $\sin x = \dfrac{1}{2}$ 2. $\tan x + 1 = 0$ 3. $2 \cos x + 1 = 0$

4. $\sec x - 1 = 0$ 5. $\tan x - \sqrt{3} = 0$ 6. $\sqrt{3} \csc x - 2 = 0$

Written   Find the general solution for each equation.

1. $2 \cos \theta - 1 = 0$ 2. $2 \sin x + \sqrt{3} = 0$ 3. $3 \tan^2 y = 1$
4. $\cos^2 A - 1 = 0$ 5. $4 \sin x - 3 = 0$ 6. $3 \tan y + 1 = 0$

Solve each equation. Find the principal values only.

7. $\cos^2 x - \sin^2 x = 1$ 8. $\cos 2y + 2 \sin^2 \left(\dfrac{1}{2}y\right) = 1$

9. $\cot A \tan 2A = 3$ 10. $\sin 2r = \cos r$

Solve such that $0 \le x < 2\pi$.

11. $\csc^2 x + 2 \sec x = 0$ 12. $\sin^2 \left(\dfrac{1}{2}x\right) + \tan^2 \left(\dfrac{1}{2}x\right) = \dfrac{3}{2}$

13. $\dfrac{\cos 3x + \cos x}{\cos 3x - \cos x} = \cot x$ 14. $\dfrac{\sin 5x - \sin 3x}{\sin 5x + \sin 3x} = \tan x$

15. $2 \sin \left(x - \dfrac{\pi}{6}\right) = \sqrt{3} \sin x$ 16. $2 \sin \left(x - \dfrac{\pi}{6}\right) + 2 \sin \left(x + \dfrac{\pi}{6}\right) = \sqrt{3}$

17. $\sin 2x = 2 \sin x$ 18. $\cos 2x + \sin x = 1$

Solve each of the following.

19. $\text{Arctan } 3x - \text{Arctan } 2x = \dfrac{\pi}{4}$ 20. $\text{Arctan } \dfrac{1}{2}x + \text{Arctan } \dfrac{2}{3}x = \dfrac{\pi}{4}$

Chapter Summary

1. A function f such that $f(x) = f(x + p)$ is a periodic function. The least constant p for which the equality is true is called the period. (127)

2. The cosine function is defined by $\{(r, x)|r \rightarrow (x, y)$ by the wrapping function$\}$. (129)

3. The sine function is defined by $\{(r, y)|r \rightarrow (x, y)$ by the wrapping function$\}$. (129)

4. The tangent function is defined by $\{\left(r, \frac{y}{x}\right)|r \rightarrow (x, y)$ by the wrapping function, $x \neq 0\}$. (129)

5. Since sine, cosine, and tangent functions are all related to a circle, they are called **circular functions**. (130)

✓ 6. For $y = A \sin(nx + \alpha)$, the period is $\frac{2\pi}{n}$, the amplitude is $|A|$, the phase shift is $\frac{\alpha}{n}$. (136)

✓ 7. For $y = A \cos(nx + \alpha)$, the period is $\frac{2\pi}{n}$, the amplitude is $|A|$, the phase shift is $\frac{\alpha}{n}$. (136)

8. The graphs of the sine and cosine functions are symmetric with respect to the origin and y-axis respectively. (136)

✓ 9. For $y = A \tan(nx + \alpha)$, the period is $\frac{\pi}{n}$ and the phase shift is $\frac{\alpha}{n}$. (136)

10. Reciprocals of sine, cosine, and tangent functions are defined as follows. (137)

$$\text{secant} = \left\{(x, y)|y = \frac{1}{\cos x}\right\}$$

$$\text{cosecant} = \left\{(x, y)|y = \frac{1}{\sin x}\right\}$$

$$\text{cotangent} = \left\{(x, y)|y = \frac{1}{\tan x}\right\}$$

11. An identity is an equation which is true for all permissible values of the variables. Some identities are listed below. (140)

$$\tan x = \frac{\sin x}{\cos x} \ (\cos x \neq 0) \qquad \sin^2 x + \cos^2 x = 1$$

correct the periods

$$\cot x = \frac{\cos x}{\sin x} \ (\sin x \neq 0) \qquad \tan^2 x + 1 = \sec^2 x$$

$$\sec x = \frac{1}{\cos x} \ (\cos x \neq 0) \qquad \cot^2 x + 1 = \csc^2 x$$

$$\csc x = \frac{1}{\sin x} \ (\sin x \neq 0)$$

12. The sum and difference formulas are listed below.   (142)

$$\cos (r_1 \pm r_2) = \cos r_1 \cos r_2 \mp \sin r_1 \sin r_2$$

$$\sin (r_1 \pm r_2) = \sin r_1 \cos r_2 \pm \cos r_1 \sin r_2$$

$$\tan (r_1 \pm r_2) = \frac{\tan r_1 \pm \tan r_2}{1 \mp \tan r_1 \tan r_2}$$

13. Values of circular functions can be used to write double number or half-number formulas.   (147)

$$\cos 2x = 2 \cos^2 x - 1 \qquad \cos \frac{x}{2} = \pm \sqrt{\frac{1 + \cos x}{2}}$$

$$= 1 - 2 \sin^2 x$$
$$= \cos^2 x - \sin^2 x$$

$$\sin 2x = 2 \sin x \cos x \qquad \sin \frac{x}{2} = \pm \sqrt{\frac{1 - \cos x}{2}}$$

$$\tan 2x = \frac{2 \tan x}{1 - \tan^2 x} \qquad \tan \frac{x}{2} = \pm \sqrt{\frac{1 - \cos x}{1 + \cos x}}$$

14. Each trigonometric relation has an inverse relation which can be restricted to define a function.   (152)

$$\text{arcsine} = \{(x, y) | x = \sin y\}$$

$$\text{arccosine} = \{(x, y) | x = \cos y\}$$

$$\text{arctangent} = \{(x, y) | x = \tan y\}$$

$$\text{Arcsine} = \left\{ (x, y | y = \arcsin x, -\frac{\pi}{2} \leq y \leq \frac{\pi}{2} \right\}$$

$$\text{Arccosine} = \{(x, y) | y = \arccos x, 0 \leq y \leq \pi\}$$

$$\text{Arctangent} = \left\{ (x, y) | y = \arctan x, -\frac{\pi}{2} < y < \frac{\pi}{2} \right\}$$

Note: Some sources use $\sin^{-1}$ for arcsine, $\cos^{-1}$ for arccosine, and $\tan^{-1}$ for arctan. Both expressions represent the inverse relations or functions of the circular functions.

Chapter Review

5-1 For each value of R, write the quadrant in which (x, y) is located if $R \rightarrow (x, y)$.

1. $\dfrac{\pi}{4}$ **2.** $-\dfrac{7\pi}{6}$ **3.** 10

Complete each of the following mappings.

4. If $\dfrac{\pi}{2} \rightarrow (0, y)$, then

$-\dfrac{\pi}{2} \rightarrow (\underline{\quad}, \underline{\quad}).$

5. If $\dfrac{\pi}{6} \rightarrow (x, y)$, then

$-\dfrac{5\pi}{6} \rightarrow (\underline{\quad}, \underline{\quad}).$

5-2 Find the value of each function.

6. If $\sin r = 0.8$, find $\cos r$.   **7.** If $\cos r = \dfrac{6}{13}$, find $\sin r$.

8. $\sin\left(-\dfrac{5\pi}{6}\right)$ **9.** $\tan\dfrac{7\pi}{4}$ **10.** $\cos\dfrac{5\pi}{3}$

5-3 **11.** Sketch the graph of $y = 2\tan\left(3x - \dfrac{\pi}{6}\right)$. Name the period, phase, and symmetry.

5-4 Find the value of each function.

12. $\csc\dfrac{5\pi}{3}$ **13.** $\sec\left(-\dfrac{\pi}{4}\right)$ **14.** $\cot\dfrac{\pi}{6}$

5-5 Simplify each of the following.

15. $\dfrac{1 + \sin x}{\cos x} + \dfrac{\cos x}{1 + \sin x}$ **16.** $\dfrac{\sec x}{\cos x} - \dfrac{\tan x}{\cot x}$

5-6 Express each of the following as a function of x.

17. $\sin\left(\dfrac{3\pi}{2} - x\right)$ **18.** $\cot(3\pi + x)$

5-7 Prove each of the following.

19. $2\sin\theta \csc 2\theta = \sec\theta$ **20.** $\left(\sin\dfrac{x}{2} + \cos\dfrac{x}{2}\right)^2 = 1 + \sin x$

5-8 Write each of the following as a product.

21. $\sin 5t + \sin 3t$ **22.** $\tan 2x \cos 7x - \cos 3x \tan 2x$

5-9 Evaluate each of the following.

23. $\csc\left(\text{Arcsin}\dfrac{12}{13}\right)$ **24.** $\sin\left(\text{Arcsin}\dfrac{1}{3} + \text{Arccos}\dfrac{1}{3}\right)$

5-10 Solve each of the following for principal values only.

25. $\tan\dfrac{\theta}{2} + \sin 2\theta - \sin\theta = 0$ **26.** $\cos 2x = 2\cos^2 x - \sin^2 x$

Chapter Test

Complete each of the following mappings. Assume a normal wrapping function.

1. If $r \rightarrow (x, y)$, then
   $$\frac{\pi}{2} - r \rightarrow (\underline{\quad}, \underline{\quad}).$$

2. If $r \rightarrow (x, y)$, then
   $$\frac{3\pi}{4} \rightarrow (\underline{\quad}, \underline{\quad}).$$

Find the values of each function.

3. If $\sin r = 0.6$, find $\cos r$.

4. If $\cos r = \frac{5}{12}$, find $\sin r$.

5. $\sin \left(-\frac{5\pi}{4} \right)$

6. $\cos \left(\frac{\pi}{6} \right)$

7. $\tan \left(-\frac{2\pi}{3} \right)$

8. Write the equation of a sine function with amplitude 4 and period π if $y = 0$ when $x = \frac{9\pi}{16}$. Then graph the function.

Find the values for the following functions for which x is undefined.

9. $\csc \left(\frac{2x}{3} - \frac{\pi}{6} \right)$

10. $\cot \left(\pi x + \frac{\pi}{4} \right)$

Simplify each of the following.

11. $\dfrac{\cos A \sec A + \csc A \cos A}{\sin A + \cos A}$

12. $\dfrac{\sin B \cot B + \cos B}{2 \cot B}$

Express each of the following as a function of x.

13. $\tan (2\pi + x)$

14. $\cos \left(\frac{7\pi}{2} - x \right)$

15. If $\tan 2\theta = \frac{3}{4}$ and θ is in the third quadrant, find $\tan \theta$.

Write each of the following as a sum or difference.

16. $-2 \sin 7x \sin (-x)$

17. $\cos \left(\frac{\pi}{4} + x \right) \cos \left(\frac{\pi}{2} - x \right)$

Evaluate each of the following.

18. $\sec \left(\arcsin \left(-\frac{\sqrt{3}}{2} \right) \right)$

19. $\text{Arcsin} \left(-\frac{\sqrt{3}}{2} \right) + \text{Arccos} \left(-\frac{\sqrt{3}}{2} \right)$

20. Solve $\sin 3x + \sin x = 0$ for x such that $0 \leq x < 2\pi$.

Computers

Peripheral Equipment

Graphics terminals can show three dimensional pictures.

Each computer requires various means of communicating to get programs and data into the machine, (INPUT), and to get results out of the machine, (OUTPUT).

The most fundamental method of INPUT is by means of toggle switches to set the binary code (see page 510) needed to identify numbers, addresses (locations for data), and program instructions. For many years such input was made almost exclusively through punched cards created with a "key punch" machine and placed in a "hopper". Similar means of input include punched paper tape and marked-sense cards. Of course special devices are required for creating and reading these materials. Data and programs may be stored on magnetic tapes, discs, or drums and read back into the computer as data or program steps.

Perhaps the most common means of input today is through the computer terminal. The simplest access is through a keyboard that sends a standardized electronic pulse to the computer for each key pressed. More advanced terminals include the capacity to create special functions and to alter the program code through an editing process before sending it to the computer. The speed with which such terminals communicate with the computer varies greatly.

Other ways of inputing data are through graphic tablets and light pens. Both of these devices allow the operator to "write" the answer. The computer can then interpret the response.

The simplest means of OUTPUT, which is used in most small installations and home computers, is a TV like monitor, referred to as a CRT display. The speed with which such monitors can operate varies greatly. Some monitors allow for display in color, and many provide for very highly resolved addressing of locations on the screen so that quite accurate reproductions of shapes, graphs and pictures are possible.

A printing terminal or separate printer produces what is often referred to as "hard copy." Some of these printers produce the output on special thermal or chemically treated paper. The majority, however, provide printouts similar to that typed by a typewriter. In large scale installations, line printers produce output copy at a truly amazing rate not even capable of being followed by the eye as it is being printed. Recent developments have included the creation of printed characters by the application of finely sprayed ink droplets onto the paper during the printing process.

Magnetic tape units store and feed data during a program.

Exercises   Write a program to output the graphs of each of the following.

1. $y = 2 \sin 3x$

2. $y = 4 \cos 3x$

3. $y = \tan x$

4. $y = 3 \sin 2x + 2 \sin 3x$

Use the double and half-number formulas to solve each of the following.

5. Given $\cos s = 0.6$ and the arc measured by s terminates in the first quadrant, find $\sin 2s$.

6. Given $\sin s = 0.8$ and the arc measured by s terminates in the second quadrant, find $\cos 2s$.

7. Given $\cos s = 0.2$ and the arc measured by s terminates in the fourth quadrant, find $\sin \frac{s}{2}$.

8. Given $\cos s = -0.3333$ and the arc measured by s terminates in the third quadrant, find $\cos \frac{s}{2}$.

The height of a building can be determined by using angles of elevation or angles of depression. Surveyors use trigonometric relationships to determine heights such as this as well as distances.

Trigonometric Functions

6-1   Circular Functions

There is a relationship between trigonometric functions and the circular functions that were previously studied. Let P be the point with ordinate r that maps onto B of the unit circle by the wrapping function. Arc AB subtends the central angle BOA. The **inital side** of the angle is $\overleftrightarrow{OA}$ and the **terminal side** is $\overline{OB}$. An angle with its vertex at the origin and its initial side along the positive x-axis is said to be in **standard position.**

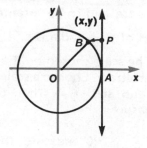

The **trigonometric functions** of $m \angle AOB$ are defined as follows.

$$\sin \angle AOB = \sin r = y \qquad \sec \angle AOB = \sec r = \frac{1}{x}$$

$$\cos \angle AOB = \cos r = x \qquad \csc \angle AOB = \csc r = \frac{1}{y}$$

$$\tan \angle AOB = \tan r = \frac{y}{x} \qquad \cot \angle AOB = \cot r = \frac{x}{y}$$

Trigonometric Functions

The **radian** is the unit of angle measure chosen. A radian is the measure of a central angle which intercepts an arc *one unit in length* on the *unit circle*. Angles measured by a *counter-clockwise* rotation have *positive* measure. Conversely, angles measured *clockwise* have *negative* measure. If an angle has a measure greater than 2π radians, it is indicated by a spiral as shown.

The symbol sin $\angle A$ is understood to mean "the sine of the measure of angle A."

$$m\angle AOC = \frac{\pi}{2} \text{ radians}$$

$$m\angle AOC = \pi \text{ radians}$$

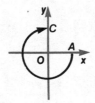

$$m\angle AOC = -\frac{3\pi}{2} \text{ radians}$$

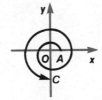

$$m\angle AOC = \frac{7\pi}{2} \text{ radians}$$

Angles in standard position which have the same terminal side are said to be **coterminal.** For example, angles with measures of $-\frac{3\pi}{2}$ radians and $\frac{\pi}{2}$ radians are coterminal.

The scale chosen on the line ℓ used in the wrapping function is arbitrary. Choose a scale on ℓ so that $90 \rightarrow C$, $180 \rightarrow D$, $270 \rightarrow E$, and $360 \rightarrow A$. Then the angles have the familiar *degree measure.*

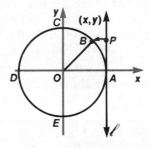

$90°$ measures the same angle as $\frac{\pi}{2}$ radians

$180°$ measures the same angle as π radians.

$270°$ measures the same angle as $\frac{3\pi}{2}$ radians.

$360°$ measures the same angle as 2π radians.

In general, a measurement of $d°$ is equivalent to $\frac{\pi d}{180}$ radians, and a measurement of r radians is equivalent to $\left(\frac{180\,r}{\pi}\right)°$.

When angle measure is in degrees the degree symbol (°) is used. When no unit is indicated, the unit is understood to be radians.

Examples

1. **Find the degree measure equivalent to $\frac{3\pi}{4}$.**

   r radians corresponds to $\left(\frac{180 \cdot r}{\pi}\right)°$

   $\frac{3\pi}{4}$ corresponds to $\left(\frac{180 \cdot \frac{3\pi}{4}}{\pi}\right)°$

   $r = \frac{3\pi}{4}$

$$\left(\left(180 \cdot \frac{3\pi}{4}\right) \div \pi\right)^\circ = \left(180 \cdot \frac{3\pi}{4} \cdot \frac{1}{\pi}\right)^\circ$$
$$= \left(\frac{3 \cdot 180}{4}\right)^\circ$$
$$= 135^\circ$$

2. **Find the degree measure equivalent to** $-\dfrac{11\pi}{4}$.

$$-\frac{11\pi}{4} \text{ corresponds to } \left(\left(180 \cdot \frac{-11\pi}{4}\right) \div \pi\right)^\circ$$
$$\left(\left(180 \cdot -\frac{11\pi}{4}\right) \div \pi\right)^\circ = \left(180 \cdot \frac{-11\pi}{4} \cdot \frac{1}{\pi}\right)^\circ$$
$$= -495^\circ$$

3. **Find the radian measure equivalent to 45°.**

$$d^\circ \text{ corresponds to } \frac{\pi d}{180}$$
$$45^\circ \text{ corresponds to } \frac{\pi(45)}{180}$$
$$\frac{45\pi}{180} = \frac{\pi}{4}$$

4. **Find the radian measure equivalent to −420°.**

$$-420^\circ \text{ corresponds to } \frac{\pi(-420)}{180}$$
$$\frac{-420\pi}{180} = -\frac{7\pi}{3}$$

The point P on the unit circle has coordinates (x_1, y_1). From the definitions of circular functions, $y_1 = \sin\theta$ and $x_1 = \cos\theta$, where θ has the same measure as $\widehat{AP}$ in radians.

Draw a circle concentric with the unit circle and with radius r. Let $Q(x_2, y_2)$ be the point of intersection of $\overrightarrow{OP}$ with the new circle. Similar right triangles OCP and OAQ are formed with a common angle θ at 0.

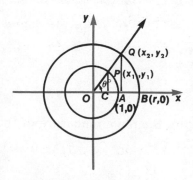

Polar Coordinates

If $0 \leq \theta < 360°$ and θ is in standard position, then every point (x, y) in the plane can be described by (r, θ), where $x = r\cos\theta$, $y = r\sin\theta$ and $\theta = \arctan\dfrac{y}{x}$.

Examples

5. The terminal side of $\angle \theta$ which is in standard position passes through (5, 12). Find $\sin \theta$, $\cos \theta$, and $\tan \theta$.

$$r = \sqrt{x^2 + y^2}$$
$$r = \sqrt{25 + 144}$$
$$r = 13$$

$$\sin \theta = \frac{12}{13}, \cos \theta = \frac{5}{13}, \tan \theta = \frac{12}{5}$$

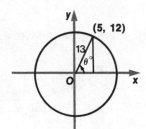

6. If $\theta = \frac{5\pi}{6}$ and $y_1 = 2$, find x_1.

$$\sin \theta = \frac{y_1}{r}$$
$$\sin \frac{5\pi}{6} = \frac{1}{2}$$
$$\frac{1}{2} = \frac{2}{r}$$
$$r = 4$$

$$x^2 + y^2 = r^2$$
$$x^2 + 4 = 16$$
$$x^2 = 12$$
$$x = 2\sqrt{3} \text{ or } -2\sqrt{3}$$

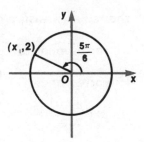

Since θ has its terminal side in the second quadrant, $x_1 < 0$. Therefore, $x_1 = -2\sqrt{3}$.

Exercises

Exploratory Write the degree measure equivalent to each radian measure below.

1. $\frac{\pi}{10}$

2. $-\frac{3\pi}{4}$

3. $\frac{6\pi}{-5}$

4. $\frac{11\pi}{3}$

5. 2

6. 3

Write the radian measure of the angle with each given degree measure.

7. $36°$

8. $-54°$

9. $160°$

10. $540°$

11. $\frac{90°}{\pi}$

12. $\frac{135°}{2\pi}$

Written The terminal side of $\angle \theta$ which is in standard position passes through the given point. Find $\sin \theta$, $\cos \theta$, and $\tan \theta$.

1. $(-4, 3)$

2. $(5, -12)$

3. $(2, -2)$

4. $(-1, \sqrt{3})$

The terminal side of $\angle\theta$ which is in standard position ($0° \le m \angle \theta < 360°$) passes through the given point. Find $m \angle\theta$ in radians and degrees.

5. $(4, 4)$ 6. $(-2, -2)$ 7. $(1, -\sqrt{3})$ 8. $(2\sqrt{3}, -2)$

Write each of the following as a function of θ.

9. $\sin(180 - \theta)°$ 10. $\cos(270 - \theta)°$ 11. $\tan(90 + \theta)°$

12. $\sec(360 + \theta)°$ 13. $\csc(90 - \theta)°$ 14. $\cot(180 + \theta)°$

Use the formulas for $\sin(x \pm y)$, $\cos(x \pm y)$ or $\tan(x \pm y)$ to find the value of each function.

15. $\sin 75°$ 16. $\cos 105°$ 17. $\tan 15°$ 18. $\sin 165°$

Use the formulas for $\sin \frac{1}{2}x$, $\cos \frac{1}{2}x$, or $\tan \frac{1}{2}x$ to find the value of each function.

19. $\sin 22\frac{1}{2}°$ 20. $\cos 15°$ 21. $\tan 15°$ 22. $\sin 105°$

Evaluate each expression.

23. $\sin 30° + \sin 60°$ 24. $\cos 60° - \cos 30°$

Write whether each pair of angles in standard position is coterminal (C) or not coterminal (NC).

25. $45°, 135°$ 26. $120°, 480°$ 27. $-20°, 340°$

28. $-70°, 70°$ 29. $1090°, 10°$ 30. $-120°, 960°$

Find the value of each function.

31. $\sin 450°$ 32. $\cos(-540°)$ 33. $\tan(-750°)$

34. $\cot 1125°$ 35. $\sec(-420°)$ 36. $\csc 780°$

6-2   Using Tables

For many angles the values of the trigonometric functions can be found by using polar coordinates. However, the values of many other angles such as $\sin 17°$ or $\cos 53°$ can be difficult to find. These values can be approximated by means of a series. Approximate values for the trigonometric functions for angles are in a table in the appendix.

For all six functions, values are given to the *nearest 10 minutes* ($60' = 1°$). The table also gives the corresponding *radian measure* for each angle. **Linear interpolation** can be used to find these values for angles which are not listed in the table.

A degree can be divided into 60 equivalent parts. Each of these parts is 1 minute, written 1'.

Examples

1. **Find sin 34° 16'.**

$$\frac{PT}{PS} = \frac{RT}{QS}$$

$QS = QB - SB$

$QS = 0.5640 - 0.5616 = 0.0024$

$PT = 6'; PS = 10'$

$$\frac{6}{10} = \frac{RT}{0.0024}$$

$RT = 0.00144$

The figure is a magnification of the sine function between 34° 10' and 34° 20'. Since △PRT and △PQS are right triangles with a common angle at P, they are similar.

$QB = sin\ 34°\ 20' = 0.5640$
$SB = sin\ 34°\ 10' = 0.5616$

Use *RM* as an approximation for sin 34° 16'.

$RM = RT + TM$

$RM = 0.0014 + 0.5616 = 0.5630$

Since $RM < NM$, this approximation is slightly too small.

34°10'   34°16'   34°20'

The solution for this example can be written in a more compact form.

$$10' \left[\begin{array}{l} \\ 6' \end{array} \left[\begin{array}{l} \rightarrow \sin 34° 20' = 0.5640 \\ \rightarrow \sin 34° 16' = \underline{\quad ? \quad} \\ \rightarrow \sin 34° 10' = 0.5616 \end{array} \right] x \right] 0.0024$$

$$\frac{6}{10} = \frac{x}{0.0024}$$

$$x = 0.00144$$

$$\sin 34° 16' = 0.5616 + 0.0014 = 0.5630$$

2. **Find csc 28° 32'.**

Since csc is a decreasing function, x is negative.

$$10' \left[\begin{array}{l} \\ 2' \end{array} \left[\begin{array}{l} \rightarrow \csc 28° 30' = 2.096 \\ \rightarrow \csc 28° 32' = \underline{\quad ? \quad} \\ \ \ \ \csc 28° 40' = 2.085 \end{array} \right] x \right] -0.011$$

$$\frac{2}{10} = \frac{x}{-0.011}$$

$$x = -0.0022$$

$$\csc 28° 32' = 2.096 - 0.002 = 2.094$$

3. **If tan θ = 1.7896, find θ to the nearest minute.**

$$10' \left[\begin{array}{l} \\ x' \end{array} \left[\begin{array}{l} \rightarrow \tan 60° 50' \doteq 1.7917 \\ \rightarrow \tan \theta \ \ \ = 1.7896 \\ \rightarrow \tan 60° 40' = 1.7796 \end{array} \right] 0.0100 \right] 0.0121$$

$$\frac{x}{10} = \frac{0.0100}{0.0121}$$

$$x = 8.3$$

$$\theta = 60° 40' + 8' = 60° 48'$$

4. If cos θ = 0.6232, find θ to the nearest minute.

$$10' \left[\begin{array}{l} x' \left[\begin{array}{l} \cos 51° 20' = 0.6248 \\ \cos \theta \quad\quad = 0.6232 \\ \cos 51° 30' = 0.6225 \end{array} \right] -0.0007 \end{array} \right] -0.0023$$

$$\frac{x}{10} = \frac{-0.0007}{-0.0023}$$

$$x = 3$$

$$\theta = 51° 30' - 3' = 51° 27'$$

Alternatively, x can be the difference θ − 51° 20'. In this case, x = 7 and θ = 51° 20' + 7' or 51° 27'.

all odd

Exercises

Exploratory Use the tables of the trigonometric functions in the appendix to find the value of each function.

1. sin 72°	**2.** cos 37° 10'	**3.** tan 73° 20'
4. sec 42° 30'	**5.** csc 63° 50'	**6.** cot 18° 10'
7. tan 43° 15'	**8.** sec 52° 26'	**9.** csc 18° 38'

Written Find the measure of each positive acute angle to the nearest minute

1. sin A = 0.3827	**2.** cos A = 0.5688	**3.** tan A = 0.7873
4. sec A = 1.166	**5.** csc A = 3.970	**6.** cot A = 0.6433

Find the value of each.

7. sin 136° 14'	**8.** cos 205° 38'	**9.** tan(−18° 32')
10. sec 249° 55'	**11.** csc(−110° 43')	**12.** cot 294° 26'

If the terminal side of each angle is in the given quadrant and 0 < θ < 2π, find each angle to the nearest minute.

13. sin θ = 0.4450; Quadrant II
14. cos θ = −0.7942; Quadrant III
15. tan θ = 0.2534; Quadrant III
16. sec θ = 1.273; Quadrant IV

6–3 Solving Right Triangles

The trigonometric functions can be used to solve right triangles. To solve a right triangle means to find the measures of the sides and angles not given.

A *unique right triangle* is determined when any of the following pairs of measures are given.

Length of the hypotenuse and length of one leg.
Length of the hypotenuse and measure of one acute angle.
Length of one leg and measure of one acute angle.
Length of both legs.

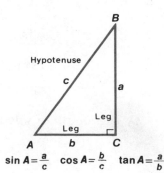

$$\sin A = \frac{a}{c} \quad \cos A = \frac{b}{c} \quad \tan A = \frac{a}{b}$$

In practical situations, measures of line segments and angles are only *approximate*. Therefore, when solving a right triangle, answers for the missing parts are no more precise than those for the given parts. The following table is useful in determining *relative accuracy* in solving right triangles. When using calculators, this table can be used to determine the number of significant digits.

Length of Side	Measure of Angle
1 significant digit	nearest 10°
2 significant digits	nearest 1°
3 significant digits	nearest 10′
4 significant digits	nearest 1′

Examples

1. **Find the measures of the remaining parts of $\triangle ABC$, given $m \angle C = 90°$, $m \angle A = 43°$, and $c = 15$.**

$$\sin 43° = \frac{a}{15}$$

$$0.6820 = \frac{a}{15}$$

$$a = 10.23 \approx 10$$

Since c is given to only 2 significant digits, the length of side a is approximately 10 units.

$$\cos 43° = \frac{b}{15}$$

$$0.7314 = \frac{b}{15}$$

$$b = 10.97 \approx 11$$

The length of side b is approximately 11 units.

$$m \angle B = 90° - 43°$$
$$= 47°$$

2. **Solve right triangle *ABC*, given *a* = 14.3 and *b* = 17.2.**

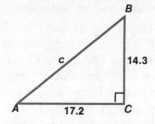

$$\tan A = \frac{14.3}{17.2} = 0.8314$$
$$m \angle A = 39° \, 40'$$
$$m \angle B = 90° - 39° \, 40'$$
$$= 50° \, 20'$$

The length of the hypotenuse can be found either by the Pythagorean Theorem or trigonometric functions.

$$\sec 39° \, 40' = \frac{c}{17.2}$$
$$c = 22.3$$

The length of side *c* is 22.3 units.

Exercises

Exploratory   **Determine with the given information which trigonometric function can be used to find the indicated part of a right triangle. Assume ∠*C* is the right angle.**

1. Given *a* and *c*. Find *m ∠ A*.
2. Given *a* and *b*. Find *m ∠ B*.
3. Given *m ∠ A* and *b*. Find *a*.
4. Given *m ∠ A* and *c*. Find *b*.

Write the number of significant digits for each measurement.

5. 7° 17'
6. 13° 10'
7. 80°
8. 79°
9. 79° 15'
10. 79° 20'

Written   **Solve the right triangle *ABC* given each pair of measures.**

1. *m ∠ A* = 23° 10'; *c* = 27.1
2. *m ∠ B* = 42° 15'; *a* = 1.912
3. *c* = 0.613; *a* = 0.126
4. *a* = 428; *b* = 797
5. *m ∠ B* = 67° 38'; *c* = 72.45
6. *b* = 4123; *c* = 8611
7. *m ∠ A* = 37° 15'; *b* = 11
8. *a* = 11, *b* = 21

Decide whether or not the right triangle *ABC* can be solved uniquely using the following information. If so, solve the right triangle. If not, describe at least two possible right triangles *ABC*.

9. One side is 3 units long and another side is 4 units long.
10. One side is 3 units long and the longest side is 4 units long.
11. Two of the three sides are 4 units long.
12. *c* = 10 and $\dfrac{a}{b} = \dfrac{3}{4}$
13. *m ∠ A* = 2 · *m ∠ B*
14. *m ∠ A* = 2 · *m ∠ B* and *a* = 3

Solve each of the following.

15. The angle of elevation is measured from the horizon upward to the object observed. The angle of elevation of the top of an observation tower is 32° when viewed from a point in the horizontal plane of the base. The distance of the observation point from the base of the tower is 300 m. What is the height of the tower?

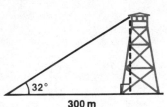

16. The angle of depression is measured from the horizon downward to the object observed. The angle of depression of an airplane on a runway as viewed from the control tower is 38°. If the controller is 110 ft. above the ground, how far is the plane from the base of the tower?

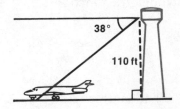

17. The guy wires holding a television tower make an angle of 55° with the ground. If they are anchored in the ground 100 m from the base, how high on the tower do the wires reach? How long are the wires?

18. An airplane flies on a compass heading of 340° at a speed of 650 mph. How far north and how far west of the starting point is the plane after 2 hours?

19. A building which is 30 m high is on top of a hill. The angles of elevation of the top and bottom of the building as viewed from a point at the foot of the hill are 63° and 60° respectively. How high is the hill?

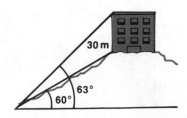

20. An 11 kg mass is placed on an inclined plane as shown. Assuming that the surfaces are frictionless, what force is necessary to keep the mass from sliding down the plane? (Hint: Find the component of $\overline{w}$ which is parallel to the inclined plane.)

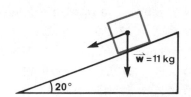

6-4 General Triangles

With the Law of Cosines and the Law of Sines, it is possible to solve any oblique triangle. An oblique triangle is a triangle in which no angle has degree measure of 90.

The Law of Cosines is as follows.
$$a^2 = b^2 + c^2 - 2bc \cos A$$
$$b^2 = a^2 + c^2 - 2ac \cos B$$
$$c^2 = a^2 + b^2 - 2ab \cos C$$

Law of Cosines

The Law of Sines is as follows.
$$\frac{\sin A}{a} = \frac{\sin B}{b} = \frac{\sin C}{c}$$

Law of Sines

The Law of Sines can be proved by circumscribing a circle about △ABC. Draw a diameter through one vertex, say from B. Let 2r represent the length of the diameter. Draw $\overline{AD}$.

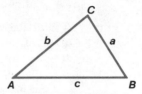

$$m \angle D = m \angle C$$
$$m \angle BAD = 90°$$
$$\sin C = \sin D = \frac{c}{2r}$$
$$\frac{\sin C}{c} = \frac{1}{2r}$$

By drawing diameters from A and C, it can also be shown that $\frac{\sin B}{b} = \frac{1}{2r}$ and $\frac{\sin A}{a} = \frac{1}{2r}$.

Therefore, $\frac{\sin A}{a} = \frac{\sin B}{b} = \frac{\sin C}{c}$.

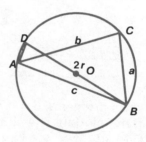

Triangle solution problems can be classified into three types according to what is given.

   I. **ASA** or **AAS** (Two angles and a side)
  II. **SSA** (Two sides and an angle)
 III. **SAS** or **SSS** (two sides and the angle between them or three sides)

In type II, the solution may not be unique.

Examples

1. In △ABC, a = 17, m ∠ A = 43°, and m ∠ B = 58°. Find m ∠ C, b, and c.

This problem is of type **I, AAS**.

Use the Law of Sines.

$$\frac{\sin 43°}{17} = \frac{\sin 58°}{b}$$

$$b = \frac{17 \sin 58°}{\sin 43°}$$

$$b = 21$$

$m \angle C = 180° - (43 + 58)° = 79°$

$$\frac{\sin 43°}{17} = \frac{\sin 79°}{c}$$

$$c = \frac{17 \sin 79°}{\sin 43°}$$

$$c = 24$$

Thus, m ∠ C = 79°, b = 21, and c = 24.

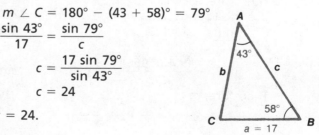

2. In $\triangle ABC$, $m \angle B = 35°$, $a = 62$, and $b = 55$. **Solve the triangle.**

This is an example of Type **II, SSA**. This type often is called the **ambiguous case** since there may be more than one solution. First find the length of the altitude h.

$$h = 62 \sin 35° = 36$$

Since $h < b < a$, there are two solutions. Solve $\triangle ABC$ and $\triangle A'BC$.

Answers should be rounded off to the correct number of significant digits.

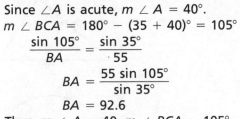

$$\frac{\sin 35°}{55} = \frac{\sin A}{62}$$

$$\sin A = \frac{62 \sin 35°}{55}$$

$$\sin A = 0.6466$$

Since $\angle A$ is acute, $m \angle A = 40°$.
$m \angle BCA = 180° - (35 + 40)° = 105°$

$$\frac{\sin 105°}{BA} = \frac{\sin 35°}{55}$$

$$BA = \frac{55 \sin 105°}{\sin 35°}$$

$$BA = 92.6$$

Thus, $m \angle A = 40$, $m \angle BCA = 105°$, and $BA = 92.6$

In $\triangle A'BC$, $m \angle BA'C = 140°$
$m \angle BCA' = 180° - (140 + 35)° = 5°$

$$\frac{\sin 5°}{BA'} = \frac{\sin 35°}{55}$$

$$BA' = \frac{55 \sin 5°}{\sin 35°}$$

$$BA' = 8.4$$

Thus, $m \angle BA'C = 140°$, $m \angle BCA' = 5°$, and $BA' = 8.4$.

In Type **II** problems, if $b < h$ (the length of the altitude), then there is no solution. The altitude must be the *shortest segment* from C to $\overrightarrow{AB}$. If $h = b$, a right triangle is the only solution. Similarly, if $b > a$, there is only one solution.

Example

3. In $\triangle ABC$, $m \angle A = 105°$, $b = 8.4$, and $c = 6.2$. **Find a, $m \angle B$, and $m \angle C$.**

This is an example of Type **III, SAS**.
Use the Law of Cosines to find a.

$$a^2 = b^2 + c^2 - 2bc \cos A$$
$$a^2 = (8.4)^2 + (6.2)^2 - 2(8.4)(6.2) \cos 105°$$
$$a = 11.7$$

Therefore, $a = 11.7$.
Use the Law of Sines to find $m \angle B$ and $m \angle C$.

$$\frac{\sin B}{8.4} = \frac{\sin 105°}{11.7}$$

$$\sin B = \frac{(8.4)(0.966)}{11.7} = 0.694$$

Therefore, $m \angle B = 44°$.

$$\frac{\sin C}{6.2} = \frac{\sin 105°}{11.7}$$

$$\sin C = \frac{(6.2)(\sin 105°)}{11.7} = 0.512$$

Therefore, $m \angle C = 31°$.

The solution of oblique triangles can be summarized as follows.

Type	Description	Number of Solutions	Theorem
I	**ASA or AAS**	one	Law of Sines
II	**SSA,** $m \angle B \geq 90°$	none if $b \leq a$	Law of Sines
II	**SSA,** $m \angle B \geq 90°$	one if $b > a$	Law of Sines
II	**SSA,** $m \angle B < 90°$	one if $b > a$	Law of Sines
II	**SSA,** $m \angle B < 90°$	one if $b = a$	Law of Sines
II	**SSA,** $m \angle B < 90°, b < a$	two if $h < b$ one if $h = b$ none if $h > b$	Law of Sines
III	**SSS or SAS**	one	Law of Cosines

Exercises

Exploratory   Write "yes" if there is a unique solution for triangle *ABC*. Write "no" if there is not a unique solution.

1. $m \angle C = 30°, b = 4, c = 2$
2. $m \angle C = 30°, b = 4, c = 5$
3. $m \angle C = 30°, b = 4, c = 3$
4. $m \angle C = 20°, b = 4, c = 2$
5. $a = b = 2c = c^2$
6. $a^2 + b^2 = c^2, c = 2a$

Written   Solve each oblique triangle *ABC*.

1. $m \angle A = 37°; m \angle B = 28°; b = 14$
2. $m \angle B = 68°; m \angle C = 47°; b = 23$
3. $m \angle A = 18°; m \angle C = 51°; b = 4.7$
4. $m \angle C = 112°; m \angle B = 25°; a = 240$
5. $a = 68, m \angle C = 71°, b = 59$
6. $a = 16; b = 14; c = 12$
7. $a = 42; b = 37; c = 26$
8. $a = 34; m \angle B = 43°; b = 28$
9. $b = 0.55; m \angle A = 62°; a = 0.51$
10. $c = 0.53; m \angle C = 28°; a = 1.3$
11. $a = 63; m \angle B = 73°; b = 54$

Solve each of the following.

12. Find the lengths of the diagonals of a parallelogram whose sides measure 14.3 and 17.2 and which has one angle with measure 37° 10′.

13. Find the measures of the angles of an isosceles triangle with base 18 units long and legs 15 units long.

14. Two ships leave the same port at 10:00 A.M. One sails on a bearing of 045°. Its speed is 12 knots. (A knot is 1 *nautical mile* per hour.) The other ship sails on a bearing of 160° at 14 knots. How many nautical miles apart are they at 1:00 P.M.?

15. Two forces of 35 kg and 42 kg have a resultant of 58 kg. Find the size of the angle between the forces.

Challenge   Solve each of the following.

1. To check the solution of a triangle, **Mollweide's Equation** can be used.

$$\frac{a - b}{c} = \frac{\sin \frac{1}{2}(A - B)}{\cos \frac{1}{2}C}$$

Prove that this equation is true for all triangles. (Hint: Find $\frac{a - b}{c}$ using the Law of Sines, $\frac{a}{c} = \frac{\sin A}{\sin C}$ and $\frac{b}{c} = \frac{\sin B}{\sin C}$.)

2. In using the Law of Cosines to solve **SAS** triangles, the calculations can be difficult to do by hand. Before electronic calculators, logarithms and the **Law of Tangents** were used to solve these problems.

$$\frac{a - b}{a + b} = \frac{\tan \frac{1}{2}(A - B)}{\tan \frac{1}{2}(A + B)}$$

Prove the Law of Tangents.

3. Type **III**, **SSS**, problems also can be solved by the **half-angle formulas.**

$$\left.\begin{array}{l} \tan \frac{1}{2}A = \dfrac{r}{s - a} \\[2mm] \tan \frac{1}{2}B = \dfrac{r}{s - b} \\[2mm] \tan \frac{1}{2}C = \dfrac{r}{s - c} \end{array}\right\} \text{ where } r = \sqrt{\dfrac{(s - a)(s - b)(s - c)}{s}} \text{ and } s = \dfrac{a + b + c}{2}$$

Prove the half-angle formulas.

6–5 Areas

Finding the area of polygons can be reduced to finding the areas of triangles. If the measures of the base and altitude of a triangle are known, then the area of the triangle can be found by using the formula $\mathcal{A} = \frac{1}{2}bh$. Suppose, however, that the measures of two sides and the included angle are known. Since $h = c \sin A$, the area of $\triangle ABC$ can be found by the formula $\mathcal{A} = \frac{1}{2}bc \sin A$. If $\angle A$ is obtuse, the formula still applies since $\sin (180 - A)° = \sin A$.

Script A will represent area.

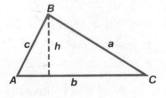

If $\mathcal{A}$ is defined to be the area of a triangle, then $\mathcal{A} = \frac{1}{2}bc \sin A$.

Area of Triangles

Examples

1. **Find the area of a triangle with two sides of length 14 and 9, if the measure of the included angle is 60°.**

$$\mathcal{A} = \frac{1}{2}(14)(9) \sin 60°.$$

$$\mathcal{A} = \frac{63\sqrt{3}}{2}$$

2. **Find the area of $\triangle ABC$, given $m \angle A = 25°$, $m \angle B = 73°$, and $b = 1.7$.**

$$m \angle C = 180° - (25 + 73)° = 82°$$

$$\frac{\sin 73°}{1.7} = \frac{\sin 82°}{c}$$

$$c = 1.8$$

$$\mathcal{A} = \frac{1}{2}(1.7)(1.8) \sin 25°$$

$$\mathcal{A} = 0.65$$

If either ASA or AAS are known, the problem can be solved by first finding the length of another side.

Answers should be rounded off to the correct number of significant figures.

3. **Find the area of $\triangle ABC$, given $a = 4.7$, $b = 5.3$, and $c = 7.6$.**

$$a^2 = b^2 + c^2 - 2bc \cos A$$

$$(4.7)^2 = (5.3)^2 + (7.6)^2 - 2(5.3)(7.6) \cos A$$

$$22.1 = 28.1 + 57.8 - 80.6 \cos A$$

$$\cos A = \frac{63.8}{80.6} = 0.792$$

Therefore, $m \angle A = 38°$.

$$\mathcal{A} = \frac{1}{2}(7.6)(5.3) \sin 38°$$

$$\mathcal{A} = 12.4$$

If SSS is given, then the Law of Cosines can be used to find an angle.

see p. 181

Hero's formula

A sector of a circle is the region bounded by an arc of a circle and the radii drawn to its endpoints.

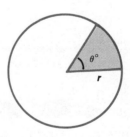

$$\mathcal{A} = \frac{\theta}{360°}(\pi r^2), \theta \text{ in degrees}$$

$$\mathcal{A} = \frac{1}{2}r^2 \theta, \theta \text{ in radians}$$

Area of a sector of a Circle

Example

4. An oscillating sprinkler can spray water up to 10 m away. If it turns only through an angle of 60°, what is the area of the surface it can spray?

$$a = \frac{1}{2}(10)^2\frac{\pi}{3}$$

$$a = \frac{50\pi}{3}$$

$$a \approx 52 \text{ m}^2$$

A segment of a circle is the region bounded by an arc and its chord. If the arc is a minor arc then the area of the segment can be found by subtracting the area of $\triangle AOB$ from the area of sector AOB.

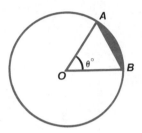

If a is the area of a segment of a circle, then $a = \frac{1}{2}r^2(\theta - \sin \theta)$ when θ is in radians.

Area of a segment of a Circle

Example

5. Find the area of a segment of a circle with radius 4 if $\theta = \frac{\pi}{6}$.

$$a = \frac{1}{2}(16)\left(\frac{\pi}{6} - \frac{1}{2}\right)$$

$$a = \frac{4\pi}{3} - 4$$

Exercises

Exploratory Find the area of $\triangle ABC$ given each set of measures.

1. $m \angle A = 45°; b = 11; c = 14$
2. $m \angle C = 60°; a = 7; b = 9$
3. $m \angle A = 43°; b = 16; c = 12$
4. $m \angle B = 30°; a = 12; c = 10$
5. $m \angle C = 148°; a = 10; b = 8.4$
6. $m \angle A = 87°; m \angle B = 15°; c = 26$
7. $m \angle C = 34°; m \angle A = 77°; a = 1.4$
8. $a = 4; b = 6; c = 8$
9. $a = 3; b = 5; c = 7$
10. $a = 5; b = 6; c = 9$

<u>Written</u>   **Find the area of each sector, given the radius of the circle and the measure of the angle between the radii.**

1. $\theta = \dfrac{\pi}{8}$; $r = 7$

2. $\theta = \dfrac{5\pi}{12}$; $r = 10$

3. $\theta = 48°$; $r = 22$

4. $\theta = 54°$; $r = 6$

Find the area of each segment.

5. $\theta = \dfrac{5\pi}{6}$; $r = 15$

6. $\theta = \dfrac{3\pi}{4}$; $r = 24$

7. $\theta = 120°$; $r = 8$

8. $\theta = 81°$; $r = 16$

Solve each of the following.

9. Find the area enclosed by a circle with radius 12 cm, and a regular inscribed hexagon.

10. Find the area of a parallelogram with two sides of length 43 cm and 67 cm, if the angle between these sides has a measure of 52°.

11. Find the area of a parallelogram with two sides of length 14.8 m and 25.6 m, if the angle between these sides has a measure of 127°.

12. Find the area of a rhombus with sides 10 units long if the length of the longer diagonal is 16 units long.

The area of a regular polygon can be found by using the formula $a = \frac{1}{2}ap$ where a is the radius of the inscribed circle and p is the perimeter of the polygon. Find the area of each of the following.

13. A regular pentagon with a side 8 units long.

14. A regular hexagon with a side 14 units long.

15. A radar antenna turns through a horizontal angle of 75°. If its range is 40 km, what area can it sweep?

Excursions in mathematics

Hero's Formula

Another way to find the area of $\triangle ABC$ when the length of the three sides are known is to use **Hero's Formula.**

$$a = \sqrt{s(s - a)(s - b)(s - c)}$$

In Hero's Formula, s represents the semiperimeter of the triangle, $s = \dfrac{a + b + c}{2}$.

Exercises   **Use Hero's Formula to find the area of each of the following triangles.**

1. $a = 3, b = 4, c = 5$

2. $a = 2, b = 7, c = 8$

3. $a = 12, b = 10, c = 14$

4. $a = 17, b = 13, c = 19$

6–6 Velocity

Suppose an object is moving in a straight line at a constant linear velocity v. Then the distance s the object travels in time t is $s = vt$, provided v and t are expressed in the same unit of time. Suppose the object is moving along a circle with radius r. The distance s it travels in this case is $s = \dfrac{\theta}{2\pi}(2\pi r) = r\theta$ where θ is measured in radians. Thus, $\dfrac{s}{t} = \dfrac{r\theta}{t}$. Since $\dfrac{s}{t} = v$, $v = r\omega$ where the number of radians "turned" per unit time is $\omega = \dfrac{\theta}{t}$, called **angular velocity.**

The symbol ω is a Greek letter called omega.

Examples

1. **A wheel with radius 10 cm is turning at 5 revolutions per second. What is the velocity of a point on the rim?**

$$v = r\omega$$
$$v = 10(5 \cdot 2\pi)$$
$$v = 100\pi$$

The angular velocity is 5 rev per sec.

The point is traveling at 100π cm per second.

2. **A trailer wheel has a diameter of 12 in. If the car pulling the trailer travels at 60 mph, what is the angular velocity of the wheel in revolutions per second?**

Convert 60 mph to inches per second.

$$60\ \frac{\text{mi}}{\text{h}} \cdot 5280\ \frac{\text{ft}}{\text{mi}} \cdot 12\ \frac{\text{in.}}{\text{ft}} \cdot \frac{1\ \text{h}}{3600\ \text{s}} = 1056\ \frac{\text{in.}}{\text{s}}$$

A velocity of 60 mph is the same as 1056 in./s.

$$v = r\omega$$
$$1056 = 6\omega$$
$$\omega = 176 \text{ radians/s}$$
$$176 \text{ radians/sec} = \frac{176}{2\pi} \text{ revolutions per second}$$

One revolution is equal to 2π radians.

The angular velocity is approximately 28 revolutions per second.

Exercises

Exploratory   Find the length of each arc, given the measure of its central angle and the radius of the circle.

1. $\theta = 45°$; $r = 10$

2. $\theta = 210°$; $r = 36$

3. $\theta = \dfrac{\pi}{6}; r = 15$ **4.** $\theta = \dfrac{2\pi}{3}; r = 8$

Find the radius of a circle given the arc length and central angle.

5. $\theta = 120°, s = 18$ **6.** $\theta = \dfrac{3\pi}{4}, s = \dfrac{\pi}{6}$

<u>Written</u> **Find the *linear velocity* of a point on a circle, given the radius of the circle and the angular velocity of the point.**

1. $r = 9$ in.; $\omega = \dfrac{2}{3}\pi$ rad/min   **2.** $r = 12$ cm; $\omega = \dfrac{5\pi}{6}$ rad/min

3. $r = 18$ cm; $\omega = 40°/s$ **4.** $r = 15$ cm; $\omega = 75°/s$

5. $r = 8$ m; $\omega = 2.5$ rev/min   **6.** $r = 21$ ft; $\omega = \dfrac{4}{3}$ rev/min

Find the angular velocity of each wheel, given its radius and linear velocity.

7. $r = 24$ in.; $v = 48$ in./s   **8.** $r = 18$ cm; $v = 108$ cm/s

9. $r = 2$ ft; $v = 30$ mph   **10.** $r = 3$ m; $v = 20$ km/h

Solve each of the following.

11. A bicycle with wheels 28 in. in diameter travels 30 mph. How fast are the wheels turning?

12. A hammer thrower whirls an iron ball at the end of a handle which is 1 m long. If he can whirl it at $1\dfrac{1}{2}$ revolutions per second, how fast is the ball traveling when it leaves his hand?

✗ do 2-9 p.56.

6-7 Complex Numbers

Complex numbers may be written in terms of trigonometric functions. Consider the graphical representation of $a + bi$.

$$a = r \cos \theta; \quad b = r \sin \theta$$
$$r = |a + bi| = \sqrt{a^2 + b^2}$$
$$\theta = \arctan \dfrac{b}{a}$$

$$a + bi = r \cos \theta + (r \sin \theta)i$$
$$= r(\cos \theta + i \sin \theta)$$

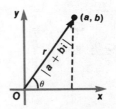

Notice that θ must be chosen so that the terminal side of θ contains $a + bi$. Complex numbers written in this way are said to be in **trigonometric form**.

Examples

1. **Write $1 + \sqrt{3}i$ in trigonometric form.**

$$r = \sqrt{1 + 3} = 2 \qquad \theta = \arctan \frac{\sqrt{3}}{1}$$

Since $1 + \sqrt{3}i$ is in the first quadrant, $\theta = \frac{\pi}{3}$.

$$1 + \sqrt{3}i = 2\left(\cos \frac{\pi}{3} + i \sin \frac{\pi}{3}\right)$$

2. **Write $3\left(\cos \frac{3\pi}{4} + i \sin \frac{3\pi}{4}\right)$ in the form $a + bi$.**

$$3\left(\cos \frac{3\pi}{4} + i \sin \frac{3\pi}{4}\right) = 3\left(-\frac{\sqrt{2}}{2} + \frac{\sqrt{2}}{2}i\right)$$
$$= \frac{-3\sqrt{2}}{2} + \frac{3\sqrt{2}}{2}i$$

Complex numbers written in trigonometric form can be multiplied and divided easily. The following theorems are useful in these operations.

Given radii r_1 and r_2 and angles θ_1 and θ_2,
$$r_1(\cos \theta_1 + i \sin \theta_1) \cdot r_2(\cos \theta_2 + i \sin \theta_2)$$
$$= r_1 r_2[\cos(\theta_1 + \theta_2) + i \sin (\theta_1 + \theta_2)].$$

Multiplying Complex Numbers

Use the formulas for sin ($\theta_1 + \theta_2$) and cos ($\theta_1 + \theta_2$).

Proof

Let $x = r_1(\cos \theta_1 + i \sin \theta_1) \cdot r_2(\cos \theta_2 + i \sin \theta_2)$.
Thus, $x = r_1 r_2[(\cos \theta_1 \cos \theta_2 - \sin \theta_1 \sin \theta_2) + i(\sin \theta_1 \cos \theta_2 + \cos \theta_1 \sin \theta_2)]$
$\qquad = r_1 r_2[\cos(\theta_1 + \theta_2) + i \sin (\theta_1 + \theta_2)]$
Therefore, $r_1(\cos \theta_1 + i \sin \theta_1) \cdot r_2(\cos \theta_2 + i \sin \theta_2) = r_1 r_2[\cos(\theta_1 + \theta_2) + i \sin (\theta_1 + \theta_2)]$

Given radii r_1 and r_2 and angles θ_1 and θ_2
$$\frac{r_1(\cos \theta_1 + i \sin \theta_1)}{r_2(\cos \theta_2 + i \sin \theta_2)} = \frac{r_1}{r_2} \cos (\theta_1 - \theta_2) + i \sin (\theta_1 - \theta_2)$$

Dividing Complex Numbers

Proof

Let $x = \dfrac{r_1(\cos \theta_1 + i \sin \theta_1)}{r_2(\cos \theta_2 + i \sin \theta_2)}$

Thus, $x = \dfrac{r_1(\cos \theta_1 + i \sin \theta_1)}{r_2(\cos \theta_2 + i \sin \theta_2)} \cdot \dfrac{(\cos \theta_2 - i \sin \theta_2)}{(\cos \theta_2 - i \sin \theta_2)}$

Remember $i^2 = -1$ and $\cos^2 \theta + \sin^2 \theta = 1$.

$\qquad = \dfrac{r_1(\cos \theta_1 \cos \theta_2 + \sin \theta_1 \sin \theta_2) + i\,(\sin \theta_1 \cos \theta_2 - \cos \theta_1 \sin \theta_2)}{r_2(\cos^2 \theta_2 + \sin^2 \theta_2)}$

$\qquad = \dfrac{r_1}{r_2}\left[\cos(\theta_1 - \theta_2) + i \sin(\theta_1 - \theta_2)\right]$

Therefore, $\dfrac{r_1(\cos \theta_1 + i \sin \theta_1)}{r_2(\cos \theta_2 + i \sin \theta_2)} = \dfrac{r_1}{r_2}\left[\cos(\theta_1 - \theta_2) + i \sin(\theta_1 - \theta_2)\right]$

Examples

3. **Find the product of $4\left(\cos \dfrac{5\pi}{6} + i \sin \dfrac{5\pi}{6}\right)$ and $2\left(\cos \dfrac{\pi}{3} + i \sin \dfrac{\pi}{3}\right)$.**

$4\left(\cos \dfrac{5\pi}{6} + i \sin \dfrac{5\pi}{6}\right) \cdot 2\left(\cos \dfrac{\pi}{3} + i \sin \dfrac{\pi}{3}\right) = 8\left[\cos\left(\dfrac{5\pi}{6} + \dfrac{\pi}{3}\right) + i \sin\left(\dfrac{5\pi}{6} + \dfrac{\pi}{3}\right)\right]$

$\qquad\qquad = 8\left(\cos \dfrac{7\pi}{6} + i \sin \dfrac{7\pi}{6}\right)$

4. **Find $\dfrac{-3 + 3i\sqrt{3}}{\sqrt{3} + i}$.**

Refer to example 1 for the numerator. For the denominator,

$\dfrac{-3 + 3i\sqrt{3}}{\sqrt{3} + i} = \dfrac{6\left(\cos \dfrac{2\pi}{3} + i \sin \dfrac{2\pi}{3}\right)}{2\left(\cos \dfrac{\pi}{6} + i \sin \dfrac{\pi}{6}\right)}$

$r = \sqrt{(\sqrt{3})^2 + 1^2} = \sqrt{4} = 2$ and $\theta = \arctan \dfrac{1}{\sqrt{3}} = \dfrac{\pi}{6}$.

$\qquad = 3\left[\cos\left(\dfrac{2\pi}{3} - \dfrac{\pi}{6}\right) + i \sin\left(\dfrac{2\pi}{3} - \dfrac{\pi}{6}\right)\right]$

$\qquad = 3\left[\cos \dfrac{\pi}{2} + i \sin \dfrac{\pi}{2}\right]$

$\qquad = 3(0 + i)$

see p.186 #5 for an example

$\qquad = 3i$

Exercises

Exploratory   Write each of the following in trigonometric form.

1. $1 + 0i$

2. $\dfrac{\sqrt{2}}{2} - \dfrac{\sqrt{2}}{2}i$

3. $-\dfrac{1}{2} + \dfrac{\sqrt{3}}{2}i$

Write each of the following in the form $a + bi$.

4. $2(\cos 30° + i \sin 30°)$

5. $12(\cos 180° + i \sin 180°)$

6. $4(\cos 135° + i \sin 135°)$

Written Perform the indicated operation. Write your answer in the form $a + bi, a, b, \in \mathcal{R}$.

1. $3(\cos 30° + i \sin 30°) \cdot 2(\cos 60° + i \sin 60°)$

2. $2(\cos 45° + i \sin 45°) \cdot 5(\cos 135° + i \sin 135°)$

3. $\sqrt{3}\left(\cos \dfrac{2\pi}{3} + i \sin \dfrac{2\pi}{3}\right) \cdot \dfrac{1}{2}\left(\cos \dfrac{\pi}{6} + i \sin \dfrac{\pi}{6}\right)$

4. $8\left(\cos \dfrac{5\pi}{6} + i \sin \dfrac{5\pi}{6}\right) \cdot \dfrac{3}{4}\left(\cos \dfrac{\pi}{3} + i \sin \dfrac{\pi}{3}\right)$

5. $4(\cos 47° + i \sin 47°) \div 2(\cos 17° + i \sin 17°)$

6. $\sqrt{3}(\cos 105° + i \sin 105°) \div 2(\cos 15° + i \sin 15°)$

7. $18(\cos 18° + i \sin 18°) \div 3(\cos 78° + i \sin 78°)$

8. $4(\cos 57° + i \sin 57°) \div 3(\cos 117° + i \sin 117°)$

Write each complex number in trigonometric form and perform the indicated operation. Check your answer by performing the operation with the complex numbers as written.

9. $(4 + 4i)(2 - 2i)$

10. $(2 + 2\sqrt{3}i)(\sqrt{3} - i)$

11. $\dfrac{-2\sqrt{3} - 2i}{4 + 4\sqrt{3}i}$

12. $\dfrac{-5 + 5i}{3 - 3i}$

13. Simplify the expression.
$$\dfrac{3(\cos 142° + i \sin 142°) \cdot 2(\cos 56° + i \sin 56°) \cdot \sqrt{3}(\cos 220° + i \sin 220°)}{\sqrt{2}(\cos 148° + i \sin 148°)}$$

14. Simplify the expression.
$$\dfrac{5(\cos 153° + i \sin 153°) \cdot 2(\cos 49° + i \sin 49°) \cdot 3(\cos 238° + i \sin 238°)}{\sqrt{5}(\cos 260° + i \sin 260°)}$$

15. Prove that the reciprocal of $r(\cos \theta + i \sin \theta)$ is $\dfrac{1}{r}(\cos \theta - i \sin \theta)$.

16. Find the reciprocal of $2\left(\cos \dfrac{\pi}{3} + i \sin \dfrac{\pi}{3}\right)$.

17. Find the reciprocal of $3\left(\cos \dfrac{5\pi}{6} + i \sin \dfrac{5\pi}{6}\right)$.

6-8 DeMoivre's Theorem

A problem in operating with complex numbers is to find the nth root of a complex number. For $n = 2$, an algebraic solution is possible.

Example

1. Find $\sqrt{5 - 12i}$.

Let $z = a + bi = \sqrt{5 - 12i}$.

Then $z^2 = (a^2 - b^2) + 2abi = 5 - 12i$.
So, $a^2 - b^2 = 5$ and $2ab = -12$.
But $|z|^2 = |z^2| = |5 - 12i|$.

Therefore, $|z| = \sqrt{\sqrt{25 + 144}}$
$= \sqrt{13}$. *So,* $\sqrt{a^2 + b^2} = \sqrt{13}$.

$$a^2 + b^2 = 13$$
$$\underline{a^2 - b^2 = 5}$$
$$2a^2 = 18$$
$$a^2 = 9$$
$$a = \pm 3$$

So, $9 - b^2 = 5$
$b^2 = 4$
$b = \pm 2$

Since $2ab = -12$, a and b have opposite signs. Thus, $\sqrt{5 - 12i} = -3 + 2i$ or $3 - 2i$.

The method used in the example is fine for finding square roots. However, it is cumbersome for finding other roots. The following is useful for finding roots.

For all real numbers r, n, and θ

$$[r(\cos \theta + i \sin \theta)]^n = r^n(\cos n\theta + i \sin n\theta).$$

DeMoivre's Theorem

DeMoivre's Theorem can be demonstrated for all values of n when n is a positive integer. A proof can be written using a technique called proof by *mathematical induction*.

For now, it is assumed that DeMoivre's Theorem is true for all real numbers.

Mathematical induction is discussed in Chapter 13.

Examples

2. Find $\sqrt{5 - 12i}$ by **DeMoivre's Theorem.**

$$5 - 12i = 13(\cos \theta + i \sin \theta) \text{ where } \theta = \arctan\left(-\frac{12}{5}\right)$$

$$\sqrt{5 - 12i} = [13(\cos \theta + i \sin \theta)]^{1/2} = 13^{1/2}\left(\cos \frac{1}{2}\theta + i \sin \frac{1}{2}\theta\right)$$

The terminal side of θ is in Quadrant IV. Therefore, $\frac{3\pi}{2} \le \theta \le 2\pi$ or $\frac{7\pi}{2} \le \theta \le 4\pi$.

If $\dfrac{3\pi}{2} \le \theta \le 2\pi$, then $\dfrac{3\pi}{4} \le \dfrac{1}{2}\theta \le \pi$.

Use half-angle formulas.

$$\cos \tfrac{1}{2}\theta = -\sqrt{\dfrac{1 + \cos \theta}{2}} \qquad\qquad \sin \tfrac{1}{2}\theta = \sqrt{\dfrac{1 - \cos \theta}{2}}$$

$$= -\sqrt{\dfrac{1 + \dfrac{5}{13}}{2}} \qquad\qquad = \sqrt{\dfrac{1 - \dfrac{5}{13}}{2}}$$

$$= -\sqrt{\dfrac{9}{13}} \qquad\qquad = \sqrt{\dfrac{4}{13}}$$

$$\cos \tfrac{1}{2}\theta = -\dfrac{3}{\sqrt{13}} \qquad\qquad \sin \tfrac{1}{2}\theta = \dfrac{2}{\sqrt{13}}$$

$$\sqrt{5 - 12i} = \sqrt{13}\left(-\dfrac{3}{\sqrt{13}} + \dfrac{2}{\sqrt{13}}i\right) = -3 + 2i$$

If $\dfrac{7\pi}{2} \le \theta \le 4\pi$, then $\dfrac{7\pi}{4} \le \dfrac{1}{2}\theta \le 2\pi$.

$$\cos \tfrac{1}{2}\theta = \sqrt{\dfrac{1 + \dfrac{5}{13}}{2}} \qquad\qquad \sin \tfrac{1}{2}\theta = \sqrt{\dfrac{1 - \dfrac{5}{13}}{2}}$$

$$\cos \tfrac{1}{2}\theta = \dfrac{3}{\sqrt{13}} \qquad\qquad \sin \tfrac{1}{2}\theta = -\dfrac{2}{\sqrt{13}}$$

$$\sqrt{5 - 12i} = 3 - 2i$$

3. **Evaluate** $\left[8\left(\cos \dfrac{3\pi}{4} + i \sin \dfrac{3\pi}{4}\right)\right]^{2/3}$.

$8\left(\cos \dfrac{3\pi}{4} + i \sin \dfrac{3\pi}{4}\right) = 8\left[\cos\left(2\pi k + \dfrac{3\pi}{4}\right) + i \sin\left(2\pi k + \dfrac{3\pi}{4}\right)\right]$, where k is an integer.

For $n = 0$, $\left[8\left(\cos \dfrac{3\pi}{4} + i \sin \dfrac{3\pi}{4}\right)\right]^{2/3} = 4\left(\cos \dfrac{2}{3}\cdot\dfrac{3\pi}{4} + i \sin \dfrac{2}{3}\cdot\dfrac{3\pi}{4}\right) = 4i$

For $n = 1$, $\left[8\left(\cos \dfrac{3\pi}{4} + i \sin \dfrac{3\pi}{4}\right)\right]^{2/3} = 4\left(\cos \dfrac{2}{3}\cdot\dfrac{11\pi}{4} + i \sin \dfrac{2}{3}\cdot\dfrac{11\pi}{4}\right) = 2\sqrt{3} - 2i$

For $n = 2$, $\left[8\left(\cos \dfrac{3\pi}{4} + i \sin \dfrac{3\pi}{4}\right)\right]^{2/3} = 4\left(\cos \dfrac{2}{3}\cdot\dfrac{19\pi}{4} + i \sin \dfrac{2}{3}\cdot\dfrac{19\pi}{4}\right) = -2\sqrt{3} - 2i$

For $n = 3$, $\left[8\left(\cos \dfrac{3\pi}{4} + i \sin \dfrac{3\pi}{4}\right)\right]^{2/3} = 4\left(\cos \dfrac{2}{3}\cdot\dfrac{27\pi}{4} + i \sin \dfrac{2}{3}\cdot\dfrac{27\pi}{4}\right) = 4i$

The root for $n = 3$ is the same as the root for $n = 0$. The root for $n = 4$ is the same as the root for $n = 1$, and so on. For a cube root only $n = 0, 1, 2$ need be considered.

In general, for an rth root, only $n = 0, 1, 2, \ldots, r - 1$ need to be considered in using DeMoivre's Theorem.

If the three cube roots in Example 3 are graphed, the terminal point of each arrow lies on a circle with radius 4. The angle between any two arrows is a multiple of $\frac{4\pi}{3}$. Once the first root, $4\left(\cos \frac{\pi}{2} + i \sin \frac{\pi}{2}\right)$, is found the others can be found by adding multiples of $\frac{4\pi}{3}$.

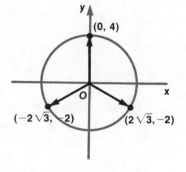

In general, to find $[r(\cos \theta + i \sin \theta)]^{m/n}$, first find $r^{m/n}\left(\cos \frac{m\theta}{n} + i \sin \frac{m\theta}{n}\right)$ and then add the next $n - 1$ multiples of $\frac{m}{n}(2\pi)$ to find the remaining roots. Graphically, these roots are arranged in a circle of radius $r^{m/n}$ with center at the origin. The angle between the arrows of any two successive roots is $\frac{m}{n}(2\pi)$.

Exercises

Exploratory   Given θ for one of the nth roots of $a + bi$. Find the other values of θ.

1. $\theta = \frac{\pi}{3}, n = 3$

2. $\theta = \frac{\pi}{6}, n = 3$

3. $\theta = \frac{\pi}{2}; n = 4$

4. $\theta = 0, n = 5$

Written   Find each power.

1. $(1 - i)^3$

2. $(1 + \sqrt{3}i)^4$

3. $(2\sqrt{3} - 2i)^2$

4. $\left(\frac{1}{2} + \frac{1}{2}i\right)^{-3}$

5. $(\sqrt{3} - i)^{2/3}$

6. $(1 + i)^{4/5}$

7. Find the three cube roots of 1.

8. Find the three cube roots of i.

9. Find all sixth roots of 64.

10. Find all fifth roots of -1.

Solve each equation over $\mathcal{C}$.

11. $z^2 = 4 - 4i$

12. $z^3 - 8 = 0$

13. $z^2 = (1 - i)^3$

14. $z^3 = (1 + i)^2$

15. Use DeMoivre's Theorem to write $\cos 3\theta$ and $\sin 3\theta$ in terms of $\cos \theta$ and $\sin \theta$. (Hint: Expand $(\cos \theta + i \sin \theta)^3$ and equate the results using DeMoivre's Theorem.)

Excursions in Mathematics

Trigonometric Functions

The values for sin x and cos x which appear in tables are calculated using the following series.

$$\sin x = x - \frac{x^3}{3!} + \frac{x^5}{5!} - \frac{x^7}{7!} + \cdots + \frac{(-1)^{n-1}x^{2n-1}}{(2n-1)!}$$

$$\cos x = 1 - \frac{x^2}{2!} + \frac{x^4}{4!} - \frac{x^6}{6!} + \cdots + \frac{(-1)^{n-1}x^{2n-2}}{(2n-2)!}$$

Using a calculator compute sin x and cos x to four decimal places, for some x in radians. Compare the values with those in the tables.

In calculating sin x and cos x using these series, only compute the value of the series to the point where addition of another term gives the same number, to the required number of significant digits.

$$\sin \frac{\pi}{4} \approx \frac{\pi}{4} - \frac{\left(\frac{\pi}{4}\right)^3}{3!} + \frac{\left(\frac{\pi}{4}\right)^5}{5!} \approx 0.707$$

If the next term, $\dfrac{\left(\frac{\pi}{4}\right)^7}{7!}$, is calculated, it is approximately 0.00003. Since the first 3 significant digits are not changed by subtracting 0.00003, the value of sin $\frac{\pi}{4}$ to 3 significant digits is 0.707.

Exercises

1. Use the series to compute sin $\frac{\pi}{5}$ to 3 significant digits.

2. Use the series to compute cos $\frac{\pi}{8}$ to 3 significant digits.

3. Use the result of Problem **1** to find sin $\frac{4\pi}{5}$.

4. Use the result of Problem **2** to find cos $\frac{7\pi}{8}$.

5. Sketch the graphs of $y = \sin x$, $y = x$, and $y = x - \frac{x^3}{3!}$ in the same coordinate plane. Which of the latter two equations seems to be a better approximation for $y = \sin x$?

6. Repeat Problem **5** for $y = \cos x$, $y = 1 - \frac{x^2}{2!}$, and $y = 1 - \frac{x^2}{2!} + \frac{x^4}{4!}$.

Chapter Summary

1. If $0 \le \theta < 360°$ and θ is in standard position, then every point (x, y) in the plane can be described by (r, θ) where $x = r \cos \theta$, $y = r \sin \theta$, and $\theta - \arctan \frac{y}{x}$. (167)

2. Linear interpolation can be used to approximate trigonometric functions which are not listed in the tables. (165)

3. Law of Cosines is for any $\triangle ABC$, $a^2 = b^2 + c^2 - 2bc \cos A$. (175)

4. Law of Sines is for any $\triangle ABC$, $\dfrac{\sin A}{a} = \dfrac{\sin B}{b} = \dfrac{\sin C}{c}$. (175)

5. The area of $\triangle ABC$ can be found by the formula $\mathcal{A} = \frac{1}{2}bc \sin A$. (178)

6. The area of a sector of a circle can be found by one of the following formulas. (179)

$$\mathcal{A} = \frac{\theta}{360°}(\pi r^2) \text{ if } \theta \text{ is in degrees}$$

$$\mathcal{A} = \frac{1}{2}r^2\theta \text{ if } \theta \text{ is in radians}$$

7. The area of a segment of a circle can be found by $\mathcal{A} = \frac{1}{2}r^2(\theta - \sin \theta)$, where θ is in radians. (180)

8. The trigonometric form of $a + bi$ is $r(\cos \theta + i \sin \theta)$, where $\theta = \arctan \frac{b}{a}$. (183)

9. Given radii r_1 and r_2 and angles θ_1 and θ_2,
$r_1(\cos \theta + i \sin \theta) \cdot r_2(\cos \theta_2 + i \sin \theta_2) = r_1 r_2[\cos(\theta_1 + \theta_2) + i \sin(\theta_1 + \theta_2)]$. (184)

10. Given radii r_1 and r_2 and angles θ_1 and θ_2,
$\dfrac{r_1(\cos \theta_1 + i \sin \theta_1)}{r_2(\cos \theta_2 + i \sin \theta_2)} = \dfrac{r_1}{r_2}[\cos(\theta_1 - \theta_2) + i \sin(\theta_1 - \theta_2)]$. (184)

11. DeMoivre's Theorem states for all real numbers r, n, and θ, $[r(\cos \theta + i \sin \theta)]^n = r^n(\cos n\theta + i \sin n\theta)$. (187)

Chapter Review

6–1 **Find the degree measure of each of the following.**

1. $\dfrac{5\pi}{3}$

2. $\dfrac{\pi}{8}$

3. 2.5

Find the radian measure of each of the following.

4. $40°$

5. $135°$

6. $145°$

6-2 Find the value of each function to 4 significant digits.

    7. $\cos 46° 17'$ **8.** $\tan 32° 17'$

Find θ to the nearest minute.

    9. $\csc \theta = 1.633$ **10.** $\sin \theta = 0.2175$

6-3 Solve the right triangle ABC given each pair of measures with $m \angle C = 90°$.

    11. $c = 36.8; m \angle A = 28° 10'$ **12.** $m \angle B = 45°; a = 1.42$

    13. A chord of a circle is 4.82 units long. It makes an angle of 65° 40′ with a diameter at its endpoint. How long is the diameter of the circle?

6-4 Solve each of the following.

    14. An isosceles triangle has base angles which measure 48° 40′. The length of the base is 248. How long is each leg?

    15. A triangle has an angle which measures 55°, side opposite the angle which measures 48 cm, and another side which measures 62 cm. Solve the triangle.

    16. A surveyor measures the angle P between two sightings to points A and B at opposite ends of a pond. If $m \angle P = 74°$, $AP = 40$ m, and $PB = 72$ m, how far is it across the pond?

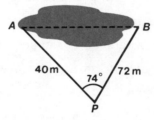

6-5   **17.** Find the area of a triangle if the lengths of its sides are 14, 16, and 18 cm.

    18. Find the area of a sector with radius 10.8 m and central angle of 36°.

6-6   **19.** Two pulleys have radii of 5 in. and 3 in. They are connected by a belt as shown. If the smaller pulley is turning at 75 revolutions per minute, what is the angular velocity of the larger pulley?

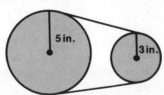

6-7   **20.** Find the product of $3\left(\cos \dfrac{5\pi}{6} + i \sin \dfrac{5\pi}{6}\right)$ and $8\left(\cos \dfrac{2\pi}{3} + i \sin \dfrac{2\pi}{3}\right)$.

6-8 Find each of the following.

    21. $(2 - 2\sqrt{3}i)^4$ **22.** The fourth roots of i

Chapter Test

Find the degree measure of each of the following.

1. $\dfrac{\pi}{4}$

2. $-\dfrac{7\pi}{8}$

3. 4

Find the radian measure of each of the following.

4. $-180°$

5. $30°$

6. $-75°$

Find the value of each function to 4 significant digits.

7. $\cos 37° \, 10'$

8. $\sin 78° \, 15'$

Find θ to the nearest minute.

9. $\cot \theta = 0.5022$

10. $\cos \theta = 0.5628$

Solve the right triangle ABC given each pair of measures.

11. $m \angle B = 37° \, 10'; \; c = 4$

12. $a = 125; \; b = 200$

13. Two forces of 25 kg and 37 kg have a resultant of 60 kg. Find the size of the angle between the forces.

Find the area of each of the following.

14. A triangle with $m \angle A = 45°$, $b = 10$, and $c = 8$.

15. A sector of a circle with $r = 10$ cm and $\theta = 64°$.

Solve each of the following.

16. A car with wheels 15 in. in diameter travels 55 mph. How fast are the wheels turning?

17. The minute hand of a town clock is 2 m long. How fast is the tip of the hand moving in meters per minute?

18. Solve $z^3 = (9 + 9i)^2$ for z over $\mathcal{C}$.

Computers

Machine Languages

Before modern computer languages such as ALGOL, FORTRAN, BASIC, COBOL, PL/1, and PASCAL were developed and standardized, it was necessary to communicate with a computer in fundamental numeric code. The computer programmer had to reserve various addresses for locations of constants and variables, to manipulate them in prescribed ways, and to store the results where needed. In addition, each step of a program carried an address and was available to be reused later in the program. Such fundamental programs were written in what is referred to as "machine language." The designer of each machine designs the machine language needed. This language uses a code that the computer can interpret. Machine language is inconvenient since it requires a complete knowledge of computers. Symbolic languages were developed to help the programmer. One type of symbolic language is "assembly language." Assembly language uses mnemonic devices for the codes of machine language.

Certain fundamental instructions have been identified and given alphabetical codes. Thus, LDA 1401 may mean "load the accumulator with the number stored in address 1401," ADD 1500 may mean "add to the number in the accumulator that number stored in address 1500," and STO 1501 may mean "store the number in the accumulator in address 1505."

An assembly language cannot be directly used by a computer. A special program called the assembler is needed to translate other languages into a form the machine can use. These other languages are called higher-level language and are relatively machine-independent. The source program deck is the main input to the assembly process. When all statements have been converted, an assembly listing and object program are produced. The object program consists of actual machine code corre-

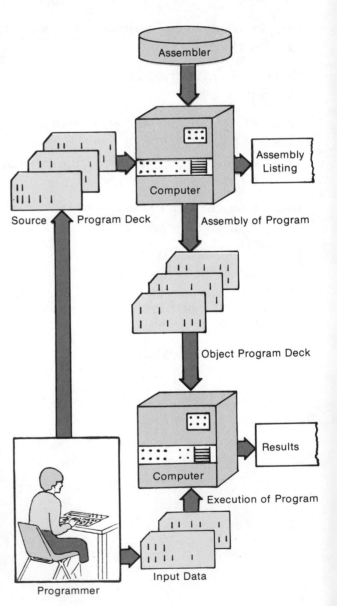

Assembler

Source — Program Deck

Computer

Assembly Listing

Assembly of Program

Object Program Deck

Computer

Results

Execution of Program

Input Data

Programmer

This is an example of machine language instruction.

**Operation
Code   Operand Number 1   Operand Number 2**

| 011100 | 010 000 010 000 000 | 101 110 100 010 010 |

Addition   Location 1   Location 2

Add the operand in location 1 to the operand in location 2.

---

sponding to the assembler language statements written by the programmer. Unlike the assembly languages and the machine languages, higher-level languages relate to the problem being programmed and thus become machine-independent. Each program written in a higher-level language needs a compiler to translate the program into the basic language of the computer being used. The compiler works in much the same way as the assembler works. The ease in learning and using these languages make them more desirable for the programmer.

Through the use of a terminal or by coding the program on the proper form, the user can run programs and produce answers with little effort.

Exercises   Write a program for each of the following. Use 3.1416 as P to stand for the value of π.

1. Given a degree measure, determine the radian measure. Arrange the output as a table. Use increments of 1° from 0° to 180°.

2. Given a radian measure, determine the degree measure. Arrange the output as a table. Use increments of 0.01 from 0 to 2.

3. Given the length of one side of a triangle and the measures of two angles neither of which is opposite the given side, find the remaining measures of the triangle using the Law of Sines.

4. Given the measure of one angle and the length of two sides neither of which is opposite to the given angle, find the remaining measures of the triangle using the Law of Sines.

5. Given two sides of a triangle and their included angle (SAS), find the area of the triangle using $a = \frac{1}{2} bc \sin A$.

6. Given a central angle θ, find the sector area. $a = \frac{1}{2}r^2\theta$ and the segment area $a = \frac{1}{2}r^2 (\theta - \sin \theta)$.

Note: In BASIC there is no built-in function for Arcsine or Arccosine. Find SIN(X) and COS(X) [the expression SQR(1 − SIN(X)↑2) may be used for COS(X)]. Then use ATN(Y/Z) where Y is the value of SIN(X) and Z is the value of COS(X). All angle measures are to be expressed in radians.

Chapter 7

One of the more important applications of vectors in physics is that of work. Work is the product of the scalar component of some force in a given direction and the distance the object moves. The higher an elevator rises, the greater the work needed to raise it.

Vectors in the Plane

7-1 Arrows and Vectors

On the number line a directed distance is uniquely represented by a single real number. The sign of the number defines direction and the absolute value of the number defines distance. In the coordinate plane, an ordered pair of numbers is used to determine uniquely a directed distance. To distinguish such an ordered pair from an ordered pair representing a point in the plane, it is written in vertical form as $\begin{pmatrix} a \\ b \end{pmatrix}$. This ordered pair is associated with a directed distance corresponding to an arrow whose terminal point is a units in the horizontal direction and b units in the vertical direction from its initial point.

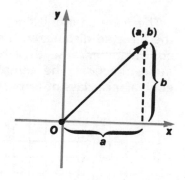

An *arrow* from A to B is different from the ray $\overrightarrow{AB}$. The ray has its initial point at A, extends through B and does not terminate. The arrow terminates at B and is symbolized as $\overrightarrow{AB}$.

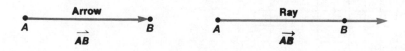

If $\overrightarrow{AB}$ is an arrow, A is the point (x_1, y_1) and B is the point (x_2, y_2), then the **directed distance** of $\overrightarrow{AB}$ is associated with $\begin{pmatrix} x_2 - x_1 \\ y_2 - y_1 \end{pmatrix}$.

Example

1. **Determine the directed distance of $\overrightarrow{AB}$ given the points $A(3, -2)$ and $B(1, 4)$.**

$$\begin{pmatrix} x_2 - x_1 \\ y_w - y_1 \end{pmatrix} = \begin{pmatrix} 1 - 3 \\ 4 - (-2) \end{pmatrix}$$
$$= \begin{pmatrix} -2 \\ 6 \end{pmatrix}$$

The slopes of $\overrightarrow{AB}$ and $\overrightarrow{BA}$ are the same but $\overrightarrow{BA}$ has opposite direction. The directed distance of $\overrightarrow{BA}$ is associated with $\begin{pmatrix} 2 \\ -6 \end{pmatrix}$.

To find the distance, use the distance formula.

$$\sqrt{(1 - 3)^2 + (4 - (-2))^2} = \sqrt{4 + 36}$$
$$= \sqrt{40}$$
$$= 2\sqrt{10}.$$

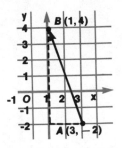

The directed distance is $2\sqrt{10}$.

There are an infinite number of arrows which correspond to the directed distance in the example above. These arrows are equivalent because they have the same magnitude and the same direction. The complete family of arrows is called an **equivalence class of arrows.**

Another example of an equivalence class is the set of fractions which names a particular rational number. The numbers $\frac{2}{4}, \frac{3}{6}, \frac{9}{18}, 0.5, \frac{100}{200}, \cdots$ belong to the same equivalence class. All can be represented by $\frac{1}{2}$. This fraction is the standard representative of the given set of fractions.

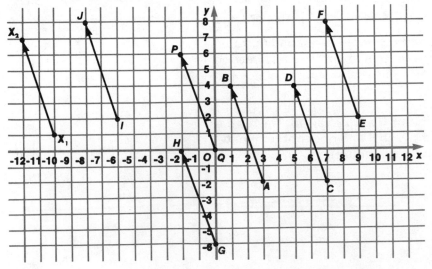

The entire equivalence class of arrows to which $\overrightarrow{AB}$ belongs is called a **vector.** Often vectors are denoted by small boldface letters such as $\mathbf{\overline{u}}, \mathbf{\overline{v}},$ and $\mathbf{\overline{w}}$.

Two vectors are equal if and only if they contain the same set of arrows.

Equal Vectors

The **magnitude** or length of a vector is the length of each arrow of the vector. The **direction** of a vector is the direction of each arrow of the vector. Any member of an equivalence class may be chosen as a representative of the entire class. It is customary to use the term *vector* when using any particular arrow of the class. In many cases, the best representative of the vector is the arrow with initial point at the origin. Such an arrow is in *standard position* and is called a **position vector.**

Different vectors have different magnitude or different directions or both.

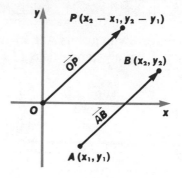

A **unit vector** is defined for each direction and has a length of 1 unit. The **zero vector** or **null vector** is considered to have any direction and has length zero.

Unit and Zero Vectors

It may appear strange to give the zero vector any direction rather than no direction. Since vectors are defined to have both magnitude and direction, this convention is appropriate. The zero vector is denoted $\overline{0}$. Its geometric representation is a single point.

The *opposite* of a vector $\overline{v}$ (written $-\overline{v}$) is the vector consisting of the class of arrows having the same slope and length as the arrows of $\overline{v}$, but with the opposite direction.

Opposite Vectors

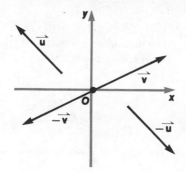

Two vectors are parallel if and only if they have the same or opposite direction.

Parallel Vectors

Thus, the vector $\vec{0}$ is parallel to every vector.

Example

2. Given points $A(3, 2)$ and $B(2, 5)$, name the position vector which represents the equivalence class of arrows $\overline{AB}$.

$$\binom{x_2 - x_1}{y_2 - y_1} = \binom{2 - 3}{5 - 2}$$

$$= \binom{-1}{3}$$

Thus, the equivalence class is represented by the vector with directed distance $\binom{-1}{3}$.

Exercises

Exploratory Name the ordered pair of the equivalence class to which the arrow described below belongs.

1. initial point, (0, 0); terminal point, (3, 5)
2. initial point, (0, 0); terminal point, (−2, 4)
3. initial point, (2, 2); terminal point, (5, −4)
4. initial point, (4, 0); terminal point (−4, 3)

Consider the triangle formed by the three points $A(3, 2)$, $B(5, -2)$, and $C(1, -2)$. Name the equivalence class of arrows associated with each of the following.

5. $\overrightarrow{AB}$
6. $\overrightarrow{BC}$
7. $\overrightarrow{AC}$
8. $\overrightarrow{BA}$
9. $\overrightarrow{CB}$
10. $\overrightarrow{CA}$

11. Complete the sentence: If the arrow $\overrightarrow{PQ}$ is associated with the equivalence class of arrows named by the ordered pair, $\binom{x_1}{y_1}$, then $\overrightarrow{QP}$ is associated with the ordered pair $\left(\dfrac{?}{?}\right)$.

Use the figures below to solve each of the following.

12. In parallelogram $ABCD$, the diagonals meet at P. List as many pairs of equal and opposite vectors as you can, using points A, B, C, D and P.

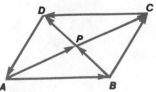

13. In $\triangle ABC$, D, E and F are midpoints of the sides. List as many equal and opposite vectors as possible.

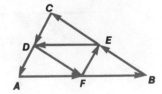

Written The ordered pair given characterizes the equivalence class of arrows. Write the ordered pair which names the initial point or the terminal point as appropriate.

Equivalence Class	Initial Point	Terminal Point		Equivalence Class	Initial Point	Terminal Point
1. $\begin{pmatrix} 2 \\ 5 \end{pmatrix}$	(3, 2)	(_?_, _?_)	2.	$\begin{pmatrix} 2 \\ -1 \end{pmatrix}$	(−2, 1)	(_?_, _?_)
3. $\begin{pmatrix} -3 \\ 4 \end{pmatrix}$	(5, −2)	(_?_, _?_)	4.	$\begin{pmatrix} 4 \\ 2 \end{pmatrix}$	(_?_, _?_)	(6, −3)
5. $\begin{pmatrix} -1 \\ -4 \end{pmatrix}$	(_?_, _?_)	(−5, −2)	6.	$\begin{pmatrix} 5 \\ -1 \end{pmatrix}$	(_?_, _?_)	(0, 0)
7. $\begin{pmatrix} a \\ b \end{pmatrix}$	(3, −4)	(_?_, _?_)	8.	$\begin{pmatrix} a \\ b \end{pmatrix}$	(_?_, _?_)	(−2, 6)

Point A is (5, 2) and B is (−3, 3). For the given point C, find the point D such that $\overrightarrow{AB}$ and $\overrightarrow{CD}$ belong to the same equivalence class.

9. $C(2, 2)$ 10. $C(-4, 3)$ 11. $C(5, -2)$

12. $C(-3, 3)$ 13. $C(0, 0)$ 14. $C(a, b)$

Given A and B, name the position vector which represents the equivalence class of arrows $\overrightarrow{AB}$ by naming its <u>terminal point</u>.

15. $A(3, 2)$, $B(2, 5)$ 16. $A(2, 5)$, $B(3, 2)$

17. $A(-3, 4)$, $B(-5, -2)$ $(-2, -6)$ 18. $A(0, 0)$, $B(3, -7)$

19. $A(a_1, a_2)$, $B(b_1, b_2)$

The vector $\overrightarrow{PQ}$ is represented by an arrow from (−2, 5) to (3, −1). Write $\overrightarrow{PQ}$, $-\overrightarrow{PQ}$ or *Neither* to describe whether each vector $\overrightarrow{RS}$ is equal to $\overrightarrow{PQ}$, the opposite of $\overrightarrow{PQ}$, or neither.

20. $R(2, 6)$, $S(7, 0)$ 21. $R(3, 1)$, $S(8, 5)$ 22. $R(-2, 4)$, $S(-7, 10)$

23. $R(-4, -4)$, $S(-9, 2)$ 24. $R(3, -1)$, $S(8, -7)$ 25. $R(-5, 6)$, $S(0, 0)$

For each vector $\overrightarrow{AB}$, write the coordinates of the point X for which $\overrightarrow{OX}$ is the position vector opposite to $\overrightarrow{AB}$.

26. $A(-4, 2)$, $B(3, 5)$ 27. $A(-3, 0)$, $B(0, -3)$

28. $A(a, b)$, $B(c, d)$ 29. $A(-3, -6)$, $B(0, 0)$

7–2 Addition and Scalar Multiplication

Physicists and other scientists have given the name vector to quantities which have *both* magnitude and direction. The arithmetic of such quantities differs from ordinary arithmetic. For example, the sum of two vectors is not, in general, a vector with direction and magnitude equal to the sums of the two directions and magnitudes. A boat ride of 3 miles east followed by one of 4 miles south does not result in the boat being 7 miles from its place of origin. Rather it is 5 miles away and in a direction southeast from its starting point.

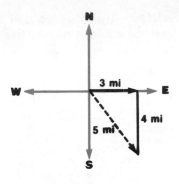

If two vectors are not parallel their sum must account for combining both magnitudes and directions. Analysis of physical situations leads to a geometric interpretation of the sum of two vectors, for which the sum of two parallel vectors is a special case.

> The sum of two vectors **ū** and **v̄** is the vector represented by the diagonal of a parallelogram. The position vectors of **ū** and **v̄** are adjacent sides of the parallelogram.

The Sum of Vectors

The sum of two vectors is referred to as their resultant.

Example

1. Show the sum of **ū** + **v̄** by a vector parallelogram.

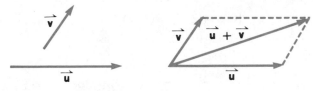

Often two vectors are added *tail-to-head*. The sum is represented by the third side of the *vector triangle*. This method is useful especially when adding three or more vectors.

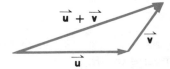

Example

2. Show the sum of **ū** + **v̄** + **w̄** + **x̄** geometrically.

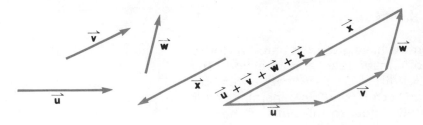

The **difference** of two vectors $\vec{u}$ and $\vec{v}$, (written, $\vec{u} - \vec{v}$), is $\vec{u} + (-\vec{v})$.

The Difference of Vectors

Example

3. **Show the difference of $\vec{u} - \vec{v}$ by a vector triangle.**

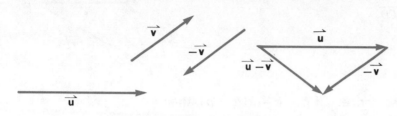

Vectors can be added tail-to-head around a polygon until the starting vertex is reached. The resultant vector is $\vec{0}$. This technique also is used to show that alternate paths from one point to another are equivalent.

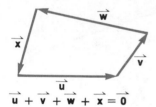

$$\vec{u} + \vec{v} + \vec{w} + \vec{x} = \vec{0}$$

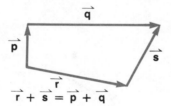

$$\vec{r} + \vec{s} = \vec{p} + \vec{q}$$

Let $k \in \mathcal{R}$ and $\vec{v} = \begin{pmatrix} a \\ b \end{pmatrix}$ be a vector, then $k\vec{v}$ is defined to be $\begin{pmatrix} ka \\ kb \end{pmatrix}$. The number k is called a **scalar** and $k\vec{v}$ is called a *scalar multiple* of $\vec{v}$.

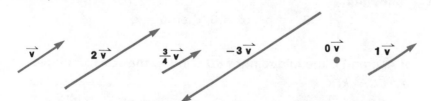

If a vector is multiplied by a positive real number, the vector is stretched or compressed. If the multiplier is *greater than one*, the vector is *stretched*. If it is *less than one*, a shrinking of the vector occurs. If the multiplier is *negative*, then the new vector has direction *opposite* to that of the original vector.

Exercises

Exploratory Consider □$ABCD$ with diagonals $\overline{AC}$ and $\overline{BD}$. $\overline{DAE}$ is a straight line. Name the simplest vector in terms of $\vec{u}$, $\vec{v}$, $\vec{w}$ or $\vec{y}$ or their opposites for each expression.

1. $\overrightarrow{MC}$
2. $\overrightarrow{BC}$
3. $\overrightarrow{CD}$
4. $\overrightarrow{DM}$
5. $\overrightarrow{AC}$
6. $\overrightarrow{EB}$
7. $\overrightarrow{AB} + \overrightarrow{BC}$
8. $\overrightarrow{AD} + \overrightarrow{AB}$
9. $\overrightarrow{AB} - \overrightarrow{DA}$
10. $\vec{w} - \vec{y}$
11. $\overrightarrow{AD} + \overrightarrow{AE}$
12. $\vec{v} + \vec{u} - 2\vec{w}$
13. $\overrightarrow{AE} + \overrightarrow{EB} + \overrightarrow{BM} + \overrightarrow{MC} + \overrightarrow{CD}$
14. $2\vec{y} + \vec{w} - \vec{u}$
15. $2\vec{w} - \vec{u} + 2\vec{y}$

16. Copy and complete this sentence: If $\vec{p} - \vec{q} = k(\vec{q} - \vec{p})$, then $k = \underline{\ ?\ }$ when $\vec{p} \neq \vec{q}$.
17. If $\vec{p} + \vec{q} = \vec{0}$, then _____. Explain your answer.

Written Copy each figure. Show the sums $\vec{u} + \vec{v}$ and $\vec{v} + \vec{u}$ by vector parallelograms. Compare the results.

1.

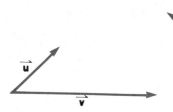

2.

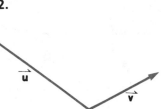

3.

4.–6. Using the vectors in Problems **1–3**, find the vector differences $\vec{u} - \vec{v}$ and $\vec{v} - \vec{u}$. Compare the results.

Show geometrically each of the following.

7. $-(\vec{p} + \vec{q}) = (-\vec{p}) + (-\vec{q})$

8. If $\vec{p} - \vec{q} = \vec{0}$, then $\vec{p} = \vec{q}$

In the figure, B is the midpoint of $\overline{AD}$, and C the midpoint of $\overline{BD}$. Find k, the scalar multiple.

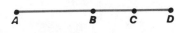

9. $\overrightarrow{AC} = k\overrightarrow{BC}$
10. $\overrightarrow{BC} = k\overrightarrow{DC}$
11. $\overrightarrow{DB} = k\overrightarrow{AC}$
12. $\overrightarrow{CA} = k\overrightarrow{BD}$

Given three points $A(3, 2)$, $B(5, -3)$, and $C(-2, 0)$, find each of the following.

13. $\overrightarrow{AB}$
14. $\overrightarrow{BC}$
15. $\overrightarrow{AC}$
16. $\overrightarrow{AB} + \overrightarrow{BC}$
17. $\overrightarrow{AB} + \overrightarrow{BC} + \overrightarrow{CA}$

For the vector $\vec{v}$ and scalar k, write the coordinates of the vector $k\vec{v}$.

18. $\begin{pmatrix} 2 \\ -5 \end{pmatrix}$, 3

19. $\begin{pmatrix} -1 \\ 3 \end{pmatrix}$, -2

20. $\begin{pmatrix} 6 \\ -10 \end{pmatrix}$, $-\dfrac{3}{2}$

21. $\begin{pmatrix} a \\ b \end{pmatrix}$, 7

22. $\begin{pmatrix} 0 \\ 0 \end{pmatrix}$, $-\dfrac{3}{5}$

23. $\begin{pmatrix} -6 \\ 5 \end{pmatrix}$, 0

24. $\begin{pmatrix} -5 \\ 4 \end{pmatrix}$, 1

25. $\begin{pmatrix} a \\ b \end{pmatrix}$, c

Prove each of the following.

26. The product of zero and any vector is $\vec{0}$.

27. $ABCD$ is a parallelogram if and only if $\overrightarrow{AB} + \overrightarrow{CD} = \vec{0}$.

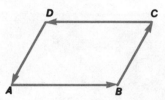

Show geometrically each of the following.

28. $m(n\vec{p}) = mn(\vec{p})$, where $\vec{p}$ is a vector and m and n are scalars

29. $(m + n)\vec{p} = m\vec{p} + n\vec{p}$, where $\vec{p}$ is a vector and m and n are scalars

Challenge In quadrilateral $PQRS$, N is the midpoint of $\overline{SQ}$, and M is the midpoint of $\overline{PR}$.

1. Write sums from the vector diagram shown to develop the relationship $4\overrightarrow{MN} = \overrightarrow{PQ} + \overrightarrow{RQ} + \overrightarrow{PS} + \overrightarrow{RS}$.

2. Determine if $4\overrightarrow{MN} = \overrightarrow{PQ} + \overrightarrow{RQ} + \overrightarrow{PS} + \overrightarrow{RS}$ is true for any four coplanar points P, Q, R, and S such as those given in the figure.

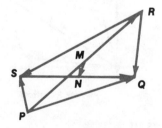

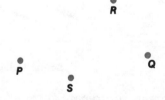

3. Show geometrically that vector addition is associative: $(\vec{a} + \vec{b}) + \vec{c} = \vec{a} + (\vec{b} + \vec{c})$. Complete the diagram.

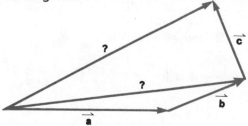

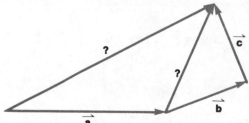

7-3 Vector Coordinates

Each arrow of a vector can be represented by the same ordered pair $\begin{pmatrix} a \\ b \end{pmatrix}$. Such an ordered pair often is used to represent the vector itself.

The various geometric properties already developed can be written in terms of **vector coordinates**.

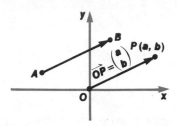

For $a, b, c, d, \ldots, k \in \mathcal{R}$, $\vec{v} = \begin{pmatrix} a \\ b \end{pmatrix}$, $\vec{u} = \begin{pmatrix} c \\ d \end{pmatrix}$.

Zero Vector: $\vec{0} = \begin{pmatrix} 0 \\ 0 \end{pmatrix}$

Opposite Vector: If $\vec{v} = \begin{pmatrix} a \\ b \end{pmatrix}$, then $-\vec{v} = \begin{pmatrix} -a \\ -b \end{pmatrix}$.

Scalar Multiple: If $\vec{v} = \begin{pmatrix} a \\ b \end{pmatrix}$, then $k\vec{v} = \begin{pmatrix} ka \\ kb \end{pmatrix}$.

Vector Addition: If $\vec{u} = \begin{pmatrix} a \\ b \end{pmatrix}$ and $\vec{v} = \begin{pmatrix} c \\ d \end{pmatrix}$,

then $\vec{u} + \vec{v} = \begin{pmatrix} a + c \\ b + d \end{pmatrix}$.

Vector Equality: $\vec{v} = \vec{u}$ if and only if $a = c$ and $b = d$.

Properties of Vectors

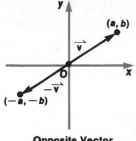

Opposite Vector

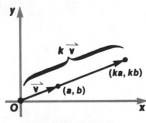

Scalar Multiple

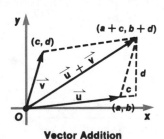

Vector Addition

Considering vectors in coordinate form allows properties of real numbers to suggest properties of vectors.

Examples

1. If $\vec{v} = \begin{pmatrix} 3 \\ -2 \end{pmatrix}$ and $\vec{u} = \begin{pmatrix} -5 \\ 4 \end{pmatrix}$, find $\vec{v} + \vec{u}$, $\vec{v} - \vec{u}$, and $3\vec{v} - 2\vec{u}$.

$$\vec{v} + \vec{u} = \begin{pmatrix} 3 \\ -2 \end{pmatrix} + \begin{pmatrix} -5 \\ 4 \end{pmatrix} = \begin{pmatrix} -2 \\ 2 \end{pmatrix} \qquad \vec{v} - \vec{u} = \begin{pmatrix} 3 \\ -2 \end{pmatrix} - \begin{pmatrix} -5 \\ 4 \end{pmatrix} = \begin{pmatrix} 8 \\ -6 \end{pmatrix}$$

$$3\vec{v} - 2\vec{u} = 3\begin{pmatrix} 3 \\ -2 \end{pmatrix} + (-2)\begin{pmatrix} -5 \\ 4 \end{pmatrix} = \begin{pmatrix} 9 \\ -6 \end{pmatrix} + \begin{pmatrix} 10 \\ -8 \end{pmatrix} = \begin{pmatrix} 19 \\ -14 \end{pmatrix}$$

2. Find r and s such that $r\vec{v} + s\vec{u} = \begin{pmatrix} 13 \\ -10 \end{pmatrix}$ when $\vec{v} = \begin{pmatrix} 3 \\ -2 \end{pmatrix}$ and $\vec{u} = \begin{pmatrix} -5 \\ 4 \end{pmatrix}$.

$$\begin{pmatrix} 3r \\ -2r \end{pmatrix} + \begin{pmatrix} -5s \\ 4s \end{pmatrix} = \begin{pmatrix} 13 \\ -10 \end{pmatrix}$$

$$\begin{array}{rl} 3r - 5s &= 13 \\ -2r + 4s &= -10 \\ \hline 6r - 10s &= 26 \\ -6r + 12s &= -30 \\ \hline 2s &= -4 \\ s &= -2 \end{array}$$

Multiply by 2.
Multiply by 3.
Add

$$\begin{array}{rl} 3r - 5(-2) &= 13 \\ 3r &= 3 \\ r &= 1 \end{array}$$

Substitute

Exercises

Exploratory Find $\vec{v} + \vec{u}$, $\vec{v} - \vec{u}$, and $r\vec{v} + s\vec{u}$ for each of the following.

1. $\vec{v} = \begin{pmatrix} 4 \\ 3 \end{pmatrix}$, $\vec{u} = \begin{pmatrix} 1 \\ -1 \end{pmatrix}$, $r = 1$, $s = 1$

2. $\vec{v} = \begin{pmatrix} 5 \\ -2 \end{pmatrix}$, $\vec{u} = \begin{pmatrix} -2 \\ 3 \end{pmatrix}$, $r = 3$, $s = -4$

3. $\vec{v} = \begin{pmatrix} 6 \\ -4 \end{pmatrix}$, $\vec{u} = \begin{pmatrix} 7 \\ 5 \end{pmatrix}$, $r = \frac{1}{2}$, $s = 0$

4. $\vec{v} = \begin{pmatrix} 3 \\ 8 \end{pmatrix}$, $\vec{u} = \begin{pmatrix} 2 \\ -3 \end{pmatrix}$, $r = 1$, $s = -1$

5. $\vec{v} = \begin{pmatrix} 4 \\ 9 \end{pmatrix}$, $\vec{u} = \begin{pmatrix} -3 \\ 4 \end{pmatrix}$, $r = a$, $s = a$

6. $\vec{v} = \begin{pmatrix} \sqrt{2} \\ \sqrt{3} \end{pmatrix}$, $\vec{u} = \begin{pmatrix} 3\sqrt{2} \\ 5 \end{pmatrix}$, $r = \sqrt{2}$, $s = \frac{\sqrt{3}}{3}$

Determine values for r and s which make each sentence true.

7. $\begin{pmatrix} 3 \\ -5 \end{pmatrix} + \begin{pmatrix} r \\ s \end{pmatrix} = \begin{pmatrix} 0 \\ 0 \end{pmatrix}$

8. $\begin{pmatrix} 2 \\ -4 \end{pmatrix} + \begin{pmatrix} r \\ s \end{pmatrix} = \begin{pmatrix} 6 \\ -3 \end{pmatrix}$

9. $\begin{pmatrix} -3 \\ 7 \end{pmatrix} + \begin{pmatrix} r \\ 6 \end{pmatrix} = \begin{pmatrix} -5 \\ s \end{pmatrix}$

10. $\begin{pmatrix} 4 \\ -6 \end{pmatrix} + \begin{pmatrix} r \\ s \end{pmatrix} = \begin{pmatrix} -4 \\ 6 \end{pmatrix}$

Written If $\vec{v} = \begin{pmatrix} 4 \\ -2 \end{pmatrix}$ and $\vec{u} = \begin{pmatrix} -3 \\ 5 \end{pmatrix}$, find each of the following.

1. $\vec{v} + \vec{u}$

2. $\vec{v} - \vec{u}$

3. $\vec{u} - \vec{v}$

4. $\frac{1}{2}\vec{v} + \frac{1}{3}\vec{u}$

5. $-3(\vec{v} + \vec{u})$

6. $2\vec{v} - 4\vec{u}$

Let $\vec{a} = \begin{pmatrix} 1 \\ 0 \end{pmatrix}$ and $\vec{b} = \begin{pmatrix} 0 \\ 1 \end{pmatrix}$. Determine r and s such that $r\vec{a} + s\vec{b} = \vec{v}$.

7. $\vec{v} = \begin{pmatrix} 3 \\ 5 \end{pmatrix}$

8. $\vec{v} = \begin{pmatrix} -2 \\ -1 \end{pmatrix}$

9. $\vec{v} = \begin{pmatrix} \frac{2}{3} \\ -\frac{4}{5} \end{pmatrix}$

10. $\vec{v} = \begin{pmatrix} 1 \\ 1 \end{pmatrix}$ **11.** $\vec{v} = \begin{pmatrix} 0 \\ 0 \end{pmatrix}$ **12.** $\vec{v} = \begin{pmatrix} m \\ n \end{pmatrix}$

Find r and s for each of the following.

13. $\vec{v} = \begin{pmatrix} 3 \\ -5 \end{pmatrix}$ and $\vec{u} = \begin{pmatrix} -1 \\ 4 \end{pmatrix}$

$$r\vec{v} + s\vec{u} = \begin{pmatrix} 7 \\ -7 \end{pmatrix}$$

14. $\vec{v} = \begin{pmatrix} 4 \\ 9 \end{pmatrix}$ and $\vec{u} = \begin{pmatrix} -5 \\ 6 \end{pmatrix}$

$$r\vec{v} + s\vec{u} = \begin{pmatrix} -\dfrac{13}{12} \\ 15 \end{pmatrix}$$

7–4 The Vector System

Many mathematical systems can be defined such as the real number system ($\mathcal{R}$), the complex number system ($\mathcal{C}$) and an even more abstract system called a field ($\mathcal{F}$). In a similar manner, a system of vectors may be defined and its properties studied.

The system of vectors is symbolized as $\mathcal{V}$. In the two-dimensional system $\mathcal{V}_2$, members (vectors) are identified as $\vec{v} = \begin{pmatrix} a \\ b \end{pmatrix}$ for $a, b, \in \mathcal{R}$. Two operations, *addition* and *scalar multiplication*, are defined.

A vector space ($\mathcal{V}$) is a mathematical system which consists of a nonempty set $\mathcal{V}$ of ordered pairs, a nonempty set S of scalars, an equivalence relation =, and two binary operations, addition and scalar multiplication. The operations are defined on $\mathcal{V}$ and satisfy the following properties.

Vector Properties

AV_1: Closure $\vec{u} + \vec{v} \in \mathcal{V}$
AV_2: Associativity $(\vec{u} + \vec{v}) + \vec{w} = \vec{u} + (\vec{v} + \vec{w})$
AV_3: Additive Identity There is an element $\vec{0} = \begin{pmatrix} 0 \\ 0 \end{pmatrix}$ $\in \mathcal{V}$ such that $\vec{v} + \vec{0} = \vec{0} + \vec{v} = \vec{v}$.
AV_4: Additive Inverse There is an element $-\vec{v}$ in $\mathcal{V}$ such that $\vec{v} + (-\vec{v}) = (-\vec{v}) + \vec{v} = \vec{0}$
AV_5: Commutativity $\vec{u} + \vec{v} = \vec{v} + \vec{u}$

Properties of Addition

SMV_1: Closure $k\vec{v} \in \mathcal{V}$
SMV_2: $k_1(k_2\vec{v}) = (k_1 k_2)\vec{v}$
SMV_3: $1\vec{v} = \vec{v}$
SMV_4: $-1\vec{v} = -\vec{v}$
SMV_5: $0\vec{v} = \vec{0}$
SMV_6: $k\vec{0} = \vec{0}$

Properties of Scalar Multiplication

DV_1: $k(\vec{v} + \vec{u}) = k\vec{v} + k\vec{u}$
DV_2: $(k_1 + k_2)\vec{v} = k_1\vec{v} + k_2\vec{v}$

Distributive Properties

Properties $AV_1 - AV_5$ are those of a commutative (or Abelian) group which also is an important mathematical system. Thus a vector space is a commutative group under addition also satisfying $SMV_1 - SMV_6$ and $DV_1 - DV_2$.

Vector properties can be verified for addition and multiplication by using the properties of real numbers.

Examples

1. **Prove property AV_3:** $\vec{v} + \vec{0} = \vec{0} + \vec{v} = \vec{v}$

   Proof

   I. 1. Let $\vec{v} = \begin{pmatrix} a \\ b \end{pmatrix}$.   *Definition of vector*

       2. $\vec{v} + \vec{0} = \begin{pmatrix} a \\ b \end{pmatrix} + \begin{pmatrix} 0 \\ 0 \end{pmatrix}$ *Uniqueness of $+$*

       3. $\vec{v} + \vec{0} = \begin{pmatrix} a + 0 \\ b + 0 \end{pmatrix}$ *Definition of vector addition*

       4. $\vec{v} + \vec{0} = \begin{pmatrix} a \\ b \end{pmatrix}$ A_3

       5. $\vec{v} + \vec{0} = \vec{v}$ $E_2\ E_3$

   II. Similarly, $\vec{0} + \vec{v} = \vec{v}$.

   III. *Uniqueness*: Suppose there is another identity element $\vec{0}'$ such that $\vec{v} + \vec{0}' = \vec{v}$.

       1. $\vec{v} + \vec{0}' = \vec{v}$ *Assumption*

       2. $\vec{0} + \vec{0}' = \vec{0}' + \vec{0}$ AV_5

       3. $\vec{0} + \vec{0}' = \vec{0}$ *Assumption*

       4. $\vec{0}' + \vec{0} = \vec{0}'$ AV_3

       5. $\vec{0} = \vec{0}'$ $E_2,\ E_3$

2. **Prove property DV_1:** $k(\vec{v} + \vec{u}) = k\vec{v} + k\vec{u}$

   Proof

   1. Let $\vec{v} = \begin{pmatrix} a \\ b \end{pmatrix}, \vec{u} = \begin{pmatrix} c \\ d \end{pmatrix}$.   *Definition of vector*

   2. $k(\vec{v} + \vec{u}) = k\begin{pmatrix} a + c \\ b + d \end{pmatrix}$ *Definition of vector addition*

   3. $k(\vec{v} + \vec{u}) = \begin{pmatrix} k(a + c) \\ k(b + d) \end{pmatrix}$ *Definition of scalar multiplication*

   4. $k(\vec{v} + \vec{u}) = \begin{pmatrix} ka + kc \\ kb + kd \end{pmatrix}$ *Distributive Property*

   5. $k(\vec{v} + \vec{u}) = \begin{pmatrix} ka \\ kb \end{pmatrix} + \begin{pmatrix} kc \\ kd \end{pmatrix}$ *Definition of vector addition*

   6. $k(\vec{v} + \vec{u}) = k\begin{pmatrix} a \\ b \end{pmatrix} + k\begin{pmatrix} c \\ d \end{pmatrix}$ *Definition of scalar multiplication*

   7. $k(\vec{v} + \vec{u}) = k\vec{v} + k\vec{u}$ *Definition of vector*

Exercises

Exploratory Name the property illustrated by each of the following.

1. $\begin{pmatrix} 1 \\ 2 \end{pmatrix} + \begin{pmatrix} -1 \\ -2 \end{pmatrix} = \vec{0}$

2. $\begin{pmatrix} -32 \\ 16 \end{pmatrix} + \begin{pmatrix} 8 \\ 4 \end{pmatrix} = \begin{pmatrix} -40 \\ 20 \end{pmatrix}$

3. $\begin{pmatrix} -1 \\ -4 \end{pmatrix} + \begin{pmatrix} 3 \\ -2 \end{pmatrix} = \begin{pmatrix} 3 \\ -2 \end{pmatrix} + \begin{pmatrix} -1 \\ -4 \end{pmatrix}$

4. $2\begin{pmatrix} 6 \\ -9 \end{pmatrix} = 6\begin{pmatrix} 2 \\ -3 \end{pmatrix}$

5. $3\left[\begin{pmatrix} 3 \\ 6 \end{pmatrix} + \begin{pmatrix} 3 \\ 4 \end{pmatrix}\right] = \begin{pmatrix} 9 \\ 18 \end{pmatrix} + \begin{pmatrix} 9 \\ 12 \end{pmatrix}$

6. $7\begin{pmatrix} 0 \\ 0 \end{pmatrix} = \begin{pmatrix} 0 \\ 0 \end{pmatrix}$

Written Prove the following properties of a Vector Two-Space. Use $k, k_1, k_2 \in \mathcal{R}$ for scalars and $\vec{v} = \begin{pmatrix} a \\ b \end{pmatrix}$ and $\vec{u} = \begin{pmatrix} c \\ d \end{pmatrix}$ as vectors.

1. Property AV_4: $\vec{v} + (-\vec{v}) = (-\vec{v}) + \vec{v} = \vec{0}$

2. Property SMV_1: $k\vec{v} \in \mathcal{V}$

3. Property DV_2: $(k_1 + k_2)\vec{v} = k_1\vec{v} + k_2\vec{v}$

4. Property SMV_2: $k_1(k_2\vec{v}) = (k_1 k_2)\vec{v}$

5. Property SMV_3: $1\vec{v} = \vec{v}$

6. Property SMV_5: $0\vec{v} = \vec{0}$

7. Property SMV_6: $k\vec{0} = \vec{0}$

8. Property SMV_4: $-1\vec{v} = -\vec{v}$

Challenge For Property AV_4: $\vec{v} + (-\vec{v}) = (-\vec{v}) + \vec{v} = \vec{0}$, prove that the additive inverse element $-\vec{v}$ is unique. (Hint: Assume the existence of another such element $\vec{w} = \begin{pmatrix} r \\ s \end{pmatrix}$ not equal to $-\vec{v}$ and such that $\vec{v} + \vec{w} = \vec{w} + \vec{v} = \vec{0}$. Show that such an assumption leads to a contradiction.)

7-5 The Norm

The magnitude of a vector $\vec{v}$ is the length of each arrow in the equivalence class which makes up $\vec{v}$. Magnitude is a scalar quantity.

The magnitude of a vector is called the **norm** of the vector and is denoted $\|\vec{v}\|$. If $\vec{v} = \begin{pmatrix} a \\ b \end{pmatrix}$, then $\|\vec{v}\| = \sqrt{a^2 + b^2}$.

Norm of a Vector

Example

1. Find the norm of $\vec{v} = \begin{pmatrix} \dfrac{3}{\sqrt{2}} \\ \dfrac{4}{\sqrt{2}} \end{pmatrix}$.

$$\|\vec{v}\| = \sqrt{\left(\frac{3}{\sqrt{2}}\right)^2 + \left(\frac{4}{\sqrt{2}}\right)^2} = \sqrt{\frac{9}{2} + \frac{16}{2}} = \sqrt{\frac{25}{2}} = \frac{5}{\sqrt{2}} \text{ or } \frac{5\sqrt{2}}{2}$$

The norm of a vector and the absolute value of a real number have closely related properties. These properties are listed as theorems.

$\|\vec{v}\| \geq 0$ for any vector $\vec{v}$.
$\|\vec{v}\| = 0$ if and only if $\vec{v} = \vec{0}$.
$\|k\vec{v}\| = |k| \cdot \|\vec{v}\|$ for any vector $\vec{v}$ and scalar k.
$\|-\vec{v}\| = \|\vec{v}\|$ for any vector $\vec{v}$.

Theorems for the Norm of a Vector

Example

2. Prove $\|-\vec{v}\| = \|\vec{v}\|$ for any vector $\vec{v}$.

   Proof:

   1. Let $\vec{v} = \begin{pmatrix} a \\ b \end{pmatrix}$. *Definition of vector*

   2. $-\vec{v} = \begin{pmatrix} -a \\ -b \end{pmatrix}$ *Definition of opposite vector*

   3. $\|\vec{v}\| = \sqrt{a^2 + b^2}$ *Definition of norm*
   4. $\|-\vec{v}\| = \sqrt{(-a)^2 + (-b)^2}$ *Definition of norm*
   5. $\|-\vec{v}\| = \sqrt{a^2 + b^2}$ *From Step 4*
   6. $\|-\vec{v}\| = \|\vec{v}\|$ E_3

$\|\vec{v} + \vec{u}\| \leq \|\vec{v}\| + \|\vec{u}\|$ for any vectors $\vec{u}$ and $\vec{v}$.

The Triangle Inequality

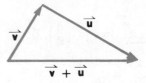

A similar theorem in geometry states that *the sum of the lengths of two sides of a triangle is greater than the length of the third side.*

Two vectors are **orthogonal** if their position vectors lie on lines which are perpendicular.

Orthogonal Vectors

A test which determines whether two vectors are orthogonal uses the norm and its properties. For $\vec{v}$ and $\vec{u}$ to be orthogonal, the vectors $\vec{v} + \vec{u}$ and $\vec{v} - \vec{u}$ must have representatives that are the diagonals of a rectangle.

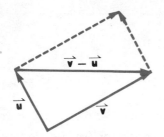 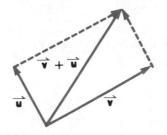

$\vec{v}$ and $\vec{u}$ are orthogonal if and only if $\|\vec{v} + \vec{u}\| = \|\vec{v} - \vec{u}\|$.

Theorem for Orthogonal Vectors

This theorem is true for $\vec{v} = \vec{0}$, $\vec{u} = \vec{0}$, or both. Thus, the zero vector is perpendicular to any other vector, including itself.

Exercises

Exploratory Find the norm of each vector.

1. $\begin{pmatrix} 0 \\ 2 \end{pmatrix}$

2. $\begin{pmatrix} 3 \\ 0 \end{pmatrix}$

3. $\begin{pmatrix} 0 \\ -2 \end{pmatrix}$

4. $\begin{pmatrix} -4 \\ 0 \end{pmatrix}$

5. $\begin{pmatrix} \frac{4}{5} \\ -\frac{3}{5} \end{pmatrix}$

6. $\begin{pmatrix} \frac{-5}{13} \\ \frac{12}{13} \end{pmatrix}$

7. $\begin{pmatrix} -\frac{1}{2} \\ \frac{\sqrt{8}}{2} \end{pmatrix}$

8. $\begin{pmatrix} \frac{3}{\sqrt{2}} \\ \frac{4}{\sqrt{2}} \end{pmatrix}$

9. $\begin{pmatrix} \frac{1}{\sqrt{5}} \\ \frac{2}{\sqrt{5}} \end{pmatrix}$

Written If $\vec{v} = \begin{pmatrix} 3 \\ 4 \end{pmatrix}$, $\vec{u} = \begin{pmatrix} -2 \\ 5 \end{pmatrix}$, and $\vec{w} = \begin{pmatrix} r \\ s \end{pmatrix}$, find each norm.

1. $\|\vec{v}\|$

2. $\|\vec{u}\|$

3. $\|\vec{w}\|$

4. $\|\vec{v}\| + \|\vec{u}\|$

5. $\|\vec{v} + \vec{u}\|$

6. $\|\vec{v} - \vec{u}\|$

7. $\|\vec{v} + \vec{w}\|$ **8.** $\|\vec{u}\| - \|\vec{w}\|$ **9.** $\|\vec{u} - \vec{w}\|$

10. $\|5\vec{v}\|$ **11.** $\|-\vec{u}\|$ **12.** $\|k\vec{w}\|$

Determine which pairs of vectors are orthogonal.

13. $\begin{pmatrix} 1 \\ 0 \end{pmatrix}, \begin{pmatrix} 0 \\ 1 \end{pmatrix}$ **14.** $\begin{pmatrix} 2 \\ 0 \end{pmatrix}, \begin{pmatrix} 0 \\ 4 \end{pmatrix}$ **15.** $\begin{pmatrix} 3 \\ 0 \end{pmatrix}, \begin{pmatrix} 0 \\ -3 \end{pmatrix}$

16. $\begin{pmatrix} 2 \\ 1 \end{pmatrix}, \begin{pmatrix} 1 \\ 2 \end{pmatrix}$ **17.** $\begin{pmatrix} 3 \\ 1 \end{pmatrix}, \begin{pmatrix} 1 \\ -3 \end{pmatrix}$ **18.** $\begin{pmatrix} -3 \\ 2 \end{pmatrix}, \begin{pmatrix} 2 \\ 3 \end{pmatrix}$

19. $\begin{pmatrix} 5 \\ -5 \end{pmatrix}, \begin{pmatrix} 2 \\ -2 \end{pmatrix}$ **20.** $\begin{pmatrix} 5 \\ -5 \end{pmatrix}, \begin{pmatrix} 2 \\ 2 \end{pmatrix}$ **21.** $\begin{pmatrix} -\frac{1}{3} \\ \frac{2}{3} \end{pmatrix}, \begin{pmatrix} \frac{4}{3} \\ \frac{2}{3} \end{pmatrix}$

Prove or disprove each of the following.

22. $\|\vec{v}\| \geq 0$

23. $\|\vec{v}\| = 0$ if and only if $\vec{v} = \vec{0}$.

24. The zero vector is orthogonal to the vector $\vec{v} = \begin{pmatrix} a \\ b \end{pmatrix}$.

25. If $\|\vec{v}\| = \|\vec{u}\|$ then it is necessarily true that $\vec{v} = \vec{u}$.

Challenge Prepare a vector algebra proof of The Triangle Inequality by comparing $\|\vec{v} + \vec{u}\| = \sqrt{(a+c)^2 + (b+d)^2}$ with $\|\vec{v}\| + \|\vec{u}\| = \sqrt{a^2 + b^2} + \sqrt{c^2 + d^2}$. (Hint: Compare the squares of these expressions.)

7-6 Projections and Components

It is convenient, especially in applied problems, to resolve a vector into its components. This is done by *projecting* the vector onto appropriate lines.

The **projection** of a vector $\vec{v}$ on a line ℓ is a vector $\vec{v}_\ell$ determined by drawing perpendiculars from the endpoints of $\vec{v}$ to the line. The initial and terminal points of the projection correspond to those of the original vector.

Projection of a vector

The line ℓ need not be horizontal.

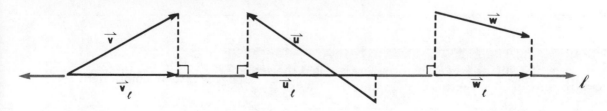

> The horizontal and vertical components of a vector are the vectors determined by projecting the vector onto the *x*- and *y*-axes.

Horizontal and Vertical Components

Examples

1. Determine the horizontal and vertical projections of the vector $\vec{v} = \begin{pmatrix} 3 \\ 5 \end{pmatrix}$.

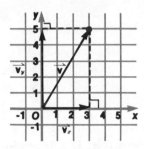

2. A ship travels at 28 knots on a course of 060°. Find the northerly and easterly components of its course.

   Since $\|\vec{v}\| = 28$, the norms of the components can be calculated.

   $$\|\vec{v}_E\| = \|\vec{v}\| \cos 30° \qquad\qquad \|\vec{v}_N\| = \|\vec{v}\| \sin 30°$$

   $$= 28 \cdot \frac{\sqrt{3}}{2} \qquad\qquad\qquad = 28 \cdot \frac{1}{2}$$

   $$= 14\sqrt{3}$$

   $$\|\vec{v}_E\| \approx 24 \text{ knots} \qquad\qquad \|\vec{v}_N\| = 14 \text{ knots}$$

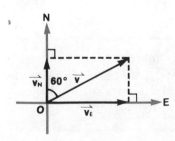

> The norm of a vector projection on a line is called the **scalar component** of that vector on the line.

Scalar Component

In the preceding example, the scalar components in the northern and eastern directions are 14 and 24, respectively.

Example

3. **Find the resultant of two vectors forming an angle of 60° and of lengths 30 units and 36 units.**

    Let $\|\vec{v}\| = 30$ and $\|\vec{u}\| = 36$.
    The resultant is $\vec{w}$.

    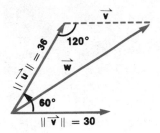

    By resolving the vector $\vec{u}$ into its horizontal and vertical components, it is possible to add these vectors and keep all calculations in right triangles.

    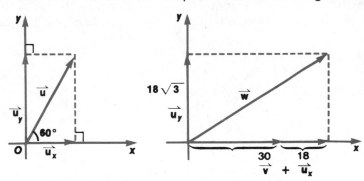

    $\|\vec{u}_x\| = \|\vec{u}\| \cos 60°$ $\qquad$ $\|\vec{u}_y\| = \|\vec{u}\| \sin 60°$

    $\qquad\quad = 36 \cdot \dfrac{1}{2}$ $\qquad\qquad\quad = 36 \cdot \dfrac{\sqrt{3}}{2}$

    $\qquad\qquad\qquad\qquad\qquad\qquad\qquad\quad = 18\sqrt{3}$

    $\|\vec{u}_x\| = 18$ $\qquad\qquad\qquad$ $\|\vec{u}_y\| \approx 31.18$

    The norm of $\vec{w}$ is $\sqrt{(18 + 30)^2 + (18\sqrt{3})^2}$ or $6\sqrt{91}$.

Exercises

Exploratory   **Determine the horizontal and vertical components of each vector.**

1. $\vec{v} = \begin{pmatrix} 3 \\ 4 \end{pmatrix}$ $\qquad\qquad\qquad\qquad\qquad$ 2. $\vec{v} = \begin{pmatrix} 1 \\ 1 \end{pmatrix}$

3. $\vec{v} = \begin{pmatrix} -3 \\ 2 \end{pmatrix}$

4. $\vec{v} = \begin{pmatrix} 0 \\ 5 \end{pmatrix}$

5. $\overrightarrow{AB}$ for $A(2, 3)$ and $B(5, 7)$

6. $\overrightarrow{AB}$ for $A(-3, -2)$ and $B(2, 5)$

7. $\overrightarrow{AB}$ for $A(-2, 4)$ and $B(3, -7)$

Written A force F is applied at angle θ with the horizontal. Find the horizontal and vertical components for each magnitude and angle.

1. $\|\vec{F}\| = 60$ lb, $\theta = 30°$ **2.** $\|\vec{F}\| = 100$ lb, $\theta = 60°$ **3.** $\|\vec{F}\| = 20$ lb, $\theta = 45°$

Solve each of the following.

4. Find the resultant of two vectors of lengths 15 and 18 which form an angle of 60°. Compare the values obtained by **(a)** The Law of Cosines and **(b)** the method of the example on page 215.

5. A wagon is pulled along level ground by a force of 18 pounds in the handle applied at an angle of 30° to the horizontal. Find the horizontal and vertical components of this vector.

6. A force F_1 of 36 pounds acts at an angle of 20° above the horizontal. Pulling in the opposing direction is a force F_2 of 48 pounds acting at an angle of 42° below the horizontal. Find the horizontal and vertical components of the resultant force.

7. An airplane flies on a heading of 090° for 210 km. It then heads on a course of 160° for 100 km. By resolving this latter vector into easterly and southerly components, determine the location of the plane from its starting place. Give its distance and direction.

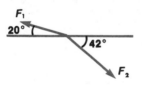

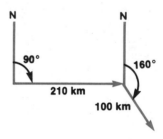

8. A weight hangs on a cable. If the system is in equilibrium, find the horizontal and vertical components acting in the brace to the wall. (Hint: The horizontal and vertical components acting at the vertex where the cable and brace meet have a vector sum of zero.)

9. An airplane flies at an air speed (speed through air) of 425 miles per hour on a heading due south. It flies against a headwind of 110 miles per hour from a direction 30° east of south. Find its ground speed (speed over the ground) and direction as well as its components in westerly and southerly directions.

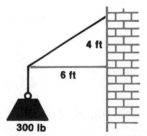

Challenge   **Solve each of the following.**

1. A trunk weighing 320 pounds is at rest on a ramp which is inclined at 15°. Three forces act on the trunk. The first is the pull of gravity, $\vec{v}_1$. The second, $\vec{v}_2$, is the push of the ramp against the trunk, perpendicular to the bottom of the trunk. The third, $\vec{v}_3$, is the force of friction parallel to the ramp which keeps the trunk from sliding down the ramp. Find the magnitude of $\vec{v}_2$ and $\vec{v}_3$. (Hint: What is the sum of the vectors acting on the trunk?)

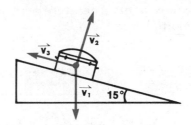

2. Find the horizontal and vertical components of the force of friction exerted on a 250 kg crate which is at rest on an incline of 22°.

3. An object weighs w pounds and is held on a ramp inclined x degrees by a force $\vec{F}$. Force $\vec{F}$ is inclined y degrees to the surface of the ramp. Resolve $\vec{F}$ and $\vec{w}$ into vector components parallel and perpendicular to the ramp. Then express $\|\vec{F}\|$ in terms of $\|\vec{w}\|$, x and y. Consider only those vectors parallel to the inclined plane.

7-7   Unit Vectors

Some vectors have norms which make them particularly useful. These vectors are the unit vectors.

The norm of a unit vector is 1.

Unit Vector

Vectors such as $\begin{pmatrix} 1 \\ 0 \end{pmatrix}$, $\begin{pmatrix} 0 \\ 1 \end{pmatrix}$, and $\begin{pmatrix} -\frac{1}{2} \\ \frac{\sqrt{3}}{2} \end{pmatrix}$ are unit vectors. The first two unit vectors are useful enough to be given special attention.

The horizontal unit vector is $\vec{i} = \begin{pmatrix} 1 \\ 0 \end{pmatrix}$. The vertical unit vector is $\vec{j} = \begin{pmatrix} 0 \\ 1 \end{pmatrix}$.

Horizontal and Vertical Unit Vectors

Any vector can be resolved into its horizontal and vertical components. Therefore each vector can be written as a sum of multiples of $\vec{i}$ and $\vec{j}$.

Examples

1. Write $\vec{v} = \begin{pmatrix} 3 \\ 2 \end{pmatrix}$ as the sum of multiples of $\vec{i}$ and $\vec{j}$.

$$\vec{v} = \begin{pmatrix} 3 \\ 2 \end{pmatrix} = 3\vec{i} + 2\vec{j}$$

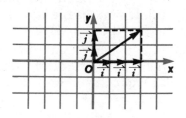

2. Write $\vec{u} = \begin{pmatrix} -4 \\ -2 \end{pmatrix}$ as the sum of multiples of $\vec{i}$ and $\vec{j}$.

$$\vec{u} = \begin{pmatrix} -4 \\ -2 \end{pmatrix} = -4\vec{i} + (-2\vec{j}) = -4\vec{i} - 2\vec{j}$$

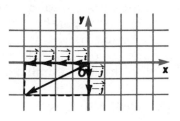

If $\vec{v} = \begin{pmatrix} a \\ b \end{pmatrix}$, then $\vec{v}$ can be expressed as $a\vec{i} + b\vec{j}$.   **Unit Vector Theorem**

Proof

1. $a\vec{i} + b\vec{j} = a \begin{pmatrix} 1 \\ 0 \end{pmatrix} + b \begin{pmatrix} 0 \\ 1 \end{pmatrix}$ *Definition of $\vec{i}$ and $\vec{j}$, Substitution*

2. $a\vec{i} + b\vec{j} = \begin{pmatrix} a \\ 0 \end{pmatrix} + \begin{pmatrix} 0 \\ b \end{pmatrix}$ *Definition of scalar multiplication*

3. $a\vec{i} + b\vec{j} = \begin{pmatrix} a + 0 \\ 0 + b \end{pmatrix}$ *Definition of vector addition*

4. $a\vec{i} + b\vec{j} = \begin{pmatrix} a \\ b \end{pmatrix}$ A_3

5. $a\vec{i} + b\vec{j} = \vec{v}$ E_3

This Theorem gives an example of a **linear combination** of vectors. The vectors $\vec{i}$ and $\vec{j}$ are combined linearly after multiplication by scalars. The vectors $\vec{v}$, $\vec{i}$ and $\vec{j}$ are said to be **linearly dependent**. The vectors $\vec{i}$ and $\vec{j}$ form a **basis** for the vector space.

It is easy to find the unit vector in the direction of a given vector. All that is required is to stretch or shrink the given vector. The unit vector in the direction of any nonzero vector $\vec{v}$ is $\frac{1}{\|\vec{v}\|}\vec{v}$.

To test this algebraically, let $\vec{v} = \begin{pmatrix} v_1 \\ v_2 \end{pmatrix}$ and find $\left\| \frac{\vec{v}}{\|\vec{v}\|} \right\|$.

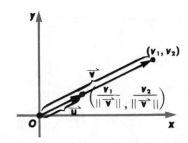

$$\left\| \frac{\vec{v}}{\|\vec{v}\|} \right\| = \left\| \frac{\begin{pmatrix} v_1 \\ v_2 \end{pmatrix}}{\sqrt{v_1^2 + v_2^2}} \right\|$$

$$= \left\| \begin{pmatrix} \dfrac{v_1}{\sqrt{v_1^2 + v_2^2}} \\ \dfrac{v_2}{\sqrt{v_1^2 + v_2^2}} \end{pmatrix} \right\|$$

$$= \sqrt{\left(\frac{v_1}{v_1^2 + v_2^2} \right)^2 + \left(\frac{v_2}{v_1^2 + v_2^2} \right)^2}$$

$$= 1$$

Example

3. Find the unit vector $\vec{u}$ in the direction of $\vec{v} = \begin{pmatrix} -3 \\ 5 \end{pmatrix}$.

$$\vec{u} = \frac{1}{\|\vec{v}\|}\vec{v}$$

$$= \frac{1}{\sqrt{(-3)^2 + 5^2}} \begin{pmatrix} -3 \\ 5 \end{pmatrix}$$

$$= \frac{1}{\sqrt{34}} \begin{pmatrix} -3 \\ 5 \end{pmatrix} \text{ or } \begin{pmatrix} \dfrac{-3}{\sqrt{34}} \\ \dfrac{5}{\sqrt{34}} \end{pmatrix}$$

Check:

$$\|\vec{u}\| = \sqrt{\left(\frac{-3}{\sqrt{34}} \right)^2 + \left(\frac{5}{\sqrt{34}} \right)^2} = \sqrt{\frac{9}{34} + \frac{25}{34}} = \sqrt{\frac{34}{34}} = 1$$

Exercises

Exploratory Determine which of the following are unit vectors.

1. $\vec{v} = \begin{pmatrix} \frac{2}{3} \\ \frac{1}{3} \end{pmatrix}$

2. $\vec{v} = \begin{pmatrix} \frac{3}{4} \\ -\frac{7}{4} \end{pmatrix}$

3. $\vec{v} = \begin{pmatrix} \frac{3}{4} \\ \frac{\sqrt{7}}{4} \end{pmatrix}$

4. $\vec{v} = \begin{pmatrix} -\frac{5}{13} \\ \frac{12}{13} \end{pmatrix}$

5. $\vec{v} = \begin{pmatrix} \frac{1}{\sqrt{3}} \\ \sqrt{\frac{2}{3}} \end{pmatrix}$

6. $\vec{v} = \begin{pmatrix} \frac{\sqrt{3}}{5} \\ \frac{2\sqrt{3}}{5} \end{pmatrix}$

Written Let $\vec{v} = \begin{pmatrix} 3 \\ -7 \end{pmatrix}$, $\vec{u} = \begin{pmatrix} -2 \\ 4 \end{pmatrix}$ and $\vec{w} = \begin{pmatrix} 1 \\ 5 \end{pmatrix}$. Write each vector in the from $r\vec{i} + s\vec{j}$.

1. $\vec{v}$

2. $\vec{v} + \vec{u}$

3. $\vec{u} - \vec{w}$

4. $5\vec{v} - 2\vec{u}$

5. $\dfrac{\vec{v} + \vec{u} + \vec{w}}{2}$

6. $\dfrac{2}{3}\vec{w} - \dfrac{1}{2}\vec{v}$

7. $a\vec{v} + b\vec{w}$

8. $\dfrac{1}{2}\left(\dfrac{\vec{v}}{\|\vec{v}\|} + \dfrac{\vec{w}}{\|\vec{w}\|}\right)$

9. Determine r and s such that $5\vec{i} + 6\vec{j} = r(2\vec{i} + 3\vec{j}) + s(3\vec{i} - 2\vec{j})$.

10. If $\vec{v}$ is of unit length and makes an angle of 60° with the x-axis, write $\vec{v}$ in the form $r\vec{i} + s\vec{j}$.

Find a unit vector which has the same direction as the given vector. Find the slope of the line containing the vector.

11. $\vec{v} = \begin{pmatrix} 3 \\ 3 \end{pmatrix}$

12. $\vec{v} = \begin{pmatrix} 2 \\ 3 \end{pmatrix}$

13. $\vec{v} = \begin{pmatrix} -3 \\ 5 \end{pmatrix}$

14. $\vec{v} = \begin{pmatrix} \frac{\sqrt{3}}{2} \\ 1 \end{pmatrix}$

15. $\vec{i} + \vec{j}$

16. $2\vec{i} - 3\vec{j}$

Solve each of the following.

17. Determine r and s so that $\vec{v} = 3\begin{pmatrix} -2 \\ 5 \end{pmatrix} - 2\begin{pmatrix} 1 \\ -7 \end{pmatrix}$ is a linear combination $r\vec{i} + s\vec{j}$.

18. A vector $\overline{PQ}$ is drawn from $P(3, -2)$ to $Q(1, 4)$. Represent the vector in the form $r\vec{i} + s\vec{j}$.

19. Find the unit vector in the direction of the resultant of $\vec{v} = 2\vec{i} - 3\vec{j}$ and $\vec{u} = \vec{i} + 2\vec{j}$.

20. Solve the equation $-2\vec{i} + 5\vec{j} = 3(\vec{i} - \vec{j}) + 2(r\vec{i} + s\vec{j})$ for r and s.

21. Prove that if $\vec{v} = r\vec{i} + s\vec{j}$ and $\vec{u} = p\vec{i} + q\vec{j}$, then $\vec{v} + \vec{u} = (r + p)\vec{i} + (s + q)\vec{j}$.

22. $\|\vec{v}\| = 5$ and the slope of the line containing $\vec{v}$ is $\sqrt{3}$. Write $\vec{v}$ as $r\vec{i} + s\vec{j}$.

23. $\|\vec{v}\| = 8$ and its direction angle is 20°. Write $\vec{v}$ as $r\vec{i} + s\vec{j}$.

7-8   Basis Vectors

Any vector may be written as a linear combination of the basis vectors i and j, the unit vectors in the horizontal and vertical directions. Because it is convenient to express vectors as linear combinations of these orthogonal unit vectors, they are most commonly used. However, other pairs of vectors can be used to form a basis for a vector space.

> **Any pair of nonzero, nonparallel vectors forms a basis for a vector space. That is, any vector $\overline{v}$ can be written as a linear combination of any two specific vectors $\overline{u}$ and $\overline{w}$ as long as they do not have the same or opposite direction.**

Basis Vectors

Proof

Let $\overline{v} = \begin{pmatrix} a \\ b \end{pmatrix}$, $\overline{u} = \begin{pmatrix} c \\ d \end{pmatrix}$ and $\overline{w} = \begin{pmatrix} e \\ f \end{pmatrix}$.

$$\overline{v} = r\overline{u} + s\overline{w}$$

$$\begin{pmatrix} a \\ b \end{pmatrix} = r\begin{pmatrix} c \\ d \end{pmatrix} + s\begin{pmatrix} e \\ f \end{pmatrix}$$

$$\begin{pmatrix} a \\ b \end{pmatrix} = \begin{pmatrix} rc \\ rd \end{pmatrix} + \begin{pmatrix} se \\ sf \end{pmatrix}$$

$$\begin{pmatrix} a \\ b \end{pmatrix} = \begin{pmatrix} rc + se \\ rd + sf \end{pmatrix}$$

$$a = rc + se \quad \text{and} \quad b = rd + sf$$

$$r = \frac{af - be}{cf - de} \quad \text{and} \quad s = \frac{cb - da}{cf - de}$$

The solution for r using determinants is as follows.

$$r = \frac{\begin{vmatrix} a & e \\ b & f \end{vmatrix}}{\begin{vmatrix} c & e \\ d & f \end{vmatrix}} = \frac{af - be}{cf - de}$$

For the values of r and s to exist, it must be true that $cf - de \neq 0$. This can be expressed as $\frac{f}{e} \neq \frac{d}{c}$, which only means that the vectors $\overline{u}$ and $\overline{w}$ cannot be parallel. This was specified in the statement of the theorem. Thus any vector can be expressed as a linear combination of any two nonzero, nonparallel vectors in the vector space.

Example

1. Write the vector $\vec{v} = \begin{pmatrix} -2 \\ 5 \end{pmatrix}$ as a linear combination of the vectors $\vec{u} = \begin{pmatrix} 2 \\ 3 \end{pmatrix}$ and $\vec{w} = \begin{pmatrix} 1 \\ -4 \end{pmatrix}$.

$$\begin{pmatrix} -2 \\ 5 \end{pmatrix} = r\begin{pmatrix} 2 \\ 3 \end{pmatrix} + s\begin{pmatrix} 1 \\ -4 \end{pmatrix}$$

$$\begin{pmatrix} -2 \\ 5 \end{pmatrix} = \begin{pmatrix} 2r + s \\ 3r - 4s \end{pmatrix}$$

$$\begin{cases} -2 = 2r + s \\ 5 = 3r - 4s \end{cases}$$

$$\begin{cases} r = \dfrac{\begin{vmatrix} -2 & 1 \\ 5 & -4 \end{vmatrix}}{\begin{vmatrix} 2 & 1 \\ 3 & -4 \end{vmatrix}} = \dfrac{8 - 5}{-8 - 3} = \dfrac{-3}{11} \\[2em] s = \dfrac{\begin{vmatrix} 2 & -2 \\ 3 & 5 \end{vmatrix}}{-11} = \dfrac{10 + 6}{-11} = -\dfrac{16}{11} \end{cases}$$

$$\vec{v} = -\frac{3}{11}\vec{u} - \frac{16}{11}\vec{w}$$

A technique for determining whether three vectors with the same initial point have collinear terminal points results from this linear combination property.

If the position vector $\overline{OX}$ terminates on $\overleftrightarrow{PQ}$, then $\overline{OX} = r\overline{OQ} + s\overline{OP}$ where $r + s = 1$, and conversely.

Linear Combination Theorem

Example

2. Determine whether or not the position vector $\vec{v} = \begin{pmatrix} 3 \\ 1 \end{pmatrix}$ terminates on the line determined by the terminal points of position vectors $\vec{u} = \begin{pmatrix} 5 \\ -2 \end{pmatrix}$ and $\vec{w} = \begin{pmatrix} 1 \\ 4 \end{pmatrix}$.

Write $\vec{v}$ as a linear combination of $\vec{v}$ and $\vec{w}$ and check the value $r + s$.

$$\vec{v} = r\vec{u} + s\vec{w}$$

$$\begin{pmatrix} 3 \\ 1 \end{pmatrix} = r\begin{pmatrix} 5 \\ -2 \end{pmatrix} + s\begin{pmatrix} 1 \\ 4 \end{pmatrix}$$

$$\begin{cases} 3 = 5r + s \\ 1 = -2r + 4s \end{cases}$$

$$r = \frac{1}{2} \quad \text{and} \quad s = \frac{1}{2}$$

Since $r + s = 1$, $\vec{v}$ terminates on the line joining the endpoints of $\vec{v}$ and $\vec{w}$.

A vector representation of a line also can be stated in terms of a single arbitrary expression called a **parameter**.

Example

3. **Write a vector representation of the line through the terminal points of position vectors $\vec{u} = \begin{pmatrix} 1 \\ 4 \end{pmatrix}$ and $\vec{w} = \begin{pmatrix} -2 \\ 5 \end{pmatrix}$.**

    Let $\vec{v}$ be a position vector terminating on the desired line. From the Linear Combination Theorem, $\vec{v} = r\vec{u} + s\vec{w}$ and $r + s = 1$.

    $$\vec{v} = r\vec{u} + s\vec{w}$$
    $$\vec{v} = r\vec{u} + (1 - r)\vec{w}$$
    $$\vec{v} = r\begin{pmatrix} 1 \\ 4 \end{pmatrix} + (1 - r)\begin{pmatrix} -2 \\ 5 \end{pmatrix}$$
    $$\vec{v} = \begin{pmatrix} r \\ 4r \end{pmatrix} + \begin{pmatrix} -2 + 2r \\ 5 - 5r \end{pmatrix}$$
    $$\vec{v} = \begin{pmatrix} -2 + 3r \\ 5 - r \end{pmatrix}$$

    The desired line is the set of all points P such that $\vec{v} = \begin{pmatrix} -2 + 3r \\ 5 - r \end{pmatrix}$ for all $r \in \mathcal{R}$ and $\vec{v}$ ends at point P. The line can be expressed in terms of r.

    $$\begin{cases} x = -2 + 3r \\ y = 5 - r \end{cases}$$

    This is the parametric form of the line.

    Each line has an infinite number of such parametric forms. The parameter r can be eliminated and the equation of the line written in terms of x and y.

    $$\begin{cases} x = -2 + 3r \\ y = 5 - r \end{cases}$$
    $$x = -2 + 3(5 - y)$$
    $$x = 13 - 3y$$
    $$x + 3y = 13$$

Exercises

Exploratory Suppose position vectors $\vec{v}$, $\vec{u}$ and $\vec{w}$ terminate at points V, U and W, respectively, which are collinear, such that $\vec{v} = r\vec{u} + s\vec{w}$ and $r + s = 1$. Determine the conditions on r and s so that each statement is true.

1. V lies on the interior of $\overline{UW}$.   2. V lies on an endpoint of $\overline{UW}$.   3. V lies on $\overleftrightarrow{UW}$.
4. V lies on $\overrightarrow{UW}$ exterior to $\overline{UW}$.   5. V lies on $\overrightarrow{WU}$.

Determine the relationships among the points V, U, and W, given each of the following.

6. $r = s = \dfrac{1}{2}$

7. $r = \dfrac{1}{3}, s = \dfrac{2}{3}$

8. $r = \dfrac{2}{5}, s = \dfrac{3}{5}$

9. $r = \dfrac{2}{3}, s = \dfrac{1}{3}$

Written Write each vector $\vec{v}$ as a linear combination of the vectors $\vec{u}$ and $\vec{w}$. That is, find r and $s \in \mathcal{R}$ such that $\vec{v} = r\vec{u} + s\vec{w}$.

1. $\vec{v} = \begin{pmatrix} 1 \\ 5 \end{pmatrix}, \vec{u} = \begin{pmatrix} -3 \\ 4 \end{pmatrix}, \vec{w} = \begin{pmatrix} 2 \\ -2 \end{pmatrix}$

2. $\vec{v} = \begin{pmatrix} \frac{1}{2} \\ -1 \end{pmatrix}, \vec{u} = \begin{pmatrix} 0 \\ 4 \end{pmatrix}, \vec{w} = \begin{pmatrix} \frac{3}{2} \\ 1 \end{pmatrix}$

3. $\vec{v} = \begin{pmatrix} 1 \\ -1 \end{pmatrix}, \vec{u} = \begin{pmatrix} 2 \\ 3 \end{pmatrix}, \vec{w} = \begin{pmatrix} \frac{3}{4} \\ 1 \end{pmatrix}$

4. $\vec{v} = \begin{pmatrix} 2 \\ -7 \end{pmatrix}, \vec{u} = \begin{pmatrix} -1 \\ -3 \end{pmatrix}, \vec{w} = \begin{pmatrix} 3 \\ 9 \end{pmatrix}$

5. $\vec{v} = \begin{pmatrix} 0 \\ 0 \end{pmatrix}, \vec{u} = \begin{pmatrix} \frac{2}{3} \\ 5 \end{pmatrix}, \vec{w} = \begin{pmatrix} -3 \\ 7 \end{pmatrix}$

Determine whether position vector $\vec{v}$ terminates on the line containing the terminal points of position vectors $\vec{u}$ and $\vec{w}$.

6. $\vec{v} = \begin{pmatrix} -1 \\ 6 \end{pmatrix}, \vec{u} = \begin{pmatrix} 5 \\ -4 \end{pmatrix}, \vec{w} = \begin{pmatrix} -4 \\ 11 \end{pmatrix}$

7. $\vec{v} = \begin{pmatrix} \frac{3}{2} \\ -1 \end{pmatrix}, \vec{u} = \begin{pmatrix} 4 \\ 3 \end{pmatrix}, \vec{w} = \begin{pmatrix} -1 \\ -5 \end{pmatrix}$

8. $\vec{v} = \begin{pmatrix} 5 \\ 4 \end{pmatrix}, \vec{u} = \begin{pmatrix} -4 \\ 2 \end{pmatrix}, \vec{w} = \begin{pmatrix} -10 \\ 1 \end{pmatrix}$

9. $\vec{v} = \begin{pmatrix} 2 \\ -2 \end{pmatrix}, \vec{u} = \begin{pmatrix} \frac{1}{5} \\ \frac{8}{5} \end{pmatrix}, \vec{w} = \begin{pmatrix} -1 \\ 4 \end{pmatrix}$

Determine the vector representation of the line through the terminal points of the two given position vectors.

10. $\vec{u} = \begin{pmatrix} -2 \\ 1 \end{pmatrix}, \vec{w} = \begin{pmatrix} 3 \\ -4 \end{pmatrix}$ 11. $\vec{u} = \begin{pmatrix} -1 \\ 5 \end{pmatrix}, \vec{w} = \begin{pmatrix} \frac{1}{2} \\ -3 \end{pmatrix}$ 12. $\vec{u} = \begin{pmatrix} 0 \\ 10 \end{pmatrix}, \vec{w} = \begin{pmatrix} 5 \\ 0 \end{pmatrix}$

13.–15. Write the equation of each line in Problems 10.–12., in vector form $\vec{v} = r\vec{u} + (1 - r)\vec{w}$ as well as in parametric form $\begin{cases} x = a + br \\ y = c + dr \end{cases}$.

Prove each of the following.

16. If V is the midpoint of $\overline{UW}$, then $\vec{v} = \frac{1}{2}(\vec{u} + \vec{w})$

17. If V is a point of trisection of $\overline{UW}$, then $\vec{v} = \frac{1}{3}\vec{u} + \frac{2}{3}\vec{w}$.

Challenge Prove each of the following.

1. If the position vector $\overrightarrow{OX}$ terminates on $\overline{PQ}$, then $\overrightarrow{OX} = r\overrightarrow{OQ} + s\overrightarrow{OP}$ where $r + s = 1$, and conversely.

2. The parametric form of a line through points (x_1, y_1) and (x_2, y_2) can be written $\begin{cases} x = x_1 + r(x_2 - x_1) \\ y = y_1 + r(y_2 - y_1) \end{cases}$.

3. If V divides $\overline{UW}$ in the ratio $s:r$, then $\vec{v} = \frac{r\vec{u} + s\vec{w}}{r + s}$ or $\vec{v} = \frac{r}{r + s}\vec{u} + \frac{s}{r + s}\vec{w}$. (This is called the Point of Division Property.)

4. If $\overline{BA}$ is divided at M in the ratio 3:1 (or $\overline{BM} = 3\overline{MA}$), then $\vec{m} = \frac{1}{4}(3\vec{a} + \vec{b})$.

7-9 The Dot Product

One of the more important applications of vectors in physics is that of work. Work is defined as the product of a force on an object and the distance it is moved. A force of 10 lb applied uniformly over a distance of 12 ft produces 120 ft-lb of work ($W = Fs = 10 \cdot 12$). Suppose the force applied to the object is in a direction other than the motion of the object. If the force F is applied in the direction of $\vec{F}$, but the object moves along the direction of $\vec{s}$, then the work accomplished is no longer Fs. The work is the product of the scalar component of $\vec{F}$ in the direction of $\vec{s}$ and the distance $s = \|\vec{s}\|$ the object moves. The vector component of $\vec{F}$ in the direction of $\vec{s}$ is $\vec{F}_s$. In addition, $\|\vec{F}_s\| = \|\vec{F}\| \cos \theta$, where θ is the angle between $\vec{F}$ and $\vec{s}$.

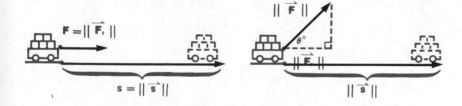

Work done by a force F applied at an angle θ to the direction of motion can now be described.

$$W = \|\vec{F}_s\|\|\vec{s}\| = \|\vec{F}\|\|\vec{s}\| \cos \theta$$

This type of expression has been given a special name because of its importance in both vector theory and application.

> The **scalar** or **dot product** of two nonzero vectors $\overline{v}$ and $\overline{u}$ is $\overline{v} \cdot \overline{u} = \|\overline{v}\|\|\overline{u}\| \cos \theta$ where θ is the angle between $\overline{v}$ and $\overline{u}$.

Dot Product

   Although this is considered to be the product of two vectors, such multiplication is not a closed operation in the system of vectors. Actually, the dot product of two vectors is a scalar. The term *scalar product* is a result of this fact. The term *dot product* results from the symbol used.

⅄ note

> Two nonzero vectors are orthogonal if and only if their dot product is zero.

Orthogonal Vectors

Proof

I.   Let $\overline{v} \cdot \overline{u} = 0$. Then $\overline{v} \cdot \overline{u} = 0 = \|\overline{v}\|\|\overline{u}\| \cos \theta$. Since neither $\overline{v}$ nor $\overline{u}$ is $\overline{0}$, then $\cos \theta = 0$ and $\theta = 90° + k \cdot 180°, k = 0, 1, 2, \ldots$

II. Let $\theta = 90° + k \cdot 180°$.

$$\overline{v} \cdot \overline{u} = \|\overline{v}\|\|\overline{u}\| \cos \theta = 0$$

   If $\overline{v}$ or $\overline{u}$ is null, then their dot product is defined to be 0. This is consistent with the zero vector being orthogonal to all vectors.

⅄ note

Example

1. Find the dot product of $\overline{v} \cdot \overline{u}$, $\overline{u} \cdot \overline{v}$ and $\overline{v} \cdot \overline{w}$ if $\overline{v} = \begin{pmatrix} 5 \\ 0 \end{pmatrix}$, $\overline{u} = \begin{pmatrix} 3 \\ 3 \end{pmatrix}$, $\|\overline{w}\| = \sqrt{3}$ and the angle between $\overline{v}$ and $\overline{w}$ is 60°.

$$\overline{v} \cdot \overline{u} = \|\overline{v}\| \|\overline{u}\| \cos 45° = 5 \cdot \sqrt{18} \cdot \frac{\sqrt{2}}{2} = 15$$

$$\overline{u} \cdot \overline{v} = \|\overline{u}\| \|\overline{v}\| \cos 45° = \sqrt{18} \cdot 5 \frac{\sqrt{2}}{2} = 15$$

$$\overline{v} \cdot \overline{w} = \|\overline{v}\| \|\overline{w}\| \cos 60° = 5 \cdot \sqrt{3} \cdot \frac{1}{2} = \frac{5\sqrt{3}}{2}$$

An expression for the dot product in terms of the components of the two vectors is possible and often convenient to use.

Apply the Law of Cosines to the triangle in the figure.

$$\|\vec{v} - \vec{u}\|^2 = \|\vec{v}\|^2 + \|\vec{u}\|^2 - 2\|\vec{v}\|\|\vec{u}\| \cos \theta$$

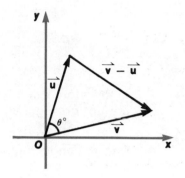

Since $\vec{v} \cdot \vec{u} = \|\vec{v}\|\|\vec{u}\| \cos \theta$, $\vec{v} \cdot \vec{u} = \frac{1}{2}[\|\vec{v}\|^2 + \|\vec{u}\|^2 - \|\mathbf{v} - \mathbf{u}\|^2]$. If $\vec{v} = \begin{pmatrix} a \\ b \end{pmatrix}$ and $\vec{u} = \begin{pmatrix} c \\ d \end{pmatrix}$, then $\|\vec{v} - \vec{u}\|$ is the distance between the points (a, b) and (c, d).

$$\|\vec{v} - \vec{u}\| = \sqrt{(a - c)^2 + (b - d)^2}$$

Substitute this expression.

$$\vec{v} \cdot \vec{u} = \frac{(a^2 + b^2) + (c^2 + d^2) - [(a - c)^2 + (b - d)^2]}{2}$$

$$\vec{v} \cdot \vec{u} = \frac{a^2 + b^2 + c^2 + d^2 - (a^2 - 2ac + c^2 + b^2 - 2bd + d^2)}{2}$$

$$\vec{v} \cdot \vec{u} = ac + bd$$

This is an expression for the dot product of two vectors in terms of their components. It proves the following theorem.

If $\vec{v} = \begin{pmatrix} a \\ b \end{pmatrix}$ and $\vec{u} = \begin{pmatrix} c \\ d \end{pmatrix}$, then $\vec{v} \cdot \vec{u} = ac + bd$.	**Dot Products in Terms of Components**

Examples

2. Find the dot products $\vec{v} \cdot \vec{u}$, $\vec{u} \cdot \vec{v}$ and $\vec{v} \cdot \vec{w}$ if $\vec{v} = \begin{pmatrix} 3 \\ -2 \end{pmatrix}$, $\vec{u} = \begin{pmatrix} 5 \\ 1 \end{pmatrix}$ and $\vec{w} = \begin{pmatrix} 2 \\ 3 \\ -4 \end{pmatrix}$.

$$\vec{v} \cdot \vec{u} = \begin{pmatrix} 3 \\ -2 \end{pmatrix} \cdot \begin{pmatrix} 5 \\ 1 \end{pmatrix} = 15 - 2 = 13$$

$$\vec{u} \cdot \vec{v} = \begin{pmatrix} 5 \\ 1 \end{pmatrix} \cdot \begin{pmatrix} 3 \\ -2 \end{pmatrix} = 13$$

$$\vec{v} \cdot \vec{w} = \begin{pmatrix} 3 \\ -2 \end{pmatrix} \cdot \begin{pmatrix} 2 \\ 3 \\ -4 \end{pmatrix} = 2 + 8 = 10$$

3. **Determine which pairs of vectors are orthogonal if** $\bar{v} = \begin{pmatrix} 3 \\ 5 \end{pmatrix}$, $\bar{u} = \begin{pmatrix} -5 \\ 3 \end{pmatrix}$ **and**

$$\bar{w} = \begin{pmatrix} \dfrac{2}{3} \\ -\dfrac{1}{5} \end{pmatrix}.$$

$$\bar{v} \cdot \bar{u} = -15 + 15 = 0$$
$$\bar{v} \cdot \bar{w} = 2 - 1 = 1 \neq 0$$
$$\bar{u} \cdot \bar{w} = \frac{-10}{3} - \frac{3}{5} \neq 0$$

Therefore $\bar{v}$ and $\bar{u}$ are orthogonal, $\bar{v}$ and $\bar{w}$ are not orthogonal, and $\bar{u}$ and $\bar{w}$ are not orthogonal.

An easy test to determine if vectors are orthogonal is now available.

4. **Find the angle between** $\bar{v} = \begin{pmatrix} 2 \\ -1 \end{pmatrix}$ **and** $\bar{u} = \begin{pmatrix} -3 \\ 8 \end{pmatrix}$.

$$\bar{v} \cdot \bar{u} = 2(-3) + (-1) \cdot 8 = -6 - 8 = -14$$

Since $\bar{v} \cdot \bar{u} = \|\bar{v}\| \|\bar{u}\| \cos \theta$

$$-14 = \sqrt{4 + 1} \cdot \sqrt{9 + 64} \cos \theta$$
$$-14 = \sqrt{365} \cos \theta$$
$$\cos \theta \approx \frac{-14}{19.10} \approx -0.733$$
$$\theta \approx 137° \ 10'$$

The dot product is useful to determine the angle between vectors.

The dot product, as an operation, has many properties. Proofs of some of these are asked for in the exercises.

Let $\bar{u}$ and $\bar{v} \in \mathcal{V}$, and $r, s, \in \mathcal{R}$.
  DP$_1$: **Commutativity ($\cdot$):** $\bar{v} \cdot \bar{u} = \bar{u} \cdot \bar{v}$
  DP$_2$: $r(\bar{v} \cdot \bar{u}) = (r\bar{v}) \cdot \bar{u}$
  DP$_3$: $(r\bar{v}) \cdot (s\bar{u}) = rs(\bar{v} \cdot \bar{u})$
  DP$_4$: **Distributivity ($\cdot$ over +):** $\bar{v} \cdot (\bar{u} + \bar{w}) = \bar{v} \cdot \bar{u} + \bar{v} \cdot \bar{w}$
  DP$_5$: $\bar{v} \cdot \bar{v} = \|\bar{v}\|^2 \geq 0$

Properties of the Dot Product

The dot product can be used to find the set of all vectors orthogonal to a given vector. Let $\bar{u} = \begin{pmatrix} c \\ d \end{pmatrix}$ be any vector orthogonal to $\bar{v} = \begin{pmatrix} a \\ b \end{pmatrix}$. Then $\bar{v} \cdot \bar{u} = 0$ or $ac + bd = 0$. For $\bar{v} = \begin{pmatrix} a \\ b \end{pmatrix}$, choose c and d such that $\frac{c}{d} = -\frac{b}{a}$. This can be done by choosing $\bar{u} = \begin{pmatrix} c \\ d \end{pmatrix} = \begin{pmatrix} -b \\ a \end{pmatrix}$ or $\bar{u} = \begin{pmatrix} c \\ d \end{pmatrix} = \begin{pmatrix} b \\ -a \end{pmatrix}$. In these two cases,

$\bar{u}$ has the same norm as $\bar{v}$. The special vector $\begin{pmatrix} -b \\ a \end{pmatrix}$ is denoted $\bar{v}_p$. Other vectors orthogonal to $\bar{v}$ are of the form $k\begin{pmatrix} -b \\ a \end{pmatrix}$ for some scalar k. Notice in particular that $(-1) \cdot \begin{pmatrix} -b \\ a \end{pmatrix} = \begin{pmatrix} b \\ -a \end{pmatrix}$.

If $\bar{v} = \begin{pmatrix} a \\ b \end{pmatrix}$ then $\bar{u} = k\begin{pmatrix} -b \\ a \end{pmatrix}$ is orthogonal to $\bar{v}$ for any scalar k.

Theorem for Orthogonal Vectors

Example

5. Find $\bar{v}_p$, $3\bar{v}_p$; and the unit vector $\dfrac{\bar{v}_p}{\|\bar{v}\|}$ all orthogonal to $\bar{v} = \begin{pmatrix} 3 \\ -7 \end{pmatrix}$.

$$\bar{v}_p = \begin{pmatrix} 7 \\ 3 \end{pmatrix}$$

$$3\bar{v}_p = 3\begin{pmatrix} 7 \\ 3 \end{pmatrix} = \begin{pmatrix} 21 \\ 9 \end{pmatrix}$$

$$\frac{\bar{v}_p}{\|\bar{v}\|} = \frac{\begin{pmatrix} 7 \\ 3 \end{pmatrix}}{\sqrt{3^2 + (-7)^2}} = \frac{\begin{pmatrix} 7 \\ 3 \end{pmatrix}}{\sqrt{58}} = \begin{pmatrix} \frac{7}{\sqrt{58}} \\ \frac{3}{\sqrt{58}} \end{pmatrix}$$

Exercises

Exploratory   Find each dot product if $\bar{v} = \begin{pmatrix} 3 \\ 1 \end{pmatrix}$, $\bar{u} = \begin{pmatrix} 2 \\ -2 \end{pmatrix}$, and $\bar{w} = \begin{pmatrix} -1 \\ 3 \end{pmatrix}$.

1. $\bar{v} \cdot \bar{u}$ 2. $\bar{v} \cdot \bar{w}$ 3. $\bar{u} \cdot \bar{w}$
4. $4(\bar{u} \cdot \bar{w})$ 5. $2(\bar{u} \cdot \bar{v})$ 6. $\bar{v} \cdot (\bar{u} + \bar{w})$
7. If $\bar{v} = \vec{i} + 2\vec{j}$ and $\bar{u} = 4\vec{i} - 3\vec{j}$, find $\bar{u} \cdot \bar{v}$.

Written   Find $\bar{v} \cdot \bar{u}$ for each set of values.

1. $\bar{v} = \begin{pmatrix} 2 \\ 3 \end{pmatrix}$, $\|\bar{u}\| = 4$ and $\theta = 30°$ 2. $\bar{v} = \begin{pmatrix} -1 \\ 5 \end{pmatrix}$, $\|\bar{u}\| = \dfrac{\sqrt{3}}{2}$ and $\theta = 45°$

Given the vectors $\bar{v} = \begin{pmatrix} 1 \\ 2 \\ 5 \end{pmatrix}$ $\bar{u} = \begin{pmatrix} -5 \\ -1 \\ 2 \end{pmatrix}$, $\bar{w} = \begin{pmatrix} -15 \\ 3 \\ 2 \end{pmatrix}$, determine if each of the following pairs are orthogonal.

3. $\bar{v}, \bar{u}$ 4. $\bar{u}, \dot{w}$ 5. $\bar{v}, \bar{w}$

Find the angle between each pair of vectors.

6. $\bar{v} = \begin{pmatrix} 4 \\ 4\sqrt{3} \end{pmatrix}, \bar{u} = \begin{pmatrix} -12 \\ 0 \end{pmatrix}$ 7. $\bar{v} = \begin{pmatrix} 3 \\ -7 \end{pmatrix}, \bar{u} = \begin{pmatrix} 1 \\ 5 \end{pmatrix}$

8. An object is moved 25 ft horizontally by exerting a force of 75 lb at an angle of 20° above the horizontal. Find the amount of work done.

Prove each of the following.

9. $\|\bar{v} + \bar{u}\|^2 = \|\bar{v}\|^2 + 2\bar{v} \cdot \bar{u} + \|\bar{u}\|^2$

10. $(\bar{v} + \bar{u}) \cdot (\bar{v} - \bar{u}) = \|\bar{v}\|^2 - \|\bar{u}\|^2.$

11. $(r\bar{v}) \cdot (s\bar{u}) = rs(\bar{v} \cdot \bar{u})$ for $r, s \in \mathcal{R}.$

12. $\bar{v} \cdot (\bar{u} + \bar{w}) = \bar{v} \cdot \bar{u} + \bar{v} \cdot \bar{w}.$

Challenge Prove each of the following.

1. $\bar{v}$ is orthogonal to $\bar{u}$ if and only if $\|\bar{v} - \bar{u}\|^2 = \|\bar{v}\|^2 + \|\bar{u}\|^2.$

2. If $\bar{v}$ and $\bar{u}$ are orthogonal, then $(\bar{v} + \bar{u}) \cdot (\bar{v} + \bar{u}) = (\bar{v} - \bar{u}) \cdot (\bar{v} - \bar{u}).$

3. $\|\bar{v}\| = (\bar{v} \cdot \bar{v})^{1/2}.$

7–10   Geometric Proofs

Certain properties of geometry lend themselves to methods of proof involving vectors.

Example

1. Prove the line segment joining the midpoints of two sides of a triangle is parallel to the third side and congruent to one-half of it.

In Geometric Terms:

Hypothesis: M midpoint of $\overline{AC}$ and N midpoint of $\overline{BC}$

Prove: $\overline{MN} \parallel \overline{AB}$ and $MN = \frac{1}{2}AB$

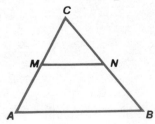

In Vector Terms:

Indicate vectors as appropriate arrows.

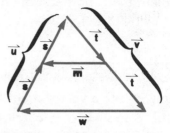

Hypothesis: $\vec{s} = \dfrac{1}{2}\vec{u}$ and $\vec{t} = \dfrac{1}{2}\vec{v}$

Prove: $\overrightarrow{m} = \dfrac{1}{2}\overrightarrow{w}$

Proof

Suppose $\vec{s} = \dfrac{1}{2}\vec{u}$ and $\vec{t} = \dfrac{1}{2}\vec{v}$. Then $-\overrightarrow{m} + \vec{t} + \overrightarrow{w} + \vec{s} = \vec{0}$ and $\overrightarrow{m} + \vec{s} + \vec{t} = \vec{0}$ because the sum of the vectors around a polygon is zero. Subtracting gives $-2\overrightarrow{m} + \overrightarrow{w} = \vec{0}$ which means $\overrightarrow{m} = \dfrac{1}{2}\overrightarrow{w}$.

Equality of length without parallelism is handled by equating norms. The properties of the dot product allow problems of perpendicularity to be handled algebraically.

 Example

2. **Prove the altitudes of a triangle are concurrent.**

   Proof

   As in strictly geometric methods, let two altitudes meet. Show that the line from the third vertex to this point is perpendicular to the third side. With vectors this treatment is convenient since vectors are orthogonal whether their representatives actually meet or not.

   Hypothesis: $\overline{u} \cdot (\overline{w} - \overline{v}) = 0$ and $\overline{v} \cdot (\overline{u} - \overline{w}) = 0$
   Prove: $\overline{w} \cdot (\overline{v} - \overline{u}) = 0$

   Proof

   1. $\overline{u} \cdot (\overline{w} - \overline{v}) = 0,\ \overline{v} \cdot (\overline{u} - \overline{w}) = 0$ *Hypothesis*
   2. $\overline{u} \cdot \overline{w} - \overline{u} \cdot \overline{v} = 0,\ \overline{v} \cdot \overline{u} - \overline{v} \cdot \overline{w} = 0$ DP_4
   3. $\overline{u} \cdot \overline{w} = \overline{u} \cdot \overline{v},\ \overline{v} \cdot \overline{u} = \overline{v} \cdot \overline{w}$ A_3
   4. $\overline{u} \cdot \overline{w} = \overline{v} \cdot \overline{w}$ E_3
   5. $\overline{v} \cdot \overline{w} - \overline{u} \cdot \overline{w} = 0$ A_4
   6. $\overline{w} \cdot (\overline{v} - \overline{u}) = 0$ DP_4

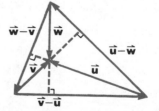

There are many ways to label a figure. One may be more

convenient than another. Determine the approach to the proof before marking the figure.

Exercises

Written **Write a vector proof for each statement.**

1. The diagonals of a parallelogram bisect each other. Use the method described in the examples.

2. The diagonals of a rhombus are perpendicular.

3. The median to the base of an isosceles triangle is perpendicular to the base.

4. An angle inscribed in a semicircle is a right angle. (Hint: Let the three radii be $\bar{\mathbf{v}}$, $-\bar{\mathbf{v}}$ and $\bar{\mathbf{u}}$. Find $(\bar{\mathbf{u}} + \bar{\mathbf{v}}) \cdot (\bar{\mathbf{u}} - \bar{\mathbf{v}})$.)

5. The quadrilateral formed by connecting the midpoints of the adjacent sides of any quadrilateral is a parallelogram.

6. The sum of the squares of the lengths of the sides of a parallelogram is equal to the sum of the squares of the lengths of the diagonals.

Challenge **Solve each of the following.**

1. The segments joining the midpoints of pairs of opposite sides of a quadrilateral bisect each other.

2. In $\square ABCD$, E and F are trisection points of diagonal $\overline{AEFC}$. Prove that $DEBF$ is a parallelogram.

Chapter Summary

1. A vector is an equivalence class of arrows. It may be represented by the arrow which is in standard position, the position vector. (198)

   a. Two vectors are equal if they contain the same set of arrows.

   b. A unit vector is defined for each direction and has a length of 1 unit. The zero vector $\begin{pmatrix} 0 \\ 0 \end{pmatrix}$, or null vector, has length zero and is considered to have any direction.

   c. The opposite of a vector $\bar{\mathbf{v}} = \begin{pmatrix} a \\ b \end{pmatrix}$ is $-\bar{\mathbf{v}} = \begin{pmatrix} -a \\ -b \end{pmatrix}$. It has the same slope and length as $\bar{\mathbf{v}}$ but has the opposite direction as $\bar{\mathbf{v}}$.

2. The sum of two vectors is the vector formed by the diagonal of the parallelogram with two vectors as adjacent sides. (204)

3. The difference of two vectors $\bar{\mathbf{u}}$ and $\bar{\mathbf{v}}$ is $\bar{\mathbf{u}} + (-\bar{\mathbf{v}})$. (203)

4. If $\bar{\mathbf{v}} = \begin{pmatrix} a \\ b \end{pmatrix}$ and k is a scalar, then $k\bar{\mathbf{v}} = \begin{pmatrix} ka \\ kb \end{pmatrix}$. (203)

5. If $\vec{v} = \begin{pmatrix} a \\ b \end{pmatrix}$ and $\vec{u} = \begin{pmatrix} c \\ d \end{pmatrix}$, then $\vec{v} + \vec{u} = \begin{pmatrix} a + c \\ b + d \end{pmatrix}$. (204)

6. Two vectors $\vec{v} = \begin{pmatrix} a \\ b \end{pmatrix}$ and $\vec{u} = \begin{pmatrix} c \\ d \end{pmatrix}$ are equal if and only if $a = c$ and $b = d$. (204)

7. The magnitude of a vector $\vec{v} = \begin{pmatrix} a \\ b \end{pmatrix}$ is called the norm of the vector, written $\|\vec{v}\|$, and $\|\vec{v}\| = \sqrt{a^2 + b^2}$. (208)

8. Two vectors are orthogonal if their arrows lie on lines which are perpendicular. (210)

9. The horizontal and vertical components of a vector are the vectors determined by projecting the vector onto the x- and y-axes. (211)

10. Any vector may be written in the form $a\vec{i} + b\vec{j}$ for some scalar multiples of $\vec{i}$ and $\vec{j}$. The unit vectors $\vec{i}$ and $\vec{j}$ form a basis for the vector space. (215)

11. Any pair of nonzero, nonparallel vectors form a basis for the vector space. (219)

12. If the position vector $\overrightarrow{OX}$ terminates on the line $\overleftrightarrow{PQ}$, then $\overrightarrow{OX} = r\overrightarrow{OQ} + s\overrightarrow{OP}$ where $r + s = 1$; and conversely. (220)

13. The dot product, or scalar product, of two vectors $\vec{v}$ and $\vec{u}$ is $\vec{v} \cdot \vec{u} = \|\vec{v}\|\|\vec{u}\| \cos \theta$ where θ is the angle between $\vec{v}$ and $\vec{u}$. (224)

14. If $\vec{v} = \begin{pmatrix} a \\ b \end{pmatrix}$ and $\vec{u} = \begin{pmatrix} c \\ d \end{pmatrix}$, then $\vec{v} \cdot \vec{u} = ac + bd$. (225)

15. If $\vec{v} = \begin{pmatrix} a \\ b \end{pmatrix}$, then $\vec{u} = k\begin{pmatrix} -b \\ a \end{pmatrix}$ is orthogonal to $\vec{v}$ for any scalar k. The special vector $\begin{pmatrix} -b \\ a \end{pmatrix}$ is denoted $\vec{v}_p$. (227)

Chapter Review

7-1 The vector $\overrightarrow{PQ}$ is represented by an arrow drawn from (4, −3) to (2, 5). Write $\overrightarrow{PQ}$, $-\overrightarrow{PQ}$ or *Neither* to describe whether each vector $\overrightarrow{RS}$ is equal to $\overrightarrow{PQ}$, the opposite of $\overrightarrow{PQ}$, or neither.

1. $R(-2, 2), S(0, 4)$　　　　　　　　2. $R(-2, -2), S(-4, 6)$
3. $R(5, 8), S(7, 0)$　　　　　　　　　4. $R(2, -7), S(-2, 9)$
5. Draw a square $ABCD$ with diagonals intersecting at E. List as many equal and opposite vectors as possible. Use vector notation.

7-2 Copy the vector figure.

6. Show the sum $\vec{u} + \vec{v}$ by a vector parallelogram.
7. Find the vector sum $\vec{u} + \vec{v}$ by a vector triangle.
8. Find the vector difference $\vec{u} - \vec{v}$ by drawing $\vec{u} + (-\vec{v})$.

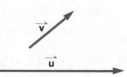

$\checkmark$ **9.** Copy and complete this sentence: If $\vec{p} = k\vec{q}$ and $\vec{p} + \vec{q} = \vec{0}$, then $k = $ __?__ .

7-3 Find $\vec{v} + \vec{u}$, $\vec{v} - \vec{u}$, and $r\vec{v} + s\vec{u}$ for each set of data.

$\checkmark$ **10.** $\vec{v} = \begin{pmatrix} 2 \\ 3 \end{pmatrix}$, $\vec{u} = \begin{pmatrix} -4 \\ 7 \end{pmatrix}$, $r = 3, s = -1$ $\checkmark$ **11.** $\vec{v} = \begin{pmatrix} 1 \\ 2 \end{pmatrix}$, $\vec{u} = \begin{pmatrix} 3 \\ 2 \end{pmatrix}$, $r = \frac{1}{2}, s = \frac{1}{2}$

Determine values for r and s which make each statement true.

$\checkmark$ **12.** $\begin{pmatrix} 2 \\ -5 \end{pmatrix} + \begin{pmatrix} r \\ s \end{pmatrix} = \begin{pmatrix} 0 \\ 0 \end{pmatrix}$ $\checkmark$ **13.** $r\begin{pmatrix} 1 \\ 0 \end{pmatrix} + s\begin{pmatrix} 0 \\ 1 \end{pmatrix} = \begin{pmatrix} -2 \\ 7 \end{pmatrix}$

7-4 **14.** Prove Property DV_2: $(k_1 + k_2)\vec{v} = k_1\vec{v} + k_2\vec{v}$ for Vector Two-Space. Use $k_1, k_2 \in \mathcal{R}$ for scalars and $\vec{v} = \begin{pmatrix} a \\ b \end{pmatrix} \in \mathcal{V}_2$ as a vector.

7-5 If $\vec{v} = \begin{pmatrix} 2 \\ -3 \end{pmatrix}$ and $\vec{u} = \begin{pmatrix} -5 \\ 1 \end{pmatrix}$, find each norm.

$\checkmark$ **15.** $\|\vec{v}\|$ $\checkmark$ **16.** $\|\vec{u}\|$ $\checkmark$ **17.** $\|-\vec{v}\|$

$\checkmark$ **18.** $\|\vec{v} + \vec{u}\|$ $\checkmark$ **19.** $\|\vec{v}\| + \|\vec{u}\|$ $\checkmark$ **20.** $\|\vec{v} - \vec{u}\|$

Determine whether each pair of vectors is orthogonal.

$\checkmark$ **21.** $\begin{pmatrix} 2 \\ 1 \end{pmatrix}, \begin{pmatrix} -2 \\ 4 \end{pmatrix}$ $\checkmark$ **22.** $\begin{pmatrix} 1 \\ 0 \end{pmatrix}, \begin{pmatrix} 1 \\ 0 \end{pmatrix}$ $\checkmark$ **23.** $\begin{pmatrix} 4 \\ 5 \end{pmatrix}, \begin{pmatrix} -5 \\ 4 \end{pmatrix}$

7-6 Determine the horizontal and vertical components of each vector.

$\checkmark$ **24.** $\vec{v} = \begin{pmatrix} -5 \\ 3 \end{pmatrix}$ $\checkmark$ **25.** $3\begin{pmatrix} 5 \\ -2 \end{pmatrix} - 2\begin{pmatrix} 7 \\ 6 \end{pmatrix}$

$\checkmark$ **26.** $\overrightarrow{AB}$ for $A(3, -7)$ and $B(-2, 9)$

27. The magnitude and direction of a force on a boat's sail is described by the vector $\vec{v}$, making an angle θ with the direction of the boat's course. Neglecting wave conditions, decide which of the following cases will make the boat go faster.
   a. $\|\vec{v}\| = 100, \theta = 45°$ **b.** $\|\vec{v}\| = 80, \theta = 30°$

7-7 **28.** Find the unit vector which has the same direction as the vector $\begin{pmatrix} 2 \\ -6 \end{pmatrix}$. Find the slope of the line containing the vector.

29. The unit vector with direction angle 30° is $\vec{u}$. Write $\vec{u}$ as $r\vec{i} + s\vec{j}$.

7-8 $ABCD$ is a parallelogram with $A(1, 1)$, $B(7, 3)$ and $C(10, 7)$. The midpoint of $\overline{AB}$ is M, and $\overline{DM}$ cuts $\overline{AC}$ at P.

30. State the coordinates of D.   **31.** Express $\overline{OM}$ in component form.

7-9 Decide which of the following statements are true (T) and which are false (F).

32. $(\vec{v} \cdot \vec{u})\vec{w}$ is a real number.   **33.** $(\vec{v} \cdot \vec{u})(\vec{u} \cdot \vec{w})$ is a vector.

7-10 **34.** Write a vector proof to prove the segment connecting the midpoints of the nonparallel sides of a trapezoid is parallel to the bases.

Chapter Test

Point A is (4, 3) and B is (−2, 2). For the given C, find the point D such that $\overrightarrow{AB}$ and $\overrightarrow{CD}$ belong to the same equivalence class.

1. $C(1, 2)$ 2. $C(0, 0)$ 3. $C(a, b)$

For each vector $\overrightarrow{AB}$, write the coordinates of the point X for which $\overrightarrow{OX}$ is a position vector opposite to $\overrightarrow{AB}$.

4. $A(2, -5), B(3, -2)$ 5. $A(-2, 3), B(6, 2)$

Copy the vector figure.

6. Show the sum $\vec{u} + \vec{v}$ by a vector parallelogram.
7. Find the vector sum $\vec{u} + \vec{v}$ by a vector triangle.
8. Find the vector difference $\vec{u} - \vec{v}$ by drawing $\vec{u} + (-\vec{v})$.

9. Prove that the product of any scalar and the zero vector is the zero vector.

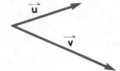

Let $\vec{v} = \begin{pmatrix} -2 \\ 4 \end{pmatrix}$, $\vec{u} = \begin{pmatrix} 1 \\ -2 \end{pmatrix}$, $r = 2$, and $s = 4$. Find each of the following.

10. $\vec{v} + \vec{u}$ 11. $\vec{v} - \vec{u}$ 12. $r\vec{v} + s\vec{u}$

13. Determine values for r and s which make $\begin{pmatrix} 2 \\ -5 \end{pmatrix} + \begin{pmatrix} r \\ s \end{pmatrix} = \begin{pmatrix} 0 \\ 0 \end{pmatrix}$ true.

14. Prove $\mathbf{SMV_5}$: $0\vec{v} = \vec{0}$ for Vector Two Space.

Find the norm of each vector.

15. $\begin{pmatrix} \sqrt{2} \\ \sqrt{2} \end{pmatrix}$ 16. $\begin{pmatrix} 3 \\ -4 \end{pmatrix}$ 17. $\begin{pmatrix} 1 \\ 0 \end{pmatrix}$

18. A pilot wishes to fly due west. She discovers a crosswind from the north of 60 miles per hour. If her airplane usually cruises at an air speed of 320 miles per hour, what heading should she use to ensure traveling west? What will be her resultant westerly speed (westerly component)?

Let $\vec{v} = \begin{pmatrix} -3 \\ 7 \end{pmatrix}$ and $\vec{u} = \begin{pmatrix} 1 \\ 5 \end{pmatrix}$. Write each vector in the form $r\vec{i} + s\vec{j}$.

19. $\vec{v}$ 20. $\vec{u}$ 21. $4\vec{v} - 3\vec{u}$

22. If $\overrightarrow{BA}$ is divided in the ratio 3:2 (or $2BM = 3MA$), show that $\vec{m} = \frac{1}{5}(3\vec{a} + 2\vec{b})$.

Find each dot product if $\vec{v} = \begin{pmatrix} 3 \\ 1 \end{pmatrix}$, $\vec{u} = \begin{pmatrix} 2 \\ -2 \end{pmatrix}$ and $\vec{w} = \begin{pmatrix} -1 \\ 3 \end{pmatrix}$.

23. $\vec{u} \cdot \vec{w}$ 24. $3\vec{v} \cdot 2\vec{u}$

25. Write a vector proof to prove the diagonals of a rectangle are congruent.

Computers

BASIC-Statements

Many higher-level languages have been developed. These languages make it possible to program computers in a relatively short time. Since many small computers use the computer language BASIC (Beginner's All-purpose Symbolic Instruction Code), special attention is given here and in subsequent computer pages. Sample programs will be given and discussed, highlighting the different types of statements possible.

```
10   REM FINDING MIDPOINTS AND DIS-
     TANCES
20   READ X1, Y1, X2, Y2
30   REM MIDPOINT OF A LINE SEGMENT
40   LET X = (X1 + X2)/2: Y = (Y1 + Y2)/2
50   PRINT
60   REM DISTANCE BETWEEN POINTS
70   LET D = ((X2 − X1)↑2 + (Y2 − Y1)↑2)↑.5
80   PRINT
90   PRINT X, Y
100  PRINT "THE DISTANCE IS"; D
110  GØTØ 20
120  DATA 3, 8, −5, −2, 10, −3, −6, 8
130  END
```

Line numbers in BASIC are part of the program and are executed in order unless a branch such as in line 110 is reached. Most programmers number lines by tens so that other lines may be inserted if needed later.

The REM statement is used as a remark to title a program or to identify parts of a program when it is listed. It is ignored by the computer when the program is run.

Each READ statement must have a DATA statement to which it refers. Every time the READ statement is reached, the next unused values in the DATA statement are assigned to the proper variables.

A variable in BASIC may be a single letter such as X, A, T or a letter followed by a digit such as B3, R1, D6. Sometimes a BASIC allows three or more characters. Subscripted variables such as A(1), A(2), A(3) are possible and will be referred to later.

Values are assigned to a variable within a program through the use of a LET statement. Either a number or an expression that can be evaluated must appear to the right of any equals sign used in a LET statement. Note that this use of an equals sign is for assignment and not as in algebra. Thus, $X = X + 1$ is nonsense in algebra, but LET $X = X + 1$ is common in BASIC.

The computer uses operational symbols similar to the ones used in algebra. For example, $*$ takes the place of $\cdot$ or $\times$ for multiplication, / is used instead of $\div$ for division, and ↑ for exponential expressions. Some BASIC languages use $**$ or $\wedge$ for exponential expressions. The $*$ must be indicated to show all multiplications. Thus, $(B ↑ 2 − 4*A*C)/(2*A)$ in BASIC is the same as $(b^2 − 4ac) \div 2a$ in algebra.

PRINT and REM can be used to leave blank lines in output or a program for ease in reading.

PRINT X, Y causes the current values of X and Y to be printed in separate print zones; that is, all variables separated by commas are output in columns. A more compact output can be caused by using a semi-colon between the variable names in a PRINT statement.

PRINT"_____" is used to output specific text such as labels or identifying words.

Most, but not all, versions of BASIC require the very last statement of a program to be identified by an END statement.

The program would have run twice because of the branching GØTØ statement and then stopped for lack of input DATA to be accessed by the READ statement.

```
10    REM   FINDING MIDPOINTS AND DI
      STANCES
20    READ X1,Y1,X2,Y2
30    REM   MIDPOINT OF A LINE SEGME
      NT
40    LET X = (X1 + X2) / 2:Y = (Y1
      + Y2) / 2
50    PRINT
60    REM  DISTANCE BETWEEN POINTS
70    LET D = ((X2 - X1) ^ 2 + (Y2 -
      Y1) ^ 2) ^ .5
80    PRINT
90    PRINT X,Y
100   PRINT
110   PRINT "THE DISTANCE IS ";D
120   GOTO 20
130   DATA  3,8,-5,-2,10,-3,-6,8
140   END

JRUN


-1              3

THE DISTANCE IS 12.8062485


2               2.5

THE DISTANCE IS 19.4164879

?OUT OF DATA ERROR IN 20
```

Exercises **Write a program for each of the following using 2-dimensional vectors.**

1. Find the ordered pair which represents $\overline{AB}$ given $A(p, q)$ and $B(r, s)$.

2. Find the norm of the vector from $A(p, q)$ to $B(r, s)$.

3. Find the scalar multiples of $\vec{u}$ and $\vec{v}$ if $\vec{u} = (p, q)$ and $\vec{v} = (r, s)$ and k is the scaler.

4. Find the unit vectors of $\vec{u}$ and $\vec{v}$ if $\vec{u} = (m, n)$ and $\vec{v} = (s, t)$.

5. Given $\vec{u}$ and $\vec{v}$ determine if the vectors are perpendicular.

6. Given $\vec{u}$ and $\vec{v}$ determine if the vectors are parallel.

7. Find the dot product of $\vec{u}$ and $\vec{v}$ where θ is the angle between $\vec{u}$ and $\vec{v}$. Use $\|\vec{v}\| \|\vec{u}\| \cos \theta$.

8. Find $\vec{u} \cdot \vec{v}$ using the terms of the vectors components.

9. Find the angle θ between $\vec{u}$ and $\vec{v}$.

Chapter 8

Geometry is a natural context in which to study vectors. Vector theory itself came from the algebraic methods devised to study certain aspects of geometry. Both physical and social scientists use vectors in a variety of settings.

Space

8–1 Coordinates in Space

A coordinate system can be placed on the plane so that figures can be studied analytically. The coordinate system can be extended to space and solid figures similarly analyzed. Let $\overrightarrow{OX}$, $\overrightarrow{OY}$, and $\overrightarrow{OZ}$ be three *mutually perpendicular* lines. These lines are called the x-, y-, and z-axes, respectively. The commonly used choices for the positive directions produces a *right-handed* system. If a right-handed screw is pointed along the positive z-axis as shown, it will advance as the positive x-axis rotates toward the positive y-axis.

The x-axis is drawn so that $\angle YOX$ appears to be obtuse, although it actually is a right angle. This perspective also gives the impression that the units on the x-axis are not the same as on the other axes.

Refer to Chapter 2.

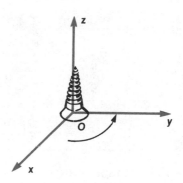

The planes determined by each pair of coordinate axes are the **coordinate planes.** These planes are called the *xy*-plane, the *xz*-plane, and the *yz*-plane.

Coordinate Planes

In establishing this coordinate system, the usual Euclidean postulates about points, lines, and planes are accepted. Other implicit assumptions will be made as the coordinate system is developed.

Let P be any point in space. Any plane which contains P and is parallel to the *yz*-plane intersects the x-axis at $x = x_1$. Similarly, planes parallel to the other coordinate planes intersect the y- and z-axes at $y = y_1$ and $z = z_1$. The three numbers $x_1, y_1,$ and z_1 written as an ordered triple (x_1, y_1, z_1) are called the *coordinates* of P.

Some assumptions are:
1. *Only one plane is perpendicular to a line at a point.*
2. *Any plane containing a line perpendicular to another plane is itself perpendicular to that plane.*

If P is in the zy-plane, then $x_1 = 0$.

The three coordinate planes separate space into eight parts called **octants.** In the octant shown, all coordinates are positive. The octants are not numbered, instead they can be specified by indicating the signs of the coordinates. For example, the octant with x negative, y positive, and z negative may be specified as $(-, +, -)$.

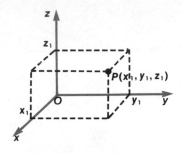

There is only one plane through P parallel to each coordinate plane. It can be proved that these three planes intersect in only one point P. For this reason, there is only one ordered triple for each point. Conversely, through the intersection on each axis, represented by $x_1, y_1,$ and z_1, there is only one plane perpendicular to the axis. This establishes a *one-to-one correspondence* between the points in space and the ordered triples of real numbers.

For convenience, the point P will be called the point (x_1, y_1, z_1) or $P(x_1, y_1, z_1)$.

The set of ordered triples with first coordinates from A, second coordinates from B, and third coordinates from C is often denoted $A \times B \times C$.

Examples

1. Find $A \times B \times C$ if $A = \{1, 2\}, B = \{5\},$ and $C = \{7, 8\}$.

   $A \times B \times C = \{(1, 5, 7), (1, 5, 8), (2, 5, 7), (2, 5, 8)\}$

2. Find $D \times E$ if $D = \{(1, 5), (2, 5)\}$ and $E = \{7, 8\}$.

   $D \times E = \{((1, 5), 7), ((1, 5), 8), ((2, 5), 7), ((2, 5), 8)\}$

Points in space are named by elements in $\mathcal{R} \times \mathcal{R} \times \mathcal{R}$. In fact, a one-to-one correspondence is postulated between $\mathcal{R} \times \mathcal{R} \times \mathcal{R}$ and the set of points in space.

Exercises

Exploratory Find $A \times B \times C$.

1. $A = \{1, 3\}, B = \{2\}, C = \{5, 6\}$
2. $A = \{4\}, B = \{2, 5\}, C = \{1, 6\}$
3. $A = \{a, b\}, B = \{a, c\}, C = \{b, c\}$
4. $A = \{x, y\}, B = \{a, e\}, C = \{7\}$

Find $A \times B$.

5. $A = \{(1, 2), (1, 3)\}, B = \{5, 9\}$
6. $A = \{(4, 7)\}, B = \{6, 1, 4, 9\}$

Name the plane in which the following points are located.

7. $(3, 4, 0)$
8. $(0, 5, 7)$
9. $(7, 0, 2)$

10. A contains m elements, B contains n elements, and C contains p elements. How many elements are in $A \times B \times C$?

Written   Describe each set of points.

1. $\{(x, y, z)|x = 4\}$
2. $\{(x, y, z)|x = -2, y = 3\}$
3. $\{(x, y, z)|y = -2\}$
4. $\{(x, y, z)|y = 1, z = -2\}$

Copy and complete each statement.

5. The xy-plane is the perpendicular bisector of the segment joining $(3, -4, 8)$ and _____.

6. The yz-plane is the perpendicular bisector of the segment joining $(-4, -6, -3)$ and _____.

7. The x-axis is the perpendicular bisector of the segment joining $(8, -3, 1)$ and _____.

8. The y-axis is the perpendicular bisector of the segment joining $(-4, 10, -7)$ and _____.

9. The origin is the midpoint of the segment joining $(4, -1, 6)$ and _____.

10. The origin is the midpoint of the segment joining $(-1, 7, 3)$ and _____.

Determine if the points in each pair are on the same side of the xy-plane.

11. $(3, -5, 2)$ and $(4, 4, 4)$
12. $(-8, -6, 4)$ and $(-7, 9, -3)$

Determine if the points in each pair are on the same side of the yz-plane.

13. $(4, -2, 7)$ and $(-10, -12, 4)$
14. $(6, 6, -2)$ and $(-4, 21, 62)$

15. A cube has its center at the origin and its faces each are perpendicular to an axis. If the cube has an edge 8 units long, what are the coordinates of the eight vertices?

Copy and complete each statement.

16. A line passes through the origin from the octant $(-, -, +)$ into the octant ____.

17. A line passes through the origin from the octant $(+, -, +)$ into the octant ____.

8–2   Distance

The distance between two points in space can be found by using the Pythagorean Theorem. Perpendiculars are drawn from two points $P(x_1, y_1, z_1)$ and $Q(x_2, y_2, z_2)$ to the xy-plane. The segment $\overline{SU}$ is called the projection of $\overline{PQ}$ on the xy-plane. In the xy-plane, the projection of $\overline{SU}$ on the y-axis is $\overline{VW}$.

$$ST = VW = |y_2 - y_1|$$
$$UT = |x_2 - x_1|$$
$$PR = SU = \sqrt{(x_2 - x_1)^2 + (y_2 - y_1)^2}$$
$$QR = |z_2 - z_1|$$

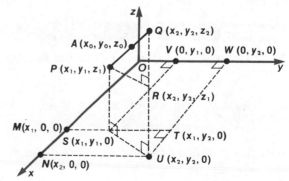

Since $\overline{PR} \perp \overline{QU}$, find PQ.

$$PQ^2 = PR^2 + QR^2$$
$$PQ^2 = (x_2 - x_1)^2 + (y_2 - y_1)^2 + (z_2 - z_1)^2$$
$$PQ = \sqrt{(x_2 - x_1)^2 + (y_2 - y_1)^2 + (z_2 - z_1)^2}$$

The distance between $P(x_1, y_1, z_1)$ and $Q(x_2, y_2, z_2)$ is $PQ = \sqrt{(x_2 - x_1)^2 + (y_2 - y_1)^2 + (z_2 - z_1)^2}.$	**Distance Formula**

Example

1. **Find the distance between $P(1, 2, 4)$ and $Q(-2, 6, -8)$.**
   $$PQ = \sqrt{(-2 - 1)^2 + (6 - 2)^2 + (-8 - 4)^2} = \sqrt{169} = 13$$

The coordinates of the point A on $\overline{PQ}$ can be found such that $\dfrac{PA}{PQ} = k$. The coordinates are (x_0, y_0, z_0) as defined below.

$$x_0 = x_1 + k(x_2 - x_1) \qquad y_0 = y_1 + k(y_2 - y_1) \qquad z_0 = z_1 + k(z_2 - z_1)$$

If A is the midpoint of $\overline{PQ}$, then $k = \dfrac{1}{2}$.

$$x_0 = \frac{x_1 + x_2}{2} \qquad y_0 = \frac{x_1 + y_1}{2} \qquad z_0 = \frac{z_1 + z_2}{2}$$

Example

2. **Find the coordinates of the midpoint B of $\overline{AC}$ when A has coordinates $(7, 3, 2)$ and C has coordinates $(-1, 0, -2)$.**

   If B is the midpoint of $\overline{AC}$, then $k = \dfrac{1}{2}$.

   $$x_0 = \frac{7 + (-1)}{2} = \frac{6}{2} = 3 \qquad y_0 = \frac{3 + 0}{2} = \frac{3}{2} \qquad z_0 = \frac{2 + (-2)}{2} = \frac{0}{2} = 0$$

   The coordinates of the midpoint are $\left(3, \dfrac{3}{2}, 0\right)$.

Exercises

Exploratory Find the length of the projection of $\overline{PQ}$ on the xy-plane and on the x-axis.

1. $P(5, -3, 1)$, $Q(8, 1, 7)$
2. $P(-2, -7, 4)$, $Q(10, -2, 6)$

Find the length of the projection of $\overline{AB}$ on the yz-plane and on the y-axis.

3. $A(4, 2, -1)$, $B(-3, -6, 14)$
4. $A(1, 1, 1)$, $B(3, 3, 3)$

Find the distance between P and Q. Then, find the midpoint of the segment PQ.

5. $P(4, -7, 1)$, $Q(1, -1, 3)$
6. $P(0, -4, -8)$, $Q(-1, 4, -4)$
7. $P(6, -1, 1)$, $Q(2, 2, -3)$
8. $P(3, 0, -10)$, $Q(1, -2, 8)$

Written Find the length of the projection of $\overline{PQ}$ on the *xy*-plane and on the *x*-axis.

1. $P(4, 1, -2), Q(-1, 4, 4)$
2. $P(9, -2, 3), Q(7, 4, -1)$
3. $P(3n, 4n, n), Q(-5n, 11n, 2n)$
4. $P(4n, -7n, 11n), Q(-2n, n, -n)$

Find the length of the projection of $\overline{AB}$ on the *xz*-plane and on the *y*-axis.

5. $A(2, 1, -4), B(8, -1, -6)$
6. $A(5, 5, 5), B(-1, -1, -1)$
7. $A(11n, -3n, 4n), B(3n, 12n, -8n)$
8. $A(r - 3, 3r + 1, 4r), B(2r - 1, r + 2, 8r)$

Find the distance between P and Q.

9. $P(9, 3, -2), Q(5, -1, 0)$
10. $P(-1, 7, 1), Q(2, 5, -2)$
11. $P(12, 4, -3), Q(-1, -2, 5)$
12. $P(6\sqrt{3}, 1, -4), Q(2\sqrt{3}, -3, 2)$

Find the midpoint of the segment PQ.

13. $P(2\sqrt{3}, 1, -5), Q(4\sqrt{3}, -2, 1)$
14. $P\left(0, 1, \frac{1}{2}\right), Q\left(1, 0, \frac{1}{2}\right)$
15. $P(a, 0, c), Q(b, d, 0)$
16. $P(2a, b, c - d), Q(4a, 5b, c + d)$

If M is the midpoint of $\overline{AB}$, find B for each M and A.

17. $A(2, 5, -1), M(3, 1, 0)$
18. $A(4\sqrt{2}, -1, 3), M(-3\sqrt{2}, 2, 11)$

Solve each of the following.

19. Show that the triangle with vertices at $A(1, 2, 1)$, $B(-3, 7, 9)$, and $C(11, 4, 2)$ is isosceles, but not equilateral.

20. Use the distance formula to show that the segments connecting the origin with $P(4, 2, 16)$ and $Q(1, 6, -1)$ are perpendicular to each other.

21. Show that the points $A(3, 4, -1), B(9, -4, 10), C(7, -2, 3)$, and $D(1, 6, -8)$ taken in order form a parallelogram. Is it enough to show that the opposite sides are equal in length?

22. Suppose (x, y, z) is any point which is 4 units from $(1, -2, 1)$. Write an equation to express this relation. What kind of locus is described?

23. Show that the points $A\left(\frac{2}{3}, 4, -\frac{1}{3}\right), B\left(\frac{8}{3}, -1, 1\right), C\left(\frac{17}{6}, -7, \frac{3}{2}\right)$ and $D\left(\frac{5}{6}, -2, \frac{1}{6}\right)$, taken in order, form a parallelogram.

24. Find the points of trisection of the segment with endpoints $A(-10, 2, 5)$ and $B(2, 4, -1)$.

25. Find the points of trisection of the segment with endpoints $A(-1, 2, 4)$ and $B(5, -10, 10)$.

26. Show that the points $A(1, 4, -3), B(7, 2, -1), C(8, 3, -3)$, and $D(2, 5, -5)$ taken in order are the vertices of a rectangle.

8–3 Vectors in Space

The study of *three-dimensional* space by means of vectors is accomplished by an extension of two-dimensional vectors. In two-space a vector was considered an equivalence class of arrows and each vector was associated with an ordered pair of numbers. In three-dimensional space, a vector is again defined

to be an equivalence class of arrows. The arrows of a particular vector have the same magnitude and direction. Each
vector in space can be associated with an ordered triple of
numbers $\begin{pmatrix} a \\ b \\ c \end{pmatrix}$.

If $\vec{u} = \begin{pmatrix} a_1 \\ b_1 \\ c_1 \end{pmatrix}$ and $\vec{v} = \begin{pmatrix} a_2 \\ b_2 \\ c_2 \end{pmatrix}$, then $\vec{u} = \vec{v}$ if and only if $a_1 = a_2$, $b_1 = b_2$, and $c_1 = c_2$.

Equivalence of Vectors

The operations of addition and scalar multiplication are the
same as for two-dimensional vectors.

$$\vec{u} + \vec{v} = \begin{pmatrix} a_1 \\ b_1 \\ c_1 \end{pmatrix} + \begin{pmatrix} a_2 \\ b_2 \\ c_2 \end{pmatrix} = \begin{pmatrix} a_1 + a_2 \\ b_1 + b_2 \\ c_1 + c_2 \end{pmatrix}$$

$$k\vec{u} = k \begin{pmatrix} a_1 \\ b_1 \\ c_1 \end{pmatrix} = \begin{pmatrix} ka_1 \\ kb_1 \\ kc_1 \end{pmatrix}, k \in \mathcal{R}$$

Examples

1. If $\vec{u} = \begin{pmatrix} 7 \\ 8 \\ 1 \end{pmatrix}$ and $\vec{v} = \begin{pmatrix} 1 \\ -3 \\ 0 \end{pmatrix}$, find $\vec{u} + \vec{v}$.

$$\begin{pmatrix} 7 \\ 8 \\ 1 \end{pmatrix} + \begin{pmatrix} 1 \\ -3 \\ 0 \end{pmatrix} = \begin{pmatrix} 8 \\ 5 \\ 1 \end{pmatrix}$$

2. If $\vec{u} = \begin{pmatrix} 2 \\ -3 \\ 6 \end{pmatrix}$ and $k = 3$, find $k\vec{u}$.

$$3 \begin{pmatrix} 2 \\ -3 \\ 6 \end{pmatrix} = \begin{pmatrix} 6 \\ -9 \\ 18 \end{pmatrix}$$

Any two position vectors are coplanar. Three position vectors
need not be coplanar. The addition of three vectors is shown in
the figure on the next page. Suppose the vectors $\vec{r}$, $\vec{v}$, and

*A position vector is a vector
which has the initial point at the
origin.*

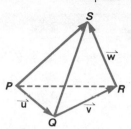

$\overline{w}$ have position vectors that are not coplanar. Then *PQRS* is a tetrahedron (triangular pyramid), and $\vec{u} + \vec{v} + \vec{w}$ is represented by $\overrightarrow{PS}$. Suppose all three position vectors are coplanar. Then it is still true that $\vec{u} + \vec{v} + \vec{w}$ is represented by $\overrightarrow{PS}$.

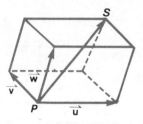

The addition of three vectors is also shown as in the figure to the right. The diagonal of the parallelepiped represents the sum of the three vectors, $\vec{u} + \vec{v} + \vec{w}$. This is similar to using the diagonal of a parallelogram to represent the sum of two vectors in two-dimensional space.

The following properties are adapted from two dimensions. They define a three-dimensional vector space, $\mathcal{V}_3$.

These properties are inherited from the properties of reals and therefore can be proved.

AV₁:	*Closure*	$(\vec{u} + \vec{v}) \in \mathcal{V}_3$
AV₂:	*Associativity*	$(\vec{u} + \vec{v}) + \vec{w} = \vec{u} + (\vec{v} + \vec{w})$
AV₃:	*Additive Identity*	$\vec{v} + \vec{0} = \vec{0} + \vec{v} = \vec{v}$, where

$$\vec{0} = \begin{pmatrix} 0 \\ 0 \\ 0 \end{pmatrix}$$

AV₄: *Additive Inverse* $\vec{v} + (-\vec{v}) = (-\vec{v}) + \vec{v} = \vec{0}$,

$$\text{where } -\vec{v} = \begin{pmatrix} -a \\ -b \\ -c \end{pmatrix} \text{ when } \vec{v} = \begin{pmatrix} a \\ b \\ c \end{pmatrix}$$

AV₅: *Commutativity* $\vec{u} + \vec{v} = \vec{v} + \vec{u}$

SMV₁: *Closure* $k\vec{v} \in \mathcal{V}_3, k \in \mathcal{R}$
SMV₂: *Associativity* $k_1(k_2\vec{v}) = (k_1 k_2)\vec{v}$
SMV₃: $1\vec{v} = \vec{v}$
SMV₄: $-1\vec{v} = -\vec{v}$
SMV₅: $0\vec{v} = \vec{0}$
SMV₆: $k\vec{0} = \vec{0}$

DV₁: $k(\vec{u} + \vec{v}) = k\vec{u} + k\vec{v}$
DV₂: $(k_1 + k_2)\vec{v} = k_1\vec{v} + k_2\vec{v}$

Properties of Addition

Properties of Scalar, Multiplication

Distributive Properties

Example

3. **Prove $(\bar{u} + \bar{v}) + \bar{w} = \bar{u} + (\bar{v} + \bar{w})$.**

Let $\bar{u} = \begin{pmatrix} a_1 \\ b_1 \\ c_1 \end{pmatrix}$, $\bar{v} = \begin{pmatrix} a_2 \\ b_2 \\ c_2 \end{pmatrix}$, and $\bar{w} = \begin{pmatrix} a_3 \\ b_3 \\ c_3 \end{pmatrix}$.

If $\bar{u} + \bar{v} = \begin{pmatrix} a_1 + a_2 \\ b_1 + b_2 \\ c_1 + c_2 \end{pmatrix}$, then $(\bar{u} + \bar{v}) + \bar{w} = \begin{pmatrix} (a_1 + a_2) + a_3 \\ (b_1 + b_2) + b_3 \\ (c_1 + c_2) + c_3 \end{pmatrix}$.

If $\bar{v} + \bar{w} = \begin{pmatrix} a_2 + a_3 \\ b_2 + b_3 \\ c_2 + c_3 \end{pmatrix}$, then $\bar{u} + (\bar{v} + \bar{w}) = \begin{pmatrix} a_1 + (a_2 + a_3) \\ b_1 + (b_2 + b_3) \\ c_1 + (c_2 + c_3) \end{pmatrix}$.

Therefore, $(\bar{u} + \bar{v}) + \bar{w} = \bar{u} + (\bar{v} + \bar{w})$ by the associative property for addition of real numbers.

Exercises

Exploratory Find the values of m, n, and p so that equality holds.

1. $\begin{pmatrix} 3 \\ n \\ p - 1 \end{pmatrix} = \begin{pmatrix} m \\ 2n - 3 \\ 4 \end{pmatrix}$

2. $\begin{pmatrix} 4 \\ -2 \\ p \end{pmatrix} = \begin{pmatrix} n \\ m \\ 5 \end{pmatrix}$

3. $\begin{pmatrix} 3m + 2 \\ n - 4 \\ 2 - 5p \end{pmatrix} = \begin{pmatrix} 11 \\ -6 \\ 5 \end{pmatrix}$

Evaluate each expression if $\bar{u} = \begin{pmatrix} -2 \\ 1 \\ 4 \end{pmatrix}$, $\bar{v} = \begin{pmatrix} 3 \\ -2 \\ 2 \end{pmatrix}$, $k = 5$, and $r = -2$.

4. $2\,\bar{u}$
5. $r\,\bar{v}$
6. $2\bar{u} + r\bar{v}$
7. $\bar{u} - \bar{v}$
8. $\bar{v} - \bar{u}$
9. $k\bar{u}$

Written Find the values of m, n, and p so that each equality holds.

1. $\begin{pmatrix} 3m + 2n \\ n - 4p \\ 2m - 5p \end{pmatrix} = \begin{pmatrix} 11 \\ -6 \\ 5 \end{pmatrix}$

2. $\begin{pmatrix} 2m - p \\ p - n \\ 3n + 2p \end{pmatrix} = \begin{pmatrix} n - 3 \\ m - 2n - 3 \\ m + 1 \end{pmatrix}$

3. $\begin{pmatrix} m + n \\ 2m \\ p - n + m \end{pmatrix} = \begin{pmatrix} p - 2 \\ p \\ 0 \end{pmatrix}$

4. $\begin{pmatrix} n + p \\ 2m + 2p \\ 4m + 2n \end{pmatrix} = \begin{pmatrix} 2 - m \\ 3n - 1 \\ p + 16 \end{pmatrix}$

Prove each of the following.

5. If $\bar{u} = \bar{v}$ and $\bar{v} = \bar{w}$, then $\bar{u} = \bar{w}$.
6. If $k = r$, then $k\bar{v} = r\bar{v}$.
7. If $k\bar{v} = r\bar{v}$, $\bar{v} \ne \bar{0}$, then $k = r$.
8. $k\bar{v} = \bar{0}$ if and only if $k = 0$ or $\bar{v} = \bar{0}$.
9. $k(r\bar{v}) = (kr)\bar{v}$
10. $k(\bar{u} + \bar{v}) = k\bar{u} + k\bar{v}$
11. $(k + r)\,\bar{v} = k\bar{v} + r\bar{v}$
12. $1\bar{v} = \bar{v}$

Challenge   Use suitable definitions for addition and scalar multiplication to show that the set of ordered quadruples $\begin{pmatrix} a \\ b \\ c \\ d \end{pmatrix}$ forms a vector space over the field of real numbers.

8–4   The Norm

The *norm* of a vector is defined by using the distance formula.

The norm of $\bar{v}$, denoted $\|\bar{v}\|$, is the length of each arrow in the equivalance class. If $\bar{v} = \begin{pmatrix} a \\ b \\ c \end{pmatrix}$, then $\|\bar{v}\| = \sqrt{a^2 + b^2 + c^2}$.

Norm

The properties of the norm can be proved using the definition of norm.

For any vectors $\bar{u}$ and $\bar{v}$ and scalar k, the following is true.

$$\|\bar{0}\| = 0$$

$$\|\bar{v}\| \geq 0$$
$$\|k\bar{v}\| = |k|\ \|\bar{v}\|$$
$$\|\bar{v} + \bar{u}\| \leq \|\bar{v}\| + \|\bar{u}\| \quad \textit{(Triangle Inequality)}$$

Properties of Norm

Three nonzero vectors are required to form a basis for Vector Three-Space. No two of their respective position vectors can be collinear. Also, the position vectors must be noncoplanar.

The vectors $\vec{i}, \vec{j}$, and $\vec{k}$ are unit vectors whose arrows lie along the positive x-, y-, and z-axes.

$$\vec{i} = \begin{pmatrix} 1 \\ 0 \\ 0 \end{pmatrix} \qquad \vec{j} = \begin{pmatrix} 0 \\ 1 \\ 0 \end{pmatrix} \qquad \vec{k} = \begin{pmatrix} 0 \\ 0 \\ 1 \end{pmatrix}$$

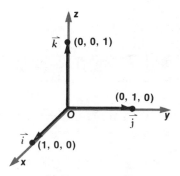

Any vector can be written as a linear combination of $\vec{i}, \vec{j}$, and $\vec{k}$. That is, if $\bar{v} = \begin{pmatrix} a \\ b \\ c \end{pmatrix}$, then $\bar{v} = a\vec{i} + b\vec{j} + c\vec{k}$.

If $\bar{v} = \begin{pmatrix} a_1 \\ b_1 \\ c_1 \end{pmatrix}$ and $\bar{u} = \begin{pmatrix} a_2 \\ b_2 \\ c_2 \end{pmatrix}$ are nonzero vectors, and the angle between the position vectors of $\bar{u}$ and $\bar{v}$ is θ, then the dot product is $\vec{v} \cdot \vec{u} = \|\vec{v}\| \cdot \|\vec{u}\| \cos \theta$. If either $\vec{v}$ or $\vec{u}$ is the zero vector, then their dot product is defined to be 0.

For any vectors $\vec{v}$ and $\vec{u}$, and scalar k, the following are properties of the dot product.

$$\vec{v} \cdot \vec{u} = a_1 a_2 + b_1 b_2 + c_1 c_2$$
$$\vec{v} \cdot (\vec{u} + \vec{w}) = \vec{v} \cdot \vec{u} + \vec{v} \cdot \vec{w}$$
$$(k\vec{v}) \cdot \vec{u} = k(\vec{v} \cdot \vec{u}), k \in \mathcal{R}$$
$$\vec{v} \cdot \vec{v} = \|\vec{v}\|^2$$

$\vec{v}$ is orthogonal to $\vec{u}$ if and only if $\vec{v} \cdot \vec{u} = 0$.

Properties of Dot Products

The direction of a two-dimensional vector is determined by the angle its position vector makes with the positive x-axis. The direction of a three-dimensional vector can be determined by the three angles its position vector makes with the positive x-, y-, and z-axes.

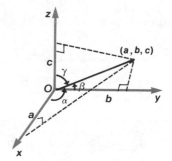

Let these angles be α, β, and γ respectively.

$$\cos \alpha = \frac{\vec{v} \cdot \vec{i}}{\|\vec{v}\|}, \cos \beta = \frac{\vec{v} \cdot \vec{j}}{\|\vec{v}\|}, \cos \gamma = \frac{\vec{v} \cdot \vec{k}}{\|\vec{v}\|}$$

$$\cos \alpha = \frac{a}{\|\vec{v}\|}, \cos \beta = \frac{b}{\|\vec{v}\|}, \cos \gamma = \frac{c}{\|\vec{v}\|}$$

These angles α, β, and γ are called the **direction angles** of $\vec{v}$. The cosines of these angles are called the **direction cosines** of $\vec{v}$. Since $\cos^2 \alpha + \cos^2 \beta + \cos^2 \gamma = \frac{a^2}{\|v\|^2} + \frac{b^2}{\|v\|^2} + \frac{c^2}{\|v\|^2}$, it follows that $\cos^2 \alpha + \cos^2 \beta + \cos^2 \gamma = 1$.

Example

1. Find the direction cosines for $\vec{v} = \begin{pmatrix} 2 \\ 3 \\ 6 \end{pmatrix}$.

$$\|\vec{v}\| = \sqrt{2^2 + 3^2 + 6^2} = 7$$

$$\cos \alpha = \frac{2}{7} \qquad \cos \beta = \frac{3}{7} \qquad \cos \gamma = \frac{6}{7}$$

Example

2. Two direction cosines for $\overrightarrow{OP}$ are $\cos \alpha = \frac{1}{9}$ and $\cos \beta = -\frac{4}{9}$. If $\|\overrightarrow{OP}\| = 9$, find the coordinates of P.

$$\cos^2 \alpha + \cos^2 \beta + \cos^2 \gamma = 1$$

$$\left(\frac{1}{9}\right)^2 + \left(-\frac{4}{9}\right)^2 + \cos^2 \gamma = 1$$

$$\frac{1}{81} + \frac{16}{81} + \cos^2 \gamma = 1$$

$$\frac{17}{81} + \cos^2 \gamma = 1$$

$$\cos^2 \gamma = 1 - \frac{17}{81} = \frac{64}{81}$$

$$\cos \gamma = \pm \frac{8}{9}$$

Hence, P has coordinates $(1, -4, 8)$ or $(1, -4, -8)$.

The direction angles are measured from the positive direction of each axis. If a direction angle is obtuse, at least one of its direction cosines will be negative.

Exercises

Exploratory Find the norm and direction cosines of $\overrightarrow{OP}$ for each point P.

1. $(1, 1, 2)$ 2. $(3, 3, 3)$ 3. $(-3, 4, 12)$ 4. $(1, -4, 8)$

Two of the direction cosines are given for $\bar{v}$. Find the third direction cosine.

5. $\cos \alpha = \frac{1}{9}$, $\cos \beta = \frac{8}{9}$ 6. $\cos \alpha = \frac{4}{13}$, $\cos \beta = \frac{-3}{13}$

Find $\bar{u} \cdot \bar{v}$.

7. $\bar{u} = \begin{pmatrix} 3 \\ 4 \\ 7 \end{pmatrix}$, $\bar{v} = \begin{pmatrix} -1 \\ 4 \\ 1 \end{pmatrix}$ 8. $\bar{u} = \begin{pmatrix} -1 \\ 2 \\ 5 \end{pmatrix}$, $\bar{v} = \begin{pmatrix} 5 \\ 2 \\ -3 \end{pmatrix}$

Written Find the norm and direction cosines of $\overrightarrow{OP}$ for each point P.

1. $(-6, 2, -3)$ 2. $(1, -4, 3)$ 3. $(6, -3, 6)$

Two of the direction cosines are given for $\bar{v}$. Find the third direction cosine.

4. $\cos \alpha = \frac{-\sqrt{5}}{35}$, $\cos \gamma = \frac{12\sqrt{5}}{35}$ 5. $\cos \beta = \frac{\sqrt{3}}{15}$, $\cos \gamma = -\frac{\sqrt{3}}{3}$

6. $\cos \alpha = -\dfrac{3}{7}, \cos \beta = \dfrac{4}{7}$ **7.** $\cos \alpha = \dfrac{3}{5}, \cos \gamma = \dfrac{-1}{5}$

Find the coordinates of P for the vector $\overrightarrow{OP}$ with each set of direction cosines and norms.

8. $\cos \gamma = \dfrac{2\sqrt{5}}{15}, \cos \beta = \dfrac{4\sqrt{5}}{15}, \cos \alpha = \dfrac{\sqrt{5}}{3}, \|\overrightarrow{OP}\| = \sqrt{5}$

9. $\cos \alpha = -\dfrac{\sqrt{6}}{6}, \cos \beta = \dfrac{\sqrt{6}}{15}, \cos \gamma = -\dfrac{11\sqrt{6}}{30}, \|\overrightarrow{OP}\| = 10\sqrt{6}$

Find $\vec{u} \cdot \vec{v}$.

10. $\vec{u} = \begin{pmatrix} -1 \\ 6 \\ 2 \end{pmatrix}, \vec{v} = \begin{pmatrix} 8 \\ 11 \\ -9 \end{pmatrix}$ **11.** $\vec{u} = \begin{pmatrix} 4 \\ 0 \\ -2 \end{pmatrix}, \vec{v} = \begin{pmatrix} 2 \\ 3 \\ -4 \end{pmatrix}$

12. $\vec{u} = 4\vec{i} - 2\vec{j} + 3\vec{k}, \vec{v} = 3\vec{i} - \vec{j} + 2\vec{k}$ **13.** $\vec{u} = 10\vec{i} + 6\vec{j} - 5\vec{k}, \vec{v} = -6\vec{i} + \vec{j} + 2\vec{k}$

Find the cosine of the angle between each pair of vectors.

14. $\vec{u} = \begin{pmatrix} 2 \\ 6 \\ 9 \end{pmatrix}, \vec{v} = \begin{pmatrix} 1 \\ 4 \\ 8 \end{pmatrix}$ **15.** $\vec{u} = -2\vec{i} + 3\vec{j} + 6\vec{k}, \vec{v} = 2\vec{i} - 7\vec{j} + 26\vec{k}$

Evaluate each expression if $\vec{u} = \begin{pmatrix} -2 \\ 1 \\ 4 \end{pmatrix}, \vec{v} = \begin{pmatrix} 3 \\ -2 \\ 2 \end{pmatrix}, k = 5,$ and $r = -2$.

16. $k\vec{u} \cdot \vec{v}$ **17.** $\vec{v} \cdot (r\vec{u} + \vec{v})$ **18.** $\|\vec{u} - \vec{v}\|$

8-5 The Cross Product

The dot product of two vectors is a scalar. Another useful multiplication rule, called the **cross product**, is defined for vectors. The cross product of two vectors is a vector.

The cross product of two vectors $\vec{v} = \begin{pmatrix} v_1 \\ v_2 \\ v_3 \end{pmatrix}$ and $\vec{w} = \begin{pmatrix} w_1 \\ w_2 \\ w_3 \end{pmatrix}$

is $\vec{v} \times \vec{w} = \begin{pmatrix} v_2 w_3 - v_3 w_2 \\ v_3 w_1 - v_1 w_3 \\ v_1 w_2 - v_2 w_1 \end{pmatrix}.$

Cross Product

The cross product is more easily remembered by writing it as an array using determinants.

$$\overline{p} = \overline{v} \times \overline{w} = \begin{pmatrix} \begin{vmatrix} v_2 & v_3 \\ w_2 & w_3 \end{vmatrix} \\ -\begin{vmatrix} v_1 & v_3 \\ w_1 & w_3 \end{vmatrix} \\ \begin{vmatrix} v_1 & v_2 \\ w_1 & w_2 \end{vmatrix} \end{pmatrix}$$

Notice that in $\overline{p}$, the subscript 1 is missing from the first determinant, the subscript 2 is missing from the second determinant, and the subscript 3 is missing from the third determinant.

The symbol, $\begin{vmatrix} a & b \\ c & d \end{vmatrix}$, in which $a, b, c,$ and d denote numbers, is called a **second order determinant**. It represents the number $ad - bc$.

The cross product has several interesting properties. Some of them are different from other operations encountered so far.

For any vectors $\overline{v}$, $\overline{u}$, and $\overline{w}$ and scalar k the following properties are true.

Anticommutative Property: $\overline{v} \times \overline{w} = -(\overline{w} \times \overline{v})$

Scalar Associative Property:
$$\overline{v} \times (k\overline{w}) = (k\overline{v}) \times \overline{w} = k(\overline{v} \times \overline{w})$$

Antiassociative Properties:
$$\overline{u} \times (\overline{v} \times \overline{w}) = (\overline{u} \cdot \overline{w})\overline{v} - (\overline{u} \cdot \overline{v})\overline{w}$$
$$(\overline{u} \times \overline{v}) \times \overline{w} = (\overline{w} \cdot \overline{u})\overline{v} - (\overline{w} \cdot \overline{v})\overline{u}$$

Distributive Property:
$$\overline{u} \times (\overline{v} + \overline{w}) = (\overline{u} \times \overline{v}) + (\overline{u} \times \overline{w})$$

Properties of Cross Product

Example

1. **Verify the anticommutative property for the vectors**

$$\overline{v} = \begin{pmatrix} 1 \\ -2 \\ 1 \end{pmatrix} \text{ and } \overline{w} = \begin{pmatrix} 2 \\ 3 \\ -1 \end{pmatrix}.$$

$$\overline{v} \times \overline{w} = \begin{pmatrix} \begin{vmatrix} -2 & 1 \\ 3 & -1 \end{vmatrix} \\ -\begin{vmatrix} 1 & 1 \\ 2 & -1 \end{vmatrix} \\ \begin{vmatrix} 1 & -2 \\ 2 & 3 \end{vmatrix} \end{pmatrix} = \begin{pmatrix} 2 - 3 \\ -(-1 - 2) \\ 3 - (-4) \end{pmatrix} = \begin{pmatrix} -1 \\ 3 \\ 7 \end{pmatrix}$$

$$\overline{w} \times \overline{v} = \begin{pmatrix} 3 - 2 \\ -(2 - (-1)) \\ -4 - 3 \end{pmatrix} = \begin{pmatrix} 1 \\ -3 \\ -7 \end{pmatrix}$$

Hence, $\overline{v} \times \overline{w} = -(\overline{w} \times \overline{v})$.

Example

2. Verify the scalar associative property for the vectors $\vec{v} = \begin{pmatrix} 1 \\ -2 \\ 1 \end{pmatrix}$ and $\vec{w} = \begin{pmatrix} 2 \\ 3 \\ -1 \end{pmatrix}$ and the scalar $k = 3$.

$$\vec{v} \times (k\vec{w}) = \begin{pmatrix} 1 \\ -2 \\ 1 \end{pmatrix} \times \begin{pmatrix} 6 \\ 9 \\ -3 \end{pmatrix} = \begin{pmatrix} 6 - 9 \\ 3 + 6 \\ 9 + 12 \end{pmatrix} = \begin{pmatrix} -3 \\ 9 \\ 21 \end{pmatrix} = 3 \begin{pmatrix} -1 \\ 3 \\ 7 \end{pmatrix} = k(\vec{v} \times \vec{w})$$

$$k\vec{v} \times \vec{w} = \begin{pmatrix} 3 \\ -6 \\ 3 \end{pmatrix} \times \begin{pmatrix} 2 \\ 3 \\ -1 \end{pmatrix} = \begin{pmatrix} 6 - 9 \\ 3 + 6 \\ 9 + 12 \end{pmatrix} = \begin{pmatrix} -3 \\ 9 \\ 21 \end{pmatrix} = 3 \begin{pmatrix} -1 \\ 3 \\ 7 \end{pmatrix} = k(\vec{v} \times \vec{w})$$

The following theorem states one geometric interpretation of $\vec{v} \times \vec{w}$.

For any two three-dimensional vectors $\vec{v} = \begin{pmatrix} v_1 \\ v_2 \\ v_3 \end{pmatrix}$ and $\vec{w} = \begin{pmatrix} w_1 \\ w_2 \\ w_3 \end{pmatrix}$, $\vec{v} \times \vec{w}$ is orthogonal to both $\vec{v}$ and $\vec{w}$.

Orthogonal Vectors

Proof

Since two vectors are orthogonal if their dot product is 0, it is necessary only to show that $(\vec{v} \times \vec{w}) \cdot \vec{v} = 0$ and $(\vec{v} \times \vec{w}) \cdot \vec{w} = 0$.

$$(\vec{v} \times \vec{w}) \cdot \vec{v} = \begin{pmatrix} \begin{vmatrix} v_2 & v_3 \\ w_2 & w_3 \end{vmatrix} \\ -\begin{vmatrix} v_1 & v_3 \\ w_1 & w_3 \end{vmatrix} \\ \begin{vmatrix} v_1 & v_2 \\ w_1 & w_2 \end{vmatrix} \end{pmatrix} \cdot \begin{pmatrix} v_1 \\ v_2 \\ v_3 \end{pmatrix} = \begin{pmatrix} v_2 w_3 - w_2 v_3 \\ w_1 v_3 - v_1 w_3 \\ v_1 w_2 - w_1 v_2 \end{pmatrix} \cdot \begin{pmatrix} v_1 \\ v_2 \\ v_3 \end{pmatrix}$$

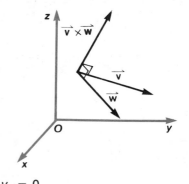

$$= v_1 v_2 w_3 - v_1 w_2 v_3 + v_2 w_1 v_3 - v_2 v_1 w_3 + v_3 v_1 w_2 - v_3 w_1 v_2 = 0$$

In the same way, $(\vec{v} \times \vec{w}) \cdot \vec{w} = 0$.

Two vectors $\vec{v}$ and $\vec{w}$ are said to be parallel if and only if $\vec{v} = k\vec{w}$ for some scalar k.

If two vectors $\vec{v} = \begin{pmatrix} v_1 \\ v_2 \\ v_3 \end{pmatrix}$ and $\vec{w} = \begin{pmatrix} w_1 \\ w_2 \\ w_3 \end{pmatrix}$ are parallel, then $\vec{v} \times \vec{w} = \vec{0}$.

Parallel Vectors

Proof

Suppose $\vec{v}$ is parallel to $\vec{w}$. Then $\vec{v} = k\vec{w}$ for some scalar k.

$$\begin{pmatrix} v_1 \\ v_2 \\ v_3 \end{pmatrix} = k\begin{pmatrix} w_1 \\ w_2 \\ w_3 \end{pmatrix} = \begin{pmatrix} kw_1 \\ kw_2 \\ kw_3 \end{pmatrix}$$

Thus, $\vec{v} \times \vec{w} = \begin{pmatrix} kw_2w_3 - kw_3w_2 \\ kw_3w_1 - kw_1w_3 \\ kw_1w_2 - kw_2w_1 \end{pmatrix} = \vec{0}$.

The converse is also true. Thus, if the cross product of two vectors is the zero vector, the vectors are parallel.

Exercises

Exploratory   Evaluate each determinant.

1. $\begin{vmatrix} 3 & 2 \\ 1 & 4 \end{vmatrix}$
2. $\begin{vmatrix} -1 & 3 \\ 5 & -2 \end{vmatrix}$
3. $\begin{vmatrix} 9 & 0 \\ -2 & 4 \end{vmatrix}$
4. $\begin{vmatrix} a & b \\ -2 & 1 \end{vmatrix}$

Find $\vec{v} \times \vec{w}$.

5. $\vec{v} = \begin{pmatrix} 1 \\ 3 \\ 2 \end{pmatrix}, \vec{w} = \begin{pmatrix} 2 \\ -1 \\ 1 \end{pmatrix}$
6. $\vec{v} = \begin{pmatrix} 4 \\ 0 \\ -2 \end{pmatrix}, \vec{w} = \begin{pmatrix} -7 \\ 1 \\ 0 \end{pmatrix}$

Written   State whether each pair of vectors is parallel (Pa), perpendicular (Pe), or neither (N).

1. $\begin{pmatrix} 4 \\ 2 \\ -10 \end{pmatrix}, \begin{pmatrix} 2 \\ 1 \\ -5 \end{pmatrix}$
2. $\begin{pmatrix} 3 \\ 7 \\ -4 \end{pmatrix}, \begin{pmatrix} 5 \\ -5 \\ -5 \end{pmatrix}$
3. $\begin{pmatrix} 8 \\ 2 \\ -1 \end{pmatrix}, \begin{pmatrix} -6 \\ 3 \\ 1 \end{pmatrix}$

4. $\begin{pmatrix} 9 \\ 0 \\ 2 \end{pmatrix}, \begin{pmatrix} 0 \\ 1 \\ -3 \end{pmatrix}$
5. $\begin{pmatrix} 2 \\ -3 \\ 0 \end{pmatrix}, \begin{pmatrix} 0 \\ 0 \\ -10 \end{pmatrix}$
6. $\begin{pmatrix} 16 \\ -20 \\ 28 \end{pmatrix}, \begin{pmatrix} -12 \\ 15 \\ -21 \end{pmatrix}$

Determine the values of a and b, if each pair of vectors is parallel.

7. $\begin{pmatrix} 2 \\ -3 \\ 5 \end{pmatrix}, \begin{pmatrix} 1 \\ a \\ b \end{pmatrix}$
8. $\begin{pmatrix} -4 \\ 9 \\ -15 \end{pmatrix}, \begin{pmatrix} a \\ -3 \\ b \end{pmatrix}$

Find a vector perpendicular to each pair of vectors.

9. $\begin{pmatrix} 8 \\ 0 \\ -2 \end{pmatrix}, \begin{pmatrix} 5 \\ 1 \\ 3 \end{pmatrix}$
10. $\begin{pmatrix} 6 \\ 2 \\ 2 \end{pmatrix}, \begin{pmatrix} 1 \\ 4 \\ -2 \end{pmatrix}$

Find a unit vector perpendicular to each pair of vectors.

11. $\begin{pmatrix} 7 \\ -2 \\ 4 \end{pmatrix}, \begin{pmatrix} -5 \\ -3 \\ 1 \end{pmatrix}$
12. $\begin{pmatrix} 2 \\ -1 \\ \frac{1}{6} \end{pmatrix}, \begin{pmatrix} 0 \\ 6 \\ 2 \end{pmatrix}$

13. $\begin{pmatrix} -2 \\ 2 \\ -\frac{1}{3} \end{pmatrix}, \begin{pmatrix} -1 \\ -2 \\ \frac{4}{3} \end{pmatrix}$

14. $\begin{pmatrix} 1 \\ 1 \\ 2 \end{pmatrix}, \begin{pmatrix} 2 \\ 0 \\ -1 \end{pmatrix}$

Prove each theorem about three-dimensional vectors.

15. $k\bar{v} \times \bar{v} = \bar{0}.$

16. $(\vec{i} \times \vec{j}) \times \vec{k} = \vec{i} \times (\vec{j} \times \vec{k})$

Challenge   Solve each of the following.

1. Show that in general
    $(\bar{u} \times \bar{v}) \times \bar{w} \neq \bar{u} \times (\bar{v} \times \bar{w}).$

2. Prove that $(\bar{u} + \bar{v}) \times (\bar{u} - \bar{v})$
    $= -2(\bar{u} \times \bar{v}).$

3. Prove that if $(\bar{u} \times \bar{u}) - (\bar{v} \times \bar{v})$
    $= (\bar{u} + \bar{v}) \times (\bar{u} - \bar{v})$, then $\bar{u}$
    is parallel to $\bar{v}$.

4. Show that there is no cancellation
    property for cross products. That is, if
    $\bar{u} \times \bar{v} = \bar{u} \times \bar{w}$ then $\bar{v}$ is not necessarily
    equal to $\bar{w}$.

8–6   Equations of the Line

Suppose ℓ is a line and $\bar{v}$ is a vector. Thus, ℓ and $\bar{v}$ are parallel if and only if the arrows of $\bar{v}$ lie on lines that are parallel to ℓ. A nonzero vector $\bar{v}$ that is parallel to a line ℓ is called a direction vector of ℓ.

If a line ℓ passes through $P(x_0, y_0, z_0)$ and has a direction vector $\bar{v}$, then the point $Q(x, y, z)$ lies on ℓ if the following equation holds.

$$\bar{q} = \bar{p} + t\bar{v} \text{ for some } t \neq 0 \text{ where } \bar{q} = \begin{pmatrix} x \\ y \\ z \end{pmatrix} \text{ and } \bar{p} = \begin{pmatrix} x_0 \\ y_0 \\ z_0 \end{pmatrix}$$

Vector Equation

This equation is called the **vector equation** of the line. If $\bar{v} = \begin{pmatrix} a \\ b \\ c \end{pmatrix}$, then any point $Q(x, y, z)$ on ℓ has the following coordinates.

$$x = x_0 + at, y = y_0 + bt, z = z_0 + ct$$

These equations are called the **parametric equations** of the line through P with a direction vector $\bar{v}$. If the parameter t is eliminated, then the resulting set of equations is said to be in **symmetric form**.

$$\frac{x - x_0}{a} = \frac{y - y_0}{b} = \frac{z - z_0}{c}$$

Of course the direction vector $\bar{v}$ cannot be the zero vector. The numbers a, b, and c are called **direction numbers**. They are proportional to the direction cosines of $\bar{v}$.

Example

1. Find the vector, parametric, and symmetric equation for the line through $P(8, 2, -5)$ with a direction vector $\vec{v} = \begin{pmatrix} 3 \\ -1 \\ 2 \end{pmatrix}$.

   The vector equation can be written as $\vec{q} = \vec{p} + t\vec{v}$ for some $t \neq 0$.

   So, $\begin{pmatrix} x \\ y \\ z \end{pmatrix} = \begin{pmatrix} 8 \\ 2 \\ -5 \end{pmatrix} + t \begin{pmatrix} 3 \\ -1 \\ 2 \end{pmatrix}$ is the vector equation.

   The parametric equations are as follows.

   $$x = 8 + 3t, \, y = 2 - t, \, z = -5 + 2t$$

   The symmetric equations are given as follows.

   $$\frac{x - 8}{3} = \frac{y - 2}{-1} = \frac{z + 5}{2}$$

The angle θ between two lines is the same as the angle between their direction vectors. Suppose the direction vectors for two lines are $\vec{u} = \begin{pmatrix} u_1 \\ u_2 \\ u_3 \end{pmatrix}$ and $\vec{v} = \begin{pmatrix} v_1 \\ v_2 \\ v_3 \end{pmatrix}$.

$$\|\vec{u}\| \, \|\vec{v}\| \cos \theta = \vec{u} \cdot \vec{v}$$

$$\cos \theta = \frac{\vec{u} \cdot \vec{v}}{\|\vec{u}\| \, \|\vec{v}\|}$$

$$\cos \theta = \frac{u_1 v_1 + u_2 v_2 + u_3 v_3}{\|\vec{u}\| \, \|\vec{v}\|}$$

If the direction cosines for $\vec{u}$ are $\cos \alpha_1$, $\cos \beta_1$, $\cos \gamma_1$, and for $\vec{v}$ are $\cos \alpha_2$, $\cos \beta_2$, $\cos \gamma_2$, then

$$\cos \theta = \cos \alpha_1 \cos \alpha_2 + \cos \beta_1 \cos \beta_2 + \cos \gamma_1 \cos \gamma_2.$$

Example

2. Find the cosine of the angle between the lines with equations

   $$\begin{pmatrix} x_1 \\ y_1 \\ z_1 \end{pmatrix} = \begin{pmatrix} 4 \\ 0 \\ -1 \end{pmatrix} + t \begin{pmatrix} 1 \\ 2 \\ 2 \end{pmatrix} \text{ and } \begin{pmatrix} x_2 \\ y_2 \\ z_2 \end{pmatrix} = \begin{pmatrix} 4 \\ 0 \\ -1 \end{pmatrix} + t \begin{pmatrix} 8 \\ -4 \\ 19 \end{pmatrix}.$$

   $$\|\vec{v}\| = \sqrt{1 + 4 + 4} = 3 \qquad \|\vec{u}\| = \sqrt{64 + 16 + 361} = 21$$

   $$\cos \theta = \frac{(1)(8) + (2)(-4) + (2)(19)}{3 \cdot 21} = \frac{8 - 8 + 38}{63} = \frac{38}{63}$$

Exercises

Exploratory   Name the direction vector for each line and give the coordinates of a point on the given line.

1. $\begin{pmatrix} x \\ y \\ z \end{pmatrix} = \begin{pmatrix} 1 \\ 4 \\ 2 \end{pmatrix} + t \begin{pmatrix} -3 \\ 1 \\ 4 \end{pmatrix}$

2. $\begin{pmatrix} x \\ y \\ z \end{pmatrix} = \begin{pmatrix} -2 \\ 3 \\ 5 \end{pmatrix} + t \begin{pmatrix} -4 \\ 2 \\ 5 \end{pmatrix}$

3. $x = 2 + 3t, y = -1 + 4t, z = 4 - 3t$

4. $x = 2t, y = -7 + 8t, z = 1$

Determine the parametric equations of a line through P with a direction vector $\vec{v}$. Then, state the equations in symmetric form.

5. $P(4, 1, 2), \vec{v} = \begin{pmatrix} 2 \\ 4 \\ -3 \end{pmatrix}$

6. $P(1, 4, 2), \vec{v} = \begin{pmatrix} 3 \\ 1 \\ 2 \end{pmatrix}$

Written   Determine the parametric equations of a line through P with a direction vector $\vec{v}$. Then, write the equations in symmetric form.

1. $P(7, 1, -1), \vec{v} = \begin{pmatrix} 2 \\ 1 \\ 2 \end{pmatrix}$

2. $P(8, 0, 0), \vec{v} = \begin{pmatrix} 1 \\ 3 \\ -2 \end{pmatrix}$

3. $P(-1, 2, \sqrt{3}), \vec{v} = \begin{pmatrix} -2 \\ 0 \\ 1 \end{pmatrix}$

4. $P(11, -6, -3), \vec{v} = \begin{pmatrix} \sqrt{2} \\ 0 \\ -\sqrt{2} \end{pmatrix}$

Write the equations of each line described below.

5. Parallel to a line whose equations in symmetric form are $\dfrac{x - 3}{2} = \dfrac{y + 5}{-1} = \dfrac{z - 2}{10}$, passes through $(4, 6, -1)$

6. Parallel to the line whose equations are $x = 5 + 3t, y = -7 + 2t, z = 8 - t$, passes through $(-7, 0, -12)$

7. Parallel to the line with vector equation $\vec{q} = \begin{pmatrix} 0 \\ 4 \\ 2 \end{pmatrix} + t \begin{pmatrix} 3 \\ 1 \\ -1 \end{pmatrix}$, passes through $(2, 0, -1)$

8. Parallel to the line with vector equation $\vec{q} = \begin{pmatrix} 11 \\ 2 \\ -3 \end{pmatrix} + t \begin{pmatrix} 6 \\ -2 \\ -3 \end{pmatrix}$, passes through $(-4, 6, 2)$

Locate the line through $P(x_0, y_0, z_0)$ with the given direction vector.

9. $\begin{pmatrix} 0 \\ b \\ c \end{pmatrix}$

10. $\begin{pmatrix} a \\ b \\ 0 \end{pmatrix}$

11. $\begin{pmatrix} 0 \\ 0 \\ c \end{pmatrix}$

12. $\begin{pmatrix} 0 \\ b \\ 0 \end{pmatrix}$

Find the parametric equations for the line through each pair of points.

13. $(3, -1, 2), (5, 1, -2)$

14. $(4, 0, -1), (7, 2, 2)$

15. $(9, -4, 2), (11, 3, -1)$

16. $(2a, 5b, c), (-3a, b, -2c)$

Find the equations for a line orthogonal at the point of intersection of the given pairs of intersecting lines.

17. $\vec{q}_1 = \begin{pmatrix} -3 \\ -1 \\ 7 \end{pmatrix} + t \begin{pmatrix} 1 \\ 4 \\ 2 \end{pmatrix}$

18. $\vec{q}_1 = \begin{pmatrix} 2 \\ 11 \\ -3 \end{pmatrix} + t \begin{pmatrix} 1 \\ 5 \\ 12 \end{pmatrix}$

$\vec{q}_2 = \begin{pmatrix} -3 \\ -1 \\ 7 \end{pmatrix} + t \begin{pmatrix} -3 \\ -9 \\ 5 \end{pmatrix}$

$\vec{q}_2 = \begin{pmatrix} 2 \\ 11 \\ -3 \end{pmatrix} + t \begin{pmatrix} -2 \\ 1 \\ -3 \end{pmatrix}$

8–7 Equation for a Plane

In Euclidean geometry, a plane perpendicular to a line at a given point is one which contains all the perpendiculars to the line at that point. This definition can be used to derive the equation for a plane.

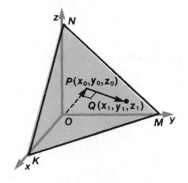

Let $\overrightarrow{OP} = \begin{pmatrix} x_0 \\ y_0 \\ z_0 \end{pmatrix}$ be a position vector with P in the plane KMN which is perpendicular to the line containing $\overrightarrow{OP}$. The vector such as $\overrightarrow{OP}$ is said to be **normal** to the plane. Let $Q(x_1, y_1, z_1)$ be any other point in the plane KMN. Since $\overrightarrow{PQ}$ is perpendicular to $\overrightarrow{OP}$, $\overrightarrow{PQ} \cdot \overrightarrow{OP} = 0$.

$$\begin{pmatrix} x_1 - x_0 \\ y_1 - y_0 \\ z_1 - z_0 \end{pmatrix} \cdot \begin{pmatrix} x_0 \\ y_0 \\ z_0 \end{pmatrix} = 0$$

$$x_1 x_0 - x_0^2 + y_1 y_0 - y_0^2 + z_1 z_0 - z_0^2 = 0$$

$$x_1 x_0 + y_1 y_0 + z_1 z_0 = x_0^2 + y_0^2 + z_0^2 = \| \overrightarrow{OP} \|^2$$

$$\frac{x_0}{\|\overrightarrow{OP}\|} x_1 + \frac{y_0}{\|\overrightarrow{OP}\|} y_1 + \frac{z_0}{\|\overrightarrow{OP}\|} z_1 = \| \overrightarrow{OP} \|$$

Suppose the direction cosines for $\overrightarrow{OP}$ are $\cos \alpha = \dfrac{x_0}{\|\overrightarrow{OP}\|}$, $\cos \beta = \dfrac{y_0}{\|\overrightarrow{OP}\|}$, $\cos \gamma = \dfrac{z_0}{\|\overrightarrow{OP}\|}$ and the distance from the origin $\|\overrightarrow{OP}\| = p$.

The equation for the plane then becomes the following.

$$x \cos \alpha + y \cos \beta + z \cos \gamma = p$$

This equation is called the **normal form** for the equation of a plane. If the normal form of the equation is multiplied by any nonzero number k, then the following equation results.

$$xk \cos \alpha + yk \cos \beta + zk \cos \gamma = pk$$

More generally, $Ax + By + Cz + D = 0$. This equation is called the **general** or **scalar form** for the equation of a plane. Notice that A, B, and C are multiples of the direction cosines. Therefore, they are direction numbers for the normal vector.

Examples

1. **Find the normal form of $4x + 8y - z + 18 = 0$. Find the distance of the plane from the origin.**

    Direction numbers for the normal vector are 4, 8, and -1.

    $$\cos \alpha = \frac{\pm 4}{\sqrt{16 + 64 + 1}}, \cos \beta = \frac{\pm 8}{\sqrt{16 + 64 + 1}}, \cos \gamma = \frac{\pm 1}{\sqrt{16 + 64 + 1}}$$

    Since p is a distance, it is positive. This is opposite to that of D so, therefore, the equation becomes $-\frac{4}{9}x - \frac{8}{9}y + \frac{1}{9}z = 2$.

    $$p = -18\left(-\frac{1}{9}\right) = 2$$

    The distance from the origin is 2.

2. **Find the equation of a plane normal to $\bar{v} = \begin{pmatrix} 3 \\ -2 \\ 1 \end{pmatrix}$ containing $Q(-1, 4, 2)$.**

    Let $P(x, y, z)$ be a point in the plane. $\overrightarrow{PQ}$ and $\bar{v}$ are perpendicular.

    $$\begin{pmatrix} x + 1 \\ y - 4 \\ z - 2 \end{pmatrix} \cdot \begin{pmatrix} 3 \\ -2 \\ 1 \end{pmatrix} = 0$$

    $$3x + 3 - 2y + 8 + z - 2 = 0$$

    Thus, $3x - 2y + z + 9 = 0$ is the equation of the plane.

3. **Find the equation of the plane through the three points $P(4, -2, -5)$, $Q(-3, 1, -3)$, and $R(2, 0, 1)$.**

    Since $\overrightarrow{PQ}$ and $\overrightarrow{PR}$ are two vectors in the plane, then $\overrightarrow{PQ} \times \overrightarrow{PR}$ is a vector normal to the plane.

    $$\overrightarrow{PQ} = \begin{pmatrix} -3 - 4 \\ 1 + 2 \\ -3 + 5 \end{pmatrix} = \begin{pmatrix} -7 \\ 3 \\ 2 \end{pmatrix} \qquad \overrightarrow{PR} = \begin{pmatrix} 2 - 4 \\ 0 + 2 \\ 1 + 5 \end{pmatrix} = \begin{pmatrix} -2 \\ 2 \\ 6 \end{pmatrix}$$

    $$\overrightarrow{PQ} \times \overrightarrow{PR} = \begin{pmatrix} \begin{vmatrix} 3 & 2 \\ 2 & 6 \end{vmatrix} \\ -\begin{vmatrix} -7 & 2 \\ -2 & 6 \end{vmatrix} \\ \begin{vmatrix} -7 & 3 \\ -2 & 2 \end{vmatrix} \end{pmatrix} = \begin{pmatrix} 14 \\ 38 \\ -8 \end{pmatrix}$$

Let X (x, y, z) be any point in the plane.

$$\overrightarrow{PX} = \begin{pmatrix} x - 4 \\ y + 2 \\ z + 5 \end{pmatrix} \text{ is a vector in the plane. So, } \overrightarrow{PX} \cdot \begin{pmatrix} 14 \\ 38 \\ -8 \end{pmatrix} = 0.$$

$$\begin{pmatrix} x - 4 \\ y + 2 \\ z + 5 \end{pmatrix} \cdot \begin{pmatrix} 14 \\ 38 \\ -8 \end{pmatrix} = 0$$

$$14x - 56 + 38y + 76 - 8z - 40 = 0$$
$$14x + 38y - 8z = 20$$

4. **Find the distance of the point $(5, -3, 1)$ from the plane $12x - 3y - 4z - 39 = 0$.**

Consider a plane parallel to the given plane containing the point $(5, -3, 1)$. The equation of the parallel plane is $12x - 3y - 4z + D = 0$.

$$12(5) - 3(-3) - 4(1) + D = 0 \qquad \textit{Substitute } (5, -3, 1) \textit{ for } (x, y, z).$$
$$60 + 9 - 4 + D = 0$$
$$-65 = D$$

The normal form for both planes are $\qquad \sqrt{(12)^2 + (3)^2 + (4)^2} = 13$

$$\frac{12}{13}x - \frac{3}{13}y - \frac{4}{13}z = 3 \qquad \text{and} \qquad \frac{12}{13}x - \frac{3}{13}y - \frac{4}{13}z = 5.$$

The distance between them is the difference $|5 - 3| = 2$.

An analysis of this problem shows that the same result can be obtained by using the following formula.

$$d = \frac{|Ax' + By' + Cz' + D|}{\sqrt{A^2 + B^2 + C^2}}$$

$$\textit{If } (x, y, z) = (0, 0, 0) \textit{ then}$$
$$d = \frac{|D|}{\sqrt{A^2 + B^2 + C^2}}.$$

In the formula, $Ax' + By' + Cz' + D = 0$ is the equation of the given plane, and (x', y', z') are the coordinates of the given point.

Exercises

Exploratory Give a set of direction numbers for the normal and find the direction cosines for each of the following planes.

1. $3x - 4y + 12z = 12$

2. $x + 4y - 8z = 11$

3. $2x - 2y + z = 7$

4. $5x + 12y = 10$

Find the equation of the plane with the given normal vector $\vec{n}$ and which contains the given point P.

5. $\vec{n} = \begin{pmatrix} 4 \\ 1 \\ 3 \end{pmatrix}$, $P(2, -5, 0)$

6. $\vec{n} = \begin{pmatrix} -1 \\ 8 \\ -4 \end{pmatrix}$, $P(3, 2, 10)$

Written   **Find the equation of each plane.**

1. The plane contains the point $(6, 1, -3)$ and is parallel to the plane $2x - 5y + z + 7 = 0$.

2. The plane contains the point $(-5, 1, 0)$ and is parallel to the plane $2x - 7y + 13z - 4 = 0$.

3. The plane contains the point $(6, -2, 5)$ and is perpendicular to the line through $(1, 2, -3)$ and $(-3, 1, 0)$.

4. The plane contains the point $(-8, -1, -3)$ and is perpendicular to the line through $(4, 1, 7)$ and $(0, 2, -3)$.

5. The plane contains the points $(1, 3, -3)$, $(5, -1, 3)$, $(9, -7, 1)$.

6. The plane contains the points $(2, 0, -4)$, $(-2, 6, 2)$, $(4, 2, -2)$.

7. The plane is determined by the intersecting lines $\dfrac{x - 3}{2} = \dfrac{y - 1}{3} = \dfrac{z + 1}{5}$ and $\dfrac{x - 3}{-1} = \dfrac{y - 1}{1} = \dfrac{z + 1}{2}$.

8. The plane is determined by the following intersecting lines.

    $$x = 2 + 4t \qquad\qquad x = 2 + t$$
    $$y = -4 + 3t \quad\text{and}\quad y = -4 + 2t$$
    $$z = 5 - t \qquad\qquad z = 5 + 2t$$

Find the distance of each of the following.

9. From the origin to the plane $12x - 4y + 3z - 5 = 0$

10. From the origin to the plane $9x + 2y - 6z + 4 = 0$

11. From the point $(-7, -4, -1)$ to the plane $x - 4y + 8z - 3 = 0$

12. From the point $(1, 1, 1)$ to the plane $12x - 12y - z + 5 = 0$

Find cos θ for each pair of planes given below. (The angle θ between two planes is the same as the angle between their normals. Use the dot product.)

13. $8x + y + 4z = 3$
     $2x - 2y - z = 7$

14. $2x + y + 4z - 5 = 0$
     $x - 5y - z - 10 = 0$

15. Show that the distance d from (x', y', z') to the plane $Ax + By + Cz + D = 0$ is given by the following formula.

$$d = \frac{|Ax' + By' + Cz' + D|}{\sqrt{A^2 + B^2 + C^2}}$$

Challenge   **Solve each of the following.**

1. Show that the equation of the plane with intercepts of $a, b,$ and c on the x-, y-, and z-axes respectively is $\dfrac{x}{a} + \dfrac{y}{b} + \dfrac{z}{c} = 1$.

2. Find the equations of the line of intersection of $3x - 2y + 6z - 10 = 0$ and $x + y - 2z + 5 = 0$.

3. Find the equations of the line of intersection of $2x - 5y + z + 12 = 0$ and $5x + y - 2z - 15 = 0$.

8–8   Loci

   In three dimensional space, there are many interesting locus problems. A few familiar shapes will be studied in this section.
   The locus of all points in space at a given distance from a

given point is a **sphere**. The given point is the center and the given distance is the radius. If the given point is $C(x_0, y_0, z_0)$, and the given distance is r, the equation of the sphere, by the distance formula, is $(x - x_0)^2 + (y - y_0)^2 + (z - z_0)^2 = r^2$. Where the center is at the origin, the equation becomes $x^2 + y^2 + z^2 = r^2$.

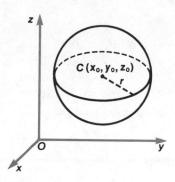

What is the locus of all points at a distance r from the z-axis? Consider a plane parallel to the xy-plane. This plane will intersect the surface in a curve with equation $x^2 + y^2 = r^2$. Since this is the equation of a circle for any value of z, the locus is a circular cylindrical surface. The z-axis is its axis. It has radius r.

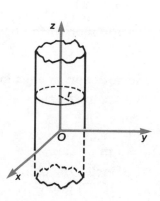

Example

1. **Find the equation of the locus of points equidistant from $P(2, 3, -5)$ and $Q(4, -5, 1)$. Describe the locus.**

   Let (x, y, z) be any point.

   $$(x - 2)^2 + (y - 3)^2 + (z + 5)^2 = (x - 4)^2 + (y + 5)^2 + (z - 1)^2$$
   $$x^2 - 4x + 4 + y^2 - 6y + 9 + z^2 + 10z + 25 =$$
   $$x^2 - 8x + 16 + y^2 + 10y + 25 + z^2 - 2z + 1$$
   $$4x - 16y + 12z - 4 = 0$$
   $$x - 4y + 3z - 1 = 0$$

   This is a plane with a normal vector $\begin{pmatrix} 1 \\ -4 \\ 3 \end{pmatrix}$. The direction vector of $\overrightarrow{PQ}$ is $\begin{pmatrix} 2 \\ -8 \\ 6 \end{pmatrix}$.

   Therefore, $\overrightarrow{PQ}$ and the plane are perpendicular. The midpoint of $\overrightarrow{PQ}$ is $(3, -1, -2)$. This point lies in the plane $x - 4y + 3z - 1 = 0$. Hence, the locus is the plane which is the perpendicular bisector of $\overrightarrow{PQ}$.

Exercises

Exploratory Find the equation of a sphere with center C and radius r.

1. $C = (7, -1, 2), r = 3$

2. $C - (2, 0, -5), r - 1$

3. $C = (3, 5, -1), r = 2$

4. $C = (0, 0, 0), r = 4$

Find the equation of a cylindrical surface with the given axis and radius.

5. x-axis, $r = 4$

6. y-axis, $r = 7$

Written Find the equation of a sphere with center C and radius r.

1. $C = (11, -2, 7), r = 5$

2. $C = (1, 0, 1), r = 7$

Find the equation of a cylindrical surface with the given axis and radius.

3. z-axis, $r = 2$

4. z-axis, $r = 3$

5. x-axis, $r = 1$

6. y-axis, $r = 5$

Find the equation of the perpendicular bisector of $\overline{PQ}$.

7. $P(4, 1, -3), Q(2, -5, 7)$

8. $P(-3, 2, 3), Q(5, -6, 1)$

Find the equation of each locus.

9. The locus of points at a distance 4 from $(-3, 9, 4)$.

10. The locus of points at a distance 7 from $(2, 11, -8)$.

11. The locus of points at a distance 12 from the z-axis.

12. The locus of points at a distance 9 from the x-axis.

13. The locus of points equidistant from $(4, -1, -2)$ and $(-2, 3, -6)$.

14. The locus of points equidistant from $(7, 4, 2)$ and $(1, 0, 0)$.

15. The locus of points equidistant from the parallel planes $2x - 3y + 6z - 7 = 0$ and $4x - 6y + 12z + 2 = 0$.

16. The locus of points equidistant from the parallel planes $6x + 8y - 24z - 5 = 0$ and $9x + 12y - 36z - 8 = 0$.

17. The locus of points at a distance 3 from the plane $x - 4y + 8z - 7 = 0$.

18. The locus of points at a distance 6 from the plane $x - 2y - 2z - 4 = 0$.

Excursions in Mathematics

A number represents a displacement along a line. An ordered pair represents a displacement or vector in the plane. An ordered triple represents a vector in space. Three-dimensional vectors have been studied by comparison with two-dimensional vectors. There is a similar analogy between three-dimensional and n-dimensional vectors. Let an n-dimensional vector be defined as $\vec{v} = \begin{pmatrix} x_1 \\ x_2 \\ x_3 \\ \vdots \\ x_n \end{pmatrix}$ where each x_i is a real number. Analogous definitions for equality, addition, and scalar multiplication can be set up.

Chapter Summary

1. There is a one-to-one correspondence between ordered triples of real numbers and points in space. (239)
2. Three mutually perpendicular axes divide space into eight octants which are named by the signs of the coordinates of points in the octant. (240)
3. If points P and Q have coordinates (x_1, y_1, z_1) and (x_2, y_2, z_2) respectively, then $PQ = \sqrt{(x_2 - x_1)^2 + (y_2 - y_1)^2 + (z_2 - z_1)^2}$. (242)
4. In three-dimensional space, a vector is defined as an equivalence class of arrows, all having the same magnitude and direction. Each vector can be associated with an ordered number triple $\begin{pmatrix} a \\ b \\ c \end{pmatrix}$. The properties of Vector Three-Space are similar to those of Vector Two-Space. (244)
5. The standard unit basis vectors in $\mathcal{V}_3$ are $\vec{i} = \begin{pmatrix} 1 \\ 0 \\ 0 \end{pmatrix}, \vec{j} = \begin{pmatrix} 0 \\ 1 \\ 0 \end{pmatrix}$, and $\vec{k} = \begin{pmatrix} 0 \\ 0 \\ 1 \end{pmatrix}$. (247)
6. Properties of the Cross Product are as follows. (251)
$$\vec{v} \times \vec{w} = -(\vec{w} \times \vec{v})$$
$$\vec{v} \times (k\vec{w}) = (k\vec{v}) \times \vec{w} = k(\vec{v} \times \vec{w})$$
$$\vec{u} \times (\vec{v} \times \vec{w}) = (\vec{u} \cdot \vec{w})\vec{v} - (\vec{u} \cdot \vec{v})\vec{w}$$
$$(\vec{u} \times \vec{v}) \times \vec{w} = (\vec{w} \cdot \vec{u})\vec{v} - (\vec{w} \cdot \vec{v})\vec{u}$$
$$\vec{u} \times (\vec{v} + \vec{w}) = (\vec{u} \times \vec{v}) + (\vec{u} \times \vec{w})$$
7. For any two three-dimensional vectors $\vec{v}$ and $\vec{w}$, $\vec{v} \times \vec{w}$ is orthogonal to both $\vec{v}$ and $\vec{w}$. (252)
8. The parametric equations for a line through $P(x_0, y_0, z_0)$ with direction vector $\vec{v} = \begin{pmatrix} a \\ b \\ c \end{pmatrix}$ are $x = x_0 + at, y = y_0 + bt$, $z = z_0 + ct$. In symmetric form these equations are $\dfrac{x - x_0}{a} = \dfrac{y - y_0}{b} = \dfrac{z - z_0}{c}$. (254)
9. The general form for the equation of a plane is $Ax + By + Cz + D = 0$, where A, B, and C are direction numbers for the normal vector and $\dfrac{|D|}{\sqrt{A^2 + B^2 + C^2}}$ is the distance of the plane from the origin. (257)
10. The general equation of a sphere with center $C(x_0, y_0, z_0)$ and radius r is $(x - x_0)^2 + (y - y_0)^2 + (z - z_0)^2 = r^2$. (261)

Chapter Review

8–1 **Describe the location of $P(x, y, z)$ given the following conditions.**

1. $x = 0$
2. $x = 0$ and $y = 0$
3. $x = k$ and $z = 0$

8–2 **Find the distance between the following points.**

4. $(4, 2, -6)$ and $(3, -4, 12)$
5. $(3, 7, -8)$ and $(-2, 2, -3)$

6. Show that in the triangle $P(-9, -12, 1)$, $Q(-3, -6, -5)$, $R(1, 6, 3)$, the segment joining the midpoints of $\overline{PQ}$ and $\overline{PR}$ is parallel to $\overline{QR}$ and equal to $\frac{1}{2}\overline{QR}$.

8–3 **Prove each of the following.**

7. If $k\vec{v} = \vec{0}$ then $k = 0$ or $\vec{v} = \vec{0}$.
8. If $k\vec{u} + k\vec{v} = \vec{w}$ then $k(\vec{u} + \vec{v}) = \vec{w}$.

8–4 **Find the norm and direction cosines of $\overrightarrow{OP}$ for each point P.**

9. $(2, 3, 4)$
10. $(-4, 1, 1)$
11. $(-5, -3, 6)$

Find $\vec{u} \cdot \vec{v}$.

12. $\vec{u} = \begin{pmatrix} 2 \\ 0 \\ 1 \end{pmatrix}, \vec{v} = \begin{pmatrix} 3 \\ -5 \\ 2 \end{pmatrix}$

13. $\vec{u} = \begin{pmatrix} 8 \\ -5 \\ -9 \end{pmatrix}, \vec{v} = \begin{pmatrix} -7 \\ 2 \\ 1 \end{pmatrix}$

8–5 **Determine whether each pair of vectors is parallel (Pa), perpendicular (Pe), or neither (N).**

14. $\begin{pmatrix} 2 \\ 4 \\ 1 \end{pmatrix}, \begin{pmatrix} 3 \\ -2 \\ 2 \end{pmatrix}$

15. $\begin{pmatrix} 5 \\ -1 \\ 7 \end{pmatrix}, \begin{pmatrix} -2 \\ -3 \\ 1 \end{pmatrix}$

16. $\begin{pmatrix} 6 \\ 0 \\ 2 \end{pmatrix}, \begin{pmatrix} 1 \\ 8 \\ -1 \end{pmatrix}$

17. Find a vector perpendicular to both $\begin{pmatrix} 4 \\ 1 \\ 2 \end{pmatrix}$ and $\begin{pmatrix} -2 \\ 3 \\ 4 \end{pmatrix}$.

8–6 **Write the equations of each line described below.**

18. Parallel to a line through $(-4, -2, 5)$ and $(-3, 1, 4)$, passes through $(7, 11, -1)$.

19. Perpendicular to the plane $4x - 2y + 3z - 12 = 0$, passes through $(4, 5, 3)$.

8–7 **Find the equation of each plane.**

20. The plane has an x-intercept twice as far from the origin as its y-intercept and passes through $(-4, 6, -9)$ and $(6, -2, 0)$.

21. The plane contains the points $(1, 3, -3)$, $(5, -1, 3)$, and $(4, 2, -2)$.

22. Find the distance from the point $(1, 1, 1)$ to the plane $x - 4y + 8z - 3 = 0$.

8–8 **Identify each three-dimensional locus.**

23. $\{(x, y, z) | x^2 + y^2 = 4\}$

24. $\{(x, y, z) | 4x - 3y - 2z + 10 = 0\}$

25. Find the equation of a cylindrical surface whose axis is the x-axis and whose radius is 4.

Chapter Test

Name the plane in which the following points are located.

1. $(4, 0, -2)$
2. $(-3, 0, -2)$
3. $(0, 1, 0)$

Find the length of the projection of $\overline{AB}$ on the xz-plane and on the y-axis.

4. $A(4, 1, -2), B(-1, 4, 4)$
5. $A(9, -2, 3), B(7, 4, -1)$
6. $A(3n, 4n, n), B(-5n, 11n, 2n)$

7. Given the points $A(0, 0, 0)$, $B(a, b, c)$, $C\left(a + \dfrac{1}{a}, b + \dfrac{1}{b}, c - \dfrac{2}{c}\right)$, and $D\left(\dfrac{1}{a}, \dfrac{1}{b}, -\dfrac{2}{c}\right)$, prove $AB = CD$.

Find the values of m, n, and p so that equality holds.

8. $\begin{pmatrix} m + n \\ m + p \\ n + p \end{pmatrix} = \begin{pmatrix} -6 \\ -2 \\ 2 \end{pmatrix}$

9. $\begin{pmatrix} m + n + p \\ m - p \\ n - p \end{pmatrix} = \begin{pmatrix} 3 \\ 1 \\ -4 \end{pmatrix}$

Find the norm and direction cosines of $\overrightarrow{OP}$ for each point P.

10. $(7, 0, 4)$
11. $(-3, 1, -5)$
12. $(4, -2, 8)$

Find $\vec{u} \cdot \vec{v}$.

13. $\vec{u} = \begin{pmatrix} 1 \\ 1 \\ 1 \end{pmatrix}, \vec{v} = \begin{pmatrix} 2 \\ -1 \\ 0 \end{pmatrix}$

14. $\vec{u} = \begin{pmatrix} -1 \\ -4 \\ -3 \end{pmatrix}, \vec{v} = \begin{pmatrix} -5 \\ 2 \\ -9 \end{pmatrix}$

15. Find a vector perpendicular to both $\begin{pmatrix} 7 \\ -2 \\ 4 \end{pmatrix}$ and $\begin{pmatrix} 2 \\ 0 \\ -1 \end{pmatrix}$.

Find the equations for the line through each pair of points.

16. $(3, -1, 2), (4, 0, -1)$
17. $(1, 4, 2), (-2, 0, 1)$

Find the equation for each plane.

18. The plane contains the point $(1, 2, -3)$ and is parallel to the plane $2x - 5y + z + 7 = 0$.

19. The plane contains the points $(0, 2, 3)$ and $(2, 0, 4)$ and is perpendicular to the plane $2x - 7y + 13z - 4 = 0$.

20. Describe the locus of $\{(x, y, z) \mid x^2 + y^2 + z^2 - 2x + 4y - 2z - 15 = 0\}$.

Computers

BASIC-Looping

Some statements in BASIC can compare numbers and, as a result can be directed to a particular statement. The following program demonstrates this branching procedure.

```
10   REM POLYNOMIAL EVALUATION USING
         IF - THEN
20   LET C = 0
30   IF C > 7 THEN 110
40   READ X
50   LET P = X↑3 − 3 ∗ X↑2 + 2 ∗ X − 5
60   PRINT "FOR X = "; X; "THE POLYNO-
         MIAL VALUE IS"; P
70   PRINT
80   LET C = C + 1
90   GØTØ 30
100  DATA −3, −2, −1, 0, 1, 2, 3
110  END
```

When using the IF-THEN statement an ex-
pression of equality or inequality follows IF and a line number follows THEN. If the statement is correctly composed, the computer will branch to the indicated statement. In some situations, an assignment might follow THEN. For example, in the statement IF $X > = Y + 2$ THEN $X = 2*Z$ if $X \geq Y + 2$, X becomes 2 times Z. The computer would then execute the next step of the program. An inequality is expressed using one of the following forms $> =$ (read "is greater than or equal to"), $< =$ (read "is less than or equal to,"), and $<>$ (read "is not equal to"). A statement with a strict less than or greater than is similarly coded.

When a program needs to be repeated several times, a counter can be used to keep tab of the number of times the program is run.

To initialize the counter C, LET C=0 is used. To increment the counter, LET C=C+1 is used. To test to see if the process is complete, the branch IF C > 7 THEN 110 is used. The program prints out a table of values of x from −3 to 3 in integer steps and the corresponding P(x) for the cubic $x^3 − 3x^2 + 2x − 5$.

```
FOR X=-3 THE POLYNOMIAL VALUE IS -65

FOR X=-2 THE POLYNOMIAL VALUE IS -29

FOR X=-1 THE POLYNOMIAL VALUE IS -11

FOR X=0 THE POLYNOMIAL VALUE IS -5

FOR X=1 THE POLYNOMIAL VALUE IS -5

FOR X=2 THE POLYNOMIAL VALUE IS -5

FOR X=3 THE POLYNOMIAL VALUE IS 1.0000001
```

Another approach to looping (repeating the program several times) is to use the FOR-NEXT statement.

```
10  REM POLYNOMIAL EVALUATION USING
      FOR-NEXT
20  FOR X = -3 TO 3
30  LET P = X↑3 + 3 * X↑2 + 2 * X - 5
40  PRINT "FOR X ="; X; "THE POLYNOMIAL
      VALUE IS"; P
50  NEXT X
60  END
```

When the FOR statement is reached, the counter is initialized and a test is made to see if the loop is finished. When the NEXT statement is reached, transfer is made back to the FOR statement, the counter is incremented and the test for completion is made. If the test fails, another loop through the program segment is made with the new value of the counter. If the test value is reached, the program branches to the line after that containing NEXT. If it is desired to increment by other than one, a STEP is added to the FOR statement. For example, FOR K = 1 TO 25 STEP 3 would indicate the program to be executed for K =1 to K = 25 but using every third number so that the second number for K would be 4.

```
10    REM   POLYNOMIAL EVALUATION US
        ING FOR-NEXT
20    FOR X =  - 3 TO 3
30    LET P = X ^ 3 + 3 * X ^ 2 + 2
        * X - 5
40    PRINT "FOR X= ";X;" THE POLYN
        OMIAL VALUE IS ";P
50    NEXT X
60    END

]RUN
FOR X= -3 THE POLYNOMIAL VALUE IS -11
FOR X= -2 THE POLYNOMIAL VALUE IS -5
FOR X= -1 THE POLYNOMIAL VALUE IS -5
FOR X= 0 THE POLYNOMIAL VALUE IS -5
FOR X= 1 THE POLYNOMIAL VALUE IS 1
FOR X= 2 THE POLYNOMIAL VALUE IS 19
FOR X= 3 THE POLYNOMIAL VALUE IS 55
```

Exercises **Write programs for each of the following using 3-dimensional vectors.**

1. Find the distance k between $\bar{u}$ and $\bar{v}$.

2. Find the dot product of $\bar{u}$ and $\bar{v}$.

3. Find the cross product of $\bar{u}$ and $\bar{v}$.

4. Determine if $\bar{u}$ and $\bar{v}$ are parallel, perpendicular, or neither.

5. Find the equation for the line passing through (x_1, y_1, z_1) and parallel to a line through (x_2, y_2, z_2) and (x_3, y_3, z_3).

6. Find the equation of the line which passes through (x_1, y_1, z_1) and is perpendicular to the planes $Ax + By + Cz + D = 0$.

Chapter 9

Many buildings have used the concepts of conic sections in their construction. For example, the ellipse has been used to build rooms in which sound travels very effectively from one point in the room to another.

Second-Degree Relations

9-1 The Circle

A **circle** may be defined as the locus of points in a plane at a given distance from a given point. Suppose the given point is (h, k) and the given distance is r units.

> The standard form of the equation of a circle with center (h, k) and radius r units is $(x - h)^2 + (y - k)^2 = r^2$.

Equation of a Circle

$$(x - h)^2 + (y - k)^2 = r^2$$
$$x^2 - 2hx + h^2 + y^2 - 2ky + k^2 = r^2$$

Since h, k, and r are constants, the standard form of the equation of a circle may be written as $x^2 + y^2 + Dx + Ey + F = 0$. This equation is called the *general form* of the equation of a circle.

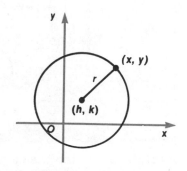

Example

1. **Find the equation in general form of the circle with endpoints of a diameter at $A(-1, 1)$ and $B(5, 3)$.**

   Let $C(h, k)$ be the midpoint of $\overline{AB}$.

   $$(h, k) = \left(\frac{-1 + 5}{2}, \frac{1 + 3}{2}\right) = (2, 2)$$

   Segment AC is a radius.

   $$r^2 = (AC)^2 = (-1 - 2)^2 + (1 - 2)^2 = 10$$

   Thus, the equation would be as follows.

   $$(x - 2)^2 + (y - 2)^2 = 10$$
   $$x^2 - 4x + 4 + y^2 - 4y + 4 = 10$$
   $$x^2 + y^2 - 4x - 4y - 2 = 0$$

   (General form)

   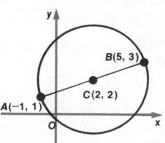

Example

2. **Find the equation of a circle tangent to the x-axis and passing through (2, 9) with center (h, k) on the line with equation x + 2y = 9.** *Since the center (h, k) lies on the graph of x + 2y = 9, it must satisfy the equation.*

An equation of all circles through (2, 9) is as follows.

$$(2 - h)^2 + (9 - k)^2 = r^2$$
$$(2 - (9 - 2k))^2 + (9 - k)^2 = r^2 \qquad \textit{Substitute } 9 - 2k \textit{ for } h.$$
$$(-7 + 2k)^2 + (9 - k)^2 = r^2$$

Since the circle is tangent to the x-axis, $|k| = r$.

$$(-7 + 2k)^2 + (9 - k)^2 = k^2$$
$$49 - 28k + 4k^2 + 81 - 18k + k^2 = k^2$$
$$4k^2 - 46k + 130 = 0 \qquad \textit{Divide through by 2.}$$
$$(2k - 13)(k - 5) = 0 \qquad \textit{Then factor.}$$
$$k = \frac{13}{2} \text{ or } k = 5$$

If $k = \frac{13}{2}$, $h = -4$ and if $k = 5$, $h = -1$.

There are two circles which satisfy the given conditions.

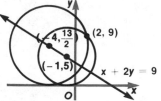

$$(x + 4)^2 + \left(y - \frac{13}{2}\right)^2 = \frac{169}{4} \qquad \text{or} \qquad (x + 1)^2 + (y - 5)^2 = 25$$

Exercises

Exploratory Find the coordinates of the center and the length of the radius of each circle for each equation below.

1. $(x - 2)^2 + (y - 1)^2 = 16$
2. $(x + 3)^2 + (y - 5)^2 = 4$
3. $x^2 + (y + 1)^2 = 9$

Write the equation of the circle with each given center at C and radius r units.

4. $C(1, 4); r = 4$
5. $C(3, -7); r = 3$
6. $C(0, 4); r = 1$
7. $C(3, 5); r = 2$
8. $C(-2, 4); r = 4$
9. $C(-1, 0); r = 5$

Written For each of the following, write the equation of the circle with each center at C and radius r units.

1. $C(a, 2a); r = a$
2. $C(3b, b); r = b$
3. $C(7, -a); r = \sqrt{2}$
4. $C(-5, 3); r = \sqrt{5}$
5. $C(0, 5); r = \sqrt{13}$
6. $C\left(-\frac{1}{4}, 1\right); r = \sqrt{3}$

Write the coordinates of the center and find the length of the radius of each circle.

7. $x^2 + y^2 - 6x + 4y - 3 = 0$
8. $x^2 + y^2 + 8x + 2y - 8 = 0$
9. $x^2 + y^2 - 2ax + 4ay + 4a^2 = 0$
10. $x^2 + y^2 + 4bx + 6by + 9b^2 = 0$

Write the equation of each circle described below.

11. Center $(-8, -3)$, tangent to the x-axis

12. Center $(5, -2)$, tangent to the y-axis

13. Center $(4, 4)$, tangent to the line $3x + 4y = 3$

14. Center $(3, -1)$, tangent to the line $y = x + 2$

15. Center on the line $2x - 5y = 9$, tangent to both axes (There are two circles.)

16. Center on the line $3x + 4y = 14$, tangent to both axes (There are two circles.)

17. Diameter $\overline{AB}$ where the coordinates of A are $(-3, 4)$ and the coordinates of B are $(1, 2)$

18. Passes through $P(5, 3)$, $Q(-2, 2)$, and $R(-1, -5)$ (Evaluate the general form, solving for D, E, and F.)

19. Passes through $A(0, -9)$, $B(7, -2)$, and $C(-5, -10)$

20. Passes through $(2, 1)$, tangent to the x-axis at $(3, 0)$

Challenge

1. Write the equation of the line which passes through the center of the circle with the equation $x^2 + y^2 - 14x + 10y + 73 = 0$ and is parallel to the line whose equation is $x + 2y = 5$.

2. Write the equation of a circle which passes through $(6, 1)$ and the points of intersection of the circles $x^2 + y^2 - 6x + 8y - 9 = 0$ and $x^2 + y^2 - 6x - 4y - 21 = 0$.

9–2 The Parabola

A **parabola** is the locus of points in a plane which are equidistant from a given point and a given line. The given point is called the **focus**. The given line is called the **directrix**.

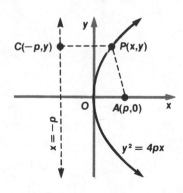

Suppose the focus of a parabola is located at $(p, 0)$ and the directrix is the line with equation $x = -p$. Then the origin is on the parabola. In fact, the origin is the point which is nearest the focus and directrix. This point is called the **vertex** of the parabola. The line which passes through the vertex and focus is called the **axis** of the parabola.

By definition, AP is equal to PC.

$$\sqrt{(x - p)^2 + y^2} = \sqrt{(x + p)^2}$$
$$x^2 - 2px + p^2 + y^2 = x^2 + 2px + p^2$$
$$y^2 = 4px$$

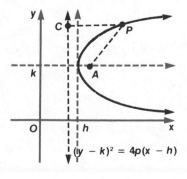

Suppose the vertex of the parabola is at (h, k), and the axis is parallel to the x-axis. The equation of the parabola in this case is $(y - k)^2 = 4p(x - h)$.

If the axis of the parabola is parallel to the y-axis, then the equation of the parabola is $(x - h)^2 = 4p(y - k)$.

The standard forms for the equation of a parabola with vertex at (h, k), where $|p|$ is the number of units from the focus to the vertex, are as follows.

$(y - k)^2 = 4p(x - h)$ $\begin{cases} \text{if the axis of the parabola} \\ \text{is parallel to the } x\text{-axis} \end{cases}$

$(x - h)^2 = 4p(y - k)$ $\begin{cases} \text{if the axis of the parabola} \\ \text{is parallel to the } y\text{-axis} \end{cases}$

Equations of a Parabola

Note that in $(y - k)^2 = 4p (x - h)$ there are two values of y for each x. Hence the graph has a horizontal axis. In $(x - h)^2 = 4p(y - k)$ there are two values of x for each y. Hence the graph has a vertical axis.

The standard forms for the equation of a parabola may by transformed to the general forms. The equations,

$$y^2 + Dx + Ey + F = 0 \quad \text{and} \quad x^2 + Dx + Ey + F = 0,$$

depend on $h, k,$ and p.

Examples

1. **Find the equation of a parabola with vertex at $(3, -5)$ and focus at $(3, -3)$.**

    $h = 3, k = -5, p = -3 - (-5) = 2$

    Since the axis is parallel to the y-axis or vertical, use the equation $(x - h)^2 = 4p(y - k)$.

    $$(x - 3)^2 = 8(y + 5)$$
    $$x^2 - 6x + 9 = 8y + 40$$
    $$x^2 - 6x - 8y - 31 = 0$$

    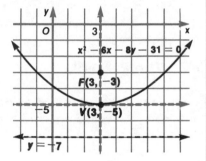

2. **Find the coordinates of the vertex and focus and the equation of the directrix of the parabola $y^2 - 12x + 2y + 25 = 0$.**

    $$y^2 - 12x + 2y + 25 = 0$$
    $$y^2 + 2y = 12x - 25$$
    $$y^2 + 2y + 1 = 12x - 25 + 1 \quad \textit{Complete the}$$
    $$(y + 1)^2 = 12x - 24 \quad \textit{square.}$$
    $$(y + 1)^2 = 12(x - 2)$$

    Therefore, $h = 2, k = -1, p = 3$. The vertex is at $(2, -1)$. Since the axis is parallel to the x-axis or horizontal, the focus is $(5, -1)$. The equation of the directrix is $x = 2 - 3$ or $x = -1$.

    When p is positive the parabola opens to the right or upward. When p is negative the parabola opens to the left or downward.

    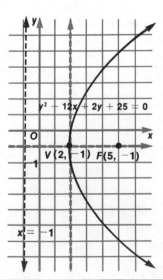

The **latus rectum** of a parabola is the line segment which is perpendicular to the axis, passes through the focus, and has endpoints on the parabola. The length of the latus rectum is $|4p|$, where $|p|$ is the distance from the focus to the vertex of the parabola.

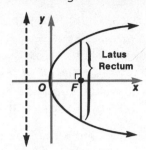

Exercises

Exploratory Find the coordinates of the vertex and the equation of the directrix of the parabola for each equation below.

1. $y^2 = 8x$
2. $(x - 1)^2 = 12(y - 1)$
3. $(x + 4)^2 = -4(y - 2)$
4. $(y + 6)^2 = 16(x + 3)$
5. $(x - 2)^2 = -8(y + 1)$
6. $(y - 3)^2 = 4x$

Write the equation of the parabola with the given vertex V and focus F.

7. $V(0, 0), F(2, 0)$
8. $V(0, 0), F(-1, 0)$
9. $V(-3, 5), F(-3, 3)$
10. $V(2, -1), F(4, -1)$
11. $V(h, 2h), F(h, 4h)$
12. $V(2a, a), F(6a, a)$

Written Sketch the parabola for each equation below.

1. $y = \frac{1}{4}x^2$
2. $x = -2y^2$
3. $(x - 2)^2 = 8(y + 1)$
4. $(y + 3)^2 = -12(x - 2)$
5. $y^2 - 4x + 2y + 5 = 0$
6. $x^2 - 8x + 8y + 32 = 0$

Write the equation of each parabola described below.

7. The parabola has vertex (4, 3), passes through (5, 2), and has a vertical axis.

8. The parabola has vertex (-7, -5), passes through (2, -1), and has a horizontal axis

9. The parabola passes through (-7 4), (-5, 5) and (3, 29), and its axis is parallel to the y-axis. (Hint: Use general form and solve for D, E, and F.)

10. The parabola passes through (7, 5), (-1, 3) and (17, 0), and its axis is parallel to the x-axis.

11. The parabola is equidistant from (-2, 0) and the line $x = 2$.

12. The parabola is equidistant from (0, 4) and the line $y = -4$.

Suppose an object is thrown vertically upward with an initial velocity V_0. The distance, s, above the ground after t seconds (neglecting air resistance) is $s = v_0 t - 16t^2$. Assume $v_0 = 64$ft/s. Solve each of the following.

13. Sketch the function $s = v_0 t - 16t^2$.

14. Find the coordinates of the vertex.

15. Discuss the significance of the distance at the vertex.

16. Determine the number of seconds it takes to hit the ground.

Solve each of the following.

17. A farmer has 96 m of fencing. He wants to enclose a rectangular field and build a fence equal to the width across the middle. Express the area of the field as a function of the width x. Sketch the graph of the relation. Determine for which value of x the area is maximum.

18. The cross section of a headlight reflector is a parabola. The reflector is 6 in. in diameter and 4 in. deep. Determine the distance from the vertex to the focus of this parabola.

Challenge Show that the length of the latus rectum is $|4p|$, where $|p|$ is the distance from the focus to the vertex of the parabola.

9-3 The Ellipse

An **ellipse** is defined as the locus of points in a plane such that the sum of the distances from two fixed points is a constant. The two fixed points are called the **foci** of the ellipse.

The equation of an ellipse can be derived from the definition. Suppose the foci are at $(c, 0)$ and $(-c, 0)$. Let (x, y) be any point on the ellipse and the sum of the distances to the foci be $2a$ units.

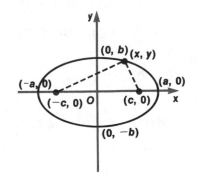

$$\sqrt{(x + c)^2 + y^2} + \sqrt{(x - c)^2 + y^2} = 2a$$

$$\sqrt{(x + c)^2 + y^2} = 2a - \sqrt{(x - c)^2 + y^2}$$
$$x^2 + 2cx + c^2 + y^2 = 4a^2 - 4a\sqrt{(x - c)^2 + y^2} + x^2 - 2cx + c^2 + y^2$$
$$4cx - 4a^2 = -4a\sqrt{(x - c)^2 + y^2}$$
$$-cx + a^2 = a\sqrt{(x - c)^2 + y^2}$$
$$a^4 - 2a^2cx + c^2x^2 = a^2x^2 - 2a^2cx + a^2c^2 + a^2y^2$$
$$a^4 - a^2c^2 = (a^2 - c^2)x^2 + a^2y^2$$
$$a^2(a^2 - c^2) = (a^2 - c^2)x^2 + a^2y^2$$
$$a^2b^2 = x^2b^2 + a^2y^2 \qquad \text{Let } a^2 - c^2 = b^2.$$
$$\frac{x^2}{a^2} + \frac{y^2}{b^2} = 1$$

If $y = 0$, then $x = \pm a$. The points $(a, 0)$ and $(-a, 0)$ are called the **vertices** of the ellipse. The distance $2a$ units is the length of the **major axis,** and a units is the length of the **semi-major axis.** Likewise, $2b$ units is the length of the **minor axis,** and b units is the length of the **semi-minor axis.**

Consider the case where $(x, y) = (0, b)$. Since the sum of the distances to the foci always is $2a$ units, the hypotenuse of the right triangle is a, and the legs are b and c. Hence, $a^2 = b^2 + c^2$.

Suppose the center of the ellipse is at (h, k). The equation of the ellipse in this case is $\dfrac{(x - h)^2}{a^2} + \dfrac{(y - k)^2}{b^2} = 1.$

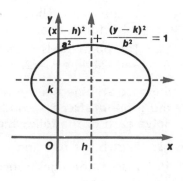

If the foci are on the y-axis at $(0, c)$ and $(0, -c)$ then the equation of the ellipse is $\dfrac{y^2}{a^2} + \dfrac{x^2}{b^2} = 1$. If the center is at (h, k), then $\dfrac{(y - k)^2}{a^2} + \dfrac{(x - h)^2}{b^2} = 1$ is the equation of the ellipse.

> **Standard forms of the equations of an ellipse with center (h, k) and sum of the distances to the foci $2a$ units are as follows.**
>
> $\dfrac{(x - h)^2}{a^2} + \dfrac{(y - k)^2}{b^2} = 1$ $\left\{\begin{array}{l}\text{if segment joining the foci}\\ \text{is parallel to the } x\text{-axis}\end{array}\right.$
>
> $\dfrac{(y - k)^2}{a^2} + \dfrac{(x - h)^2}{b^2} = 1$ $\left\{\begin{array}{l}\text{if segment joining the foci}\\ \text{is parallel to the } y\text{-axis}\end{array}\right.$

Equations of an Ellipse

The general form of the equation of an ellipse with major axis parallel to a coordinate axis is $Ax^2 + Cy^2 + Dx + Ey + F = 0$ where $A \neq 0$, $C \neq 0$ and A and C have the same sign. If $A = C$, the figure is a circle which is a special case of the ellipse.

The **eccentricity** e of an ellipse is defined as $e = \dfrac{c}{a}$. Since $0 < c < a$, then $0 < e < 1$. If e is close to zero, then the two foci are near the center of the ellipse. In this case, the ellipse looks nearly like a circle. If e is close to one, then the foci are near the ends of the major axis and the ellipse is very elongated.

The semi-major axis is always a. The fraction which has the larger denominator will indicate the orientation of the major axis. It is horizontal if a is in the "x" fraction, and vertical if a is in the "y" fraction.

Example

1. **Sketch the graph of $16x^2 + 25y^2 - 32x + 100y - 284 = 0$. Find the coordinates of the center, vertices, and foci. Determine the eccentricity of this ellipse.**

    $$16x^2 + 25y^2 - 32x + 100y - 284 = 0$$
    $$16(x^2 - 2x) + 25(y^2 + 4y) = 284$$
    $$16(x^2 - 2x + 1) + 25(y^2 + 4y + 4) = 284 + 16 + 100 \qquad \textit{Complete the square.}$$
    $$16(x - 1)^2 + 25(y + 2)^2 = 400$$
    $$\frac{(x - 1)^2}{25} + \frac{(y + 2)^2}{16} = 1$$

    The center is at $(1, -2)$.
    Since $a = 5$, the vertices are $(6, -2)$ and $(-4, -2)$.

    $$b^2 + c^2 = a^2$$
    $$16 + c^2 = 25$$
    $$c = 3 \qquad c^2 = 9$$

    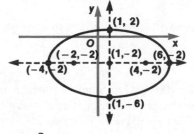

    The foci are at $(4, -2)$ and $(-2, -2)$. The eccentricity is $\dfrac{c}{a}$ or $\dfrac{3}{5}$.

Example

2. Find the equation of the ellipse with foci at (2, 7) and (2, −1) and eccentricity $\frac{4}{5}$.

$$h = 2 \qquad k = \frac{7 + (-1)}{2} = 3$$

The center of the ellipse is the midpoint of the segment between the foci.
The foci lie on a vertical line.

So, $\dfrac{(y-3)^2}{a^2} + \dfrac{(x-2)^2}{b^2} = 1.$

The distance between the foci is 8, so $c = 4$.

$$e = \frac{c}{a} \qquad\qquad b^2 + c^2 = a^2$$
$$\frac{4}{5} = \frac{4}{a} \qquad\qquad b^2 + 16 = 25$$
$$a = 5 \qquad\qquad b^2 = 9$$

The equation of the ellipse is $\dfrac{(y-3)^2}{25} + \dfrac{(x-2)^2}{9} = 1.$

In standard form, the equation is $25x^2 + 9y^2 - 100x - 54y - 44 = 0$.

The **latus rectum** of an ellipse is the chord which is perpendicular to the major axis at the focus. The length of the latus rectum for the ellipse $\dfrac{x^2}{a^2} + \dfrac{y^2}{b^2} = 1$ is $\dfrac{2b^2}{a}$ units.

Exercises

Exploratory Write the equation for an ellipse with the given center, the measure of the semi-major axis, and the measure of the semi-minor axis. Assume the major axis is horizontal.

1. $C(4, 3)$, $a = 5$, $b = 3$
2. $C(-2, 1)$, $a = 4$, $b = 1$
3. $C(-5, -9)$, $a = 6$, $b = 2$

Find the coordinates of the center and the vertices for each of the following.

4. $\dfrac{(x-2)^2}{4} + \dfrac{(y-1)^2}{1} = 1$
5. $\dfrac{(y-3)^2}{16} + \dfrac{x^2}{36} = 1$
6. $\dfrac{(x+7)^2}{9} + \dfrac{(y-1)^2}{25} = 1$

Find the eccentricity given the following information.

7. $a = 5$, $b = 3$
8. $a = 10$, $b = 8$
9. $c = 9$, $b = 12$
10. $a = 13$, $c = 5$

Written For each equation of an ellipse given, (a) determine the coordinates of the center, vertices, and foci; (b) determine the eccentricity; and (c) sketch the graph.

1. $\dfrac{(x-1)^2}{4} + \dfrac{(y-2)^2}{16} = 1$
2. $\dfrac{(y+2)^2}{4} + \dfrac{(x-3)^2}{1} = 1$
3. $x^2 + 4y^2 - 14x - 8y + 53 = 0$
4. $x^2 + 9y^2 + 10x + 36y + 52 = 0$

Write the equation of each ellipse described below.

5. Center (3, 3), vertex, (3, 8), $e = \frac{4}{5}$

6. Center (−2, −5), vertex (3, −5), $e = \frac{3}{5}$

7. Vertices (5, 1) and (−3, 1), focus (2, 1)

8. Vertices (0, 4) and (0, −2), focus (0, 3)

9. The sum of the distances from the foci (3, 0) and (−3, 0) is 10.

10. The sum of the distances from the foci (0, 4) and (0, −4) is 10.

Solve each of the following.

11. The orbit of the earth about the sun is an ellipse. The sun is at one focus, and the eccentricity is about 0.017. The length of the semi-major axis is about 149 million kilometers. What is the greatest and least distance of the earth from the sun?

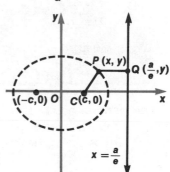

12. A satellite is in an elliptic orbit around the earth. Its perigee (nearest point) is 480 km. Its apogee (farthest point) is 800 km. The diameter of the earth is 12,800 km. The earth is at one focus of the elliptic orbit. What is the eccentricity of the orbit? (See figure above.)

Challenge

1. Prove that the length of the latus rectum for the ellipse $\frac{x^2}{a^2} + \frac{y^2}{b^2} = 1$ is $\frac{2b^2}{a}$.

2. There is another way to describe an ellipse. Suppose a fixed point is $C(c, 0)$ and a fixed line has the equation $x = \frac{a}{e}$. The ratio $\frac{PC}{PQ} = e$ where $e = \frac{c}{a}$. Show that the locus is the ellipse with equation $\frac{x^2}{a^2} + \frac{y^2}{b^2} = 1$. *(Hint: $a^2 = b^2 + c^2$.)*

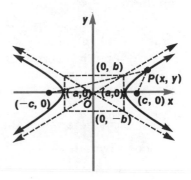

9–4 The Hyperbola

A **hyperbola** is the locus of points in a plane such that the difference of the distances from two fixed points is a constant. The two fixed points are called the **foci** of the hyperbola.

Let the foci be at $(c, 0)$ and $(-c, 0)$. Let the *constant difference* be $2a$ units.

$$\sqrt{(x - c)^2 + y^2} - \sqrt{(x + c)^2 + y^2} = 2a$$

$$\sqrt{(x - c)^2 + y^2} = 2a + \sqrt{(x + c)^2 + y^2}$$

$$-4xc - 4a^2 = 4a\sqrt{(x + c)^2 + y^2} \quad \textit{Square and combine.}$$

$$x^2c^2 + 2a^2xc + a^4 = a^2x^2 + 2a^2xc + a^2c^2 + a^2y^2$$

$$x^2(c^2 - a^2) - a^2y^2 = a^2(c^2 - a^2) \quad \textit{Collect terms and factor.}$$

$$x^2b^2 - a^2y^2 = a^2b^2 \quad \textit{Let } c^2 - a^2 = b^2.$$

$$\frac{x^2}{a^2} - \frac{y^2}{b^2} = 1$$

The **center** of this hyperbola is at the origin. The **vertices** are at $(a, 0)$ and $(-a, 0)$. The line segment which has its endpoints at the vertices is called the **transverse axis**. The segment perpendicular to the transverse axis at its midpoint and with endpoints $(0, b)$ and $(0, -b)$ is called the **conjugate axis**.

If the equation $\dfrac{x^2}{a^2} - \dfrac{y^2}{b^2} = 1$ is solved for y, then $y = \pm\dfrac{b}{a}\sqrt{x^2 - a^2}$. As x becomes very large, $x^2 - a^2$ comes close to x^2 and y comes close to $\pm\dfrac{b}{a}x$. The lines $y = \pm\dfrac{b}{a}x$ are **asymptotes** of the hyperbola.

The foci are on a line parallel to the x-axis.

If the foci of the hyperbola are at $(0, c)$ and $(0, -c)$, then the equation becomes $\dfrac{y^2}{a^2} - \dfrac{x^2}{b^2} = 1$. The vertices of this hyperbola then are at $(0, a)$ and $(0, -a)$. The asymptotes are $y = \pm\dfrac{a}{b}x$.

The foci are on a line parallel to the y-axis.

The standard forms of the equation of a hyperbola with center at (h, k) and difference of the distances from the foci $2a$ units are as follows.

$$\dfrac{(x - h)^2}{a^2} - \dfrac{(y - k)^2}{b^2} = 1 \quad \left\{ \begin{array}{l} \text{if the transverse} \\ \text{axis is horizontal} \end{array} \right.$$

$$\dfrac{(y - k)^2}{a^2} - \dfrac{(x - h)^2}{b^2} = 1 \quad \left\{ \begin{array}{l} \text{if the transverse} \\ \text{axis is vertical} \end{array} \right.$$

Equations of a Hyperbola

The general equation of a hyperbola which has axis parallel to a coordinate axes is $Ax^2 + Cy^2 + Dx + Ey + F = 0$ where $A \neq 0$, $C \neq 0$, and A and C have different signs.

The distance from the center to the vertex is always a. This value will always appear in the positive fraction. The positive fraction indicates the direction of the transverse axis.

The lines ℓ and m are the asymptotes with the equations $(y - k) = \dfrac{b}{a}(x - h)$ and $(y - k) = -\dfrac{b}{a}(x - h)$, respectively. The focus A has coordinates $(-c + h, k)$, and focus D has coordinates $(c + h, k)$. The vertex B has coordinates $(-a + h, k)$ and vertex C has coordinates $(a + h, k)$.

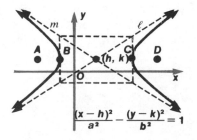

Eccentricity determines the shape of a hyperbola. The **eccentricity** of a hyperbola is defined as $e = \dfrac{c}{a}$. Since $c > a$, it follows that $e > 1$.

Examples

1. **Find the center, vertices, foci, and eccentricity of the hyperbola with equation $9x^2 - 4y^2 - 36x + 8y - 4 = 0$.**

$$9x^2 - 4y^2 - 36x + 8y - 4 = 0 \qquad \textit{Find the standard form of the equation.}$$
$$9x^2 - 36x - 4y^2 + 8y = 4$$
$$9(x^2 - 4x) - 4(y^2 - 2y) = 4$$
$$9(x^2 - 4x + 4) - 4(y^2 - 2y + 1) = 4 + 36 - 4$$
$$9(x - 2)^2 - 4(y - 1)^2 = 36$$
$$\frac{(x - 2)^2}{4} - \frac{(y - 1)^2}{9} = 1$$

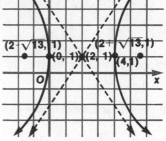

The center has the coordinates (2, 1). Since $a = 2$, the vertices are at (4, 1) and (0, 1).

$$c^2 = a^2 + b^2$$
$$c^2 = 4 + 9$$
$$c = +\sqrt{13}$$

The foci are at $(2 + \sqrt{13}, 1)$ and $(2 - \sqrt{13}, 1)$. The eccentricity is $\dfrac{\sqrt{13}}{2}$.

2. **Write the equation of a hyperbola with eccentricity $\dfrac{5}{4}$, center at (−2, 3), and one vertex at (−2, −1).**

With one vertex at (−2, −1) and the center at (−2, 3), a can be found.

$$a = 3 - (-1) = 4 \qquad \textit{The transverse axis is vertical.}$$

Since $e = \dfrac{c}{a}$ or $\dfrac{5}{4}$, $c = 5$.

$$c^2 = a^2 + b^2$$
$$25 = 16 + b^2$$
$$9 = b^2$$

The equation is $\dfrac{(y - 3)^2}{16} - \dfrac{(x + 2)^2}{9} = 1$.

A **latus rectum** is defined as the line segment perpendicular to the transverse axis at the focus and with endpoints on the hyperbola. If the hyperbola is $\dfrac{x^2}{a^2} - \dfrac{y^2}{b^2} = 1$ then the length of the latus rectum is $\dfrac{2b^2}{a}$ units.

Exercises

Exploratory For each of the following write the equation of the hyperbola with the given center and values of a and b. Assume a horizontal transverse axis.

1. $C(4, 7)$, $a = 3$, $b = 2$ 2. $C(-3, 3)$, $a = 5$, $b = 4$ 3. $C(0, 0)$, $a = 1$, $b = 1$

Find the coordinates of the center and the vertices of each of the following.

4. $\dfrac{x^2}{9} - \dfrac{y^2}{4} = 1$ 5. $\dfrac{(x - 1)^2}{25} - \dfrac{(y - 3)^2}{49} = 1$ 6. $\dfrac{(y + 2)^2}{16} - \dfrac{(x + 1)^2}{9} = 1$

Find the eccentricity given the following information.

7. $a = 5$, $b = 12$ 8. $a = 6$, $c = 10$ 9. $b = 15$, $c = 17$

Written For each equation of a hyperbola given write **(a)** the coordinates of the center, foci, and vertices; **(b)** the eccentricity; **(c)** the slopes of the asymptotes; and **(d)** sketch the graph.

1. $x^2 - 4y^2 = 64$ 2. $4y^2 - 9x^2 = 36$

3. $\dfrac{(y - 3)^2}{25} - \dfrac{(x - 2)^2}{16} = 1$ 4. $\dfrac{(x + 6)^2}{36} - \dfrac{(y + 3)^2}{9} = 1$

5. The hyperbolas $\dfrac{x^2}{4} - \dfrac{y^2}{9} = 1$ and $\dfrac{y^2}{9} - \dfrac{x^2}{4} = 1$ are called conjugate hyperbolas. Show that they share the same asymptotes.

Write the equation of each hyperbola described below.

6. Foci at $(6, 0)$ and $(-6, 0)$, $e = \frac{3}{2}$

7. Foci at $(0, 8)$ and $(0, -8)$, $e = \frac{4}{3}$

8. Vertices at $(6, 2)$ and $(-6, 2)$, $e = \frac{5}{3}$

9. Vertices at $(1, 4)$ and $(1, -1)$, $e = \frac{3}{2}$

10. Center $(3, -1)$, vertex $(6, -1)$, one asymptote with equation $2x - 3y = 9$

11. Center $(4, 2)$, vertex $(4, 6)$, one asymptote with equation $4y - 3x = -4$

12. Center $(0, 4)$, one focus at $(0, 9)$, $e = \frac{5}{4}$

13. Center $(5, 1)$, one focus at $(0, 1)$, $e = \frac{5}{3}$

14. The difference of the distances from $(10, 0)$ and $(-10, 0)$ is 16.

15. The difference of the distances from $(0, 5)$ and $(0, -5)$ is 8.

Challenge

1. Prove that the length of the latus rectum of the hyperbola $\dfrac{x^2}{a^2} - \dfrac{y^2}{b^2} = 1$ is $\dfrac{2b^2}{a}$.

2. By rotating the axes through 45°, show that $xy = k$ represents a hyperbola with perpendicular asymptotes.

3. A hyperbola also may be described another way. A hyperbola is the locus of points P such that the ratio of the distance from P to a fixed point and from P to a fixed line is a constant. Show that if the ratio $e > 1$, then the equation is that of a hyperbola. Suppose the fixed point is $C(c, 0)$ and the fixed line is $x = \dfrac{a}{e}$. The ratio $\dfrac{PC}{PQ}$ is e, where $e = \dfrac{c}{a}$. Show that the locus is the hyperbola with equation $\dfrac{x^2}{a^2} - \dfrac{y^2}{b^2} = 1$. (Hint: $a^2 + b^2 = c^2$.)

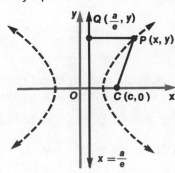

9–5 General Second-Degree Equations

The circle, parabola, ellipse, and hyperbola are called the **conic sections.** If a plane intersects a cone, the intersection is a *conic section*.

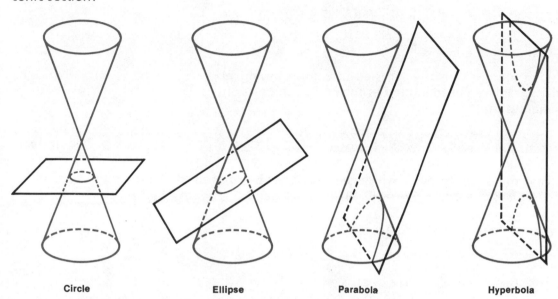

| Circle | Ellipse | Parabola | Hyperbola |

If the plane passes through the vertex of the conical surface, the intersection is a *degenerate case*. The degenerate cases are a point, a line, and two intersecting lines.

The general second degree equation in two variables is $Ax^2 + Bxy + Cy^2 + Dx + Ey + F = 0$. Whenever $B = 0$, the equation is a conic section or one of the degenerate cases (unless the equation has no graph at all).

If $B \neq 0$, a suitable rotation of axes will be made to transform a second-degree equation to a simpler form. Under a counterclockwise rotation through an angle θ, the given point in the xy-plane is related to the same point in the $x'y'$-plane by the equations of rotation, $x = x' \cos \theta - y' \sin \theta$ and $y = x' \sin \theta + y' \cos \theta$.

Substituting the equations of rotation into the general second-degree equation gives its new form in the $x'y'$-plane.

$$A'x'^2 + B'x'y' + C'y'^2 + D'x' + E'y' + F' = 0$$
where $A' = A \cos^2 \theta + B \sin \theta \cos \theta + C \sin^2 \theta$
$B' = B(\cos^2 \theta - \sin^2 \theta) - (A - C)(2 \sin \theta \cos \theta)$
$\quad = B \cos 2\theta - (A - C) \sin 2\theta$
$C' = A \sin^2 \theta - B \sin \theta \cos \theta + C \cos^2 \theta$
$D' = D \cos \theta + E \sin \theta$
$E' = E \cos \theta - D \sin \theta$
$F' = F$

A second-degree equation has no graph in the real number plane if it has no real number solutions. For example, consider $x^2 + y^2 + 4 = 0$.

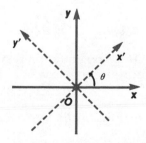

The most convenient choice of θ is the one for which $B' = 0$.

$B' = 0$

$B \cos 2\theta - (A - C) \sin 2\theta = 0$

$B \cos 2\theta = (A - C) \sin 2\theta$

$\dfrac{B}{A - C} = \tan 2\theta$ if $A \neq C$ or $B \cos 2\theta = 0$ if $A = C$

When $B' = 0$, the problem is reduced to the cases where the axes are vertical or horizontal.

If $A = C$ then $2\theta = \dfrac{\pi}{2}$ and $\theta = \dfrac{\pi}{4}$.

Once the equation can be expressed in a form having no $x'y'$-term, its graph can be identified as one of the conic sections or a degenerate case.

Example

1. **Find the angle through which the axes must be rotated to eliminate the xy-term in $8x^2 + 4xy + 5y^2 = 40$. Then, find A' and C'. Identify the conic.**

$$\tan 2\theta = \frac{B}{A - C}$$

$$\tan 2\theta = \frac{4}{3}$$

$$\frac{2 \tan \theta}{1 - \tan^2 \theta} = \frac{4}{3}$$

$$6 \tan \theta = 4 - 4 \tan^2 \theta$$

$$2 \tan^2 \theta + 3 \tan \theta - 2 = 0$$

$$(2 \tan \theta - 1)(\tan \theta + 2) = 0$$

$$2 \tan \theta - 1 = 0 \quad \text{or} \quad \tan \theta + 2 = 0$$

$$\tan \theta = \frac{1}{2} \quad \text{or} \quad \tan \theta = -2$$

$\dfrac{B}{A - C} = \dfrac{4}{8 - 5}$

$\tan 2\theta = \dfrac{2 \tan \theta}{1 - \tan^2 \theta}$

The two values of θ represent angles which differ by $90°$.

For $\theta = \arctan \dfrac{1}{2}$, $\sin \theta = \dfrac{1}{\sqrt{5}}$ and $\cos \theta = \dfrac{2}{\sqrt{5}}$.

$$A' = 8\left(\frac{2}{\sqrt{5}}\right)^2 + 4\left(\frac{1}{\sqrt{5}}\right)\left(\frac{2}{\sqrt{5}}\right) + 5\left(\frac{1}{\sqrt{5}}\right)^2$$

$$= 8\left(\frac{4}{5}\right) + 4\left(\frac{2}{5}\right) + 5\left(\frac{1}{5}\right) = 9$$

$$C' = 8\left(\frac{1}{\sqrt{5}}\right)^2 - 4\left(\frac{1}{\sqrt{5}}\right)\left(\frac{2}{\sqrt{5}}\right) + 5\left(\frac{2}{\sqrt{5}}\right)^2$$

$$= 8\left(\frac{1}{5}\right) - 4\left(\frac{2}{5}\right) + 5\left(\frac{4}{5}\right) = 4$$

$A' = A \cos^2 \theta + B \sin \theta \cos \theta + C \sin^2 \theta$

$C' = A \sin^2 \theta - B \sin \theta \cos \theta + C \cos^2 \theta$

The new equation is $9x'^2 + 4y'^2 = 40$. Since both A' and C' have the same sign, the figure is an ellipse.

The expression $B^2 - 4AC$ is called the discriminant of the second-degree equation. The discriminant remains invariant under any rotation. That is, $B^2 - 4AC = B'^2 - 4A'C'$. If θ is chosen so that $B' = 0$, then $B^2 - 4AC = -4A'C'$.

> Consider the following cases for the discriminant.
>
> 1. If $B^2 - 4AC < 0$, then $A'C' > 0$, A' and C' have the same sign. The figure is a circle, an ellipse, or degenerate.
> 2. If $B^2 - 4AC > 0$, then $A'C' < 0$, A' and C' have opposite signs. The figure is a hyperbola or degenerate.
> 3. If $B^2 - 4AC = 0$, then $A' = 0$ or $C' = 0$. The figure is a parabola or degenerate.

Cases for the Discriminant

Examples

2. **Identify the conic with equation $4x^2 - 5xy + 16y^2 = 32$.**

$$B^2 - 4AC = 5^2 - 4(4)(16) = 25 - 256 = -231$$

Since $B^2 - 4AC < 0$, the figure is a circle, an ellipse or degenerate. Since no circle has an equation with an xy-term, the figure is an ellipse or degenerate.

3. **Identify the conic with equation $16x^2 - 24xy + 9y^2 - 30x - 40y = 0$.**

Assume that the conic exists and is not degenerate.

$$B^2 - 4AC = (-24)^2 - 4(16)(9) = 576 - 576 = 0$$

Since $B^2 - 4AC = 0$, the conic is a parabola.

Exercises

Exploratory   Identify the conic with each equation.

1. $x^2 + y^2 = 4$
2. $xy - 4x + y = 10$
3. $y^2 = 4x + 8$
4. $2x + 3y = 4x^2 - 9y^2$

Describe the degenerate cases possible for each conic.

5. parabola
6. ellipse
7. circle
8. hyperbola

Find $\tan 2\theta$ for each set of values for A, B, and C.

9. 3, 5, 2
10. 4, 0, -9
11. 5, 12, 5
12. 7, 1, 0

Written   Identify the conic with each equation. Assume that each conic exists and is not degenerate.

1. $x^2 + y^2 - 4x + 2y + 1 = 0$
2. $2x^2 - 4x + y - 3 = 0$

3. $y^2 = x - 2y + 5$

4. $x^2 - y^2 + 6x + 6y + 9 = 0$

5. $x^2 - xy - 2y^2 - x + 2y = 0$

6. $5x^2 + 2xy + 5y^2 - 12 = 0$

Show each of the following is true for any rotation of the axes.

7. $A + C = A' + C'$

8. $B^2 - 4AC = B'^2 - 4A'C'$

Eliminate the parameter t in each pair of equations. Show that each is a conic. Identify the conic.

9. $\begin{cases} x = 4 - t \\ y = 4t - t^2 \end{cases}$
10. $\begin{cases} x = 2 \sin t \\ y = 3 \cos t \end{cases}$
11. $\begin{cases} x = 2 - \sin t \\ y = 3 + \cos^2 t \end{cases}$
12. $\begin{cases} x = 1 - \cos^2 t \\ y = 2 + \sin t \end{cases}$

Rotate the axes through a positive acute angle so that the xy-term in each equation is eliminated. Identify the conic. Sketch the graph.

13. $7x^2 + 12xy - 2y^2 = 10$

14. $5x^2 - 4xy + 5y^2 = 12$

Challenge A conic may be defined as the locus of points such that the ratio of the distance from a given point to the distance from a given line is a constant.

1. Establish a coordinate system such that the fixed point is (1, 0) and the fixed line is the y-axis. Let $e = \dfrac{D_1}{D_2}$ where D_1 is the distance from the curve to the fixed point and D_2 is the distance from the curve to the fixed line. Show the equation $e = \dfrac{\sqrt{(x-1)^2 + y^2}}{|x|}$ formed by the ratio defines a conic.

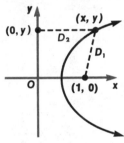

3. Show that if $e < 1$, the figure is an ellipse.

2. Show that if $e = 1$, the figure is a parabola.

4. Show that if $e > 1$, the figure is a hyperbola.

Excursions in mathematics

Matrices and Conics

An arrangement of numerals in rows and columns is called a matrix. $\begin{bmatrix} 1 & 9 & 5 & 7 \\ 6 & 4 & 12 & 2 \end{bmatrix}$ is a 2 by 4 matrix. *It has two rows and four columns.*

Each square matrix has a value called the determinant of the matrix. The determinant of $\begin{bmatrix} 2 & 1 \\ 3 & 4 \end{bmatrix}$ is denoted by $\det \begin{bmatrix} 2 & 1 \\ 3 & 4 \end{bmatrix}$ or $\begin{vmatrix} 2 & 1 \\ 3 & 4 \end{vmatrix}$. *$\det \begin{bmatrix} 2 & 1 \\ 3 & 4 \end{bmatrix} = 2 \cdot 4 - 3 \cdot 1 = 5$*

If $N = \begin{bmatrix} a & b & c \\ d & e & f \\ g & h & i \end{bmatrix}$, then $\det N = aei + bfg + cdh - gec - hfa - idb$.

In terms of determinants, a conic is degenerate if $\begin{vmatrix} 2A & B & D \\ B & 2C & E \\ D & E & 2F \end{vmatrix} = 0$.

9-6   Quadric Surfaces

Second-degree equations in *two* variables describe curves in a *plane*. A second-degree equation also may contain *three* variables. Such equations describe *surfaces* which are called **quadric surfaces**. This section investigates only simple surfaces which can be described using conic sections.

Quadric surfaces can be studied by looking at sections formed by planes which are *parallel* to the *coordinate axes*. Sections made by the coordinate planes are called the **traces** of the surface. The traces on the coordinate planes are found by letting $x = 0$, $y = 0$, or $z = 0$.

Some quadric surfaces are shown below.

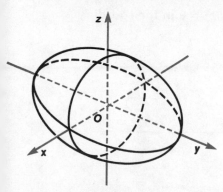

Ellipsoid

$$\frac{x^2}{a^2} + \frac{y^2}{b^2} + \frac{z^2}{c^2} = 1$$

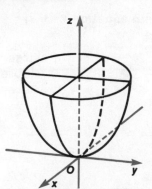

Elliptic Paraboloid

$$\frac{x^2}{a^2} + \frac{y^2}{b^2} = \frac{z}{c}$$

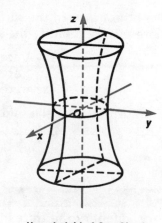

Hyperboloid of One Sheet

$$\frac{x^2}{a^2} + \frac{y^2}{b^2} - \frac{z^2}{c^2} = 1$$

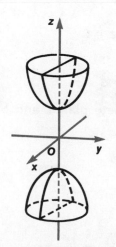

Hyperboloid of Two Sheets

$$\frac{z^2}{c^2} - \frac{x^2}{a^2} - \frac{y^2}{b^2} = 1$$

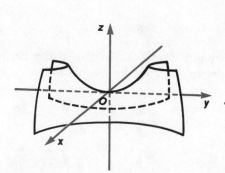

Hyperbolic Paraboloid

$$\frac{y^2}{b^2} - \frac{x^2}{a^2} = \frac{z}{c}$$

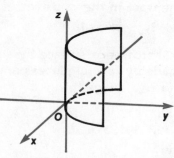

Parabolic Cylinder

$$y = x^2$$

Examples

1. **Describe the surface with equation $x^2 + y^2 - z = 0$.**

   The plane with equation $z = k, k \geq 0$, is parallel to the xy-plane. It intersects the surface in the curve $x^2 + y^2 = k$ which is a circle for all k except $k = 0$. At $k = 0$ the surface passes through the origin.

   The plane with equation $x = p$ intersects the surface in the curve $y^2 = z - p^2$ which is a parabola for all values of p.

   Likewise, the plane with equation $y = q$ intersects the surface in the curve $x^2 = z - q^2$ which is a parabola for all q.

   Therefore, the surface is *parabolic* in *two vertical* directions and *circular* in the *horizontal* direction. This surface is called a **paraboloid**.

2. **Find the traces of the surface with equation $x^2 + 2y^2 + 5z^2 = 8$ in the coordinate planes. Identify the surface.**

   xy-trace: $x^2 + 2y^2 = 8, z = 0$; ellipse
   yz-trace: $2y^2 + 5z^2 = 8, x = 0$; ellipse
   xz-trace: $x^2 + 5z^2 = 8, y = 0$; ellipse

   The surface is an **ellipsoid**.

Exercises

Exploratory Identify the trace in the xy-plane.

1. $x^2 + 4y^2 + z^2 = 16$

2. $4x^2 - 9y^2 - 4z = 36$

Identify the trace in the yz-plane.

3. $x^2 + y^2 + 9z^2 = 1$

4. $y^2 - 4x^2 + z^2 - 4x - z = 0$

Identify the trace in the xz-plane.

5. $12x^2 + 9y^2 - z^2 = 18$

6. $10x^2 - 2y^2 + 4y - z = 9$

Written Sketch each surface by showing its traces in the three coordinate planes and by sections made by several planes parallel to the coordinate planes.

1. $x^2 + y^2 + z^2 = 16$

2. $x^2 - 2y^2 + 3z^2 = 6$

3. $x^2 + y^2 - z = 0$

4. $x^2 + z^2 - 2y = 0$

5. $4x^2 - 9y^2 + 18z = 36$

6. $y^2 = 4x$

7. $\dfrac{x^2}{1} + \dfrac{y^2}{4} - \dfrac{z^2}{4} = 1$

8. $\dfrac{x^2}{1} + \dfrac{y^2}{9} + \dfrac{z^2}{16} = 1$

Write the equation of the surface which is the locus satisfying the following conditions.

9. The square of the distance to a point from the z-axis is $\frac{3}{4}$ of its distance from the xy-plane.

10. The square of the distance to a point from the y-axis is $\frac{2}{3}$ of the distance from the xz-plane.

Excursions in Mathematics

Duality

Ordered Pairs of numbers (x, y) have been used to label points in the plane. For instance, two points on the line $\frac{x}{a} + \frac{y}{b} = 1$ are the intercepts $(a, 0)$ and $(0, b)$.

By labeling lines with ordered pairs $[X, Y]$, a new system of coordinates in the plane can be found. First, rewrite the equation $\frac{x}{a} + \frac{y}{b} = 1$ in the form $\left(-\frac{1}{a}\right)x + \left(-\frac{1}{b}\right)y + 1 = 0$. Now let $X = \left[-\frac{1}{a}\right]$ and $Y = \left[-\frac{1}{b}\right]$. Then the line is named by the ordered pair $[X, Y]$. For example, the line $-\frac{x}{3} + \frac{y}{4} + 1 = 0$ is named $\left[\frac{1}{3}, -\frac{1}{4}\right]$.

Equations have been formed using a pair of points in the old (x, y) coordinate system by writing the ratios of the change in y divided by the change in x. The same can be done in the new $[X, Y]$ coordinate system by using a pair of lines which contain $(2, 2)$. For the lines $\left[-\frac{1}{4}, -\frac{1}{4}\right]$ and $\left[-\frac{1}{6}, -\frac{1}{3}\right]$, the ratio is as follows.

$$\frac{Y - \left(-\frac{1}{4}\right)}{X - \left(-\frac{1}{4}\right)} = \frac{-\frac{1}{3} - \left(-\frac{1}{4}\right)}{-\frac{1}{6} - \left(-\frac{1}{4}\right)}$$

$$2X + 2Y + 1 = 0$$

It has been shown how to find an equation $pX + qY + 4 = 0$ in our new coordinate system. This is the equation of a point in the plane. All lines $[X, Y]$ through a point satisfy the equation of that point.

Systems of equation have been solved in the old coordinate system, usually finding an ordered pair (x, y).

$$\begin{cases} 2X + 2Y + 1 = 0 \\ 3X + (-2)Y + 1 = 0 \end{cases}$$

Solving the system of equations in the new system picks out the line $\left[-\frac{2}{5}, -\frac{1}{10}\right]$ which contains the points $(2, 2)$ and $(3, -2)$.

In the study of geometry many statements appeared in pairs. For example:

Two points determine one line.   Two lines determine one point.

Except for the difference in position of the words point and line, the statements are identical. For centuries, geometers, suspected that for any true statement involving points and lines, they could obtain another true statement just by interchanging the words points and lines. Plücker proved this true in 1829 using techniques similar to those we have used. He noted the similarity of the equations $ax + by + c = 0$ and $pX + qY + r = 0$.

The principle of duality is an extremely powerful statement in mathematics. Two theorems are developed for the price of one each time a statement is proved concerning points and lines.

Chapter Summary

1. The equations of a circle, center at (h, k), radius r units are as follows. (269)

    Standard form: $(x - h)^2 + (y - k)^2 = r^2$

    General form: $x^2 + y^2 + Dx + Ey + F = 0$

2. The equations of a parabola with vertex at (h, k) and with distance p units from focus to vertex are as follows. (272)

    Standard forms:
    $$\begin{cases} (y - k)^2 = 4p(x - h) & \text{if axis is horizontal} \\ (x - h)^2 = 4p(y - k) & \text{if axis is vertical} \end{cases}$$

    General forms:
    $$\begin{cases} y^2 + Dx + Ey + F = 0 & \text{if axis is horizontal} \\ x^2 + Dx + Ey + F = 0 & \text{if axis is vertical} \end{cases}$$

3. The latus rectum of a parabola is the line segment which is perpendicular to the axis and passes through the focus. The length of the latus rectum of a parabola is $4p$ units. (273)

4. For an ellipse, $a^2 = b^2 + c^2$, where a is the length of the semi-major axis, b is the length of the semi-minor axis, and c is the distance from the center to a focus. (274)

5. The equation of an ellipse with center (h, k) and sum of distances from foci $2a$ is as follows. (275)

    Standard forms:
    $$\begin{cases} \dfrac{(x - h)^2}{a^2} + \dfrac{(y - k)^2}{b^2} = 1 & \text{if segment joining foci is horizontal} \\ \dfrac{(y - k)^2}{a^2} + \dfrac{(x - h)^2}{b^2} = 1 & \text{if segment joining foci is vertical} \end{cases}$$

6. For an ellipse, the eccentricity $e = \dfrac{c}{a}$ and $e < 1$. (275)

7. The length of a latus rectum of an ellipse is $\dfrac{2b^2}{a}$ units. (276)

8. The equation of a hyperbola with center at (h, k) and difference of the distances from the foci $2a$ units is as follows. (278)

    Standard forms:
    $$\begin{cases} \dfrac{(x - h)^2}{a^2} - \dfrac{(y - k)^2}{b^2} = 1 & \text{if the transverse axis is horizontal} \\ \dfrac{(y - k)^2}{a^2} - \dfrac{(x - h)^2}{b^2} = 1 & \text{if the transverse axis is vertical} \end{cases}$$

9. For a hyperbola, $e = \dfrac{c}{a}$ and $e > 1$. (278)

10. The length of a latus rectum of a hyperbola is $\dfrac{2b^2}{a}$ units. (279)

11. The general second degree equation in two variables is $Ax^2 + Bxy + Cy^2 + Dx + Ey + F = 0$. (281)
12. The discriminant $B^2 - 4AC$ may be used to identify a conic. (283)

    1. If $B^2 - 4AC < 0$, then $A'C' > 0$, A' and C' have the same sign. The figure is a circle, an ellipse, or degenerate.

    2. If $B^2 - 4AC > 0$, then $A'C' < 0$, A' and C' have opposite signs. The figure is a hyperbola or degenerate.

    3. If $B^2 - 4AC = 0$, then $A' = 0$ or $C' = 0$. The figure is a parabola or degenerate.

13. Quadric surfaces are described by the sections made when planes parallel to the coordinate axes intersect the surface. (285)
14. Sections formed by the intersection of a surface and a coordinate plane are called the traces of the surface in the coordinate plane. (285)

Chapter Review

9-1 Write the equation of each circle described below.

1. Center $(-3, 5)$, tangent to y-axis
2. Passes through $(-2, 1)$, $(5, 6)$, and $(-3, 6)$

Write the coordinates of the center and find the length of the radius of each circle.

3. $3x^2 + 3y^2 = 81$
4. $x^2 = 6y - y^2$
5. $x^2 + y + y^2 = 12 - 3x$
6. $x^2 + 14x + y^2 + 6y = 23$

9-2 Find the coordinates of the vertex and the equation of the directrix of each parabola for each equation below.

7. $(x - 7)^2 = 8(y - 3)$
8. $y^2 - 2x + 10y + 27 = 0$

Write the equation of each parabola described below.

9. Vertex (2, 1), passes through (−6, 9), horizontal axis

10. Focus (3, 5), the equation of the directrix $y = 1$

9-3 For each equation of an ellipse given, **(a)** determine the coordinates of the center, vertices, and foci; **(b)** determine the eccentricity; and **(c)** sketch the graph.

11. $\dfrac{x^2}{16} + \dfrac{y^2}{12} = 1$

12. $\dfrac{y^2}{25} + \dfrac{x^2}{9} = 1$

13. $x^2 - 12x + 3y^2 + 12y + 39 = 0$

14. $x^2 - 2x + 2y^2 - 4y - 6 = 0$

Write the equation of each ellipse described below.

15. Center (0, 0), Vertex (2, 0), $e = \dfrac{3}{4}$

16. Foci (2, 1) and (−4, 1), $e = \dfrac{3}{5}$

17. Foci (5, −1), and (−1, −1), $2a = 10$

18. Foci (3, 0) and (3, 4), $e = \dfrac{1}{2}$

9-4 For each equation of a hyperbola given, **(a)** write the coordinates of the center, foci, and vertices; **(b)** write the eccentricity; **(c)** write the slopes of the asymptotes; and **(d)** sketch the graph.

19. $2x^2 - y^2 = 8$

20. $y^2 - 5x^2 + 20x = 50$

21. $9x^2 - 16y^2 - 36x + 96y + 36 = 0$

22. $2(x - 5)^2 - (y - 1)^2 = 8$

Write the equation of each hyperbola described below.

23. Vertices (1, 2) and (1, −2), $b = 3$

24. Foci at $(\sqrt{34}, 0)$ and $(-\sqrt{34}, 0)$, $e = \dfrac{\sqrt{34}}{3}$

25. Center (4, −2), focus (7, −2), vertex (6, −2)

26. Center (3, 3), focus (8, 3), vertex (6, 3)

9-5 Identify the conic with each equation. Assume that each conic exists and is not degenerate.

27. $x^2 - 8x + y^2 = -11$

28. $x^2 - 6x - 4y + 9 = 0$

29. $9x^2 + 25y^2 - 54x - 50y = 119$

30. $x^2 + y^2 + 6y - 8x = -24$

31. $4y^2 + 4y + 8x - 15 = 0$

32. $x^2 - 4y^2 + 10x - 16y = -5$

33. $3y^2 + 24y - x^2 - 2x = -41$

34. $9y^2 + 27x^2 - 6y - 108x + 82 = 0$

9-6 Sketch each surface by showing its traces in the three coordinate planes and by sections made by several planes parallel to the coordinate planes.

35. $3x^2 + 4y^2 - 12z^2 = 0$

36. $x^2 + \dfrac{1}{9}y^2 - \dfrac{1}{9}z^2 = 1$

37. $x^2 + y^2 + z^2 = 25$

38. $\dfrac{1}{4}x^2 + \dfrac{1}{25}y^2 = z$

39. $\dfrac{1}{16}y^2 - \dfrac{1}{36}x^2 = z$

40. $x^2 = 8y$

Chapter Test

Write the coordinates of the center and find the length of the radius of each circle.

1. $x^2 + y^2 - 2x + 4y - 11 = 0$

2. $x^2 + y^2 + 6x - 10y - 2 = 0$

3. $x^2 + y^2 + 2x = 0$

4. $x^2 + y^2 + 6x - 4y + 4 = 0$

Write the equation of each parabola described below.

5. Vertex (2, 4), focus (2, 6)

6. Vertex (−2, 5), focus (−2, −8)

7. Vertex (4, 3), passes through (5, 2), vertical axis

8. Vertex (−7, −5), passes through (2, −1), horizontal axis

For each equation of an ellipse given, (a) determine the coordinates of the center, vertices, and foci; (b) determine the eccentricity; and (c) sketch the graph.

9. $\dfrac{(x - 5)^2}{25} + \dfrac{y^2}{4} = 1$

10. $\dfrac{(y - 3)^2}{16} + \dfrac{x^2}{9} = 1$

11. $4y^2 - 4y + 16x^2 + 16x - 11 = 0$

12. $12x^2 + 36x + 16y^2 + 32y - 5 = 0$

Write the equation of each hyperbola described below.

13. Center (0, 4), focus (0, 9), $e = \dfrac{5}{4}$

14. Center (3, −1), focus (3, −4), $e = \dfrac{3}{2}$

15. Vertices (5, −1) and (5, 7), $e = 2$

16. Vertices (−3, 1) and (7, 1), $e = \dfrac{6}{5}$

Identify the conic with each equation. Assume that each conic exists and is not degenerate.

17. $-9x^2 + y^2 - 4y = 5$

18. $y^2 + 6y - 3x + 12 = 0$

19. $36x^2 + 36y^2 - 108x - 180y = -273$

20. $9x^2 + 4y^2 + 18x + 24y + 9 = 0$

Sketch each surface by showing its traces in the three coordinate planes and by sections made by several planes parallel to the coordinate planes.

21. $100z = 4x^2 + 2y^2$

22. $x^2 + y^2 + z^2 = 144$

23. $\dfrac{y^2}{49} - \dfrac{x^2}{64} = z$

24. $\dfrac{x^2}{36} + \dfrac{y^2}{81} = z^2$

25. $16z^2 - 20x^2 - 25y^2 = 400$

Computers

BASIC-Functions

In place of READ and DATA, often a program will allow the user to type in the data as the program is run. For this purpose the INPUT statement is used. Each time the statement is reached, the computer responds with a "?" and the operator types in the necessary data for that run.

Subscripts in BASIC are typed as A(1), X(5), R(K-4), and the like. Some versions of BASIC require subscripted variables to be dimensioned to the maximum size to be used such as, DIM A(10) or DIM X (20,30) in the case of a doubly subscripted variable or matrix. Most versions of BASIC provide very powerful means of handling matrix algebra.

BASIC also has built-in functions. These are actual subprograms stored in the computer which can be used when needed.

SQR	(X)	square root of X
ABS	(X)	absolute value of X
INT	(X)	greatest integer not greater than X
RND	(X)	yields a random number between 0 and 1
SIN	(X)	For X in radians, sine of X
COS	(X)	For X in radians, cosine of X
TAN	(X)	For X in radians, tangent of X
LOG	(X)	natural logarithm of X
EXP	(X)	yields e^x
ATN	(X)	Arctangent of X

String variables are used to handle expressions which are sequences of symbols. Such expressions are called alphanumeric, groups of alphabetical and/or numeric symbols. The numeric symbols are treated as symbols alone and do not carry their numeric values.

Consider the following example of using strings.

Write a program to print a chessboard which has eight rows and eight columns of squares as suggested by the figure.

```
10  REM CHESSBOARD USING STRINGS
20  DIM A$ (32), B$ (32)
30  LET A$ = "****____****____
              ****____****____"
40  LET B$ = "____****____****
              ____****____****"
50  FOR I = 1 to 4
60    FOR J = 1 TO 3
70      PRINT A$
80    NEXT J
90    FOR K = 1 TO 3
100     PRINT B$
110   NEXT K
120 NEXT I
130 END
```

Strings, like subscripted variables, must be dimensioned so that their maximum size may be assigned to an appropriate address by the computer. The $ is used to change a regular variable to a string variable. Note the "nested" FOR-NEXT loops. Each FOR must be matched with a corresponding NEXT. Indentation helps

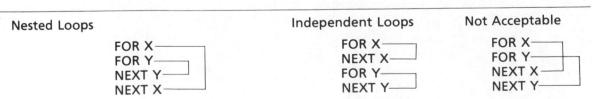

Nested Loops	Independent Loops	Not Acceptable
FOR X FOR Y NEXT Y NEXT X	FOR X NEXT X FOR Y NEXT Y	FOR X FOR Y NEXT X NEXT Y
The loops do *not* cross. They are nested.	The loops do *not* cross.	The loops cross.

in following the program. Often the computer provides this indenting even when the programmer does not. Nesting must be done carefully to avoid crossing from one loop into another.

BASIC is a language designed mainly for mathematics and science but can be applied to other areas such as business and social studies. It is frequently used as a teaching language because it is easily learned.

Exercises Write programs for each of the following.

1. Find the center and radius of a circle given by the equation $Ax^2 + Cy^2 + Dx + Ey + F = 0$.

2. Find the center and radius of a circle given by the equation $Ax^2 + Cy^2 + F = 0$.

The equation of a parabola with focus (h, k) and directrix parallel to the x-axis is $(x - h)^2 = 4p(y - k)$.

3. Find the coordinates of the vertex.

4. Find the coordinates of the focus.

The standard form of the equation of a hyperbola with center (h, k) and transverse axis of length $2a$, parallel to the x-axis, is $\dfrac{(x - h)^2}{a^2} - \dfrac{(y - k)^2}{b^2} = 1$.

5. Find the coordinates of the foci.

6. Find the length of the latera recta.

Find the point(s) of intersection of a conic section with each of the following equations and the circle $x^2 + y^2 = r^2$.

7. $ax^2 + bx + c = y$

8. $\dfrac{x^2}{a^2} - \dfrac{y^2}{b^2} = 1$

9. $(x - h)^2 + (y - k)^2 = s^2$

Chapter 10

The graph of a polynomial equation is a smooth curve. Many buildings use designs based on a combination of polynomial equations.

Polynomial Functions

10–1 Polynomials

Linear and quadratic polynomials and their corresponding equations already are familiar.

A **polynomial function,** P, is one which may be expressed as $P(x) = a_n x^n + a_{n-1} x^{n-1} + a_{n-2} x^{n-2} + \cdots + a_1 x + a_0$ where $n \in W$, $a_n \neq 0$.

✻ note symbolism

Polynomial Function

$W = \{0, 1, 2, 3, \ldots\}$

The numbers $a_n, a_{n-1}, a_{n-2}, \ldots, a_1, a_0$ are called **coefficients.** The expression $a_n x^n + a_{n-1} x^{n-1} + a_{n-2} x^{n-2} + \cdots + a_1 x + a_0$ is a *polynomial*. The coefficients may be complex numbers but are usually restricted to the real numbers unless otherwise specified. Polynomials may be defined over any *field*. They can be defined over the field of real numbers with the usual operations of addition (+) and multiplication (·) of real numbers.

The **degree** of a polynomial is the exponent of the highest power of x, namely n. The only exception to this definition is the case in which the polynomial is zero. The *zero polynomial* has no degree.

$P(x) = 0$ is called the zero polynomial and is not assigned a degree.

✻ note: this last subtlety will not be tested

The addends $a_n x^n$, $a_{n-1} x^{n-1}$, $a_{n-2} x^{n-2}, \ldots, a_1 x$, a_0 are the **terms** of the polynomial. The **constant term** is a_0. The **leading term** is $a_n x^n$.

Polynomial	Degree	Leading coefficient	Constant term	Special name
$3x^2 + 2x - 1$	2	3	-1	quadratic function
$\sqrt{5}x + 4$	1	$\sqrt{5}$	4	linear function
-7	0	-7	-7	constant function
0	none	none	0	zero polynomial

Often in this chapter no distinction will be made between a polynomial expression such as $3x^2 + 5x - 6$ and its corresponding function $y = 3x^2 + 5x - 6$. This is done frequently. In most cases it is not confusing. For each *polynomial* there is a corresponding polynomial equation. A *polynomial equation* is formed by setting $P(x) = 0$.

✳ note

✳ note relationship between zeros and roots

✳

The **roots** of a polynomial equation are those values of x for which $P(x) = 0$. Such a value also is called a **zero** of the polynomial.

Roots of a Polynomial Equation

Examples

1. If $P(x) = 3x^3 - 2x^2 - 5x$, find $P(-2)$.
$$P(-2) = 3(-2)^3 - 2(-2)^2 - 5(-2)$$
$$= -24 - 8 + 10$$
$$= -22$$

✳ note symbolism for substitution

2. If $P(x) = 3x^3 - 2x^2 - 5x$, find the zeros of P.
$$3x^3 - 2x^2 - 5x = 0$$
$$x(3x^2 - 2x - 5) = 0$$
$$x(3x - 5)(x + 1) = 0$$
$$x = 0, 3x - 5 = 0, \text{ or } x + 1 = 0$$
$$x = 0, x = \frac{5}{3} \text{ or } x = -1$$

✳ reminder about factoring

For each polynomial P and each value c in the domain of P, it always is possible to find $P(c)$. However, finding the zeros of P is not always easy.

Exercises

Exploratory Identify the expressions which are polynomials, giving the degree, leading coefficient, and constant term for each. Explain why the other expressions are not polynomials.

1. $3x^2 - 2x$
2. $3x^2 - 2x + 1$
3. $0.25x^3 - 0$
4. $2x^0$
5. $\sqrt{5}x^7 - \sqrt{2}$
6. $3\sqrt{x} + 5$
7. $ix^7 + 3x^5 - 2$
8. $2x^{-2} + 5x^{-1} + 3$
9. 17
10. $4x^3 + (i - 2)x^2 + 6$

Written Find $P(0)$, $P(1)$, $P(-1)$ and $P(2)$ for each polynomial P. Identify each quadratic function (Q), linear function (L), or constant function (C).

1. $3x - 5$
2. $x^2 - 2x + 4$
3. $2x^3 - 7$
4. $2x^5$
5. $x^7 - 3x + 2$
6. 5
7. $ix^2 + (i - 2)x$
8. $-x + 1$

Find the zeros of each polynomial.

9. $x^2 - 5x$
10. $x^2 - 5x + 6$
11. $x^2 - 5x - 6$
12. $4x^2 - 25$ (Hint: Use the quadratic formula.)
13. $2x^2 - 7x + 4$
14. $x^3 - 13x^2 + 42x$
15. $2x^2 + 32$ (Hint: Consider imaginary zeros.)
16. $5x^2 - 12$ (Hint: Consider irrational zeros)

10–2 Graphing Polynomials

Most properties of polynomials are related closely to properties of polynomial graphs. Consider the *general form* of a polynomial function.

✳ note use table on next page to assist in understanding this discussion

$$P(x) = a_n x^n + a_{n-1} x^{n-1} + \cdots + a_1 x + a_0$$

For now, restrict the domain and all a_i to the set of real numbers. For each $x = c$, $P(c)$ is calculated by using multiplication and addition.

If $P(c + \epsilon)$ is calculated for some arbitrarily small real number ϵ, the result is very close to $P(c)$. For example, if $P(x) = x^2 + 5x + 3$, then $P(1.1) = 9.71$, $P(1.01) = 9.0701$, $P(1.001) = 9.007001, \ldots$.

ϵ is the Greek letter epsilon.

Nothing in the nature of polynomials causes the graph to have jump discontinuities or point discontinuities.

For all polynomials which have degree ≥ 1, $|P(x)| \to \infty$ as $x \to \pm\infty$. Whether $P(x) \to \infty$ or $P(x) \to -\infty$ depends on the sign and the degree of the leading term. As $x \to \pm\infty$, the leading term in the polynomial dominates over the others. That is, $\frac{a_n x^n}{P(x)} \to 1$ for polynomials which have degree ≥ 1.

✳ note

✳ use table at bottom

Example

1. Find $P(x)$ as $x \to \pm\infty$ for $P(x) = x^3 - 4x^2 + 2x - 1$.

✳ use righthand column

x	1	10	100	1000
x^3	1	1000	1,000,000	1,000,000,000
$-4x^2$	-4	-400	$-40,000$	$-4,000,000$
$2x$	2	20	200	2000
-1	-1	-1	-1	-1
$P(x)$	-2	619	960,199	996,001,999

Clearly, x^3 dominates as $x \to \infty$. Similarly, x^3 dominates as $x \to -\infty$. Therefore, $P(x) \to \infty$ as $x \to \infty$ and $P(x) \to -\infty$ as $x \to -\infty$.

A polynomial P is dominated by its leading term $a_n x^n$ when $|x|$ is large. If $a_n > 0$ and n is even, the graph of $y = P(x)$ rises without bound as $x \to \infty$ and as $x \to -\infty$. The table summarizes all cases.

✳ use sketches on next page to aid in understanding this table

a_n	n	$x \to$	$P(x) \to$	a_n	n	$x \to$	$P(x) \to$
>0	even	∞	∞	<0	even	∞	$-\infty$
>0	even	$-\infty$	∞	<0	even	$-\infty$	$-\infty$
>0	odd	∞	∞	<0	odd	∞	$-\infty$
>0	odd	$-\infty$	$-\infty$	<0	odd	$-\infty$	∞

Examples

2. Find $P(x)$ as $x \rightarrow \pm \infty$ for $P(x) = 4x^5 + 3x^2 - 1$.

$a_5 = 4$ which is greater than 0.

$n = 5$ which is odd.

So as $x \rightarrow \infty$, $P(x) \rightarrow \infty$ and as $x \rightarrow -\infty$, $P(x) \rightarrow -\infty$.

3. Find $P(x)$ as $x \rightarrow \pm \infty$ for $P(x) = -3x^6 + 2x^3 + x$.

$a_6 = -3$ which is less than 0.

$n = 6$ which is even.

Therefore as $x \rightarrow \infty$, $P(x) \rightarrow -\infty$ and as $x \rightarrow -\infty$, $P(x) \rightarrow -\infty$.

It was previously shown that if all terms of a polynomial P are of odd degree, then P is *symmetric with respect to the origin*. This is called an **odd function**. If all terms of P are of even degree, then P is *symmetric with respect to the y-axis*. This is called an **even function**. Even functions may or may not cross the x-axis.

The patterns of symmetry are helpful in each case.

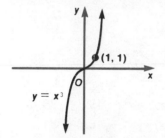

$y = x^3$

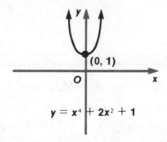

(0, 1)

$y = x^4 + 2x^2 + 1$

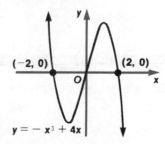

(−2, 0)   (2, 0)

$y = -x^3 + 4x$

In general, the graph of a polynomial P has these properties.
  1. It is a smooth curve.
  2. It is continuous. Therefore, it has no breaks or holes.
  3. The leading term $a_n x^n$ dominates. The graph rises or falls without bound as $x \rightarrow +\infty$ or $x \rightarrow -\infty$.

note

Assume an accurate graph is needed. Then many points $(c, P(c))$ are plotted and connected by a smooth curve. Usually a sketch of the general shape and tendencies of the curve is all that is needed. The intercepts are plotted if they can be found. The x-intercepts are easy to find if the polynomial can be factored. The y-intercept is $(0, P(0))$.

The emphasis is on determining shape and tendency, not precisely calculated values.

x-intercepts are the zeros of the polynomial

discuss use of T-tables

Example

4. **Draw the graph of $P(x) = x^3 - 3x^2 + 2x$.**

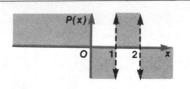

$P(x) = x^3 - 3x^2 + 2x$.
$P(x) = x(x^2 - 3x + 2)$
$P(x) = x(x - 2)(x - 1)$

The x-intercepts are $(0, 0)$, $(2, 0)$, and $(1, 0)$.
The y-intercept is $(0, P(0)) = (0, 0)$.
   Since $x = 0$ and $x = 1$ are zeros of the polynomial, to draw the graph find at least one point between $(0, 0)$ and $(1, 0)$. Similarly, find at least one point between $(1, 0)$ and $(2, 0)$. Also, points $(c, P(c))$ for at least one value of $c < 0$ and one value of $c > 2$ should be found.

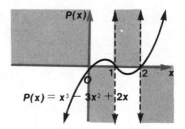

$P(x) = x^3 - 3x^2 + 2x$

x	-1	0	$\dfrac{1}{2}$	1	$\dfrac{3}{2}$	2	3
$P(x)$	-6	0	$\dfrac{3}{8}$	0	$-\dfrac{3}{8}$	0	6

Exercises

Exploratory   State whether each polynomial is even, odd, or neither.

1. $P(x) = x^3 - x$
2. $P(x) = x^3 - x^2 - 6x$
3. $P(x) = x^4 - 13x^2 + 36$
4. $P(x) = 2x^3 + 7x^2 - 15x$
5. $P(x) = x^3 - x^2 - x + 1$
6. $P(x) = x^4 - 18x^2 + 81$

Written   Factor each polynomial, if possible. Sketch each polynomial function.

1. $P(x) = x^3 - x$
2. $P(x) = x^3 - x^2 - 6x$
3. $P(x) = x^4 - 13x^2 + 36$
4. $P(x) = 2x^3 + 7x^2 - 15x$
5. $P(x) = x^3 - x^2 - x + 1$
6. $P(x) = x^4 - 18x^2 + 81$

Sketch each polynomial. Compare each graph with the graph of $P(x) = x^2 - 1$.

7. $P(x) = -x^2 + 1$
8. $P(x) = 4x^2 - 4$
9. $P(x) = 4x^2 - 3$

Find a polynomial P with zeros $x = 0$ and $x = 1$ which satisfies the given conditions. Give at least two answers, if possible.

10. The degree of P is 2.
11. $P(3) = 0$

12. Degree $P \geq 4$, $P\left(\frac{1}{2}\right) < 0$.

13. Degree $P \geq 4$, $P\left(\frac{1}{2}\right) > 0$.

14. The graph of $y = P(x)$ is tangent to the x-axis at $x = 1$.

15. Degree P is odd and $P(x) \to \infty$ as $x \to \infty$.

16. Degree P is even and $P(x) \to -\infty$ as $x \to -\infty$.

10–3 The Division Algorithm and the Remainder Theorem

Finding a particular value of a polynomial is related closely to dividing one polynomial by another.

Example

1. Divide $6x^4 + 3x^3 - 5x^2 + 7x - 2$ by $2x^2 - 3x + 1$.

$$
\begin{array}{r}
3x^2 + 6x + 5 \\
2x^2 - 3x + 1 \overline{) 6x^4 + 3x^3 - 5x^2 + 7x - 2} \\
\underline{6x^4 - 9x^3 + 3x^2} \\
12x^3 - 8x^2 + 7x \\
\underline{12x^3 - 18x^2 + 6x} \\
10x^2 + x - 2 \\
\underline{10x^2 - 15x + 5} \\
16x - 7
\end{array}
$$

Notice that $(6x^4 + 3x^3 - 5x^2 + 7x - 2) \div (2x^2 - 3x + 1) = Q(x) + \dfrac{R(x)}{2x^2 - 3x + 1}$, where $Q(x) = 3x^2 + 6x + 5$ is the quotient and $R(x) = 16x - 7$ is the numerator of the remainder. Multiply both sides of the equation by the divisor $2x^2 - 3x + 1$.

$6x^4 + 3x^3 - 5x^2 + 7x - 2 = (2x^2 - 3x + 1) \cdot (3x^2 + 6x + 5) + (16x - 7)$

The following relations also hold.

degree $Q(x)$ = degree $(6x^4 + 3x^3 - 5x^2 + 7x - 2)$ − degree $(2x^2 - 3x + 1)$
degree $R(x)$ < degree $(2x^2 - 3x + 1)$

The previous example illustrates an important theorem.

If P is a polynomial of degree m, and D is a polynomial of degree n, where $m \geq n$, then there exist polynomials Q and R such that $P(x) = D(x) \cdot Q(x) + R(x)$ and degree R < degree D or R is the zero polynomial.

The Division Algorithm for Polynomials

The **Remainder Theorem** is a basic consequence of the preceding theorem.

If a polynomial P is divided by $x - c$, where $c \in \mathcal{C}$, then the remainder is $P(c)$.

The Remainder Theorem

To see that this is so, use the Division Algorithm to find $Q(x)$ and $R(x)$ such that $P(x) = (x - c) \cdot Q(x) + R(x)$ where $R(x) = 0$ or $R(x)$ has degree less than that of $(x - c)$. In either case, $R(x) = k$ for some constant k. Also, $P(c) = (c - c) \cdot Q(X) + k = 0 \cdot Q(x) + k = k$.

The Remainder Theorem is the basis for evaluating polynomials by synthetic substitution or synthetic division.

Example

2. **Use the Remainder Theorem to find $P(3)$ if $P(x) = 2x^3 - 3x^2 + 2$.**

$$
\begin{array}{r}
2x^2 + 3x\ + 9 \\
x - 3 \overline{)\ 2x^3 - 3x^2 + 0x +\ \ 2} \\
\underline{2x^3 - 6x^2} \\
3x^2 + 0x \\
\underline{3x^2 - 9x} \\
9x +\ \ 2 \\
\underline{9x - 27} \\
29
\end{array}
$$

Therefore, $P(3) = 29$. Check by direct substitution.

$$P(3) = 2 \cdot 3^3 - 3 \cdot 3^2 + 2 = 54 - 27 + 2 = 29$$

The Remainder Theorem and the Division Algorithm can be used to find values of a polynomial function. **Synthetic substitution** can be used for the same purpose. The two processes are related closely. In fact, synthetic substitution sometimes is called **synthetic division.**

To find $P(3)$ by synthetic substitution, write the *detached coefficients* of $P(x)$ on the top line and the value c for which $P(c)$ is desired to the left. Perform the operations indicated.

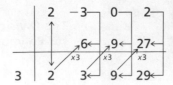

Again, $P(3)$ is found to be 29. The numbers 2, 3, and 9 written before 29 are the coefficients of the *quotient* in the example.

$$(2x^3 - 3x^2 + 2) \div (x - 3) = (2x^2 + 3x + 9) + \frac{29}{x - 3}$$

If a polynomial has any coefficients which are zero, these must be included in the row of detached coefficients. This applies even though they are ignored in direct substitution. The detached coefficients must be in descending order $a_n, a_{n-1}, \ldots, a_0$. Look again at the division in the example. Rewrite the division using only coefficients.

$$
\begin{array}{r}
2 \quad\; 3 \quad\; 9 \qquad\qquad \\
-3\overline{)2 \;-3 \quad\; 0 \quad\; 2} \\
2 \;-6 \qquad\qquad \\
\overline{3 \quad\; 0 \qquad} \\
3 \;-9 \qquad \\
\overline{\;9 \quad\; 2} \\
9 \;-27 \\
\overline{\;29}
\end{array}
$$

$$
\begin{array}{r}
2 \quad\; 3 \quad\; 9 \qquad\qquad \\
-3\overline{)2 \;-3 \quad\; 0 \quad\; 2} \\
2 \;-6 \qquad\qquad \\
\overline{3 \;-9 \qquad} \\
9 \;-27 \\
\overline{\;29}
\end{array}
$$

Eliminate the lines of numbers which are copied from the dividend.

$$
\begin{array}{r}
2 \quad\; 3 \quad 9 \qquad\qquad \\
3\overline{)2 \;-3 \quad\; 0 \quad\; 2} \\
2 \quad\; 6 \qquad\qquad \\
\overline{3 \quad\; 9 \qquad} \\
9 \quad 27 \\
\overline{\;29}
\end{array}
$$

Exchange the subtraction for easier addition.

$$
\begin{array}{r}
3\overline{)2 \;-3 \quad\; 0 \quad\; 2} \\
6 \quad\; 9 \quad 27 \\
\overline{2 \quad\; 3 \quad\; 9 \quad 29}
\end{array}
$$

Move the lines.

$$
\begin{array}{r|rrrr}
 & 2 & -3 & 0 & 2 \\
 & & 6 & 9 & 27 \\
\hline
3 & 2 & 3 & 9 & 29
\end{array}
$$

This is synthetic division again.

Examples

3. Use synthetic division to find $P(x) \div (x - 4)$ and $P(4)$, if $P(x) = x^5 - 3x^2 - 2x + 1$.

$$
\begin{array}{r|rrrrrr}
 & 1 & 0 & 0 & -3 & -2 & 1 \\
 &   & 4 & 16 & 64 & 244 & 968 \\
\hline
4 & 1 & 4 & 16 & 61 & 242 & 969
\end{array}
$$

Be careful of the signs.

Therefore, $P(4) = 969$.

$$P(x) \div (x - 4) = x^4 + 4x^3 + 16x^2 + 61x + 242 + \frac{969}{x - 4}$$

4. Use synthetic division to find $P(x) \div (x + 2)$ and $P(-2)$, if $P(x) = 2x^4 - 3x^3 + x + 4$.

$$
\begin{array}{r|rrrrr}
 & 2 & 3 & 0 & 1 & 4 \\
 &   & -4 & 14 & -28 & 54 \\
\hline
-2 & 2 & -7 & 14 & -27 & 58
\end{array}
$$

Remember the divisor must be in the form $x - c$.

Therefore $P(-2) = 58$

$$P(x) \div (x + 2) = 2x^3 - 7x^2 + 14x - 27 + \frac{58}{x + 2}$$

This shortened division process is valid only for division by a linear expression of the form $x - c$.

Exercises

Exploratory Find $P(c)$ for each of the following polynomials.

1. $P(2), P(x) = x^3 + 2x^2 - 3x + 5$
2. $P(-1), P(x) = 4x^3 - 3x^2 - 7$
3. $P(-3), P(x) = 3x^4 + 6x^2 - 5x - 1$
4. $P(2), P(x) = x^4 - x^3 - 10x^2 + 4x + 24$
5. $P(-2), P(x) = 2x^3 + 9x^2 - 2x + 7$
6. $P(4), P(x) = x^5 - 3x^3 + 2x - 8$

Written Use synthetic division to find the quotient and remainder if $P(x)$ is divided by $x - c$.

1. $P(x) = x^3 + 2x^2 - 3x + 5; c = 2$
2. $P(x) = 4x^3 - 3x^2 - 7; c = -1$
3. $P(x) = 3x^4 + 6x^2 - 5x - 1; c = -3$
4. $P(x) = x^4 - x^3 - 10x^2 + 4x + 24; c = 2$
5. $P(x) = 2x^3 + 9x^2 - 2x + 7; c = -2$
6. $P(x) = x^5 - 3x^3 + 2x - 8; c = 4$
7. $P(x) = x^7 - 140; c = -1$
8. $P(x) = 12x^4 + x^3 - 13x + 6; c = \frac{2}{3}$

Make a table of values for $P(c)$ for the given $P(x)$ if $c \in \{-3, -2, -1, 0, 1, 2, 3\}$. Then, graph the points.

9. $P(x) = 2x^3 + 3x^2 - 5x - 4$
10. $P(x) = x^4 - 4x^2 - 2x + 1$

Challenge   Find the value of k for each of the following.

1. $P(x) = kx^3 + 2x^2 - 10x + 3$
and $P(-2) = 15$

2. $P(x) = 3x^4 - 2x^3 - 10x^2 + 3kx + 3$
and $-\dfrac{1}{3}$ is a zero.

10–4   The Factor Theorem

Following directly from the Remainder Theorem is the **Factor Theorem.** This theorem can be used to factor a polynomial completely.

> The complex number c is a zero of a polynomial P if and only if $x - c$ is a factor of P.

The Factor Theorem

Proof

If c is a zero of a polynomial P then $x - c$ is a factor of P.

1. c is a zero of P.	Hypothesis
2. $P(c) = 0$	Definition of a zero
3. $P(x) = (x - c) \cdot Q(x) + P(c)$	Remainder Theorem
4. $P(x) = (x - c) \cdot Q(x) + 0$	Substitution
5. $x - c$ is a factor of P.	Definition of factor

If $x - c$ is a factor of P, then c is a zero of P.

1. $x - c$ is a factor of P.	Hypothesis
2. $P(x) = (x - c) \cdot Q(x)$	Definition of factor
3. $P(c) = (c - c) \cdot Q(c)$	Substitution
4. $P(c) = 0$	Substitution
5. c is a zero of P.	Definition of a zero

Examples

1.   Show that $x - 2$ is a factor of $P(x) = 2x^3 - 5x + 6$.

If it can be shown that $P(2) = 0$, then $x - 2$ is a factor.

$$
\begin{array}{r|rrrr}
 & 2 & 0 & -5 & 6 \\
 &   & 4 & 8 & 6 \\
\hline
2 & 2 & 4 & 3 & 12
\end{array}
$$

Since $P(2) = 12 \neq 0$, $x - 2$ is not a factor of P.

2. **Find the values of k for which $x + \dfrac{1}{3}$ is a factor of $P(x) = 3x^4 - 2x^3 - 10x^2 + 3kx + 3$.**

$$
\begin{array}{r|ccccc}
 & 3 & -2 & -10 & 3k & 3 \\
\hline
-\dfrac{1}{3} & 3 & -3 & -9 & 3k+3 & 2-k
\end{array}
$$

Often synthetic division is used without the middle line copied.

For $x + \dfrac{1}{3}$ to be a factor of P, $2 - k = 0$ or $k = 2$.

The Factor and Remainder Theorems, together with the technique of synthetic division, provide a method for factoring polynomials of higher degree.

Example

3. **Factor completely the polynomial $P(x) = x^3 - x^2 - 10x - 8$. Use synthetic division.**

Look for values c such that $P(c) = 0$.

$$
\begin{array}{r|cccc}
 & 1 & -1 & -10 & -8 \\
\hline
1 & 1 & 0 & -10 & -18 \\
-1 & 1 & -2 & -8 & 0
\end{array}
$$

$P(1) \neq 0$
$P(-1) = 0$

Since $P(-1) = 0$, $x + 1$ is a factor of P.

$$P(x) = [x - (-1)] \cdot Q(x) = (x + 1)(x^2 - 2x - 8)$$

The polynomial $x^2 - 2x - 8$ can be factored by synthetic division, by inspection, or by the quadratic formula. Thus, $P(x) = (x + 1)(x - 4)(x + 2)$.

A polynomial P of degree $n \geq 0$ has no more than n zeros.

Zeros of a Polynomial

Proof

If the degree of $P = 0$, then P is a nonzero constant and has no zeros. Also, the theorem is a true statement for any polynomial having degree n and having no zeros, since $n \geq 0$ for any $n \in W$. Therefore, in the rest of the proof, attention will be given only to polynomials with degree $n > 0$ which have at least one zero.

Let c_1 be a zero of P. Then by the Factor Theorem, $P(x) = (x - c_1) \cdot Q_1(x)$ and degree $Q_1 = n - 1$. If Q_1 has no zeros, then the proof is completed. This is because $1 \leq n$.

Suppose Q_1 has a zero c_2. Then $Q_1(x) = (x - c_2)Q_2(x)$ and degree $Q_2 = n - 2$. Thus $P(x) = (x - c_1)(x - c_2)Q_2(x)$. Again if Q_2 has no zeros, the proof is completed. If Q_2 does have a zero c_3, a new factorization $P(x) = (x - c_1)(x - c_2)(x - c_3)Q_3(x)$ with degree $Q_3 = n - 3$ is possible.

Continuing in this manner, P can be factored so that $P(x) = (x - c_1)(x - c_2) \cdots (x - c_n) \cdot Q_n(x)$ with degree $Q_n = n - n = 0$. Since Q_n is a constant function with no zeros, there can be no more factors. Therefore, there are at most n factors of the form $(x - c)$. And, there are at most n zeros. If all the c_i are different, then P has exactly n zeros, if it has any.

Exercises

Exploratory Solve each of the following.

1. When is $(x - a)$ a factor of $P(x) = x^3 - 6ax^2 + 8a^2x + 3a^2$?

Determine the value of k for which the following is a zero of $P(x) = x^4 - kx^3 + k^2x - 6$.

2. 2   3. -2 4. 3

5. Find a polynomial P with zeros 3, -2, 1, and -1. Is P unique? Explain.

Written Factor each polynomial completely.

1. $x^3 - 4x^2 + x + 6$ 2. $x^4 + x^3 - 3x^2 - 4x - 4$

3. $2x^3 + 3x + 5$ 4. $x^3 - 6x^2 - 2x - 35$

5. $x^4 - 2x^3 - x^2 - 4x - 6$ 6. $6x^4 - 5x^3 - 14x^2 - x + 2$

Challenge Solve each of the following.

1. Factor $x^6 - 2x^5 - 2x^4 + 2x^3 + x^2 + 4x + 4$ completely.

2. Prove that $(x - c)$ is a factor of $x^n - c^n$ for all $n \in Z^+$.

10–5 The Fundamental Theorem of Algebra

Some relationships between an algebraic expression and the graph of a polynomial have been investigated. If the leading coefficient of a polynomial is positive, this is the general shape of the graph.

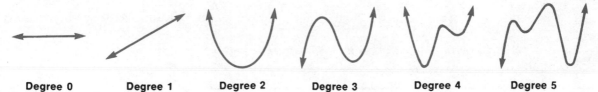

Degree 0   Degree 1   Degree 2   Degree 3   Degree 4   Degree 5

Some polynomial functions have certain coefficients equal to zero. The shape of the graph is distorted accordingly. The tendencies as $x \to \pm\infty$ are retained.

  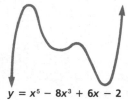

$y = x^3$ $y = x^4$ $y = x^5 - 8x^3 + 6x - 2$

Every polynomial function of degree $n > 0$ over the field of complex numbers has at least one zero.

The Fundamental Theorem of Algebra

This famous theorem is accepted here without proof. Many proofs are known, but each is essentially nonalgebraic. The theorem was proved first by C. F. Gauss in 1799. The Fundamental Theorem merely guarantees the *existence* of a zero for each polynomial. It does not say how *to find* such a zero.

The Fundamental Theorem and its corollaries ensure that every polynomial of degree n has exactly n zeros if all multiplicities are considered.

Every polynomial function of degree $n > 0$ over the field of complex numbers has at least n zeros.

Zeros of a Polynomial

The proof is similar to the proof that a polynomial of degree $n \geq 0$ has no more than n zeros. Two or more of the zeros can be identical. They are, however, considered as separate zeros.

A zero z of a polynomial P of degree $n > 0$ has multiplicity k if P can be factored as

$$P(x) = (x - z)^k Q(x)$$

where $Q(x)$ is a polynomial of degree $n - k$ and z is not a zero of $Q(x)$.

Multiplicity of Polynomials

Now another corollary of the Fundamental Theorem of Algebra can be stated.

> For a polynomial of degree $n > 0$ over the field of complex numbers, the sum of the multiplicities of all its distinct zeros is n.

Sum of Multiplicities

Example

1. Find all of the factors of P, where $P(x) = x^5 + 3x^4 + 7x^3 + 13x^2 + 12x + 4$. Sketch P.

$$
\begin{array}{r|rrrrrr}
 & 1 & 3 & 7 & 13 & 12 & 4 \\
\hline
1 & 1 & 4 & 11 & 24 & 36 & 40 \\
-1 & 1 & 2 & 5 & 8 & 4 & 0 \\
\end{array}
$$

Therefore, $P(x) = (x + 1)(x^4 + 2x^3 + 5x^2 + 8x + 4)$.

Check to see if -1 is a zero of higher multiplicity.

This is done by using synthetic substitution on the second factor $Q(x)$. If the remainder is zero the divisor is a zero of P and the number of terms in the quotient is reduced by 1.

$$
\begin{array}{r|rrrrr}
 & 1 & 2 & 5 & 8 & 4 \\
\hline
-1 & 1 & 1 & 4 & 4 & 0 \\
-1 & 1 & 0 & 4 & 0 \\
\end{array}
$$

Since the remaining factor has three terms, find its factors by inspection or if necessary by the quadratic formula. Write the complete factorization.

$$P(x) = (x + 1)^3(x^2 + 4)$$

$$P(x) = (x + 1)^3(x - 2i)(x + 2i)$$

The sum of the multiplicities of all the zeros is 5.

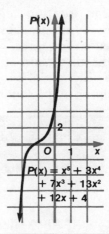

$P(x) = x^5 + 3x^4 + 7x^3 + 13x^2 + 12x + 4$

Exercises

Exploratory State the maximum number of zeros expected for each polynomial.

1. $x^5 - 3x^4 + x^3 + 5x^2 - 6x + 2$

2. $x^4 - 7x^3 + 9x^2 + 11x - 6$

3. $x^5 + 3x^4 - 6x^3 - 10x^2 + 2x - 9$

4. $x^6 - 3x^5 - 3x^4 + 11x^3 + 6x^2 - 12x - 8$

5. $x^5 + x^4 - 2x^3 - 2x^2 + x + 1$

6. $x^4 - 4x^3 - 4x^2 + 24x - 9$

Written Factor each polynomial completely. List all the zeros and their multiplicities. Sketch the graph of each polynomial.

1. $x^5 - 3x^4 + x^3 + 5x^2 - 6x + 2$

2. $x^4 - 7x^3 + 9x^2 + 11x - 6$

3. $x^5 + 3x^4 - 6x^3 - 10x^2 + 21x - 9$

4. $x^6 - 3x^5 - 3x^4 + 11x^3 + 6x^2 - 12x - 8$

5. $x^5 + x^4 - 2x^3 - 2x^2 + x + 1$

6. $x^4 - 4x^3 - 4x^2 + 24x - 9$

7. $2x^3 + x^2 - 25x + 12$

Find at least one expression for P if it has zeros as given. Sketch P.

8. -1 of multiplicity two, 2 of multiplicity three

9. $1, -1,$ $\sqrt{2}, -\sqrt{2}$

10. $1, -2, 3,$ $i, -i$

11. 0 of multiplicity three, $2 + \sqrt{3}, 2 - \sqrt{3}$

12. 2 of multiplicity five

Challenge Find a proof of the Fundamental Theorem of Algebra and be able to explain it to the class.

10–6 Locating Zeros

So far, locating zeros of polynomials has been a random process. Synthetic substitution is an ideal method for a systematic search for zeros.

In the discussion of graphs of polynomials, it was assumed that a polynomial is *continuous*. This theorem states an important property of continuous functions.

> If a function f is continuous on the interval $[a, b]$ and t is a real number such that $f(a) < t < f(b)$, then there exists at least one real number c such that $a < c < b$ and $f(c) = t$.

The Intermediate Value Theorem

The figure shows three possible values for c such that $f(c) = t$. The theorem only guarantees *at least one* such number. The graph of a continuous curve drawn from a lower point $(a, f(a))$ to a higher point $(b, f(b))$ must cross every horizontal line between the horizontal lines $y = f(a)$ and $y = f(b)$.

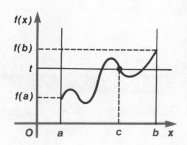

If f is a continuous function and $f(a)$ and $f(b)$ have opposite signs for $a, b \in \mathcal{R}$, then f has at least one zero between a and b.

The Location Principle

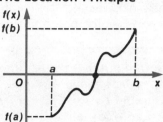

The Location Principle is used to locate zeros *between* appropriate values of x. These are often between consecutive integers.

Example

1. **Locate all zeros and graph $P(x) = x^3 + 2x^2 - 12x - 24$.**

	1	2	-12	-24
-5	1	-3	3	-39
-4	1	-2	-4	-8
$z_1 \rightarrow$ -3	1	-1	-9	3
$z_2 \rightarrow$ -2	1	0	-12	0
-1	1	1	-13	-11
0				-24
1				-33
2	1	4	-4	-32
3	1	5	3	-15
$z_3 \rightarrow$ 4	1	6	12	24

The left column gives the value of x used. The right column gives the corresponding y value. By the Remainder Theorem, this value is P(x).

Since $P(-2) = 0$, -2 is a zero of P.
Set $Q(x) = x^2 + 0x - 12$ equal to zero. Then, solve for the other zeros.

$$x^2 - 12 = 0$$
$$x = \pm 2\sqrt{3}$$
$$x \approx \pm 3.5$$

Since $P(-4)$ and $P(-3)$ have opposite signs, there is a zero between $x = -4$ and $x = -3$. Similarly, there is a zero between $x = 3$ and $x = 4$. An arrow $\rightarrow$ identifies the location of each zero.

Scanning the right column from top to bottom indicates the shape of the graph of P. The graph is negative, moves upward, crosses the x-axis between -4 and -3, rises very little above the x-axis, crosses again at $x = -2$. Then it drops below the x-axis, levels off near $x = 1$, and rises to cross again between $x = 3$ and $x = 4$.

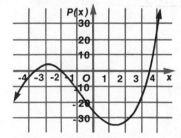

All the zeros have been located, since a maximum of three are expected by the Fundamental Theorem of Algebra.

Some zeros might be nonreal. They could not be shown by the Location Principle. Unless the coefficients are particularly large or small, the real zeros are clustered reasonably close to the y-axis. Inspect the leading coefficients. Often they will show beyond which points it is useless to look for zeros.

A real number u such that no zero of a function f is greater than u is called an **upper bound** for the zeros of f. A real number l such that no zero of a function f is less than l is called a **lower bound** for the zeros of f.

Bounds for Zeros

In the previous example it would have been useless to look for a zero more positive than 4 or more negative than -5. Using synthetic division, it is clear that all values of the quotient line would be larger positive values than 1, 6, 12 if $x - 5$ was the divisor. Therefore, the remainder, or $P(5)$, would be larger than 24. Similarly, continuation of negative values beyond -5 would produce alternate signs and yield $P(x)$ more negative than -39.

Thus, in this example, an upper bound, u, is 4, and a lower bound, l, is -5. In general, u is reached when $Q(x)$ and $R(x)$ have all signs alike. And l is reached when $Q(x)$ and $R(x)$ have alternate signs.

Exercises

Exploratory   State the maximum number of zeros expected for each polynomial.

1. $x^3 - 4x^2 - 2x + 13$
2. $2x^4 - x^3 - 17x^2 + x + 25$
3. $x^3 - 16x - 15$
4. $x^3 - 9x^2 + 20x - 8$
5. $x^3 - 4x^2 - 2x + 15$
6. $x^3 - 4x^2 - 2x - 13$

Written   Locate all real zeros of each polynomial between consecutive integers. Give the greatest integer lower bound for each. Give the least integer upper bound for each. Sketch each graph.

1. $P(x) = x^3 - 4x^2 - 2x + 13$
2. $P(x) = 2x^4 - x^3 - 17x^2 + x + 25$
3. $P(x) = x^3 - 16x - 15$
4. $P(x) = x^3 + 9x^2 + 20x - 8$
5. $P(x) = x^3 - 4x^2 - 2x + 15$
6. $P(x) = x^3 - 4x^2 - 2x + 13$
7. $P(x) = x^3 - 4x^2 - 2x + 21$
8. $P(x) = x^4 - 4x^3 - 4x^2 + 20x - 5$

Challenge   Determine the range of values for k so that the given condition is satisfied.

1. $P(x) = x^3 - 4x^2 - 2x + k$
    has a zero between -1 and -2.
2. $P(x) = x^4 - 2x^3 - 5x + k$
    has a zero between 3 and 4.

3. State the Intermediate Value Theorem for $f(b) < f(a)$. Is this theorem true? Does the theorem apply if $f(b) = f(a)$?

10-7 Rational Zero Theorem

There are relationships between the zeros and the coefficients of a polynomial.

> **Suppose that $P(x) = a_n x^n + a_{n-1} x^{n-1} + \cdots + a_1 x + a_0$ is a polynomial with integer coefficients. If $\dfrac{p}{q}$ is a rational zero of P with p and q relatively prime integers, and $\dfrac{p}{q} \neq 0$, then p is a factor of a_0 and q is a factor of a_n.**

The Rational Zero Theorem

Proof

Assume that p and q have no common factor. That is, suppose the fraction $\dfrac{p}{q}$ is reduced to lowest terms. Since $\dfrac{p}{q}$ is a zero, the following is true.

$$P\left(\frac{p}{q}\right) = 0$$

$$0 = a_n\left(\frac{p}{q}\right)^n + a_{n-1}\left(\frac{p}{q}\right)^{n-1} + \cdots + a_1\left(\frac{p}{q}\right) + a_0$$

$$0 = a_n p^n + a_{n-1} p^{n-1} q + \cdots + a_1 p q^{n-1} + a_0 q^n$$

$$-a_n p^n = a_{n-1} p^{n-1} q + \cdots + a_1 p q^{n-1} + a_0 q^n$$

$$-a_n p^n = q(a_{n-1} p^{n-1} + \cdots + a_1 p q^{n-2} + a_0 q^{n-1})$$

All factors are integers. Since q is an exact factor of the right side of the last equation, it must be an exact factor of the left side, $-a_n p^n$. By assumption, p and q are relatively prime. So q does not divide p^n. Therefore, q must be an exact factor of a_n. Similarly p can be shown to be an exact factor of a_0.

The **Integer Zero Theorem** is an immediate corollary to the Rational Zero Theorem.

> **If a polynomial $P(x) = 1 \cdot x^n + a_{n-1} x^{n-1} + \cdots + a_1 x + a_0$ has leading coefficient 1, integral coefficients, and $a_0 \neq 0$, then any rational zeros of the polynomial are integers and divide a_0.**

The Integer Zero Theorem

Example

1. **List all possible rational zeros of $P(x) = x^4 - 12x^3 + 7x + 13$.**

   Since $a_n = 1$, any rational zero must be an integer and a factor of 13. Thus, $z \in \{\pm 1, \pm 13\}$.

The following steps are a method of attack for finding zeros of a polynomial P.

1. Is the leading coefficient 1? Look for possible integer zeros which are factors of the constant term.
2. Look for rational zeros.
3. Each time a zero is found, repeat Steps **1** and **2** for the reduced polynomial Q. Try each zero again on Q, if reasonable, since a zero may have multiplicity greater than 1.
4. Find upper and lower bounds for the zeros. Isolate any real zero between two integers.
5. Find sufficient zeros to reduce Q to a quadratic factor if possible, where remaining nonreal or irrational factors are found easily.
6. If the above steps do not result in a final linear or quadratic factor, approximate methods may be used.

Example

2. **Find as many zeros of $P(x) = 4x^4 + 12x^3 + x^2 - 22x - 30$ as possible.**

   Here are some possible rational zeros. $\pm 1, \pm 2, \pm 3, \pm 5, \pm 6, \pm 10, \pm 15, \pm 30,$
   $\pm\frac{1}{2}, \pm\frac{1}{4}, \pm\frac{3}{2}, \pm\frac{3}{4}, \pm\frac{5}{2}, \pm\frac{5}{4}, \pm\frac{15}{2}, \pm\frac{15}{4}$

   This is a formidable list. The Location Principle narrows the search. The $+$ designates a large positive number.

		4	12	1	-22	-30
$l \rightarrow$	-4	4	-4	17	-90	$+$
$z_1 \rightarrow$	-3	4	0	1	-25	45
	-2	4	4	-7	-8	-14
	-1	4	8	-7	-15	-15
	0					-30
	1					-35
$z_2 \rightarrow$ $u \rightarrow$	2	4	20	41	60	$+$

   The integer zero possibilities are eliminated. Of the fractional possibilities, only $-\frac{5}{2}, \frac{3}{2}$, and $\frac{5}{4}$ are still candidates.

$$\begin{array}{r|rrrrr} & 4 & 12 & 1 & -22 & -30 \\ z_1 \rightarrow \quad \dfrac{-5}{2} & 4 & 2 & -4 & -12 & 0 \end{array}$$

$$P(x) = \left(x + \frac{5}{2}\right)Q(x)$$

$$P(x) = \left(x + \frac{5}{2}\right)(4x^3 + 2x^2 - 4x - 12)$$

The remaining zeros of P must be zeros of Q. Only $\dfrac{3}{2}$ is a possible zero. If $P\left(\dfrac{3}{2}\right) \neq 0$, then the remaining zeros must be irrational or nonreal.

$$\begin{array}{r|rrrr} & 4 & 2 & -4 & -12 \\ z_2 \rightarrow \quad \dfrac{3}{2} & 4 & 8 & 8 & 0 \end{array}$$

$$P(x) = \left(x + \frac{5}{2}\right)\left(x - \frac{3}{2}\right)(4x^2 + 8x + 8)$$

$$P(x) = 4\left(x + \frac{5}{2}\right)\left(x - \frac{3}{2}\right)(x^2 + 2x + 2)$$

Use the quadratic formula to find z_3 and z_4.

$$x^2 + 2x + 2 = 0$$

$$x = \frac{-2 \pm \sqrt{4 - 4 \cdot 2}}{2}$$

$$x = -1 \pm i$$

Thus $z_3 = -1 + i$ and $z_4 = -1 - i$.
Therefore, all zeros are determined.

Exercises

Exploratory   State a polynomial defined by the given zeros.

1. $3, -2, 1$
2. $-2, 5, 4, 1$
3. $\dfrac{2}{3}, \dfrac{1}{6}, 2$
4. $1, \sqrt{2}, -\sqrt{2}$
5. $0, -1, 1 + \sqrt{3}, 1 - \sqrt{3}$

Written   Find all zeros for each polynomial.

1. $P(x) = 3x^3 - 14x^2 + 11x - 2$
2. $P(x) = x^4 + 2x^3 - 4x^2 - 5x + 6$
3. $P(x) = x^4 - 3x^3 - x + 3$
4. $P(x) = 4x^3 - 4x^2 - x + 1$
5. $P(x) = 6x^3 + 5x^2 + 7x + 2$
6. $P(x) = 2x^4 - x^3 - 4x^2 + x + 2$
7. Two of the zeros of a cubic polynomial are -3 and 5. Suppose $P(x) = 2x^3 - 5x^2 - 28x + 15$. Find the other zero.
8. One zero of $P(x)$ is 4. Find all other zeros if $P(x) = x^3 - 4x^2 + 5x - 20$.
9. Find all rational zeros if $P(x) = x^5 - 4x^4 + 4x^3 - 3x^2 - x + 3$.

10–8 Complex Zeros

Some polynomials with real coefficients have nonreal zeros. The quadratic polynomial gives an example. The quadratic formula generates two **complex conjugates** of the form $a \pm bi$, where $a, b \in \mathcal{R}$. The sum of such conjugates is a real number, $2a$. Their product is a real number, $a^2 + b^2$. Nonreal zeros must occur in pairs, as is shown by the following theorem.

If $a + bi$ is a zero of a polynomial $P(x) = a_n x^n + a_{n-1} x^{n-1} + \ldots + a_1 x + a_0$ with real coefficients, then its conjugate $a - bi$ is a zero.

The Complex Conjugate Theorem

Proof

Suppose that $a + bi$ is a zero of P, a polynomial with real coefficients. If $b = 0$, then $a + bi = a - bi$, and $a - bi$ is also a zero. Therefore, assume $b \neq 0$. In that case $a + bi$ is nonreal. Since P has real coefficients, this means that the degree of P must be at least 2. This follows from the fact that all polynomials of degree 1 with real coefficients have exactly one real zero. Notice too that $[x - (a + bi)] \cdot [x - (a - bi)]$ has degree 2. Therefore,

$$P(x) = [x - (a + bi)] \cdot [x - (a - bi)] \cdot Q(x) + R(x)$$

for some Q and R where degree of $R \leq 1$ or R is the zero polynomial.

The divisor, $[x - (a + bi)] \cdot [x - (a - bi)]$, is equal to $x^2 - 2ax + (a^2 + b^2)$. Thus, the divisor too is a polynomial with real number coefficients. In that case, the quotient, $Q(x)$, and the remainder, $R(x)$, must have real number coefficients.

Since $P(a + bi) = 0$, and $[x - (a + bi)] \cdot [x - (a - bi)] \cdot Q(x)$ is zero when x is replaced by $a + bi$, then $0 = P(a + bi) = 0 + R(a + bi)$. So, R has real coefficients, the degree of $R \leq 1$, and R has value zero for a nonreal number. Therefore, R must be the zero polynomial. Thus,

$$P(x) = [x - (a + bi)] \cdot [x - (a - bi)] \cdot Q(x) + R(x)$$
$$= [x - (a + bi)] \cdot [x - (a - bi)] \cdot Q(x)$$

From this last equation it follows that $[x - (a - bi)]$ is a factor of $P(x)$, and therefore $a - bi$ is a zero of P.

If $a, b \in \mathcal{R}$, $b \neq 0$, why is it impossible for $R(x) = ax + b$ to have a nonreal zero?

Example

1. **Find a polynomial with integer coefficients and lowest possible degree such that its zeros include $\frac{1}{2}$ and $2 - i$.**

By the complex Conjugate Theorem, $2 + i$ also is a zero. P can be factored as follows.

$$P(x) = a_n\left(x - \frac{1}{2}\right)[x - (2 - i)][x - (2 + i)]$$

$$P(x) = a_n\left(x - \frac{1}{2}\right)[(x - 2) + i][(x - 2) - i]$$

$$P(x) = a_n\left(x - \frac{1}{2}\right)[(x - 2)^2 - i^2]$$

$$P(x) = a_n\left(x - \frac{1}{2}\right)(x^2 - 4x + 4 + 1)$$

$$P(x) = a_n\left(x - \frac{1}{2}\right)(x^2 - 4x + 5)$$

$$P(x) = a_n\left(x^3 - \frac{9}{2}x^2 + 7x - \frac{5}{2}\right)$$

Since P is to have integer coefficients, a_n must be an even integer. Suppose $a_n = 2$.

$$P(x) = 2\left(x^3 - \frac{9}{2}x^2 + 7x - \frac{5}{2}\right)$$

$$P(x) = 2x^3 - 9x^2 + 14x - 5$$

Notice that P(x) is not unique. Let $a_n = 10$, then $P(x) = 10x^3 - 45x^2 + 70x - 25$ has the same zeros as before.

Lowering the x-axis brings the zeros closer together, until they finally merge into a single zero of multiplicity 2. A further lowering of the axis forces both real zeros to disappear.

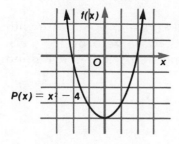

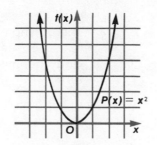

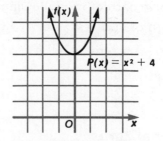

The polynomial $P(x) = x^2 - 4$ has two real zeros $z_1 = -2$ and $z_2 = 2$.

The Polynomial $P(x) = x^2$ has one real zero $z_1 = 0$ of multiplicity two.

The polynomial $P(x) = x^2 + 4$ has two imaginary zeros $z_1 = -2i$ and $z_2 = +2i$.

The Complex Conjugate Theorem proves that nonreal zeros occur in pairs. So if $a + bi$ is a root, $a - bi$ is also a root.

Exercises

Exploratory Name the conjugates of each of the following.

1. i

2. $2 + i$

3. $-3i$

4. $4 - 2i$

5. $\dfrac{1}{2} + \dfrac{\sqrt{3}}{2}i$

6. $3 - i\sqrt{2}$

7. $\sqrt{5} + 3i\sqrt{2}$

8. $2 - 5i$

9. $5 - 4i$

Written Given $P(x)$, find all other zeros.

1. $P(x) = x^3 - 2x^2 + 4x - 8;\ z_1 = 2i$

2. $P(x) = x^3 - 3x^2 + x - 3;\ z_1 = i$

3. $P(x) = x^3 - 10x^2 + 34x - 40;$
   $z_1 = 3 - i$

4. $P(x) = 2x^3 - 11x^2 + 26x - 21;$
   $z_1 = 2 + \sqrt{3}i$

5. $P(x) = x^4 + 13x^2 + 36;$
   $z_1 = 2i, z_2 = 3i$

6. $P(x) = x^4 - 5x^3 + 9x^2 - 5x;$
   $z_1 = 2 + i$

7. $P(x) = 2x^4 - 13x^3 + 34x^2 - 82x - 40;\ z_1 = 1 + 3i$ (Hint: Find $P(x) \div [(x - z_1)(x - z_2)].$)

Write a polynomial with integer coefficients of lowest possible degree which has the zeros listed.

8. $2, 3i$

9. $-4, 2 + i$

10. $\dfrac{2}{3}, i$

11. $2i, -5i$

12. $3 - i, 1 + i$

13. $3 + \sqrt{2}i, \dfrac{2}{3}, \dfrac{3}{4}$

14. $0, 0, -2, -2, i$

15. A polynomial P of degree 3 has integer coefficients. Its zeros are $\dfrac{1}{2}$, 2, and 3. Find P.

Challenge Solve each of the following.

1. If z is a zero of $P(x) = x^3 + kx^2 + kx + 1$, prove that $\dfrac{1}{z}$ is a zero.

2. The polynomial $P(x) = x^3 - 6x^2 + \cdots$ with real coefficients has a zero of $1 + i\sqrt{5}$. Find the missing zeros and the missing terms.

10-9 Irrational Zeros

Many methods are available for approximating real zeros as accurately as desired. Since such calculations usually are tedious, a calculator or computer is desirable. In this section, linear interpolation is used to approximate irrational zeros. This method is based on the assumption that the graph of a function is approximately a straight line between two points close together on the curve.

Suppose that P is a polynomial and $P(a) < 0$ and $P(b) > 0$ for $a < b$. By the Location Principle, there is a real number z such that $a < z < b$ and $P(z) = 0$.

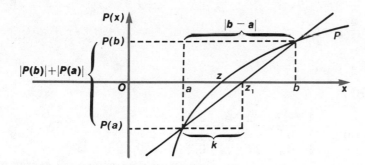

The line drawn through $(a, P(a))$ and $(b, P(b))$ intersects the x-axis at z_1, the first approximation to z. The number k identifies the fraction of the distance from a to b where z_1 is located. Consider similar triangles.

$$\frac{k}{|P(a)|} = \frac{|b - a|}{|P(a)| + |P(b)|}$$

$$k = \frac{|P(a)|}{|P(a)| + |P(b)|} \cdot |b - a|$$

The first approximation is $z_1 = a + k$. Evaluate $P(z_1)$. If z_1 is not a zero, then the above process is repeated to find another approximation z_2. In this approximation, use $(a, P(a))$ and $(z_1, P(z_1))$ if $P(z_1) > 0$ and use $(z_1, P(z_1))$ and $(b, P(b))$ if $P(z_1) < 0$.

Example

1. **Find all zeros of $P(x) = x^3 - 3x^2 - 2x - 2$.**

    Possible rational zeros are $\pm 1, \pm 2$.

		1	-3	-2	-2
$l \rightarrow$	-1	1	-4	2	-4
	0	1			-2
	1	1			-6
	2	1	-1	-4	-10
	3	1	0	-2	-8
$\begin{matrix} z \rightarrow \\ u \rightarrow \end{matrix}$	4	1	1	2	6

Since there are no rational zeros, only irrational and nonreal zeros are possible. One irrational zero z is between 3 and 4.

$$k = \frac{|P(3)|}{|P(3)| + |P(4)|} \cdot |4 - 3|$$

$$= \frac{|-8|}{|-8| + |6|} \cdot |1|$$

$$= \frac{4}{7}$$

$$k \approx 0.6$$

$$z_1 \approx 3 + 0.6 = 3.6$$

Check to see if z_1 is a zero of P.

$$
\begin{array}{c|cccc}
 & 1 & -3 & -2 & -2 \\
\hline
3.6 & 1 & 0.6 & 0.2 & -1.3 \\
z_2 \rightarrow \quad 3.7 & 1 & 0.7 & 0.6 & 0.2 \\
\end{array}
$$

The next approximation z_2 is between 3.6 and 3.7.

$$k = \frac{|P(3.6)|}{|P(3.6)| + |P(3.7)|} \cdot |3.7 - 3.6|$$

$$= \frac{|-1.3|}{|-1.3| + |0.2|} \cdot |0.1|$$

$$= \frac{1.3}{1.5}(0.1)$$

$$k \approx 0.09$$

$$z_2 \approx 3.6 + 0.09 = 3.69$$

Check to see if z_2 is a zero.

$$
\begin{array}{c|cccc}
 & 1 & -3 & -2 & -2 \\
\hline
3.69 & 1 & 0.69 & 0.55 & 0.03 \\
z_2 \rightarrow \quad 3.68 & 1 & 0.68 & 0.51 & -0.12 \\
\end{array}
$$

Since $P(3.69)$ is closer to 0 than $P(3.68)$, $z \approx 3.69$ to two decimal places.
The other two zeros are, approximately, solutions to $x^2 + 0.69x + 0.55 = 0$. This equation was obtained by dividing $P(x)$ by $(x - 3.69)$.

$$x = \frac{-0.69 \pm \sqrt{(0.69)^2 - 4 \cdot 1 \cdot (0.55)}}{2}$$

$$\approx \frac{-0.69 \pm \sqrt{-1.72}}{2}$$

$$\approx \frac{-0.69 \pm 1.31i}{2}$$

$$\approx -0.35 \pm 0.66i$$

Thus P has one irrational and two nonreal zeros. These are approximately 3.69, $-0.35 + 0.66i$ and $-0.35 - 0.66i$, correct to two decimal places.

Exercises

Exploratory Name the possible rational zeros for each of the following.

1. $P(x) = x^3 - x - 3$
2. $P(x) = x^3 - 2x^2 - x + 1$
3. $P(x) = x^3 - 3x^2 + 7x - 11$
4. $P(x) = x^3 + 2x^2 - 23x - 70$
5. $P(x) = 2x^3 - x^2 - 3x + 3$
6. $P(x) = x^4 - 10x^2 - 4x + 5$

Written Find all zeros correct to two decimal places for each polynomial.

1. $P(x) = x^3 - x - 3$
2. $P(x) = x^3 - 2x^2 - x + 1$
3. $P(x) = x^3 - 3x^2 + 7x - 11$
4. $P(x) = x^3 + 2x^2 - 23x - 70$
5. $P(x) = x^3 + 6x^2 - 10x - 1$
6. $P(x) = x^3 - 3x^2 - 2x + 3$
7. $P(x) = 2x^3 - x^2 - 3x + 3$
   (Hint: Use $P(-x)$ or $-P(-x)$.)
8. $P(x) = x^3 + 3x^2 - 6x + 4$
9. $P(x) = x^4 - 4x^2 - 8x - 4$
10. $P(x) = x^4 - 10x^2 - 4x + 5$

10–10 Rational Functions

Many relations are combinations of more elementary relations. Some of their properties are related closely to those of their component parts. Other properties are unique.

> **A rational function** is the quotient of two polynomial functions. It has the form $y = \dfrac{P(x)}{Q(x)}$, where P and Q are polynomials and $Q(x) \neq 0$.

Rational Functions

Unique properties of a rational function include the following.

1. The zeros of the function are zeros of the numerator.
2. Vertical asymptotes may be found by identifying zeros of the denominator.

The numerator and denominator of the rational function should be factored completely over the reals. Any factors common to both numerator and denominator should be removed. Any zeros of common factors are excluded from the domain of the function. The degree of any factor in the numerator or denominator is significant.

A factor of the numerator which appears to an odd degree indicates that the curve crosses the x-axis at the point which is the zero of that factor. An even degree indicates that the curve does not cross the x-axis at the value determined by the zero of the factor. Rather, the curve is *tangent* to the x-axis at this point. Consider values of $f(x)$ as $x \rightarrow a$ in the factor $(x - a)^n$. If n is odd and $x \rightarrow a^+$, then $(x - a)^n > 0$. If $x \rightarrow a^-$, $(x - a)^n < 0$ and the graph crosses the x-axis. If n is even, $(x - a)^n > 0$ for any x near a. The higher the degree of any factor of the numerator, the *flatter* the curve in the vicinity of the zero. This is true because, for $|x - a| < 1$, higher powers of $(x - a)$ produce smaller values than lower powers. Consider, for example, $(x - 2)$ and $(x - 2)^3$ when x equals 2.1. The former is 0.1 while the latter is 0.001.

Similarly, the degree of a factor of the denominator of a rational function is important. If $(x - a)^n$ appears with n odd, the vertical asymptote $x = a$ is approached from one side as $y \rightarrow +\infty$ and from the other as $y \rightarrow -\infty$. If n is even, then $x = a$ is approached from both sides as $y \rightarrow +\infty$ or as $y \rightarrow -\infty$, depending on the sign of the function.

Examples

1. **Sketch the graph of the function** $y = \dfrac{x^2(x - 1)}{(x + 1)^3(3x - 2)^2}$**. Shade the regions which are excluded.**

In the interval	y is	so exclude
$\langle \leftarrow, -1 \rangle$	positive	$y < 0$
$\langle -1, 0 \rangle$	negative	$y > 0$
$\left\langle 0, \dfrac{2}{3} \right\rangle$	negative	$y > 0$
$\left\langle \dfrac{2}{3}, 1 \right\rangle$	negative	$y > 0$
$[1, \rightarrow)$	nonnegative	$y \leq 0$

Zeros occur at $x = 0$ (multiplicity 2 since $x^2 = (x - 0)^2$) and at $x = 1$ (multiplicity 1 since $(x - 1) = (x - 1)^1$). Therefore, the curve crosses the x-axis at $x = 1$. It does not cross, and therefore is tangent to, the axis at $x = 0$.

Vertical asymptotes occur at $x = -1$ and at $x = \dfrac{2}{3}$. The function is of the form $\dfrac{(+)\,(-)}{(+)\,(+)}$ near $x = \dfrac{2}{3}$. Since 2 is even, the line $x = \dfrac{2}{3}$ is approached from both sides at the same end as $y \rightarrow -\infty$. The line $x = -1$ is approached from opposite ends, since 3 is odd. To determine which end of $x = -1$ the curve approaches as x moves from left to right, consider the form of the function expression. As $x \to -1^-$, the form is $\frac{(+)\,(-)}{(-)\,(+)}$. As $x \to -1^+$, the form is $\frac{(+)\,(-)}{(+)\,(+)}$.

Thus, the curve approaches the asymptote from the top left and bottom right.

Horizontal asymptotes are found by considering the behavior of the function as $x \to \pm\infty$. When $x \to +\infty$, the form of the function is $\frac{(+)\,(+)}{(+)\,(+)}$. Since the denominator approaches $+\infty$ faster than does the numerator, $y \to 0^+$ as $x \to +\infty$. When $x \to -\infty$, the form of the function is $\frac{(+)\,(-)}{(-)\,(+)}$. This indicates $y \to 0^+$ in this instance also. Another way to find the horizontal asymptotes is to solve for x in terms of y.

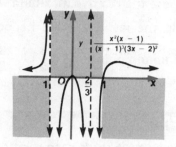

$$y \quad \frac{x^2(x-1)}{(x+1)^3(3x-2)^2}$$

2. **Sketch the graph of the function $y = \dfrac{x(x-2)}{x+1}$.**

   Zeros occur at $x = 0$ (multiplicity 1) and $x = 2$ (multiplicity 1). A vertical asymptote occurs at $x = -1$. For $x < -1$ the form is $\frac{(-)\,(-)}{(-)}$. Therefore, the curve approaches from the bottom left. Since $x + 1$ occurs as a factor only once, the curve approaches the asymptote from the top right. Alternately, the form for $x > -1$ is $\frac{(-)\,(-)}{(+)}$. Horizontal asymptotes do not occur since the ordinates are unbounded as $x \to \pm\infty$. Slant asymptotes are possible since degree $P(x)$ is exactly one more than $Q(x)$. By long division, $y = x - 3 + \dfrac{3}{x+1}$. As $x \to \pm\infty$, the last term approaches 0, and the curve is very close to the line $y = x - 3$.

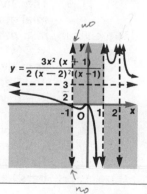

$$y = \frac{x\,(x-2)}{x+1}$$
$$y = x - 3$$

3. **Sketch the graph of the function $y = \dfrac{3x^2(x+1)}{2(x-2)^2(x-1)}$.**

   Zeros occur at $x = 0$ (multiplicity 2) and $x = -1$ (multiplicity 1). Vertical asymptotes occur at $x = 2$ (approaching from both sides at the top) and at $x = 1$ (approaching from left bottom and top right). Horizontal asymptotes are found by considering what happens as $x \to \pm\infty$. The highest degree terms in $P(x)$ and $Q(x)$ dominate the nature of the function for extremely large x. Therefore, the function is close to the function $y = \dfrac{3x^3}{2x^3}$ or $y = \dfrac{3}{2}$. This is the horizontal asymptote.

$$y = \frac{3x^2\,(x+1)}{2\,(x-2)^2(x-1)}$$

The previous examples make clear that the general shape of the curve can be sketched. Most graphs have turning points. For now all that can be done is to locate a point on the curve near where the **relative maximum** and **minimum points** might exist.

In the last example, the point $\left(\frac{3}{2}, f\left(\frac{3}{2}\right)\right)$ is near a relative minimum point and $f\left(\frac{3}{2}\right)$ is $\frac{135}{2}$.

Exercises

Written Sketch each relation.

1. $y = \dfrac{1}{x - 1}$

2. $y = \dfrac{x}{x - 1}$

3. $y = \dfrac{x(x + 1)}{(x + 1)(x - 1)}$

4. $y = \dfrac{x^2}{x - 1}$

5. $y = \dfrac{x}{(x - 1)^2}$

6. $y = \dfrac{x}{x^2 - 1}$

7. $y = \dfrac{x - 1}{x}$

8. $y = \dfrac{x - 1}{x^2}$

9. $y = \dfrac{(x - 1)^2}{x}$

10. $y = \dfrac{(x - 1)^2}{x^2}$

11. $y = \dfrac{x + 2}{x(x - 1)}$

12. $y = \dfrac{x^3 - 1}{x}$ *(Hint: $f \to a$ parabola as $x \to \pm\infty$)*

13. $y = \dfrac{(x + 2)^2(x - 1)}{x^2}$ *(Hint: Slant asymptote)*

14. $y = \dfrac{(x + 2)(x - 1)}{x^2}$

15. $y = \dfrac{2x^3}{x^3 - 1}$

Chapter Summary

1. A polynomial function, P, is one which may be expressed as $P(x) = a_n x^n + a_{n-1} x^{n-1} + a_{n-2} x^{n-2} + \cdots + a_1 x + a_0$ where $n \in W, a_n \neq 0$. (295)

2. As $x \to \pm\infty$, the highest power of x in a polynomial dominates the other powers. (298)

3. The Division Algorithm for Polynomials: If P is a polynomial of degree m and D is a polynomial of degree n, where $m \geq n$, then there exist polynomials Q and R such that $P(x) = D(x) \cdot Q(x) + R(x)$ and degree $R <$ degree D or R is the zero polynomial. (301)

4. The Remainder Theorem: If a polynomial P is divided by $x - c$, where $x \in \mathcal{C}$, then the remainder is $P(c)$. (302)

5. The Factor Theorem: The complex number c is a zero of a polynomial P if and only if $x - c$ is a factor of P. (305)

6. The Fundamental Theorem of Algebra: Every polynomial function of degree $n > 0$ over the field of complex numbers has at least one zero. (308)

7. A zero z of a polynomial P of degree $n > 0$ has multiplicity k if P can be factored as $P(x) = (x - z)^k Q(x)$ where $Q(x)$ is a polynomial of degree $n - k$ and z is not a zero of $Q(x)$. (308)

8. Given a polynomial of degree $n > 0$ over the field of complex numbers, the sum of the multiplicities of all its distinct zeros is n. (309)

9. The Intermediate Value Theorem: If a function f is continuous on the interval $[a, b]$ and t is a real number such that $f(a) < t < f(b)$, then there exists at least one real number c such that $a < c < b$ and $f(c) = t$. (310)

10. The Location Principle: If f is a continuous function and $f(a)$ and $f(b)$ have opposite signs for $a, b \in \mathcal{R}$, then f has at least one zero between a and b. (311)

11. The Rational Zero Theorem: Suppose that $P(x) = a_n x^n + a_{n-1} x^{n-1} + \cdots + a_1 x + a_0$ is a polynomial with integer coefficients. If $\dfrac{p}{q}$ is a rational zero of P, and $\dfrac{p}{q} \neq 0$, then p is a factor of a_0 and q is a factor of a_n, providing p and q are relatively prime. (313)

12. The Integer Zero Theorem: If a polynomial $P(x) = 1 \cdot x^n + a_{n-1} x^{n-1} + \cdots + a_1 x + a_0$ has leading coefficient 1, integral coefficients, and $a_0 \neq 0$, then any rational zeros are integers and divide a_0. (313)

13. The Complex Conjugate Theorem: If $a + bi$ is a zero of a polynomial with real coefficients, then its conjugate $a - bi$ also is a zero. (316)

14. A rational function has the form $y = \dfrac{P(x)}{Q(x)}$, where P and Q are polynomials and $Q(x) \neq 0$. (321)

Chapter Review

10–1 **Find the zeros of each polynomial. (Hint: Factor as much as possible.)**

1. $x^2 - 9x$

2. $x^2 - 1$

3. $2x^2 - x - 3$

4. $2x^2 + 50$

10–2 **For each polynomial, factor where possible. Determine excluded regions. Sketch each function.**

5. $P(x) = x^3 + x$

6. $P(x) = x^4 - 5x^2 + 4$

Find a polynomial P with zeros $x = 1$ and $x = -1$ which satisfy the given conditions. Give at least two answers when possible.

7. Degree $P \geq 4$, $P\left(\dfrac{3}{2}\right) < 0$.

8. Degree P is odd and $P(x) \to -\infty$ as $x \to \infty$.

10-3 Use synthetic division to write each polynomial in the form $P(x) = (x - c) \cdot Q(x) + R(x)$.

    9. $P(x) = 3x^3 - 2x^2 + x - 2;\ c = -3$ **10.** $P(x) = 4x^4 - x^2 + 7;\ c = 2$

    11. Make a table of values showing $P(c)$ if $P(x) = 2x^4 \quad 3x^3 + x^2 - 7$ and $c \in \{-3, -2, -1, 0, 1, 2, 3\}$.

    12. For what values of k is $P(2) = 36$, if $P(x) = kx^3 + 2x^2 - kx - 2$?

10-4 Factor each polynomial as completely as possible.

    13. $x^3 + 6x^2 - x - 30$ **14.** $x^4 - 10x^3 + 35x^2 - 50x + 24$

10-5 Factor each polynomial completely. List all the zeros and their multiplicities. Sketch the graph of each polynomial.

    15. $x^5 + x^4 - 5x^3 - 5x^2 + 4x + 4$ **16.** $x^6 - 64$

    17. $x^5 + 6x^4 + 3x^3 - 46x^2 - 108x - 72$

    Find at least one expression for P if it has zeros as given. Sketch P.

    18. -3 of multiplicity three, 3 of multi-   **19.** $2 + \sqrt{3},\ 2 - \sqrt{3},\ 0$
plicity two

    20. $1,\ \dfrac{1}{2} + \dfrac{\sqrt{3}i}{2},\ \dfrac{1}{2} - \dfrac{\sqrt{3}i}{2}$

10-6 Locate all real zeros of the given polynomials. Give a lower bound and upper bound. Sketch each polynomial.

    21. $P(x) = x^3 + 3x^2 - 5x - 15$ **22.** $P(x) = x^3 + x^2 - 19x + 5$

    23. Determine the range of values for k so that $P(x) = 2x^3 - 3x^2 + 2x - k$ has a zero between 1 and 2.

10-7 Find as many zeros as possible for each polynomial.

    24. $P(x) = 2x^3 - 7x^2 - 17x + 10$ **25.** $P(x) = 16x^4 - 160x^3 + 383x^2 + 10x - 24$

10-8 Given $P(x)$ and any zeros listed, find all other zeros.

    26. $P(x) = x^3 + 2x^2 + 9x + 18;\ z_1 = 3i$ **27.** $P(x) = x^4 + 5x^2 + 4;\ z_1 = i$

    Write a polynomial with integer coefficients of lowest possible degree which has the zeros listed.

    28. $3, 2i$ **29.** $2 - \sqrt{5}i,\ \dfrac{1}{4}$

    Find all zeros correct to two decimal places.

    30. $P(x) = 3x^3 - 7x^2 - x - 1$ **31.** $P(x) = x^4 - 4x^3 - 4x^2 + 20x - 5$

    Sketch the graph of each relation

    32. $y = \dfrac{x}{x^2 - 1}$ **33.** $y = \dfrac{(x - 3)^2}{x^3 - 27}$

    35. $y = \dfrac{3x^3 - x^2 + 1}{x^2 + 1}$

Chapter Test

Find the zeros of each polynomial. (Hint: Factor as much as possible.)

1. $3x^2 - 5x$

2. $3x^4 + 27x^2$

For each polynomial, factor where possible. Determine excluded regions. Sketch each function.

3. $3x^3 - x^2 + 2x$

4. $x^3 - 5x^2 - 24x$

Find a polynomial P with zeros $x = 1$ and $x = -1$ which satisfy the given conditions. Give at least two answers when possible.

5. Degree P is even and $P(x) \to +\infty$ as $x \to \infty$

6. Degree $P \geq 2$, $P\left(\dfrac{1}{2}\right) < 0$

Use synthetic division to write each polynomial in the form $P(x) = (x - c) \cdot Q(x) + R(x)$.

7. $P(x) = x^3 - 5x^2 - x + 8$; $c = 5$

8. $P(x) = x^3 + x^2 - 4x - 4$; $c = 2$

9. Make a table of values showing $P(c)$ if $P(x) = x^3 - 3x^2 - 4x + 6$ and $c \in \{-2, -1, 0, 1, 2\}$.

Factor each polynomial as completely as possible. List all the zeros and their multiplicities.

10. $x^2 + 8x - 20 = 0$

11. $x^4 - 8x^2 + 16 = 0$

Locate all real zeros of the given polynomials. Give a lower bound and upper bound. Sketch each polynomial.

12. $x^2 - 3x + 1$

13. $x^3 - 2$

Given $P(x)$ and any zeros listed, find all other zeros.

14. $x^3 - 2x^2 - x + 2$, $z_1 = -1$

15. $x^3 - 3x^2 - 4x - 12$, $z_1 = 2i$

Write a polynomial with integer coefficients of lowest possible degree which has the zeros listed.

16. $1, i$

17. $\dfrac{1}{2}, 2 - i$

18. $0, 2 - i$

19. Find all zeros correct to two decimal places for $P(x) = x^3 + x^2 - 5x - 5$.

20. Sketch the graph of $y = \dfrac{x}{x^2 - 2}$.

Computers

User Languages

Besides BASIC, which is heavily used in home computers and in schools, the most common languages currently in use are FORTRAN (FORmula TRANslation), COBOL (COmmon Business-Oriented Language), PL/1, and PASCAL.

FORTRAN was developed early in the history of programming languages primarily for scientific use. It has had a wide usage, is quite standardized, and is still used extensively. FORTRAN's symbol expressions follow that of ordinary algebra quite carefully. Since it was developed during the era of exclusive input through punched cards, it still has traces of keypunch requirements. For example, in FORTRAN the BASIC statement IF K < 10 THEN 200 would be written IF(K.LT.10) GOTO 200 because early keypunch machines did not have inequality keys. FORTRAN has very specific ways of formatting all input and output statements, and the programmer must be very careful with numeric sizes and types (e.g. real numbers versus integers).

COBOL translates about 250 reserved words and phrases common to business English to instructions for the computer. Each COBOL program has four major divisions: Procedure, Identification, Environment, and Data. The experienced COBOL programmer can easily follow another's program since its design is quite carefully dictated and the symbols and words are so commonly used in business applications. Because output in business is usually needed in very precise formatted displays for particular forms used, the output is very carefully specified.

PL/1 is a language that combines the best features of FORTRAN and COBOL and allows for easier use by those users who need to com-

bine features of each. For instance, FORTRAN does not permit easy manipulation of large amounts of data, while COBOL uses rather complicated means to do normal arithmetic and algebra. PL/1 was designed to allow a single language to be more powerful and general than either of the other two more specialized languages.

PASCAL is a language quite recently developed and was designed to overcome many of the difficulties encountered with other high-level languages. It is an example of what is called a structured language. The main body of a program is relatively simple and easy to follow. It usually is traversed just once in what is referred to as a "flow through" process. One strength of PASCAL is that the main body of the program calls upon various external parts called procedures. Because these procedures can identify their own variables and data types, each procedure is quite independent of the others and of the main program. Programming is then reduced to writing appropriate modules which are used by the main program itself. These modules may be altered quite easily and independently, even by other programmers without affecting the rest of the program. Other strengths of PASCAL lie in the ability to define data types in each part of the program and in simple control structures so that branching within the program is almost unheard of. With PASCAL it is truly possible to write a program which follows a problem carefully rather than working to express a problem in terms which the computer requires.

The languages do have statements that parallel each other. For example, if a programmer needs to find the square roots for 1 through 10, the forms will be different as illus-

trated below but the results will be the same.

```
BASIC        10  FOR X = 1 TO 10
             20  LET Y = SQR (X)
             30  NEXT X


FORTRAN          DO 30 X = 1, 10
                 Y = SQRT (X)
             30  CONTINUE


PL/1             DO X = 1 TO 10;
                 Y = SQRT (X);
                 END;
```

It is difficult to compare languages since each language has been developed for a different purpose. There are sometimes different compilers for the same language which means there is more than one version of a language. The preference of the programmer, the purpose of the program, and the available language for a computer determines the language to be used.

Exercises Write programs for each of the following.

1. Evaluate $f(x) = x^4 - x^3 + x^2 - x + 1$ for integral values of x from -6 to 6 inclusive.

2. Find the values of x for which $ax^2 + bx + c > 0$ given a, b, and c.

3. Output the graph $P(x) = x^3 - x$.

4. Determine if an equation of the form $ax^2 + bx + c$ has real roots.

5. Use the Factor Theorem to find factors of the polynomial $P(x) = ax^3 + bx^2 + cx + d$.

6. Find the integers which are factors of x given that x is an integer.

7. Use the Rational Zero Theorem to find all possible rational roots of the equation $ax^3 + bx^2 + cx + d = 0$ given that $a, b, c,$ and d are integers.

8. Approximate to the nearest hundredth the positive real zero(s) of the function $f(x) = 2x^3 - 4x^2 - 3$.

Chapter 11

The exponential function is used for steadily increasing or decreasing phenomena such as population. To find a increase in population an equation such as $y = y_0e^{kt}$ is used.

Transcendental Functions

11–1 The Exponential Function

Functions are classified as either *algebraic* or *transcendental*. The most common algebraic functions are the polynomial functions. The circular functions are examples of **transcendental functions.**

A **transcendental function** is a function which cannot be expressed by a finite number of algebraic operations. A **transcendental number** is a number which cannot be the zero of any algebraic function.

Transcendental Function
Transcendental Number

Algebraic operations include addition, subtraction, multiplication, division, and raising to a rational power.

If $a \in \mathcal{R}$ and n is a natural number, then a to the nth power is $a^n = a \cdot a \cdot \cdots \cdot a$, where there are n factors of a. Similarly the nth root of a (symbolized $\sqrt[n]{a}$) is the real number b such that $b^n = a$. It is possible that b does not exist such as if $b = \sqrt[4]{-16}$. The two expressions $\sqrt[n]{a}$ and $a^{1/n}$ are equivalent.

With these definitions, the following properties were developed earlier for $a, b \in \mathcal{R}$ and $m, n \in \mathrm{N}$.

EX$_1$: $a^m a^n = a^{m+n}$

EX$_2$: $\dfrac{a^m}{a^n} = a^{m-n}$

EX$_3$: $(a^m)^n = a^{mn}$

EX$_4$: $a^m b^m = (ab)^m$

EX$_5$: $\dfrac{a^m}{b^m} = \left(\dfrac{a}{b}\right)^m$

EX$_6$: $a^{m/n} = (a^{1/n})^m$, if $a^{1/n}$ exists

Properties of Exponents

EX$_7$: $a^0 = 1, a \neq 0$

EX$_8$: $a^{m-n} = \dfrac{1}{a^{n-m}}$

EX$_9$: $a^{p/q} = \sqrt[q]{a^p}$

Properties of Exponents

Examples

1. **Simplify** $\dfrac{16^2 \cdot 5^{1/2}}{2^3 \cdot 5^{1/3}}$.

$$\frac{16^2 \cdot 5^{1/2}}{2^3 \cdot 5^{1/3}} = \frac{(2^4)^2}{2^3} \cdot \frac{5^{1/2}}{5^{1/3}} = 2^{8-3} \cdot 5^{1/2 - 1/3} = 2^5 \cdot 5^{1/6} = 2^5 \sqrt[6]{5}$$

2. **Simplify** $\sqrt{2\sqrt{32}}$.

$$\sqrt{2\sqrt{32}} = [2(2^5)^{1/2}]^{1/2} = 2^{1/2} \cdot 2^{5/4} = 2^{1/2 + 5/4}$$
$$= 2^{7/4} = \sqrt[4]{2^7} = 2\sqrt[4]{2^3} = 2\sqrt[4]{8}$$

An extension of the Properties **EX$_1$ − EX$_9$** gives meaning to the expression a^x for x any real number.

What is meant by $2^{\sqrt{3}}$ or 3^π? Consider the graph of the function $y = 2^x$, where $x \in Z$.

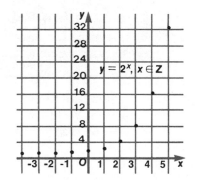

x	-4	-3	-2	-1	0	1	2	3	4	5
2^x	$\dfrac{1}{16}$	$\dfrac{1}{8}$	$\dfrac{1}{4}$	$\dfrac{1}{2}$	1	2	4	8	16	32

Suppose the domain of $y = 2^x$ is expanded to include the rational numbers. Approximate values are given for some x-values.

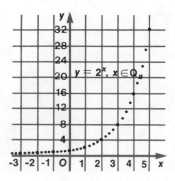

x	-2.00	-1.75	-1.50	-1.25	-1.00	-0.75	-0.50	-0.25
2^x	0.25	0.30	0.35	0.42	0.50	0.59	0.71	0.84
x	0.00	0.25	0.50	0.75	1.00	1.25	1.50	1.75
2^x	1.00	1.19	1.41	1.68	2.00	2.38	2.83	3.36
x	2.00	2.25	2.50	2.75	3.00	3.25	3.50	3.75
2^x	4.00	4.76	5.66	6.73	8.00	9.51	11.31	13.45

To expand the domain of $y = 2^x$ to include both rational and irrational numbers, consider a possible meaning for an expression such as $2^{\sqrt{3}}$. Since $1.7 < \sqrt{3} < 1.8$, it seems clear that $2^{1.7} < 2^{\sqrt{3}} < 2^{1.8}$. By using better approximations to $\sqrt{3}$, better approximations to $2^{\sqrt{3}}$ are possible.

$$2^{1.7} < 2^{\sqrt{3}} < 2^{1.8}$$
$$2^{1.73} < 2^{\sqrt{3}} < 2^{1.74}$$
$$2^{1.732} < 2^{\sqrt{3}} < 2^{1.733}$$
$$2^{1.7320} < 2^{\sqrt{3}} < 2^{1.7321}$$
$$2^{1.73205} < 2^{\sqrt{3}} < 2^{1.73206}$$

By sequences, $\sqrt{3}$ is the least upper bound of the sequence of numbers 1.7, 1.73, 1.732, 1.7320, 1.73205, ... Also $\sqrt{3}$ is the greatest lower bound of the sequence 1.8, 1.74, 1.733, 1.7321, 1.73206, ... Similarly, $2^{\sqrt{3}}$ can be defined as the least upper bound of the sequence of numbers $2^{1.7}$, $2^{1.73}$, $2^{1.732}$, $2^{1.7320}$, $2^{1.73205}$, ...

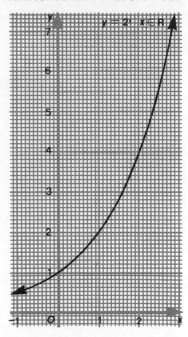

Exponential Functions

> An exponential function $y = a^x$, $a > 1$, has domain $\mathcal{R}$; for each $x_i \in \mathcal{R}$, the corresponding real number y_i in the range is the least upper bound of $S = \{y|y = a^t,\ t$ is a rational number, and $t < x_i\}$.

If $0 < a < 1$, *least upper bound* is replaced by *greatest lower bound* in the definition. If $a = 1$, then $y = a^x = 1$ for all $x \in \mathcal{R}$. An exponential function is not defined for $a < 0$, because a^x sometimes is nonreal.

Example

3. **Use the graph of $y = 2^x$ and the properties of exponents to evaluate each expression to the nearest tenth.**

    a. $y = 2^{2.4}$ **b.** $6.5 = 2^x$ **c.** $y = 2^{5.8}$ **d.** $24 = 2^x$

    a. $y = 2^{2.4}$
        From the graph; $y \approx 5.3$

    b. $6.5 = 2^x$
        From the graph; $x \approx 2.7$

    c. $y = 2^{5.8}$
       $= 2^5 \cdot 2^{0.8}$
       $\approx 32(1.7)$ $2^{0.8} = 1.7$
       ≈ 54

    d. $2^x = 24$
       $2^x = 8 \cdot 3$
       $2^x = 2^3 \cdot 2^{1.6}$ $2^{1.6} = 3$
       $2^x = 2^{4.6}$
       $x \approx 4.6$

The graph of $y = 2^x$ can be used for approximations in bases other than 2.

Example

4. **Estimate $y = 3^{2.3}$.**

    From the graph of $y = 2^x$, $3 \approx 2^{1.6}$.

$$3^{2.3} \approx (2^{1.6})^{2.3}$$
$$\approx 2^{3.68}$$
$$\approx 2^3 \cdot 2^{0.68}$$
$$\approx 8(1.6) \text{ or } 12.8$$

The figure shows graphs of $y = a^x$ for several values of the base a.

The following statements are true for any exponential function $y = a^x$. Remember, a must be greater than zero.

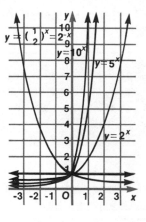

1. For $a \neq 1$, $a^{x_1} = a^{x_2}$ if and only if $x_1 = x_2$.
2. If $a \neq 1$, the function is 1–1.
3. For $a > 1$, $a^{x_2} > a^{x_1}$ if and only if $x_2 > x_1$.
4. If $a > 1$, the function is increasing.
5. For $a < 1$, $a^{x_2} < a^{x_1}$ if and only if $x_2 > x_1$.
6. If $a < 1$, the function is decreasing.
7. If $a = 1$, the function is 1 everywhere.
8. For every x, $a^x \neq 0$.
9. If $a > 1$ and $x > 0$, then $a^x > 1$. If $a > 1$ and $x < 0$, then $0 < a^x < 1$.
10. If $0 < a < 1$ and $x > 0$, then $0 < a^x < 1$. If $0 < a < 1$ and $x < 0$, then $a^x > 1$.
11. Since $a^0 = 1$, $(0, 1)$ is a point on every graph.
12. Since $a^1 = a$, $(1, a)$ is a point on every graph.
13. The graph of $y = \left(\frac{1}{a}\right)^x$ is symmetric to the graph of $y = a^x$ about the y-axis since $\left(\frac{1}{a}\right)^x = a^{-x}$.

Exercises

Exploratory Simplify each expression. Leave no negative or fractional exponents.

1. $10^{-1} \cdot 2^2$
2. $\sqrt{2} \cdot \sqrt[4]{2}$
3. $3^{-3} \cdot 81^{1/3}$
4. $25^{-2} \div 5^{-4}$

5. $(32^{1/2})^{-4/5}$ **6.** $3^{-2} + \left(\dfrac{1}{2}\right)^{-3}$

Use the graph of $y = 2^x$ to find x or y to the nearest tenth.

7. $y = 2^{1.8}$ **8.** $y = 2^{3.6}$ **9.** $y = 2^{-1.2}$

10. $y = 2^{4.7}$ **11.** $y = 2^{12.5}$ **12.** $y = 2^{\sqrt{2}}$

Written **Simplify each expression. Leave no negative or fractional exponents.**

1. $(2^{3/2} + 3^{2/3})(2^{3/2} - 3^{2/3})$ **2.** $(\pi^{\sqrt{2}})^{-3\sqrt{2}}$

3. $\left(\dfrac{-32a^{10}}{2b^{-5}}\right)^{-1/5}$ **4.** $\sqrt{\sqrt[3]{729a^{12}}}$

5. $\dfrac{3}{4} \cdot 8^{2/3} + \dfrac{3}{4} \cdot 8^{-2/3}$ **6.** $\dfrac{a^{-2} - b^{-2}}{a^{-1} + b^{-1}}$

Use the graph of $y = 2^x$ to find x or y to the nearest tenth.

7. $3.7 = 2^x$ **8.** $7.2 = 2^x$ **9.** $0.2 = 2^x$

10. $18 = 2^x$ **11.** $32.6 = 2^x$ **12.** $\sqrt{5} = 2^x$

Estimate the value for x or y from the graph of $y = 2^x$.

13. $y = 3^{1.6}$ **14.** $y = 4^{2.6}$ **15.** $y = 5^{0.8}$

16. $y = 12^{3.2}$ **17.** $10.4 = 3^x$

Challenge **Graph each of the following.**

1. $y = 2^{|x|}$ **2.** $y = 3^x$ and $y = \left(\dfrac{1}{3}\right)^x$ on the same axes

3. $y = 10^x$ and its inverse on the same axes.

11–2 The Number e

Using base ten for an exponential function is convenient when the system of numeration is a base ten place-value system. It is easy to name 10^x if $x \in Z$. If $x \notin Z$, then x may be written as $q + p$ when $q \in Z$ and $0 \le p < 1$. For example, $10^{3.68} = 10^{3 + 0.68} = 10^3 \cdot 10^{0.68} = 1000 \times 10^{0.68}$. Recall that common log tables work with 10^p where $0 \le p < 1$.

Using base two for an exponential function is sometimes convenient because the basic building block in many computers is the on-off switch (off = 0, on = 1). A place-value numeration system which uses only two characters is, of course, a base two numeration system.

A third important base used for an exponential function

comes from calculus. This number is named by the letter e. It is defined as the limit of this sequence.

$$\left(1 + \frac{1}{1}\right)^1, \left(1 + \frac{1}{2}\right)^2, \left(1 + \frac{1}{3}\right)^3, \ldots, \left(1 + \frac{1}{n}\right)^n \ldots.$$

Here are the first five terms of this sequence.

$$2, \frac{9}{4}, \frac{64}{27}, \frac{625}{256}, \frac{7776}{3125}$$

Expressed as decimal expansions to five places, the first five terms are 2.00000, 2.25000, 2.37037, 2.44141, 2.48832, ...

It appears that this sequence has an upper bound between 2 and 3. Its least upper bound is named e. The expression $\lim\limits_{n \to \infty}$ is read "the limit as n increases without bound."

$$e = \lim_{n \to \infty} \left(1 + \frac{1}{n}\right)^n$$

Definition of e

To find a decimal approximation for e it is helpful to expand $\left(1 + \frac{1}{n}\right)^n$. With some work the expansions of expressions like $(a + b)^2$ and $(a + b)^3$ can be found. The expansion of $(a + b)^n$ is given by the **Binomial Theorem**.

If n is a positive integer, then $n! = n(n - 1)(n - 2) \cdots 2 \cdot 1$. The expression $n!$ is read n *factorial*.

If $a, b \in \mathcal{R}$ and n is a natural number, then the following formula holds.

$$(a + b)^n = a^n + na^{n-1}b + \frac{n(n - 1)}{2!}a^{n-2}b^2$$

$$+ \frac{n(n - 1)(n - 2)}{3!}a^{n-3}b^3$$

$$+ \cdots + \frac{n(n - 1)(n - 2) \cdots (n - k + 1)}{k!} a^{n-k}b^k$$

$$+ \cdots + \frac{n(n - 1)(n - 2) \cdots 2}{(n - 1)!}ab^{n-1} + b^n$$

Binomial Theorem

Using the Binomial Theorem the expression $\left(1 + \frac{1}{n}\right)^n$ can be expanded.

$$\left(1 + \frac{1}{n}\right)^n = 1^n + n \cdot 1^{n-1} \cdot \left(\frac{1}{n}\right) + \frac{n(n-1)}{2!} \cdot 1^{n-2}\left(\frac{1}{n}\right)^2 + \frac{n(n-1)(n-2)}{3!}\left(\frac{1}{n}\right)^3 + \cdots + \left(\frac{1}{n}\right)^n$$

$$= 1 + n\left(\frac{1}{n}\right) + \frac{n(n-1)}{2!}\left(\frac{1}{n}\right)^2 + \frac{n(n-1)(n-2)}{3!}\left(\frac{1}{n}\right)^3 + \cdots + \left(\frac{1}{n}\right)^n$$

$$= 1 + 1 + \frac{n-1}{2!n} + \frac{(n-1)(n-2)}{3!n^2} + \cdots + \left(\frac{1}{n}\right)^n$$

$$= 1 + 1 + \frac{\left(1 - \frac{1}{n}\right)}{2!} + \frac{\left(1 - \frac{1}{n}\right)\left(1 - \frac{2}{n}\right)}{3!} + \cdots + \left(\frac{1}{n}\right)^n$$

$$e = \lim_{n \to \infty}\left(1 + \frac{1}{n}\right)^n = 1 + 1 + \frac{1}{2!} + \frac{1}{3!} + \cdots$$

As n gets large, the fractions with n in the denominator get small. In fact, it can be proved that as n gets large $\left(1 + \frac{1}{n}\right)^n$ approaches $1 + 1 + \frac{1}{2!} + \frac{1}{3!} + \cdots$. Therefore, $e = 1 + 1 + \frac{1}{2!} + \frac{1}{3!} + \cdots$.

The following computation for e is correct to six significant digits.

$$e = 1 + 1 + \frac{1}{2!} + \frac{1}{3!} + \frac{1}{4!} + \frac{1}{5!} + \frac{1}{6!} + \frac{1}{7!} + \frac{1}{8!} + \frac{1}{9!} + \cdots$$

$$= 1 + 1 + \frac{1}{2} + \frac{1}{6} + \frac{1}{24} + \frac{1}{120} + \frac{1}{720} + \frac{1}{5040} + \frac{1}{40320} + \frac{1}{362880} + \cdots$$

$$= 1 + 1 + 0.5 + 0.166667 + 0.041667 + 0.008333 + 0.001389 + 0.000198 + 0.000025 + 0.000003 + \cdots$$

$e \approx 2.718282$

Continuing terms $\frac{1}{10!}, \frac{1}{11!}, \frac{1}{12!}, \ldots$ of the expression for e will not affect the first six decimal places. The value of e correct to twelve decimal places is 2.718281828590. The number e is irrational and transcendental.

The Binomial Theorem can also be used if n is any real number. Since $e^x = \lim_{n \to \infty}\left[\left(1 + \frac{1}{n}\right)^n\right]^x = \lim_{n \to \infty}\left(1 + \frac{1}{n}\right)^{nx}$.

$$e^x = 1 + x + \frac{x^2}{2!} + \frac{x^3}{3!} + \cdots$$

Example

1. A table of values for $y = e^x$ and $y = e^{-x}$ is given on page 547. Use this table or a calculator to evaluate each expression to three decimal places.

   a. $y = e^{2.3}$ b. $y = e^{4.8}$ c. $y = e^{-0.8}$

   a. $y = e^{2.3}$
   From the table, $y = 9.974$.

   b. $y = e^{4.8}$
   From the table, $y = 121.510$.

   c. $y = e^{-0.8}$
   From the table, $y = 0.449$.

   Many calculators have e^x function keys on them making calculations with powers of e very easy. If no such key is available, the y^x key may be used with 2.71828 as y.

Exercises

Exploratory Use the table of values for $y = e^x$ and $y = e^{-x}$ to find each approximation.

1. $y = e^{1.2}$

2. $y = e^{-0.5}$

3. $y = e^{5.4}$

4. $y = 1.6^{2.2}$

5. $10.6 = e^x$

6. $8 = 3^x$

7. $y = 3\sqrt{e}$

8. $y = 5\sqrt[3]{e^2}$

Written Expand each of the following by using the binomial theorem.

1. $(a + b)^4$

2. $(2x + y)^4$

3. $(a - b)^5$

4. $\left(2xy - \dfrac{1}{2}\right)^5$

5. Compute, correct to six decimal places, the values of $\dfrac{1}{10!}$ and $\dfrac{1}{11!}$ to verify that they do not affect the first six decimal places of the given value of e.

6. What approximate value for e is obtained by using $n = 10$ in $e = \left(1 + \dfrac{1}{n}\right)^n$? Compute the answer correct to four significant digits.

Use $e^x = 1 + x + \dfrac{x^2}{2!} + \dfrac{x^3}{3!} + \cdots$ to find the value for e^x to three decimal places for each of the following. Use the table to check the estimates.

7. e^2

8. e^3

9. e^7

10. e^8

11. Start with any value of e^x, such as $e^1 = 2.7$ and find $e^{x+0.7}$. Test a few values and make a conjecture on these observations.

12. Estimate $e^{3.5}$ and e^4 by using the conjecture from Problem **11**.

Challenge Solve each of the following.

1. Graph the function $f(n) = \left(1 + \dfrac{1}{n}\right)^n$ for $n > 0$. What is the least upper bound of f?

2. Graph the function $y = e^x$. Find the slope of the tangent to the curve at various points. Make a conjecture about the slope of the tangent line in terms of each corresponding y-value.

Excursions in Mathematics

Euler's Formula

Many remarkable properties of e are the result of raising e to the imaginary exponent $i\theta$. The expression $e^{i\theta}$ can be interpreted as a unit vector with inclination θ with respect to the real axis.

The vector $e^{i\theta}$ ends at the point $(\cos\theta, i\sin\theta)$ which leads to an expression known as Euler's Formula.

$$e^{i\theta} = \cos\theta + i\sin\theta$$

Euler's Formula

Such an expression is true for any value of θ including n times θ.

$$e^{in\theta} = \cos n\theta + i\sin n\theta \qquad \textit{This is DeMoivre's Theorem.}$$

But $e^{in\theta} = (e^{i\theta})^n = (\cos\theta + i\sin\theta)^n$ so $(\cos\theta + i\sin\theta)^n = \cos n\theta + i\sin n\theta$.
By using Euler's Formula and letting $\theta = \pi$,

$$e^{i\pi} = \cos\pi + i\sin\pi = -1$$

The form $e^{i\pi} + 1 = 0$ is sometimes called the most powerful statement in mathematics. It links the 5 most important constants $e, i, \pi,$ 1 and 0.

Exercises

1. Expand Euler's Formula by letting $\theta = A + B$.

$$e^{i\theta} = \cos\theta + i\sin\theta$$

Then consider $e^{i(A+B)} = e^{iA}e^{iB} = (\cos A + i\sin A)(\cos B + i\sin B)$. Find the product. Equate the real and imaginary parts obtained from the two expressions. Compare the results to the expressions in Chapter 5 for $\cos(A + B)$ and $\sin(A + B)$.

2. Use $x = i\theta$ in the series for e^x. Equate the real and imaginary parts to those in Euler's Formula. Use this to derive the series.

$$\cos\theta = 1 - \frac{\theta^2}{2!} + \frac{\theta^4}{4!} - \frac{\theta^6}{6!} + \cdots \quad \text{and} \quad \sin\theta = \theta - \frac{\theta^3}{3!} + \frac{\theta^5}{5!} - \cdots$$

3. Use $e^{i\theta}$ to show that $i^i = e^{-\pi/2}$.

11–3 The Logarithmic Function

The function $f:y = a^x$ is *increasing* for $a > 1$ and *decreasing* for $0 < a < 1$. Therefore, it is $1 - 1$ and has an inverse which also is $1 - 1$. If f is written $y = a^x$, then f^{-1} can be written $x - a^y$. For convenience, f^{-1} also is written $y = \log_a x$, and is read *the log of x to the base a* or simply *log base a of x*. It is called a **logarithmic function.** *Note:* $y = \log_a x$ *is the reflection of* $y = a^x$ *in the line* $y = x$.

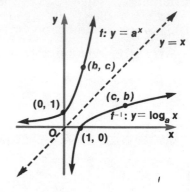

Logarithmic Function

The logarithmic function $y = \log_a x,\ x > 0$ and $a \neq 1$, is the inverse of the function $y = a^x$.

Thus $y = \log_a x$ if and only if $x = a^y$. Notice that *a logarithm is an exponent.*

Examples

1. **Evaluate $\log_3 9 = y$.**

$$\log_3 9 = y \text{ Thus, } 3^y = 9.$$
$$y = 2$$

2. **Evaluate $\log_{10} x = -\dfrac{1}{4}$.**

$$\log_{10} x = -\frac{1}{4} \text{ Thus, } 10^{-1/4} = x.$$

$$\frac{1}{\sqrt[4]{10}} = x$$

Since the exponential and logarithmic functions are inverses of each other, $(f \circ f^{-1})\ (x) = x$ for every $x \in D(f^{-1})$ and $(f^{-1} \circ f)(x) = x$ for every $x \in D(f)$.

$$(f^{-1} \circ f)(x) = \log_a a^x = x$$
$$(f \circ f^{-1})(x) = a^{\log_a x} = x$$

Since a logarithm is an exponent, properties of logarithms are based on properties of exponents.

For $a, b > 0, a, b \neq 1$ and $x, y \in \mathcal{R}$ the following properties apply.

L_1: $\log_a xy = \log_a x + \log_a y$

L_2: $\log_a \dfrac{x}{y} = \log_a x - \log_a y$

L_3: $\log_a x^y = y \log_a x$

L_4: Reciprocal Law: $\log_a x = \dfrac{1}{\log_x a}$

L_5: Change of Base Law: $\log_a x = \dfrac{\log_b x}{\log_b a}$ or
$$\log_a x \cdot \log_b a = \log_b x$$

L_6: $\dfrac{\log_a x}{\log_a y} = \dfrac{\log_b x}{\log_b y}$

L_7: $\log_a \dfrac{1}{x} = -\log_a x$

L_8: $\log_{1/a} x = -\log_a x$

L_9: $\log_a 1 = 0$

L_{10}: If $f{:}y = \log_a x$, then $D(f) = \{x \mid x \in \mathcal{R}, x > 0$ and $R(f) = \mathcal{R}.\}$

L_{11}: If $a > 1$ and $x_2 > x_1$, then $\log_a x_2 > \log_a x_1$.
If $0 < a < 1$ and $x_2 > x_1$, then $\log_a x_2 < \log_a x_1$.

L_{12}: If $x_2 = x_1$, then $\log_a x_2 = \log_a x_1$ and conversely.

Properties of Logarithm

Examples

3. **Prove L_1: $\log_a xy = \log_a x + \log_a y$.**

Let $x = a^m$ and $y = a^n$. Thus $\log_a x = m$ and $\log_a y = n$. *But, $m = \log_a x$ and $n = \log_a y$.*

$$x \cdot y = a^m \cdot a^n = a^{m+n}$$
$$= \log_a(x \cdot y) = \log_a a^{x+y} = x + y$$
$$\log_a xy = \log_a x + \log_a y$$

4. **Prove L_5: $\log_a x = \dfrac{\log_b x}{\log_b a}$.**

Let $\log_a x = p$ or $a^p = x$.

$$\log_b a^p = \log_b x$$
$$p \log_b a = \log_b x$$
$$\log_a x \cdot \log_b a = \log_b x$$
$$\log_a x = \dfrac{\log_b x}{\log_b a}$$

The properties of logarithms are used to compute values of logarithms.

5. **Evaluate $\log_5 2$ by changing to base 10.**

$$\log_5 2 = \frac{\log_{10} 2}{\log_{10} 5} \approx \frac{0.3010}{0.6990} \approx 0.4306$$

A log table or a calculator with a log key can be used.

6. **Evaluate $\log_e 0.7$ by changing to base 10.**

$$\log_e 0.7 = \frac{\log_{10} 0.7}{\log_{10} e} = -\frac{0.1549}{0.4343} = -0.3567$$

Base ten logarithms are called **common logarithms**. They are frequently used for calculations. In calculus and areas of science and economics where growth problems occur often, base e logarithms are more useful. They are called **natural logarithms**. It is customary to write ln x instead of $\log_e x$.

Tables of values for natural logarithms are printed on pages 548 and 549.

The use of the natural logarithm table is different from the use of the common logarithm table. *Natural logarithms do not have a characteristic or mantissa.* In the table, ln N is given for values of N between 1.00 and 9.99, inclusive. The whole number value is given in the column under 0. It is not repeated in columns 1–9. If the whole number value increases by 1 in any of columns 1–9, the value in that column is preceded by an asterisk (*).

7. **Find ln 12.6.**

$$\begin{aligned}
\text{ln } 12.6 &= \text{ln}(1.26 \cdot 10) \\
&= \text{ln } 1.26 + \text{ln } 10 \\
&\approx 0.2311 + 2.3026 \text{ or } 2.5337
\end{aligned}$$

8. **Find ln 0.0623.**

$$\begin{aligned}
\text{ln } 0.0623 &= \text{ln}(6.23 \cdot 10^{-2}) \\
&= \text{ln } 6.23 + \text{ln } 10^{-2} \\
&= \text{ln } 6.23 - 2 \text{ ln } 10 \\
&\approx 1.8294 - 4.6052 \text{ or } -2.7758
\end{aligned}$$

Sometimes ln x is known to have a value b but x itself is not known. Then x is called the **antilogarithm** of b.

Example

9. Find x if ln $x = 3.9824$.

$\ln x = 3.9824$ rewrite as antiln 3.9824

$\text{antiln } 3.9824 = \text{antiln } (2.3026 + 1.6798)$ *Note:* $\ln 10 = 2.3026$
$= 10 \cdot 5.364$ $\ln 5.364 = 1.6798$
$= 53.64$

Exercises

Exploratory   Write each expression in logarithmic notation.

1. $a^b = c$
2. $3^{1/2} = \sqrt{3}$
3. $5^{-3} = \dfrac{1}{125}$
4. $4^0 = 1$
5. $3^{\sqrt{2}} = t$
6. $(\sqrt{2})^3 = 2^{3/2}$
7. $0.01^3 = 0.000001$
8. $10^{-6} = \dfrac{1}{1,000,000}$

Use the Table of Natural Logarithms to find each of the following.

9. ln 7.88
10. ln 2.76
11. ln 5.35
12. ln 34.6
13. ln 0.0672
14. antiln 1.5790
15. antiln 2.1017
16. antiln 0.6686
17. antiln 5.1169

Written   Find the value of the variable in each expression.

1. $\log_2 x = -3$
2. $\log_x 5 = 1$
3. $\log_3 1 = y$
4. $\log_5 5\sqrt{5} = t$
5. $\log_2 \sqrt[5]{4} = r$
6. $\log_y \dfrac{1}{8} = -\dfrac{3}{2}$
7. $\log_{32} t = 0.6$
8. $\log_x 256 = 0.375$
9. $0 = \log_6 t$
10. $r = \log_{27} \dfrac{1}{9}$
11. $0 = \log_b 1$
12. $a = \log_2 \dfrac{1}{2}\sqrt[3]{4}$

Find the value of x in each statement.

13. $a^{\log_a t} = t$
14. $x^{\log_2 7} = 7$
15. $5^{\log_5 x} = 8$
16. $x = 4 \log_2 8$
17. $x = \log_3 3^4$
18. $0 = \dfrac{2}{3} \log_5 2^x$
19. $x = 5^{1 + \log_5 3}$
20. $x = 7^{\log \sqrt{7}3}$
21. $x = e^{\ln 2 + \ln t}$
22. $x = e^{t + \ln t}$

Change each expression to one in terms of the given base.

23. ln 10, base 10

24. $\log_{10} 5$, base e

25. ln 3.8, base 5

26. $\log_a t$, base 10

27. $\log_a t$, base e

28. $\log_{10} e$, base e

29. Sketch carefully $y = \log_{10} x$ and $y = \ln x$ on the same set of axes.

Find f^{-1} for each of the following.

30. $f(x) = \sqrt{1 + e^x}$

31. $f(x) = x^e$

32. $f(x) = e^x + e^{-x}$

Prove each of the following.

33. L_9: $\log_a 1 = 0$

34. L_2: $\log_a \dfrac{x}{y} = \log_a x - \log_a y$

35. L_4: $\log_a x = \dfrac{1}{\log_x a}$

36. L_7: $\log_a \dfrac{1}{x} = -\log_a x$

Consider logarithms of both sides of the exponential expressions to evaluate the following.

37. $5^x = 17$

38. $3.2^x = 10$

39. $e^x = 42$

40. $y^{4.8} = 20$

41. $y^{-3.25} = 12$

42. $(3e)^{12} = t$
(Hint: What base should you use?)

Challenge Sketch each of the following.

1. $y = \ln |x|$

2. $y = |\ln x|$

3. $y = x \ln x$

4. Prove L_{11}: If $a > 1$ and $x_2 > x_1$, then $\log_a x_2 > \log_a x_1$. If $0 < a < 1$ and $x_2 > x_1$, then $\log_a x_2 < \log_a x_1$.

11–4 Exponential and Logarithmic Equations

Solutions to equations involving exponential expressions are based on the fact that if $b^{x_1} = b^{x_2}$ for some base b and $x_1, x_2 \in \mathcal{R}$, then $x_1 = x_2$.

Examples

1. Solve if $2^{3x-1} = 2^{2x}$.

   If $2^{3x-1} = 2^{2x}$ then $3x - 1 = 2x$.

   $$3x - 1 = 2x$$
   $$-1 = -x$$
   $$1 = x$$

   Since the bases are equal, the exponents must be equal.

2. **Solve if $5^x = 3.2^{2x-5}$**

$$5^x = 3.2^{2x-5}$$
$$(e^{1.61})^x = (e^{1.16})^{2x-5}$$
$$e^{1.61x} = e^{2.32x-5.8}$$
$$1.61x = 2.32x - 5.8$$
$$-0.71x = -5.8$$
$$x = 8.17$$

Use e as the common base.

Interpolation is needed to help find a good approximation.

A more accurate value computed by calculator is $x = 8.1128$.

If the unknown x appears in only one exponent of an equality, logarithms are useful in solving for x.

Examples

3. **Solve if $5^{2x+1} = 96$.**

$$5^{2x+1} = 96$$
$$\log_{10}5^{2x+1} = \log_{10}96$$
$$(2x+1)\log_{10}5 = \log_{10}96$$
$$2x+1 = \frac{\log_{10}96}{\log_{10}5}$$
$$2x+1 = \frac{1.9823}{0.6990}$$
$$2x+1 = 2.836$$
$$x = 0.918$$

In this problem it is necessary to divide one logarithm by another.

(Caution: Do not subtract these logarithms.)

4. **Solve if $e^x = 10$.**

$$e^x = 10$$
$$\ln e^x = \ln 10$$
$$x \ln e = \ln 10$$
$$x \cdot 1 = 2.3026$$
$$x = 2.30$$

If $y = \ln e$, then $e^y = e$ and $y = 1$.

Solutions to equations involving logarithms also are solved by using the fact that logarithmic functions are $1-1$. If an equation has sums or differences of logarithms, remember that such sums or differences can be changed to logarithms of products or quotients.

Example

5. Solve $\log_{1/2}5 = \log_2 t^2 - \log_2 5t$ for $t \neq 0$.

$$\log_{1/2}5 = \log_2 t^2 - \log_2 5t$$
$$-\log_2 5 = \log_2 t^2 - \log_2 5t$$
$$0 = \log_2 t^2 - \log_2 5t + \log_2 5$$
$$0 = \log_2\left(\frac{5t^2}{5t}\right), \ t \neq 0$$
$$0 = \log_2 t$$
$$2^0 = t$$
$$t = 1$$

Check: $\log_{1/2}5 = -\log_2 5$
$\log_2 t^2 - \log_2 5 \cdot 1 = 0 - \log_2 5$
$= -\log_2 5$

Check each solution, at least by estimates. Sometimes checking is merely reworking the problem using specific values. If accuracy is not needed, an estimate is sufficient. In some equations, apparent or extraneous solutions appear. These must be discarded.

Example

6. Solve $\log_{10}(2x - 4) - \log_{10}(x + 2) = 1$ for x.

$$\log_{10}(2x - 4) - \log_{10}(x + 2) = 1$$

$$\log_{10}\frac{2x - 4}{x + 2} = \log_{10}10$$
$$\frac{2x - 4}{x + 2} = 10$$
$$2x - 4 = 10x + 20$$
$$x = -3$$

The domain of $y = \log_{10}(2x - 4)$ does not contain -3. This is because $\log_{10}[2(-3)-4] = \log_{10}(-10)$. The logarithm of a negative number is not defined. The solution set is empty.

Exercises

Exploratory Solve each equation.

1. $3^x \cdot 27 = 243$

2. $3^{x+4} = \dfrac{1}{81}$

3. $2^{x-3} = \dfrac{1}{20}$

4. $16 \cdot 4^{-x^2} = 1$

5. $3^{t^2} = 1.4$

6. $5^{r+2} \cdot 5^{2r} = 100$

7. $3^{\log_2 64} = 5a + 20$

8. $\log_{10}x^2 - \log_{10}\dfrac{x}{5} = 3$

Written Solve each of the following.

1. $2^x < 5$
2. $e^{-3x^2} - 2 = 0$
3. $e^{7x^2} - 12.4 = 0$

4. $\ln 3x = 2.0477$
5. $\log_5 x = 2.8222$
6. $e^{-0.5x^2} - 4 = 0$

7. $e^{0.5x^2} - 4 = 0$
8. $(\log_{10} x)^2 - 2(\log_{10} x) = 3$

(Hint: Treat as a polynomial in $\log_{10} x$.)

9. $\log_{10}(x^2 - 4x + 4) - \log_{10}(x - 2) + \log_{10}(x - 3) = \log_{10} 6$

10. $\log_5(x^2 + 5x + 6) - \log_5(x + 3) + \log_5(x - 1) = \log_5 4$

11. $\log_5(x - 2) = 3$
12. $\dfrac{1.05^n - 1}{0.07} = 1000$

13. $x = \log_{121} 8$
14. $x = \log_{42} 19$

15. $\sqrt{3^{b-2}} = 2^b$
16. $3^{v-2} = 2^{2v}$

17. $5^{20x} = 10,000$
18. $\log_{10} 15x = 3$

19. $\log_3(x^2 - 9) - \log_3(x + 3) = 1$
20. $\ln(2 - x^2) = -3$

Solve each of the following for x.

21. $y = ce^{-hx}$
22. $y = \ln(x - 1)^2$
23. $y = \log_x 6$

Find the values of x for which y is defined given the following.

24. $y = \log_{10}(2x - 1) - \log_{10}(6x + 2)$
25. $y = \ln(x^2 - 4) - \ln(x + 5)$

26. Solve $\log_{10}(x + 97) - \log_{10}(x - 2) = 2$ for x.

Challenge If x is any positive real number, tell which of the following functions are equivalent to the function $y = x$. Defend each answer.

1. $y = e^{\ln x}$
2. $y = x^{\ln e}$
3. $y = 10^{\log_{10} x}$

4. $y = x \cdot 10^{\ln 1}$
5. $y = \log_{10} 10^x$

6. Since $\ln x^2 = 2 \ln x$, if $f : x \to \ln x^2$ and $g : x \to 2 \ln x$, then $f = g$. Comment on this conclusion.

7. Given the definitions and properties of logarithms but *not* those of exponents, prove that $\dfrac{a^s}{a^t} = a^{s-t}$.

11–5 Growth and Decay Functions

For steadily increasing or decreasing phenomena of many kinds, the exponential function is well suited as a mathematical model. For example, under ideal conditions some bacteria can double in number during a specified time period.

Example

1. A sample count of bacteria in a culture indicates that it is doubling in size each 20 minutes. If the estimated count was 24,000 at time 60, what is the initial size of the culture at time 0? What is the estimated count at time 300?

   At $t = 0$ let the initial count be y_0.

   $$y = y_0 \cdot 2^{t/20}$$ *y is the amount at any time t.*

   To compute y_0, substitute the given values.

   $$24{,}000 = y_0 \cdot 2^{60/20}$$ *y = 24,000, t = 60*
   $$24{,}000 = 8y_0$$
   $$3000 = y_0$$

   Therefore, $y = 3000 \cdot 2^{t/20}$ is the desired function.
   At time $t = 300$,

   $$y = 3000 \cdot 2^{300/20}$$
   $$= 3000 \cdot 2^{15}$$
   $$= 3000 \cdot 32768$$
   $$= 98{,}304{,}000$$

   This problem was idealized since such factors as environmental conditions were not considered.

In general, a growth problem may be expressed by the function $y = y_0 2^{t/k}$ where k is the growth rate factor of time doubling.

$$y = y_0 2^{t/k}$$ **Growth Formula**

Radioactive material decays at exponential rates. Half-life is the amount of time during which a given amount of material decays until one half of it is left. The shape of the curve is the same as that of $y = y_0 \left(\dfrac{1}{2}\right)^{kt}$ or $y = y_0 \cdot 2^{-kt}$. At $t = 0$, $y = y_0$, the initial amount; k is determined by the particular substance in question. If T is the half-life of a substance then at time T, $y = \dfrac{y_0}{2}$.

$$\frac{y_0}{2} = y_0 \cdot \left(\frac{1}{2}\right)^{kT}$$

So $kT = 1$ and $k = \dfrac{1}{T}$. This form is the so-called **half-life formula**.

$$y = y_0 \cdot \left(\frac{1}{2}\right)^{t/T} \text{ or } y = y_0 \cdot 2^{-t/T}$$

Half-life Formula

Example

2. A given radioactive substance has a half-life of 2.5 years. Find how much remains of a 5-pound sample after 17.5 years.

$$y = 5 \cdot \left(\frac{1}{2}\right)^{17.5/2.5}$$

$$\approx 5 \cdot \left(\frac{1}{2}\right)^{7}$$

$$\approx \frac{5}{128} = 0.039 \text{ lb}$$

Many people are aware of one common application of the exponential function. This is the investment of money at compound interest. To compound interest means to leave both the principal and the interest to earn interest during following investment periods.

The use of the computer has brought changes in banking. Lending institutions now compound interest monthly, weekly, daily, and even "continuously." To compute interest compounded continuously use the **Compound Interest Law.**

$$A = Pe^{it}$$

Compound Interest Law

A is the amount realized after successive periods of compounding at annual interest rate i for a principal P invested for t years.

Example

3. A person invests $100 at 12% for five years compounded continuously. Find the amount realized.

$$A = Pe^{it}$$
$$= 100 \cdot e^{(12/100) \cdot 5}$$
$$= 182.21$$

The value $e^{0.6}$ may be read from the table of e^x values or from a calculator.

Exercises

Written   Solve each of the following.

1. A bacteria culture doubles every $\frac{1}{4}$ hour. At time $1\frac{1}{4}$ hours an estimate of 64,000 bacteria is taken. What was the initial count? What is it after $2\frac{1}{2}$ hours?

2. A bacteria culture has an initial count estimate of 4000. After 20 minutes the count is 22,400. Approximately how many minutes did it take for the culture to double?

3. A radioactive substance has a half-life of 420 years. How much remains of a 2-ounce sample after 200 years?

4. An isotope of sodium has a half-life of 15 hours. How many hours will it take for 40% of a given amount to remain?

5. Altaville had a population of 20,000 in 1980. The town grows by the function $y = y_0 e^{kt}$ where $k = 0.023$.
    a.   What will be the population of Altaville by the year 1990?
    b.   By what year will its population be double that of 1980?

6. Stratustown had a population of 12,000 in 1945 and 32,000 in 1980. With an increase proportional to its population ($y = y_0 e^{kt}$ holds), what will be the population of the town in the year 2000?

7. What amount is reached by investing $425 for 6 years at 10% interest compounded continuously?

8. How much money must be invested at 9% interest compounded continuously to yield $650 after 2 years?

9. How long must an amount of money be invested at 9% interest compounded continuously before it is doubled?

10. At what rate of interest compounded continuously will an amount of money double in 20 years?

11. A friend invests a sum of money at $8\frac{1}{2}$% interest compounded continuously. How much must she invest now to have a total of $10,000 in ten years?

12. The amperage, I, in an alternating current circuit obeys the law $I = I_0 e^{-kt}$ for t seconds after the voltage is shut off. In a given circuit, $k = 300$. Find the current remaining 0.005 seconds after opening the switch when the circuit initially carries 8.5 amps.

Excursions in Mathematics

Hyperbolic Functions

Certain combinations of the functions $y = e^x$ and $y = e^{-x}$ occur in applied and theoretical work very often. For this reason they have been given special names. These functions are called the hyperbolic sine, $\sinh x = \dfrac{e^x - e^{-x}}{2}$, and hyperbolic cosine, $\cosh x = \dfrac{e^x + e^{-x}}{2}$ functions. The hyperbolic functions are related to the coordinates of the hyperbola in much the same way that circular functions are related to the coordinates of a circle.

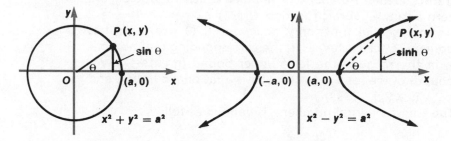

Definitions for tanh x and the reciprocal functions coth x, sech y and csch x are exact counterparts to those of the circular functions.

The graphs of the hyperbolic functions are easy to derive from those of e^x and e^{-x}. For instance, let us determine the graph of $y = \cosh x$. Use addition of ordinates, noting that cosh x is an even function since $\cosh (-x) = \cosh x$, and cosh x is the average of e^x and e^{-x}.

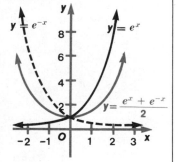

The curve looks remarkably like a parabola. Actually it is that of a catenary, the curve which a flexible cord suspended at two points assumes of its own weight. For example, a telephone or power wire hangs in a catenary. So does the cable of a suspension bridge prior to the roadway being hung from it. This is shown in Figure **a**. A catenary uniformly weighted is stretched into a parabola. Figure **b** shows the parabola formed after the roadway is built.

a.

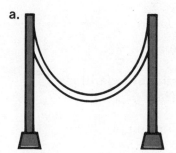

b.

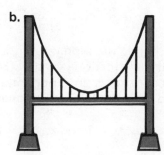

The Memorial Arch in St. Louis is in the shape of a catenary. The force of the arch's weight acts along the leg of the arch directly into the ground. This ensures the maximum stability of the arch.

Chapter Summary

1. A transcendental function is a function which cannot be expressed by a finite number of algebraic operations. A transcendental number is a number which cannot be the zero of any algebraic function. (331)

2. An exponential function $y = a^x$, $a > 1$ $(0 < a < 1)$, has domain $\mathcal{R}$, for each $x_i \in \mathcal{R}$, the corresponding real number y_i in the range is the least upper bound (greatest lower bound) of the set $S = \{y | y = a^t, t$ is a rational number, and $t \le x_i (t \ge x_i)\}$. (333)

3. The transcendental number e is defined as follows

$$e = \lim_{n \to \infty} \left(1 + \frac{1}{n}\right)^n \quad (336)$$

4. The Binomial Theorem is the expansion of $(a + b)^n$ if $a, b \in \mathcal{R}$ and n is a natural number. (337)

$$(a + b)^n = a^n + na^{n-1}b + \frac{n(n-1)}{2!} a^{n-2}b^2$$

$$+ \frac{n(n-1)(n-2)}{3!} a^{n-3}b^3$$

$$+ \cdots + \frac{n(n-1)(n-2) \cdots 2}{(n-1)!} ab^{n-1} + b^n$$

5. The number e and the exponential function $y = e^x$ can be written as series. (337)

$$e = 1 + 1 + \frac{1}{2!} + \frac{1}{3!} + \frac{1}{4!} + \cdots$$

$$e^x = 1 + x + \frac{x^2}{2!} + \frac{x^3}{3!} + \frac{x^4}{4!} + \cdots$$

6. The logarithmic function $y = \log_a x$, $a > 0$ and $a \ne 1$, is the inverse of the function $y = a^x$. (340)

7. Since a logarithm is an exponent, properties of logarithms are based on properties of exponents. (340)

For $a, b > 0$, $a, b \ne 1$ and $x, y \in \mathcal{R}$ the following properties apply.

L_1: $\log_a xy = \log_a x + \log_a y$

L_2: $\log_a \frac{x}{y} = \log_a x - \log_a y$

L_3: $\log_a x^y = y \log_a x$

L_4: Reciprocal Law: $\log_a x = \dfrac{1}{\log_x a}$

L_5: Change of Base Law: $\log_a x = \dfrac{\log_b x}{\log_b a}$ or

$$\log_a x \cdot \log_b a = \log_b x$$

L_6: $\dfrac{\log_a x}{\log_a y} = \dfrac{\log_b x}{\log_b y}$

L_7: $\log_a \dfrac{1}{x} = -\log_a x$

L_8: $\log_{1/a} x = -\log_a x$

L_9: $\log_a 1 = 0$

L_{10}: If $f : y = \log_a x$, then $D(f) = \{x \mid x \in \mathcal{R}, x > 0\}$ and $R(f) = \mathcal{R}$.

L_{11}: If $a > 1$ and $x_2 > x_1$, then $\log_a x_2 > \log_a x_1$.
If $0 < a < 1$ and $x_2 > x_1$, then $\log_a x_2 < \log_a x_1$.

L_{12}: If $x_2 = x_1$ then $\log_a x_2 = \log_a x_1$ and conversely.

8. The growth formula is $y = y_0\, 2^{t/k}$. (348)

9. The half-life formula is $y = y_0\left(\dfrac{1}{2}\right)^{t/T}$ or $y = y_0 \cdot 2^{-t/T}$. (349)

10. The compound interest law is $A = Pe^{it}$. (349)

Chapter Review

11-1 **Simplify each expression leaving no negative or fractional exponents.**

1. $\left(\sqrt[3]{216}\right)^2$
2. $(2a)^{1/3}(a^2 b)^{1/3}$
3. $\dfrac{a^{-3} + b^{-3}}{a^{-2} - b^{-2}}$
4. $(5\,ac)^{1/3}(a^2 c^3)^{1/3}$
5. $\left(\sqrt[3]{125} \cdot \sqrt[4]{16}\right)^2$
6. $\left(\sqrt{\sqrt{81}x^4}\right)(ya)^{-1/2}$

Use the graph of $y = 2^x$ to find x or y to one decimal place.

7. $y = 2^{1.5}$
8. $y = 2^{5.2}$
9. $6.2 = 2^x$

10. Graph $y = \left(\dfrac{3}{2}\right)^x$ and $y = \left(\dfrac{2}{3}\right)^x$ on the same axes.

11-2 **Use the table of $y = e^x$ to find approximations for each of the following.**

11. $y = e^{2.7}$
12. $y = e^{-0.1}$
13. $y = 5^{1.8}$
14. $8.8 = e^x$
15. $7 = 3^x$
16. $y = 2\sqrt[5]{e^3}$

Use the series $e^x = 1 + x + \dfrac{x^2}{2!} + \dfrac{x^3}{3!} + \dfrac{x^4}{4!} + \cdots$ to compute each of the following correct to two decimal places.

17. $e^{1.1}$
18. $e^{2.01}$
19. $e^{0.001}$
20. $e^{-1.01}$

11-3 **Find the value of each variable.**

21. $\log_2 x = -5$ **22.** $\log_y \dfrac{1}{27} = 3$ **23.** $\log_5 0.04 = t$

Find the value of x.

24. $x^{\log_3 8} = 8$ **25.** $x = \log_2 2^{-2}$

26. $x = e^{(\ln 2 - \ln t)}$ **27.** $x = 4^{\log_2 3}$

Change each expression to an expression in terms of the given base.

28. $\log_4 7$, base 10   **29.** $\log_{10} e$, base e

30. $\ln 100$, base 10   **31.** $\ln 2$, base 2

32. If $f{:}y = x^{2e}$, find f^{-1}.

Use the Table of Natural Logarithms or a calculator to find each of the following.

33. $\ln 4.72$ **34.** $\ln 47.2$ **35.** $\ln 7.826$

36. antiln 1.8856   **37.** antiln 1.0890   **38.** antiln 9.018

11-4 **Solve each equation.**

39. $4^{3y} = 5^{y+2}$ **40.** $\log_{12} 8 + \log_{12} 18 = x$

41. $\ln(x - 4) = 5$

Solve $5^{2x} = 2.04$ by the following methods and compare the solutions.

42. base ten logarithms   **43.** base five logarithms using the change of base rule

44. 2^x graph   **45.** e^x table or a calculator

46. Solve $\ln (x^2 - 1) = y$ for x.

11-5 **Solve each of the following.**

47. The population of single-celled organisms in a pond doubles every 5 days. If the initial count of organisms is 5000 and the final count is 25,000 how many days have passed?

48. A certain radioactive substance has a half-life of 5.5 years. If 0.0469 kilograms are remaining from an initial sample of 6 kilograms, how many years have passed?

49. Mr. Hammond invests a sum of money at 18% interest compounded continuously. If he makes his investment on January 1, 1985, and has $10,000 in his account by January 1, 2000, what was his original investment?

50. How much money must be invested at $11\frac{1}{2}$% interest compounded continuously to yield $3,000 after 2 years?

51. At what rate of interest compounded continuously will $200 triple in 25 years?

52. In 7 days a sample of a radioactive substance decreases from 200 grams to 40 grams. Find the half-life of this substance.

Chapter Test

Simplify each expression leaving no negative or fractional exponents.

1. $\dfrac{a^{-1} + b^{-1}}{a^{-3} + b^{-3}}$

2. $(16)^{3/2}\sqrt[3]{27(a^2)^3}$

Estimate each of the following from the graph of $y = 2^x$.

3. $y = 2^{0.8}$

4. $y = (2^{1.4})^2$

Find approximations for each of the following.

5. $e^{2.9} = y$

6. $y = e^{12.5}$

Find the value of each variable.

7. $\log_3 x = -5$

8. $\log_x \dfrac{1}{64} = 3$

9. $x = 7^{\log_3 4}$

10. $x = e^{\ln 2}$

Change each expression to an expression in terms of the given base.

11. $\log_3 4.5$, base 5

12. $\ln 15$, base 10

Solve each equation.

13. $\log_2 4 + \log_2 6 = \log_2 x$

14. $\log_9 5x = \log_9 6 + \log_9(x - 2)$

Solve each of the following.

15. An isotope of nitrogen loses 40% of its mass in 7 minutes. Find its half-life.

16. What rate of interest compounded continuously would be required to yield $50 interest after one year on a $1000 investment?

Computers

Transportation

Since the beginning of air travel, airlines have had increased problems with reservations, traffic control and scheduling. All of these problems have been lessened by the use of computers.

Nothing is more annoying than to have travel plans interrupted by a confusion in reservations. Computers are being used to control reservations. Computers provide airline clerks and travel agents with almost immediate access to up-to-the-minute information on space availability for all flights. The agent can get a picture of the availability of seats close to departure time by entering the proper code on a keyboard. As new reservations enter the system, the computer includes this information on all subsequent reports. If space is not available, the person can be put on one or more waiting lists. When cancellations are received the person next on the list can be put on the flight and the proper agent notified.

Traffic control is another area greatly helped by computers. Once a plane is airborne, air traffic controllers monitor its speed, altitude, and location. Computers help in this monitoring by plotting each plane on the controller's display scope. In this way, air traffic controllers know exactly where each plane is located at any given time. In the future computers may more directly alert pilots of an approaching plane on a collision course and direct the planes to safety.

Anyone who travels knows how important schedules are. Computers can help plan schedules so that connecting flights are available on the most traveled routes. Also, computers can schedule crews so that each crew does not extend itself beyond safety limits.

Computers are used in radar systems for air travel.

Computers also help in supplies, parts inventory, freight control, and ordering control. All of these items are important in the running of an efficient airline.

Besides airline travel, computers have helped spacecraft travel. Hundreds of computers are used in NASA control centers. Many advances in the computer field are a direct spinoff from this application. Computers help guidance control, testing, medical monitoring, communication, and many more systems. Each of these uses have been adapted to concrete needs in our everyday lives.

Computers can be used in similar ways in other forms of transportation. Railroads, for instance, have the same needs for control as the airlines. It is important to know the speed, direction, and location of trains to avoid major collisions. The BART system in the San Francisco Bay Area is the first completely automated rail system in the world. The computers control, schedule, and monitor the system. Truckers also use computers to get information concerning loads both on new jobs as well as updates on old jobs.

Computers are becoming very important in transportation. Airlines have experienced growth, freight traffic has quadrupled, mail volume is six times as great as it was a decade ago. People must learn to use computers efficiently and to maintain careful supervision of their capabilities, power, and limitations.

Exercises   Write programs for each of the following.

1. Find logarithms of n to the base eight for $n = 1, 2, 3, \ldots 50$.

2. Output the graph of $y = 3^x$ and $y = \left(\dfrac{1}{3}\right)^x$ on the same axis.

3. Estimate the value of e by evaluating $(1 + x)^{1/x}$ for values of x close to 0. Let $x = 1, 0.1, 0.01, 0.001, 0.0001$, and 0.00001.

4. Find which value is larger, e^π or π^e.

5. The formula for the amount of money accumulated, A, on an investment, P, deposited for t years at $r\%$ interest rate, and compounded n times annually is $A = P\left(1 + \dfrac{r}{n}\right)^{nt}$. Find the amount of interest earned on $2500 for 5 years at interest rates of 5.5%, 5.75%, 6.00%, $\ldots$, 12% compounded quarterly.

6. When the interest is compounded continuously, the formula in Problem 5 becomes $A = Pe^{rt}$ where e is approximately 2.718. If $1000 is deposited in a savings account at an interest rate of 10% compounded continuously, when will the money be double the original amount?

7. A radioactive substance decays according to the equation, $A = A_0 \times 10^{-0.024t}$ where t is in hours. Find the half life of the substance (when $A = 0.5A_0$).

8. A piece of machinery valued at $50,000 depreciates 10% per year. The value at the end of n years is $V(n) = 50,000 \times 0.9^n$. Make a table which shows the value of the machine after 1 to 20 years for each year.

Chapter 12

Some curves like the one pictured above are called classical curves. These curves can be more easily drawn using polar coordinates.

Polar Coordinates

12-1 Polar Representation

It is possible to locate points in the plane using trigonometry and vectors. In the plane choose a fixed point O called the **pole**. From this point a ray is drawn usually in a horizontal direction. This fixed ray is called the **polar axis**. Every point P in the plane can be located using polar coordinates (r, θ).

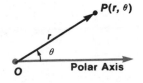

In the ordered pair (r, θ), $|r|$ is the *magnitude* of the *radius vector* $\overrightarrow{OP}$; θ is the *angle of rotation* of $\overrightarrow{OP}$ from the polar axis. If $\theta > 0$ then the rotation is counterclockwise. If $\theta < 0$ then the rotation is clockwise.

Unlike rectangular coordinates, polar representation is *not unique*. Other names for point P in the figure are $(-4, -150°)$ and $(4, 750°)$. If r is negative, then reflect $\overrightarrow{OP}$ in the origin.

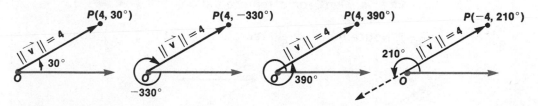

Suppose the point P is represented by both polar coordinates and rectangular coordinates when the pole and the origin coincide and the polar axis falls on the positive x-axis. Then the polar coordinates and rectangular coordinates of P are related this way.

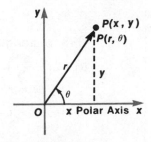

Polar Coordinates

$$x = r \cos \theta \qquad r^2 = x^2 + y^2$$

$$y = r \sin \theta \qquad \theta = \text{Arctan}\, \frac{y}{x} + k\pi, x \neq 0, k \in \mathbf{Z}$$

When r is positive, k is even. When r is negative, k is odd. Notice that if P is the origin or any point on the line $\theta = \frac{\pi}{2}$, then arctan $\frac{y}{x}$ is not defined. In this case θ is defined to be $\frac{\pi}{2} + k\pi$, $k \in Z$. The origin is named $(0, \theta)$ for any angle θ.

Examples

1. **Find polar coordinates for the point $P(-\sqrt{3}, 1)$.**

    $$r^2 = x^2 + y^2 \qquad\qquad \theta = \text{Arctan } \frac{y}{x} + k\pi$$

    $$r = \pm\sqrt{x^2 + y^2} \qquad\qquad \theta = \text{Arctan } \left(-\frac{1}{\sqrt{3}}\right) + k\pi$$

    $$r = \pm\sqrt{(-\sqrt{3})^2 + 1^2} \qquad \theta = \frac{\pi}{-6} + k\pi, \ k \in Z$$

    $$r = \pm 2$$

    The principal value of arctan $\left(-\frac{1}{\sqrt{3}}\right)$ is $-\frac{\pi}{6}$. Since P is in Quadrant II, if $r = 2$ is chosen then $\theta = -\frac{\pi}{6} + k\pi$ and k is odd. So P is represented by $\left(2, \frac{5\pi}{6}\right)$, $\left(2, -\frac{7\pi}{6}\right)$, $\left(2, \frac{17\pi}{6}\right)$ or in general by $\left(2, -\frac{\pi}{6} + (2k + 1)\pi\right)$. If $r = -2$ is chosen, then $\theta = -\frac{\pi}{6} + k\pi$ and k is even. Some representations are $\left(-2, \frac{11\pi}{6}\right)$, $\left(-2, -\frac{\pi}{6}\right)$, or $\left(-2, \frac{23\pi}{6}\right)$. Notice that $\left(2, \frac{5\pi}{6}\right)$ represents P but $\left(-2, \frac{5\pi}{6}\right)$ does not.

2. **Find rectangular coordinates for the point whose polar coordinates are $B\left(-2, -\frac{5\pi}{6}\right)$.**

    $$x = r \cos \theta \qquad\qquad y = r \sin \theta$$

    $$x = (-2) \cos \frac{-5\pi}{6} \qquad y = (-2) \sin \left(-\frac{5\pi}{6}\right)$$

    $$x = (-2)\left(-\frac{\sqrt{3}}{2}\right) \qquad y = -2\left(-\frac{1}{2}\right)$$

    $$x = \sqrt{3} \qquad\qquad y = 1$$

    The rectangular coordinates are $B(\sqrt{3}, 1)$.

Exercises

Exploratory   State three equivalent polar pairs for each of the following.

1. $\left(2, \frac{\pi}{4}\right)$

2. $\left(\sqrt{3}, -\frac{2\pi}{3}\right)$

3. $(-1, 120°)$

4. $(-4, -335°)$

5. $\left(1.6, \frac{7\pi}{6}\right)$

6. $(-2.5, -740°)$

Written   For each point named write an equivalent polar pair.

1. $(3, -20°), r < 0, 0° < \theta < 180°$

2. $\left(-2, \frac{5\pi}{6}\right), r > 0, -2\pi < \theta < 0$

3. $\left(1.5, -\frac{3\pi}{2}\right), r > 0, 2\pi < \theta < 4\pi$

4. $(-4, 210°), r > 0, 360° < \theta < 540°$

Graph the locus of points.

5. $(-2, -30°)$

6. $(3, 0°)$

7. $r = 2.7$

8. $r = -2.7$

9. $r = 0$

10. $m \angle \theta = 23°$

11. $m \angle \theta = -23°$

12. $m \angle \theta = 0°$

13. Show graphically that each point (r, θ) also can be written as $(r, \theta + 2k\pi)$ or $(-r, \theta + (2k + 1)\pi)$ for $k \in Z$.

Find polar coordinates of the points named by the rectangular coordinates below.

14. $(2, -\sqrt{3})$

15. $(-1, -1)$

16. $(0, -3)$

17. $(2, -8.02)$

18. $(-\sqrt{3}, 3)$

19. $(-\sqrt{2}, 0)$

Find the rectangular coordinates of the points named by the polar coordinates below.

20. $\left(2, \frac{\pi}{2}\right)$

21. $\left(-3, \frac{7\pi}{6}\right)$

22. $(4, -330°)$

23. $(-1.7, 15°)$

24. $(-\sqrt{2}, -210°)$

25. $\left(\sqrt{3}, \frac{8\pi}{3}\right)$

Write equations in x and y that define the same locus in a rectangular coordinate system. (Refer to Problems 7, 9, 10, and 12.)

26. $r = 2.7$

27. $r = 0$

28. $m \angle \theta = 23°$

29. $m \angle \theta = 0°$

Challenge   Show that each point (r, θ) can also be written as $((-1)^k r, \theta + k\pi), k \in Z$.

12–2 Polar Graphs

Sometimes the expression for defining a curve is simpler in polar form than in rectangular form. The equation of a circle with center at the origin and radius 2 in rectangular form is $x^2 + y^2 = 4$.

The equation in polar form is $r = 2$.

Example

1. **Change $r = 6 \cos \theta$ from polar to rectangular form. Identify the curve.**

   Since $x^2 + y^2 = r^2$ and $\cos \theta = \dfrac{x}{r}$, the following is true.

   $$r = 6 \cos \theta$$
   $$r = 6\left(\frac{x}{r}\right)$$
   $$r^2 = 6x$$
   $$\text{Thus, } x^2 + y^2 = 6x.$$
   $$x^2 - 6x + y^2 = 0$$
   $$x^2 - 6x + 9 + y^2 = 9$$
   $$(x - 3)^2 + y^2 = 9$$

   The curve is a circle with center at (3, 0) and radius 3.

The general polar form of $r = 6 \cos \theta$ is $r = 2a \cos \theta$. The corresponding rectangular form is $(x - a)^2 + y^2 = (a)^2$. The graph is a circle with diameter $|2a|$, center $(a, 0)$, and radius $|a|$.

To find a general polar form for a circle with center on the line $\theta = \dfrac{\pi}{2}$ or at the origin, the **polar distance formula** is needed. Let $P_1(r_1, \theta_1)$ and $P_2(r_2, \theta_2)$ be two points.

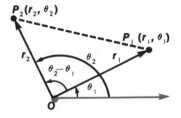

The **polar distance formula** for the distance between $P_1(r_1, \theta_1)$ and $P_2(r_2, \theta_2)$ is $(P_2P_1)^2 = r_2^2 + r_1^2 - 2r_2r_1 \cos(\theta_2 - \theta_1)$.

Polar Distance Formula

The theorem follows directly from the Law of Cosines.

Example

2. **Find the polar form of a circle with center $\left(a, \dfrac{\pi}{2}\right)$ and radius $|a|$.**

   The points $P(r, \theta)$, $A\left(2a, \dfrac{\pi}{2}\right)$ and $O(0, \theta)$ form a right triangle. This is because $\angle OPA$ is inscribed in a semicircle. Use the Pythagorean Theorem and the polar distance formula.

   $$(OA)^2 = (OP)^2 + (PA)^2$$
   $$|2a|^2 = r^2 + (PA)^2$$
   $$4a^2 = r^2 + 4a^2 + r^2 - 4ar \cos\left(\frac{\pi}{2} - \theta\right)$$

$$r^2 = 2ar \cos\left(\frac{\pi}{2} - \theta\right)$$
$$r = 2a \sin\theta \ (\text{if } r \neq 0)$$

Notice the diagram shows $a > 0$ but the development also holds for $a < 0$.

Therefore, a circle with center $\left(a, \frac{\pi}{2}\right)$ and radius $|a|$ units has polar equation $r = 2a \sin\theta$.

Sometimes it is desirable to change from polar to rectangular form in order to graph a relation. However, it is important also to be able to graph a relation expressed in polar form without changing to rectangular form.

A major problem in graphing is that the polar representation of a point is not unique. It may be that some polar coordinates of a point satisfy a given condition. Other equivalent polar coordinates of that point may not. The **polar graph** of a given relation is the set of all points which have at least one pair of polar coordinates that satisfy the conditions.

A table of values of r and θ can be generated by choosing values for one variable and solving for the other variable. Often the relation is stated in the form $r = f(\theta)$. Values of θ chosen every 30° or $\frac{\pi}{6}$ radians, from 0° to 360° or less usually are sufficient to show the shape of the curve. After finding the corresponding values of r, points can be graphed using polar coordinates. Polar coordinate paper is sometimes used.

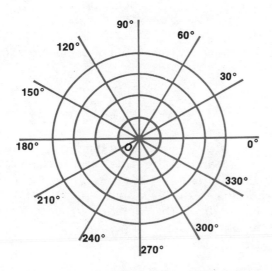

This is an example of polar coordinate paper.

Example

3. Show that $P\left(-\sqrt{5}, \dfrac{4\pi}{3}\right)$ does not satisfy $r^2 = 10 \cos \theta$ but an equivalent form does.

$P\left(-\sqrt{5}, \dfrac{4\pi}{3}\right)$, $r^2 = 10 \cos \theta$

$$r^2 = 10 \cos \frac{4\pi}{3}$$

$$(-\sqrt{5})^2 = 10\left(-\frac{1}{2}\right) = -5$$

$$5 \neq -5$$

$\theta = \dfrac{4\pi}{3}$

$r = (-\sqrt{5})$

An equivalent expression for $\left(-\sqrt{5}, \dfrac{4\pi}{3}\right)$ is $\left(\sqrt{5}, \dfrac{\pi}{3}\right)$.

$$(\sqrt{5})^2 = 10 \cos \frac{\pi}{3}$$

$$= 10\left(\frac{1}{2}\right)$$

$$= 5$$

Therefore, P lies on the graph of $r^2 = 10 \cos \theta$.

Some relations have corresponding equations which look different, but have identical graphs. This is true because for every point (r, θ) on a graph, the point $(-r, \theta + \pi)$ also is on the graph even though only one set of coordinates may satisfy the given equation.

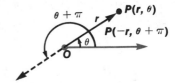

Example

4. Find an alternate expression for the relation $r = a(\cos \theta - 1)$ by replacing (r, θ) with $(-r, \theta + \pi)$.

$$-r = a[\cos (\theta + \pi) - 1]$$
$$-r = a(-\cos \theta - 1)$$
$$r = a(\cos \theta + 1)$$

The equations $r = a(\cos \theta - 1)$ and $r = a(\cos \theta + 1)$ define the same relation and have the same graph. This does not mean that the same r and θ are paired in each equation. For example, $(0, 0)$ satisfies $r = a(\cos \theta - 1)$ but not $r = a(\cos \theta + 1)$. The point having coordinates $(0, 0)$ is on the graph of $r = a(\cos \theta + 1)$ because it also has coordinates $(0, \pi)$. The point having coordinates $(2a, 0)$ also satisfies the first equation, but not the second.

Exercises

Exploratory Find the distance between the given points.

1. $\left(4, \frac{\pi}{2}\right), (0, \pi)$

2. $\left(3, \frac{\pi}{6}\right), \left(4, \frac{\pi}{3}\right)$

3. $(5, \pi), \left(-6, -\frac{\pi}{2}\right)$

4. $\left(-3, \frac{\pi}{6}\right), \left(2, \frac{\pi}{2}\right)$

5. $(4, -330°), (-1.7, 15°)$

6. $\left(2, \frac{\pi}{4}\right), \left(\sqrt{3}, -\frac{2\pi}{3}\right)$

Written Change each equation from polar to rectangular form. Identify the curve where possible.

1. $r = 3 \sin \theta$

2. $r = 6$

3. $r = 3 - \cos \theta$

4. $r = 2 + \sin \theta$

5. $r^2 \sin 2\theta = 4$

6. $r = \dfrac{1}{1 + \cos \theta}$

7. $r = \sin \theta \cos^2 \theta$

8. $r^2 = 9 \cos 2\theta$

9. $r^2 = \sec^2\theta \tan \theta$

10. $r = \dfrac{1}{1 - \sin \theta}$

11. $r = 2 \sin 3\theta$

12. $r = 4\theta$

Change each equation from rectangular to polar form.

13. $x^2 + y^2 = 10$

14. $x^2 - 8x + y^2 = 0$

15. $x^2 + y^2 + 3y = 0$

16. $x - y = 0$

17. $y^2 = 3x$

18. $xy = 8$

19. $x^2 + 2x + y^2 - 6y = 0$

20. $x + y = -xy$

21. $(x^2 + y^2)^2 = 25(x^2 - y^2)$

22. $x^2 = 1 - 3y$

23. $(x^2 + y^2)^2 = \sqrt{5}x^2y$

24. $x^2 + y^2 = 3\left(\text{Arctan } \dfrac{y}{x}\right)^2$

Find the polar form of the curve described.

25. Circle with diameter of $|2a|$ units and center at $\left(a, \dfrac{3\pi}{2}\right)$.

26. A line through $\left(b, \dfrac{\pi}{2}\right)$ parallel to the polar axis.

Find an alternate form, if any, by replacing (r, θ) with $(-r, \theta + \pi)$ in each relation.

27. $r = a(1 + \sin \theta)$

28. $r = 3 \cos \theta$

29. $r = 2 \tan \theta$

30. $r = \sec \theta - 1$

Challenge Solve each of the following.

1. Show that the polar distance formula $(P_1P_2)^2 = r_2^2 + r_1^2 - 2r_2r_1 \cos(\theta_2 - \theta_1)$ is true if
   a. P_1 is in Quadrant I and P_2 is in Quadrant II.
   b. P_1 is in Quadrant II and P_2 is in Quadrant IV.

2. Derive the polar distance formula by using the rectangular distance formula $(P_1P_2)^2 = (x_2 - x_1)^2 + (y_2 - y_1)^2$ using $x = r \cos \theta$ and $y = r \sin \theta$.

Show that $P(r, \theta)$ lies on the graph of the relation although P does not satisfy the equation.

3. $r = 3(1 + \sin \theta); P\left(-6, \dfrac{3\pi}{2}\right)$

4. $r^2 = 2 \sin \theta; P\left(1, -\dfrac{\pi}{6}\right)$

12–3 Equations of Lines and Circles

The term *polar axis* refers to the polar axis and its extension, and hence its equation is $\theta = 0$ or $\theta = \pi$. Lines parallel to the polar axis are said to be *horizontal*.

The line perpendicular to the polar axis at the pole has equation $\theta = \dfrac{\pi}{2}$ or $\theta = \dfrac{3\pi}{2}$. Lines perpendicular to the polar axis are said to be *vertical*.

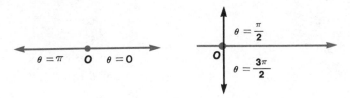

Suppose that a vertical line intersects the polar axis at $(a, 0)$. Using trigonometry, $\cos \theta = \dfrac{a}{r}$. Therefore, $r \cos \theta = a$ is the equation of the line.

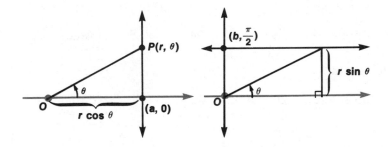

Similarly, a horizontal line intersecting the line $\theta = \dfrac{\pi}{2}$ at $\left(b, \dfrac{\pi}{2}\right)$ has equation $r \sin \theta = b$.

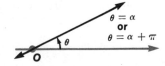

Equation of a Line through the Pole

> The equation of any line through the pole with inclination α is $\theta = \alpha$ or $\theta = \alpha + \pi$.

Suppose that ℓ is an oblique line not passing through the pole. Let $P(r, \theta)$ represent any point on line ℓ. Let B be a point on ℓ such that $\overline{OB} \perp \ell$. The distance ρ from the pole O to ℓ is $\rho = OB$. Since $\triangle OPB$ is a right triangle, $\cos (\theta - \omega) = \dfrac{\rho}{r}$. Multiplying by r gives the **general polar form of a line**.

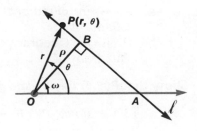

$$r \cos (\theta - \omega) = \rho$$

General Polar Form of a Line

Each formula derived so far in this section is a special case of this form. Verify that this form holds even when $\theta < \omega$.

Examples

1. Write the polar form of a horizontal line containing the point $\left(-3, \dfrac{\pi}{2}\right)$.

$$r \sin \theta = -3$$

2. Write the polar form of an oblique line containing the point (4, 0) having an inclination of $\dfrac{5\pi}{6}$.

Since $\theta = \dfrac{5\pi}{6}$, $\omega = \dfrac{\pi}{3}$. Since $\cos \omega = \dfrac{\rho}{4}$, $\rho = 4 \cos \omega = 4 \cos \dfrac{\pi}{3} = 2$. Therefore, the equation of the line is $r \cos \left(\theta - \dfrac{\pi}{3}\right) = 2$.

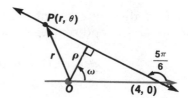

Suppose that a circle has center $C(c, \phi)$ and radius $|a|$ units. Let $P(r, \theta)$ be a point on the circle. Apply the polar distance formula for the distance between P and C. This gives the **general polar equation of a circle**.

$$a^2 = r^2 + c^2 - 2rc \cos (\theta - \phi)$$

General Polar Equation of a Circle

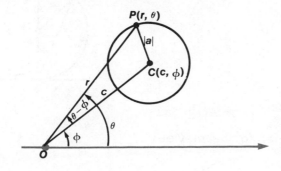

Example

3. Find the polar equation of the circle with center $\left(2.5, \dfrac{3\pi}{4}\right)$ and radius 1.3 units.

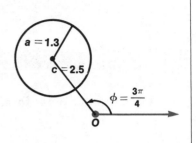

$$a = 1.3, c = 2.5, \phi = \frac{3\pi}{4}$$

$$a^2 = r^2 + c^2 - 2rc \cos(\theta - \phi)$$

$$(1.3)^2 = r^2 + (2.5)^2 - 2r(2.5) \cos\left(\theta - \frac{3\pi}{4}\right)$$

$$1.69 = r^2 + 6.25 - 5r \cos\left(\theta - \frac{3\pi}{4}\right)$$

To find the equation of a circle which passes through the pole, let $a = c$, and replace c with a in the general equation.

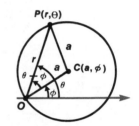

$$a^2 = r^2 + a^2 - 2ra \cos(\theta - \phi)$$
$$r^2 = 2ra \cos(\theta - \phi)$$
$$r = 2a \cos(\theta - \phi) \text{ if } r \neq 0$$

To find the equation of a circle which passes through the pole but whose center lies on the polar axis, let $a = c$ and $\phi = 0$.

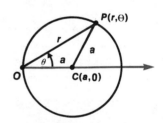

$$\phi = 0$$
$$r = 2a \cos(\theta - 0)$$
$$r = 2a \cos \theta$$

Suppose the circle passes through the pole but the center lies on the line with equation $\phi = \dfrac{\pi}{2}$.

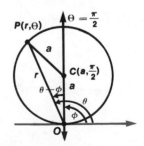

$$\phi = \frac{\pi}{2}$$

$$r = 2a \cos\left[\theta - \frac{\pi}{2}\right]$$

$$r = 2a \sin \theta$$

Do these equations seem familiar? Refer to the previous section.

Exercises

Exploratory Copy and complete the table below for each line.

	Inclination	Through point	Intercepts	Polar equation
1.	$-\dfrac{\pi}{4}$	pole	?	?
2.	$\dfrac{7\pi}{6}$	pole	?	?
3.	vertical	$(-3, 0)$	?	?
4.	horizontal	$\left(\sqrt{2}, \dfrac{3\pi}{4}\right)$	?	?
5.	?	?	$(6, \pi)\left(2\sqrt{3}, \dfrac{3\pi}{2}\right)$	?
6.	$160°$	$(10, 0)$	?	?

Written Choose convenient points and graph each line.

1. $r = \dfrac{3}{\cos\left(\theta - \dfrac{\pi}{6}\right)}$

2. $r = \dfrac{2}{\cos\left(\theta + \dfrac{\pi}{3}\right)}$

3. $r = \dfrac{1}{2\cos\theta + \sin\theta}$

4. $r = \dfrac{\sqrt{5}}{\cos\left(\theta - \dfrac{7\pi}{6}\right)}$

Find the polar form of each circle with center C passing through the pole.

5. $C\left(3, \dfrac{\pi}{2}\right)$

6. $C(2, -\pi)$

7. $C\left(-5, \dfrac{3\pi}{2}\right)$

8. $C(2.3, 0)$

9. $C\left(-\sqrt{2}, \dfrac{\pi}{2}\right)$

10. $C\left(3, \dfrac{\pi}{3}\right)$

11. $C\left(-4.2, \dfrac{7\pi}{6}\right)$

12. $C(6, 143°)$

Find the polar form of each circle with center C and radius a.

13. $C\left(2, \dfrac{3\pi}{4}\right)$, $a = 1$

14. $C\left(-3, \dfrac{2\pi}{3}\right)$, $a = 2$

15. $C(4.8, 210°)$, $a = 4$ **16.** $C(0.6, 25°)$, $a = 3$

17. $C\left(2\sqrt{3}, -\dfrac{\pi}{4}\right)$, $a = \sqrt{2}$

Find the polar form of each circle with center on the given ray and passing through the given two points.

18. $\theta = \dfrac{2\pi}{3}$, pole, $\left(6, \dfrac{2\pi}{3}\right)$ **19.** $\theta = \dfrac{\pi}{4}$, pole, $\left(3, \dfrac{\pi}{2}\right)$

20. $\theta = -\dfrac{5\pi}{6}$, pole, $(-6, 0)$ **21.** $\theta = -\dfrac{\pi}{6}$, $\left(8, -\dfrac{\pi}{6}\right)$, $\left(6, -\dfrac{\pi}{3}\right)$

Challenge Write each of the following equations in the rectangular general form. Change it to polar form and calculate the distance from the line to the origin using both the rectangular and the polar forms.

1. $3x + 4y = 5$ **2.** $\sqrt{3}x + y = 4$

Prove each of the following.

3. The equation $r(a \cos \theta + b \sin \theta) = c$ represents a straight line if a and b are not both zero.

4. The equation $r = a \cos \theta + b \sin \theta$ represents a circle.

12–4 Graphing Techniques

Graphing in the polar coordinate system can be simplified. This is done by considering properties such as symmetry, intercepts, tangents, and extent.

> **The graph of the relation S is symmetric with respect to**
>
> **I.** the polar axis if $(r, -\theta) \in S$ whenever $(r, \theta) \in S$.
>
> **II.** the line $\theta = \dfrac{\pi}{2}$ if $(r, \pi - \theta) \in S$ whenever $(r, \theta) \in S$.
>
> **III.** the pole if $(-r, \theta) \in S$ whenever $(r, \theta) \in S$.

Symmetry of a Graph

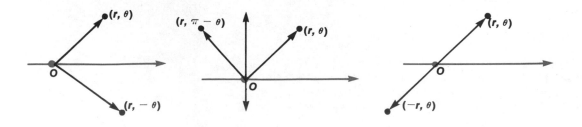

If any two of the conditions for symmetry are satisfied then the third one follows automatically. The above rules can be extended to include the following cases. This is true because (r, θ) and $(-r, \theta + \pi)$ name the same point.

What similarities do you notice between the conditions for symmetry using rectangular coordinates and those stated above?

> **The graph of the relation S is symmetric with respect to**
>
> Ia.   the polar axis if $(-r, \pi - \theta) \in S$ whenever $(r, \theta) \in S$.
>
> IIa.   the line $\theta = \dfrac{\pi}{2}$ if $(-r, -\theta) \in S$ whenever $(r, \theta) \in S$.
>
> IIIa.   the pole if $(r, \pi + \theta) \in S$ whenever $(r, \theta) \in S$.

Symmetry of a Graph

Any of the rules are *sufficient* to show symmetry. Points do *not* have unique polar representation. For this reason, the coordinates tested may fail to satisfy a defining equation even though the point named does belong to the relation.

Example

1. **Test $r = 1 + 2 \cos \theta$ for symmetry.**

   I.   Since $\cos(-\theta) = \cos \theta$, $1 + 2 \cos \theta = 1 + 2 \cos(-\theta)$.
   Therefore, $(r, -\theta) \in S$ whenever $(r, \theta) \in S$ and the graph is symmetric with respect to the polar axis.

   II.   Since $\cos(\pi - \theta) = -\cos \theta$, $1 + 2 \cos(\pi - \theta) \neq 1 + 2 \cos \theta$.
   Therefore $(r, \pi - \theta) \notin S$ and the test does not show symmetry with respect to $\theta = \dfrac{\pi}{2}$. However, such symmetry is still possible.

   III.   Since $-r = -(1 + 2 \cos \theta)$, $(-r, \theta) \notin S$ where $(r, \theta) \in S$ and the test does not show symmetry with repsect to the pole. Again, such symmetry is still possible.

> **The graph of $r = 1 + 2 \cos \theta$ is a curve called a limaçon.**

Definition of Limaçon

Intercepts of the polar axis or the line $\theta = \dfrac{\pi}{2}$ are found by testing multiples of $\dfrac{\pi}{2}$ and solving for the corresponding r values.

The graph contains the pole if $(0, \theta)$ satisfies the equation for some θ.

Example

2. Test the limaçon $r = 1 + 2 \cos \theta$ for intercepts.

$$\text{If } r = 0 \text{ then } 0 = 1 + 2 \cos \theta.$$

$$\cos \theta = -\frac{1}{2}$$

$$\theta = \frac{2\pi}{3}, \frac{4\pi}{3}$$

Therefore, the pole is on the graph.

If $\theta = \quad 0$ then $r = 1 + 2 \cos 0 = 3$

If $\theta = \dfrac{\pi}{2}$ then $r = 1 + 2 \cos \dfrac{\pi}{2} = 1$

If $\theta = \quad \pi$ then $r = 1 + 2 \cos \pi = -1$

If $\theta = \dfrac{3\pi}{2}$ then $r = 1 + 2 \cos \dfrac{3\pi}{2} = 1$

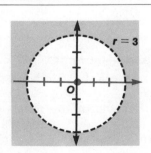

Intercepts are at $(3, 0)$, $\left(1, \dfrac{\pi}{2}\right)$, $(-1, \pi)$, $\left(1, \dfrac{3\pi}{2}\right)$ and the pole. The cycle repeats for $\theta < 0$ and $\theta > 2\pi$.

For some equations, intercepts occur for values of $\theta > 2\pi$ but not for $\theta \leq 2\pi$. An intercept of $r = 3 \cos \dfrac{2\theta}{5}$ occurs at $\theta = \dfrac{5\pi}{2}$. It does not occur at $\theta = \dfrac{5\pi}{2} - 2\pi = \dfrac{\pi}{2}$.

The *extent* of a polar graph is found by determining bounds on r. Often the extent of r is determined by the fact that $|\sin \theta| \leq 1$ and $|\cos \theta| \leq 1$. Restrictions on θ seldom need to be found. Considering $\theta < 0$ or $\theta > 2\pi$ often retraces the curve for $0 \leq \theta \leq 2\pi$, especially when the relation contains trigonometric functions of θ.

Example

3. Test the limaçon $r = 1 + 2 \cos \theta$ for extent.

$$-1 \leq \cos \theta \leq 1$$
$$-2 \leq 2 \cos \theta \leq 2$$
$$-1 \leq 1 + 2 \cos \theta \leq 3$$
$$-1 \leq r \leq 3$$

Therefore, $-1 \leq r \leq 3$.

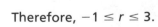

The test for *tangents at the pole* is similar to the test for tangents at the origin in rectangular coordinates. To approximate the tangents, set $r = 0$ in the equation being graphed.

The symbol $r \to 0$ is read *r approaches zero* and means that r gets *very close to zero*.

Example

4. **Test the limaçon $r = 1 + 2 \cos \theta$ for tangents to the curve at the pole.**

If $r = 0$ then $0 = 1 + 2 \cos \theta$.

$$\cos \theta = -\frac{1}{2}$$

$$\theta = \frac{2\pi}{3}, \frac{4\pi}{3}$$

If $r \to 0$ then $1 + 2 \cos \theta \to 0$.

$$\theta \to \frac{2\pi}{3} \text{ or } \theta \to \frac{4\pi}{3}$$

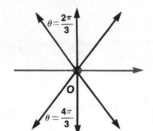

The lines $\theta = \frac{2\pi}{3}$ and $\theta = \frac{4\pi}{3}$ are tangents to the curve at the pole. They are the best linear approximations when $r = 0$.

The graph of $r = 1 + 2 \cos \theta$ now can be sketched. Using the information already found, locate the intercepts, extent, and tangents. Then plot points at intervals of $\frac{\pi}{6}$ or $\frac{\pi}{4}$ as needed until repetition due to symmetry begins.

θ	0	$\frac{\pi}{6}$	$\frac{\pi}{4}$	$\frac{\pi}{3}$	$\frac{\pi}{2}$	$\frac{7\pi}{12}$	$\frac{2\pi}{3}$	$\frac{3\pi}{4}$	$\frac{5\pi}{6}$	π	$\frac{7\pi}{6}$	$\frac{5\pi}{4}$	$\frac{4\pi}{3}$
r	3	2.7	2.4	2	1	0.5	0	−0.4	−0.7	−1	−0.7	−0.4	0

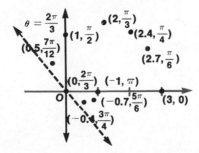

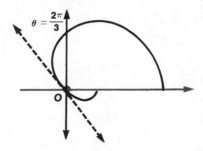

Points for $0 \le \theta \le \pi$ are plotted. A smooth curve is drawn through them. Repetition occurs for $\theta > \pi$, and the curve is symmetric with respect to the polar axis. Therefore, the rest of the curve is sketched easily.

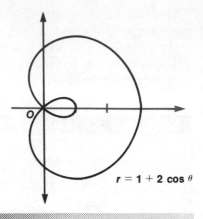

$r = 1 + 2 \cos \theta$

Example

5. **Graph the polar relation $r^2 = a^2 \sin \theta$.**

    Symmetry

        I.   For $(r, -\theta)$, $a^2 \sin (-\theta) = -a^2 \sin \theta = -r^2$
        II. For $(r, \pi - \theta)$, $a^2 [\sin (\pi - \theta)] = a^2 \sin \theta = r^2$
        III. For $(-r, \theta)$, $(-r)^2 = r^2 = a^2 \sin \theta$

    Since conditions **II** and **III** hold, condition **I** must hold also, even though Test **I** failed. Therefore, the graph is symmetric with respect to the polar axis, the line $\theta = \dfrac{\pi}{2}$ and the origin.

    Intercepts

    If $r = 0$ then $0 = a^2 \sin \theta$. Then, $\theta = 0 + k\pi$, $k \in \mathbb{Z}$. The curve therefore contains the pole and the point $(0, 0)$ is an intercept of the polar axis. Also, if $\theta = \dfrac{\pi}{2}$ then $r^2 = a^2$. Then the points $\left(a, \dfrac{\pi}{2}\right)$ and $\left(-a, \dfrac{\pi}{2}\right)$ are intercepts of the line $\theta = \dfrac{\pi}{2}$.

    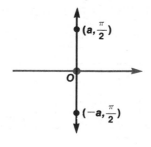

    Because of the symmetry of the curve, only intercepts for $\theta = 0$ or $\theta = \dfrac{\pi}{2}$ need to be considered. Similarly, only points in the first quadrant need to be plotted.

    Extent

    If $-1 \le \sin \theta \le 1$ then $-a^2 \le a^2 \sin \theta \le a^2$.
    $$-a^2 \le r^2 \le a^2$$
    $$|r| \le |a|$$

Since $r^2 > 0$, $a^2 > 0$, and $r^2 = a^2 \sin \theta$, $\sin \theta > 0$.

If $\sin \theta > 0$ then $0 < \theta < \pi$.

The graph exists in Quadrant III and IV, even though θ is limited to Quadrants I and II.

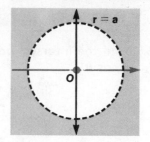

Tangents at the Pole

If $r = 0$ then $0 = a^2 \sin \theta$.
So $\sin \theta \to 0$ as $r \to 0$.

Therefore, the polar axis is tangent to the curve on both sides of the pole.

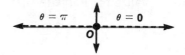

A few points in Quadrant I are needed to determine the shape of the curve. The rest is sketched by symmetry.

θ	0	$\dfrac{\pi}{6}$	$\dfrac{\pi}{4}$	$\dfrac{\pi}{3}$	$\dfrac{\pi}{2}$
r^2	0	$\dfrac{a^2}{2}$	$\dfrac{a^2}{\sqrt{2}}$	$\dfrac{a^2 \sqrt{3}}{2}$	a^2
r	0	$0.71a$	$0.84a$	$0.93a$	a

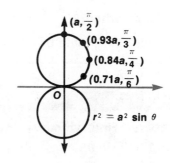

Suppose it is necessary to find the points of intersection of the graphs of two polar equations. Pairs of Cartesian equations can be solved analytically. With polar equations this is not always the easiest method. This is because the polar representation of a point is not unique. To find the points of intersection of two polar equations, graph both polar equations on the same polar coordinate system.

Example

6. Find the intersection of the graphs whose equations are $r = 4 \sin \theta$ and $r = 4 \cos \theta$.

$$4 \sin \theta = 4 \cos \theta$$
$$\sin \theta = \cos \theta$$
$$\tan \theta = 1 \text{ if } \cos \theta \neq 0$$
$$\theta = \frac{\pi}{4}, \frac{5\pi}{4}$$

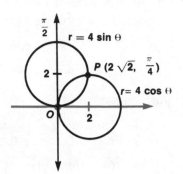

To find the points of intersection, substitute the value for θ in the first equation.

$$r = 4 \sin \frac{\pi}{4} \qquad r = 4 \sin \frac{5\pi}{4}$$
$$= 4 \cdot \frac{\sqrt{2}}{2} \qquad = 4 \cdot \left(\frac{-\sqrt{2}}{2}\right)$$
$$= 2\sqrt{2} \qquad = -2\sqrt{2}$$

The point $\left(2\sqrt{2}, \frac{\pi}{4}\right)$ is the same point as $\left(-2\sqrt{2}, \frac{5\pi}{4}\right)$. Substituting the value for θ in the second equation also gives $\left(2\sqrt{2}, \frac{\pi}{4}\right)$ and $\left(-2\sqrt{2}, \frac{5\pi}{4}\right)$. This indicates the graphs have only one point in common. A sketch shows that the graphs actually have two points in common, $\left(2\sqrt{2}, \frac{\pi}{4}\right)$ and the pole. The first equation contains the pole when $\theta = 0 + k\pi$, while the second contains the pole when $\theta = \frac{\pi}{2} + k\pi$. Thus, they both contain the pole although not for the same value of θ.

Exercises

Exploratory   Find symmetry, intercepts, extent, and tangents at the pole for each relation.

1. $r = 1 + 3 \sin \theta$
2. $r = 2 - 1 \cos \theta$
3. $r = 2 + 2 \sin \theta$
4. $r = 4 \sin \theta$
5. $r = \dfrac{1}{1 + \cos \theta}$
6. $r^2 = 9 \cos 2\theta$
7. $r = 3 \cos 2\theta$ (Hint: Use symmetry.)
8. $r^2 = \dfrac{1}{2} \sec^2 \theta \tan \theta$
9. $r = \dfrac{2}{\cos\left(\theta - \dfrac{\pi}{6}\right)}$

Written   Sketch the curve for each of the following.

1. $r = 1 + 3 \sin \theta$
2. $r = 2 - 1 \cos \theta$

3. $r = 2 + 2 \sin \theta$

4. $r = 4 \sin \theta$

5. $r = \dfrac{1}{1 + \cos \theta}$

6. $r^2 = 9 \cos 2\theta$

7. $r = 3 \cos 2\theta$ (Hint: Use symmetry.)

8. $r^2 - \dfrac{1}{2} \sec^2 \theta \tan \theta$

9. $r = \dfrac{2}{\cos\left(\theta - \dfrac{\pi}{6}\right)}$

Find the intercepts of each curve whose equation is listed below.

10. $r = 3 \cos \dfrac{2\theta}{3}$

11. $r = 4 \sin \left(\theta - \dfrac{\pi}{4}\right)$

Find the intersection of the graphs of each pair of equations.
- **(a.)** Solve the equations using analytical methods.
- **(b.)** Graph both equations in the same polar coordinate system.
- **(c.)** Which method is easier in each case? Why?

12. $r = 4$ and $r = 6 \cos \theta$

13. $r = \sin \theta$ and $r = 1 - \sin \theta$

14. $r = -2 \sin \theta$ and $r = 4 \cos \theta$

15. $r = \dfrac{4}{2 + \cos \theta}$ and $r = 2 + 4 \cos \theta$

Challenge Find a relation whose graph is symmetric but fails to satisfy the condition given.

1. I.

2. II.

3. III.

Prove each of the following Symmetric Properties

4. Ia

5. IIa

6. IIIa

7. Compare the three conditions for symmetry given at the beginning of this section to those which deal with rectangular coordinates as in Chapter 4. Which one is different?

12–5 Classical Curves

Many curves follow interesting patterns or have important applications. Such classical curves include roses, lemniscates, limaçons, cardioids, and spirals.

> **A rose** is a curve with equation of the form $r = a \cos n\theta$ or $r = a \sin n\theta, n \in N$.

Definition of Rose

The orientation to the polar axis is determined by the equation.

Example

1. **Determine the characteristics of and graph the rose $r = 3 \cos 2\theta$.**

   Symmetry   The curve is symmetric with respect the polar axis and the pole. Thus, although the test fails, the curve is also symmetric with respect to the line $\theta = \frac{\pi}{2}$. Because of the symmetry, only points for which $0 \le \theta \le \frac{\pi}{2}$ need to be plotted.

   Extent

   $$-3 \le r \le 3$$

   Intercepts

   Horizontal intercepts are $(3, 0)$ and $(3, \pi)$. Vertical intercepts are $\left(-3, \frac{\pi}{2}\right)$ and $\left(-3, \frac{3\pi}{2}\right)$. The pole is an intercept.

   Tangents at the pole

   If $r = 0$ then $3 \cos 2\theta = 0$

   $$2\theta = \pm\frac{\pi}{2}$$

   $$\theta = \pm\frac{\pi}{4}$$

   If $r \to 0$ then $\theta \to \frac{\pi}{4}$ or $\theta \to -\frac{\pi}{4}$

   Points for which $0 \le \theta \le \frac{\pi}{2}$ are plotted to determine the shape of the leaves of the rose.

θ	0	$\frac{\pi}{6}$	$\frac{\pi}{3}$	$\frac{\pi}{2}$
r	3	$\frac{3}{2}$	$\frac{-3}{2}$	-3

   Figure **a** is the graph of $r = 3 \cos 2\theta$ for $0 \le \theta \le \frac{\pi}{2}$. Figure **b** shows the completion of the graph by symmetry. The curve is graphed in the following order.

1. $0 \le \theta \le \dfrac{\pi}{4}$ **2.** $\dfrac{\pi}{4} \le \theta \le \dfrac{3\pi}{4}$

3. $\dfrac{3\pi}{4} \le \theta \le \dfrac{5\pi}{4}$ **4.** $\dfrac{5\pi}{4} \le \theta \le \dfrac{7\pi}{4}$

5. $\dfrac{7\pi}{4} \le \theta \le 2\pi$

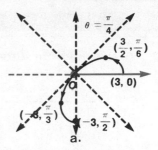

a.

The curve is a four-leaved rose.

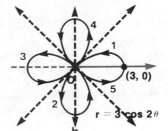

b.

A lemniscate is a curve with equation of the form $r^2 = a^2 \cos 2\theta$ or $r^2 = a^2 \sin 2\theta$.

Definition of Lemniscate

Lemniscates are symmetric with respect to the pole because of the r^2–term. Only lemniscates of the type $r^2 = a^2 \cos 2\theta$ are symmetric with respect to the polar axis and the vertical axis.

The extent of r is $-a \le r \le a$. Since $r^2 \ge 0$, $\sin 2\theta \ge 0$ or $2\theta \le \pi$. Therefore $\theta < \dfrac{\pi}{2}$ for $r^2 = a^2 \sin 2\theta$. Both forms of the curve contain the origin. Intercepts are the pole, $(a, 0)$, and (a, π) for the cosine form. The pole is the only intercept for the sine form.

Tangents at the pole differ for each form.

How is θ restricted for $r^2 = a^2 \cos 2\theta$?

If $\cos 2\theta = 0$ then $2\theta = \dfrac{\pi}{2}, \dfrac{3\pi}{2}$.

$$\theta = \dfrac{\pi}{4}, \dfrac{3\pi}{4}$$

If $\sin 2\theta = 0$ then $2\theta = 0, \pi$.

$$\theta = 0, \dfrac{\pi}{2}$$

Example

2. Graph the lemniscate $r^2 = 9 \sin 2\theta$.

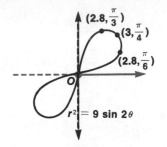

θ	0	$\frac{\pi}{6}$	$\frac{\pi}{4}$	$\frac{\pi}{3}$	$\frac{\pi}{2}$
r	0	± 2.8	± 3	± 2.8	0

A limaçon is a curve with equation of the form $r = a + b \cos \theta$ or $r = a + b \sin \theta$.

Definition of Limaçon

The shape of a limaçon depends on the relative sizes of a and b. If $|a| = |b|$, then the limaçon is called a **cardioid.** The graph of the cardioid is heart-shaped. If $|a| > |b|$, then $r > 0$. The graph is shaped like a kidney bean. If $|a| < |b|$, then r can be negative for some values of θ. The graph contains an inner loop.

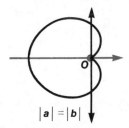

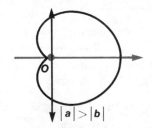

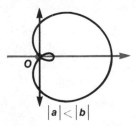

Example

3. Graph the cardioid $r = 2(1 + \cos \theta)$.

Symmetry

With respect to the polar axis.

Extent

$0 \le r \le 4$

Intercepts

pole, $(4, 0)$, $\left(2, \frac{\pi}{2}\right)$, $\left(2, \frac{3\pi}{2}\right)$

Tangents at the pole

$\theta = \pi$ *Notice that* $\theta = 0$ *is not a tangent at the pole.*

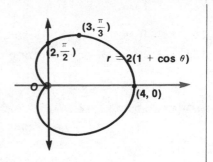

θ	0	$\dfrac{\pi}{6}$	$\dfrac{\pi}{4}$	$\dfrac{\pi}{3}$	$\dfrac{\pi}{2}$	$\dfrac{2\pi}{3}$	$\dfrac{3\pi}{4}$	$\dfrac{5\pi}{6}$	π
r	4	3.73	3.41	3	2	1	0.59	0.27	0

A *spiral* is not periodic, but has a unique value of θ for each possible value of r. The most common spiral is the *Spiral of Archimedes*.

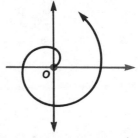

The **Spiral of Archimedes** has the equation of the form $r = a\theta$.

Definition of the Spiral of Archimedes

Exercises

Exploratory   Find symmetry, intercepts, extent, and tangents at the pole for each rose curve.

1. $r = 3 \sin 2\theta$ **2.** $r = 4 \cos 3\theta$ **3.** $r = 4 \sin 3\theta$

4. $r = 6 \cos 4\theta$ **5.** $r = 4 \cos 5\theta$

In Problems 6–9, copy and complete each statement.

6. For n an even natural number, the rose has __?__ leaves.

7. For n an odd natural number, the rose has __?__ leaves.

8. The significance of the value of a in $r = a \cos n\theta$ is __?__.

9. Replacing cosine by sine forces the graph to __?__.

Written   Study each relation for symmetry, extent, intercepts and tangents at the origin. Identify each curve and sketch the graph.

1. $r = 3(1 + \cos \theta)$ **2.** $r = 4(1 - \cos \theta)$ **3.** $r = 2(1 + \sin \theta)$

4. $r^2 = 4 \cos 2\theta$ **5.** $r^2 = 10 \sin 2\theta$ **6.** $r = 3 + 2 \cos \theta$

7. $r = 3 - 2 \cos \theta$ **8.** $r = 2 - 3 \cos \theta$ **9.** $r = 1 + 4 \sin \theta$

10. $r = 1 - 2 \sin \theta$ **11.** $r = 4\theta$

Study and graph each miscellaneous curve.

12. $r = 2 \sin \dfrac{1}{2} \theta$ **13.** $r = 2 \csc \theta + 3$ (Conchoid)

14. $r = 3 \tan \theta$

15. $r^2 = \dfrac{4}{\theta}$ (Lituus)

16. $r = 4(\sec \theta - \cos \theta)$ (Cissoid)

17. $r = 2 \sin \theta \cos^2 \theta$ (Bifolium)

18. $r = 3 \cos 2\theta \sec \theta$ (Strophoid)

19. $r^2 = -5 \sin 2\theta$

Chapter Summary

1. Every point P in the plane can be located using polar coordinates. In the ordered pair (r, θ), $|r|$ is the magnitude of the radius vector $\overline{OP}$ and θ is the angle of rotation of $\overline{OP}$ from the polar axis. (359)

2. The polar distance formula for the distance between two points $P_1(r_1, \theta_1)$ and $P_2(r_2, \theta_2)$ is $(P_1P_2)^2 = r_2^2 + r_1^2 - 2r_2r_1 \cos(\theta_2 - \theta_1)$. (362)

3.

Polar equations of lines	
horizontal line through pole	$\theta = 0$ or $\theta = \pi$
vertical line through pole	$\theta = \dfrac{\pi}{2}$ or $\theta = \dfrac{3\pi}{2}$
vertical line through $(a, 0)$	$r \cos \theta = a$
horizontal line through $\left(b, \dfrac{\pi}{2}\right)$	$r \sin \theta = b$
line through pole with inclination α	$\theta = \alpha$ or $\theta = \alpha + \pi$
general polar form of line	$r \cos(\theta - \omega) = \rho$

(366)

4. The graph of the relation S is symmetric with respect to
   I. the polar axis if $(r, -\theta) \in S$ whenever $(r, \theta) \in S$.
   II. the line $\theta = \dfrac{\pi}{2}$ if $(r, \pi - \theta) \in S$ whenever $(r, \theta) \in S$.
   III. The pole if $(-r, \theta) \in S$ whenever $(r, \theta) \in S$. (370)

5. The graph of the relation S is symmetric with respect to
   Ia. the polar axis if $(-r, \pi - \theta) \in S$ whenever $(r, \theta) \in S$.
   IIa. the line $\theta = \dfrac{\pi}{2}$ if $(-r, -\theta) \in S$ whenever $(r, \theta) \in S$.
   IIIa. the pole if $(r, \pi + \theta) \in S$ whenever $(r, \theta) \in S$. (371)

6. The classical curves are listed below with their equations.
   Rose $r = a \cos n\theta$ or $r = a \sin n\theta$, if $n \in N$
   Lemniscate $r^2 = a^2 \cos 2\theta$ or $r^2 = a^2 \sin 2\theta$
   Limaçon $r = a + b \cos \theta$ or $r = a + b \sin \theta$
   Cardioid $r = a + a \cos \theta$ or $r = a + a \sin \theta$
   Spiral of Archimedes $r = a\theta$ (381)

Chapter Review

12–1 **Plot each point. State three equivalent polar pairs for each.**

1. $\left(2, \dfrac{5\pi}{6}\right)$ **2.** $\left(-1, -\dfrac{\pi}{4}\right)$ **3.** $(3, 180°)$

Express each point in polar coordinates.

4. $(1, -1)$ **5.** $(-1, \sqrt{3})$ **6.** $(2, 0)$

Express each point in rectangular coordinates.

7. $\left(3, -\dfrac{\pi}{2}\right)$ **8.** $(-2, 225°)$ **9.** $(4, 22°)$

12–2 **Find the distance between the given points.**

10. $\left(9, \dfrac{\pi}{2}\right)$, $(0, 0)$ **11.** $\left(-6, \dfrac{\pi}{6}\right)$, $\left(2, \dfrac{\pi}{3}\right)$

Change each expression from polar to rectangular form. Identify the curve where possible.

12. $r = -3$ **13.** $r = \theta$

Change each expression from rectangular to polar form.

14. $x^2 + y^2 - 4x + 4 = 0$ **15.** $x + y = 2$

Find an alternate form, if any, by replacing (r, θ) with $(-r, \pi + \theta)$ in each relation.

16. $r = a(1 - \cos \theta)$ **17.** $r = 1 + \csc \theta$

12–3 **Copy and complete the table. Find the polar equation of each line from the given data.**

	Inclination	Through point	Polar equation
18.	$\dfrac{\pi}{3}$	pole	?
19.	horizontal	$\left(-2, \dfrac{\pi}{2}\right)$	?
20.	225°	$(2, 1)$	?

21. Find the equation of the line tangent to the circle $r = 2$ at the point $\left(2, \dfrac{\pi}{4}\right)$.

Choose convenient points and graph each equation.

22. $r = \dfrac{2}{\cos \theta - \sin \theta}$ **23.** $r = 7 \cos \theta$

Copy and complete the table. Find the polar equation of each circle from the data given.

	Center	Radius	Through points	Polar form
24.	$\left(2.5, \frac{\pi}{6}\right)$	—	pole	?
25.	$\left(4, \frac{\pi}{2}\right)$	—	pole	?
26.	$(1.2, 20°)$	2	—	?
27.	$\left(-0.6, \frac{\pi}{3}\right)$	0.5	—	?
28.	on ray $\theta = \frac{\pi}{6}$	—	pole, $\left(3, \frac{\pi}{2}\right)$	?
29.	on ray $\theta = \frac{\pi}{4}$	—	pole, $\left(1, \frac{\pi}{4}\right)$	?

12-4 For each relation, find symmetry, intercepts, extent, and tangents at the pole. Sketch each curve.

30. $r = 2 + \sin\theta$ **31.** $r = \cos 4\theta$

32. $r = 1 + \cos\theta$ **33.** $r = 3\sin\theta$

Find the intercepts of each of the following curves.

34. $r = 2\sin\frac{3}{2}\theta$ **35.** $r = \sin\left(\theta - \frac{\pi}{4}\right)$

12-5 Identify each classical curve. Find symmetry, intercepts, extent, and tangents at the pole. Graph each curve.

36. $r = 2\cos 4\theta$ **37.** $r = 2 - 2\sin\theta$

38. $r = 4\sin 2\theta$ **39.** $r = 1 - 2\cos\theta$

40. $r = 2 - \cos\theta$ **41.** $r = \theta$

Graph each of the following curves.

42. $r^2 = \frac{9}{\theta}$ **43.** $r = 4\tan\theta$

44. $r = 2\sin\theta\cos^2\theta$ **45.** $r = 3\cos 2\theta\sec\theta$

Chapter Test

Plot each point. State three equivalent polar pairs for each.

1. $(-3, 50°)$

2. $\left(2, \dfrac{\pi}{4}\right)$

3. $(1.5, -110°)$

Express each point in polar coordinates.

4. $(-\sqrt{3}, -3)$

5. $(5, 5)$

6. $(3, -2)$

Express each point in rectangular coordinates.

7. $\left(6, \dfrac{\pi}{4}\right)$

8. $\left(2, -\dfrac{\pi}{6}\right)$

9. $(-2, 2.3)$

Change each expression from polar to rectangular form. Identify the curve where possible.

10. $r = 2\cos\theta$

11. $\cos^2\theta + \sin^2\theta = \dfrac{25}{r^2}$

Change each expression from rectangular to polar form.

12. $y^2 = -x$

13. $x^2 + y^2 = 4y$

14. Find the polar form of the vertical line through $(2, 0)$.

Find the polar equation of each line given.

15. A line with inclination $45°$ through the pole

16. A vertical line through the point $(-4, 0)$

17. A line through the points $\left(2, \dfrac{\pi}{2}\right)$ and $(4, 0)$

18. A horizontal line through the point $\left(1, \dfrac{\pi}{2}\right)$

19. Choose convenient points and plot the line $r = \dfrac{5}{\cos\theta - \sin\theta}$.

For each relation, find symmetry, intercepts, extent, and tangents at the pole. Sketch each curve.

20. $r = 4 + 4\cos\theta$

21. $r^2 = 3^2\sin 2\theta$

22. $r = 6$

23. $r = 2 + 3\sin\theta$

Identify each classical curve.

24. $r = \theta$

25. $r = -6\sin 4\theta$

26. $-6 + 5\cos\theta = r$

27. $r^2 = 25\sin 2\theta$

Computers

Predicting Weather

Computers are used in predicting the weather by analyzing equations and plotting graphs. The National Weather Service located in Silver Springs, Maryland has one of the most extensive computer systems for predicting weather. There are also private companies such as Weather Services International in Bedford, Massachusetts, that provide information to local radio, television, and newspapers for weather prediction. Any such source would use parametric equations based on wind patterns and pressure systems. The atmosphere has two layers. One layer is at a low level and has patterns that move clockwise and counterclockwise. It is also associated with high and low pressure systems. The other layer is higher and contains stirring winds which direct the motion of the lower level.

To aid in predicting the path of a storm, imagine an (x, y) coordinate system placed so the origin is under an upper-air low. Let the center of the storm be 310 miles due east of the origin. Thus, the initial coordinates of the storm are (310,0). With a storm approaching the origin at 9 mph the parametric equations are

$$x = (310-9t) \cos (t/31)$$
$$y = (310-9t) \sin (t/31)$$

Assume the movement at a 45 degree bearing and using the Pythagorean Theorem, the path of the storm can be predicted by the following parametric equations.

$$x = 5\sqrt{2}t + (310-9t) \cos (t/31)$$
$$y = 5\sqrt{2}t + (310-9t) \sin (t/31)$$

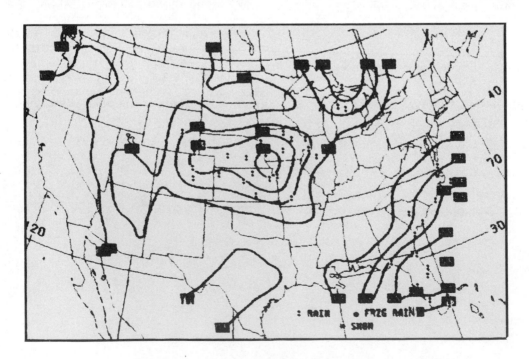

: RAIN   • FRZG RAIN
* SNOW

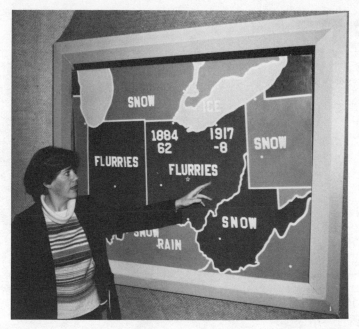

Weather forecasters use computers to help in predicting the weather.

The above system of equations uses the assumption that the upper air force is constant. Any change in the storm will obviously affect the movement of the storm. In order to do any prediction the storm's movement would be studied and monitored.

The computers analyze many such equations and then plot the movement on a chart. When the graphs of several such kinds of data are used by forecasters, weather patterns can be determined. The better the graphs are, the better the predictions can be. The use of computers makes it possible for the graphs to be completed quickly and frequently. Thus, the forecasters have up-to-date information and are able to more accurately predict the weather. Of course, since so many things affect the weather, a change in any one factor will change the weather. Even with computers, the weather forecasters are sometimes wrong. However, the percentage of correct predictions is increasing each year as more advancements are found.

Exercises **Write programs for each of the following.**

1. Given the polar coordinates of a point, find its rectangular coordinates.

2. Given the rectangular coordinates of a point, find its polar coordinates. (Use the ATN function.)

3. Change the polar equation $r = \sin x + \cos x$ to an equation in rectangular coordinates.

4. Change the equation $x^2 + y^2 = r^2$ into an equation in polar coordinates.

5. Find the intercepts of $r = a \cos bx$.

6. Find the extent and tangents for $r^2 = a^2 \sin 2\theta$.

7. Identify $r = 4 - \sin \theta$ as rose, lemniscate, limaçon, cardioid, or a spiral.

8. Output the graph for $r = \cos 4\theta$.

Chapter 13

Many structures like the one pictured seem to converge to a point. Sequences are a special class of functions with a unique domain which can converge to a number called a limit.

Sequences and Series

13-1 Sequences

Aptitude tests often contain questions such as this one.

What are the next three terms in each sequence?

    a. 2, 4, 6, 8, . . .
    b. 2, 3, 5, 7, 11, . . .
    c. 1, 2, 6, 24, . . .

To answer such questions, look for a pattern in the given numbers. Assuming that the pattern continues, it can be used to generate the next terms of the sequence. For the above patterns the following rules work for finding subsequent terms.

    a. The nth term is $2n$.
    b. The nth term is the nth prime number.
    c. The nth term is obtained by multiplying the value of the $(n - 1)$th term by n.

These are possible answers. Rules for forming sequences are not uniquely determined by listing the first few terms.

Using these rules, here are possible answers to the example.

    a. 10, 12, 14
    b. 13, 17, 19
    c. 120, 720, 5040

> A **sequence** is a function with domain N. A sequence may be defined by a formula or by listing ordered pairs of the sequence.

Definition of Sequence

Example

1. Define the sequence $1, \frac{1}{2}, \frac{1}{3}, \frac{1}{4}, \ldots$ by using a formula and by listing ordered pairs.

    1. $F(n) = \dfrac{1}{n}, n \in N$ **2.** $\{(1, 1), (2, \frac{1}{2}), (3, \frac{1}{3}), (4, \frac{1}{4}), \ldots\}$

Sequences are often represented by listing only the range elements in order since the domain element denotes the place in the sequence. These range elements are called the **terms** or **elements** of the sequence. For Example 1, the sequence could be defined as follows.

Remember sequences are functions, even though most of the work with sequences deals only with the range elements.

$$1, \frac{1}{2}, \frac{1}{3}, \frac{1}{4}, \ldots$$

When the sequence is written this way it is understood the third number is $f(3)$ and the nth number is $f(n)$. The number $\frac{1}{4}$ is called the 4th term. Its place in the sequence indicates the element of the domain. Another way to write the nth term is a_n. Notice that a_n represents the range element corresponding to the domain element n. The sequence $F(n) = \frac{1}{n}$ can be indicated by $\left\{\frac{1}{n}\right\}$.

A sequence also may be defined **recursively**, or by a **recursion formula**. This is done by specifying the first term of the sequence and then defining the relationship between any term and its successor.

Example

2. Find the first four terms of the sequence $\{a_n\}$ defined such that $a_1 = 3$ and $a_{n+1} = 2a_n + 1$.

$$a_1 = 3 \qquad a_2 = 2(3) + 1 = 7 \qquad a_3 = 2(7) + 1 = 15$$
$$a_4 = 2(15) + 1 = 31$$

The first four terms of the sequence are 3, 7, 15, 31.

Exercises

Exploratory State the first four terms of each sequence.

1. $a_n = 2n$

2. $\left\{\frac{2}{n}\right\}$

3. $a_n = n^2$

4. $a_1 = \frac{1}{2}; a_{n+1} = 1 - a_n$

Find a simple formula for the nth term of a sequence having the first four terms as given.

5. $1, 3, 5, 7, \ldots$

6. $2, 3, 4, 5, \ldots$

7. $1, \frac{1}{2}, \frac{1}{4}, \frac{1}{8}, \ldots$

8. $3, 6, 9, 12, \ldots$

9. $1, 4, 9, 16, \ldots$

10. $2, 5, 8, 11, \ldots$

Written Write the first four terms of each sequence.

1. $f(n) = n!$

2. $\{3^n\}$

3. $\left\{\dfrac{n(n-1)(2n+1)}{6}\right\}$

4. $a_n = n(n + 1)$ **5.** $f(n) = (-1)^n \cdot 3n$ **6.** $\{1 + 0.5(n - 1)\}$

7. $a_1 = 2; a_{n+1} = n \cdot a_n$ **8.** $a_1 = 1; a_{n+1} = \frac{1}{2}a_n$

Find a simple formula for the nth term of a sequence, having the first four terms as given.

9. $\frac{1}{3}, \frac{1}{9}, \frac{1}{27}, \frac{1}{81}, \ldots$ **10.** $\frac{3}{2}, \frac{9}{4}, \frac{27}{8}, \frac{81}{16}, \ldots$

11. $1, \frac{1}{2}, \frac{1}{3}, \frac{1}{4}, \ldots$ **12.** $1, -1, 1, -1, \ldots$

13. $1, 0, 1, 0, \ldots$ **14.** $1, 3, 7, 15, \ldots$

15. $1, -\frac{1}{2}, \frac{1}{4}, -\frac{1}{8}, \ldots$ **16.** $-1, \frac{1}{3}, -\frac{1}{9}, \frac{1}{27}, \ldots$

17. $-\frac{1}{2}, \frac{1}{2}, -\frac{1}{2}, \frac{1}{2}, \ldots$ **18.** $0, 1, 0, 1, \ldots$

19. $\frac{1}{2}, \frac{1}{6}, \frac{1}{12}, \frac{1}{20}, \ldots$ **20.** $\frac{1}{2}, \frac{2}{3}, \frac{3}{4}, \frac{4}{5}, \ldots$

21. $9, 3, 1, \frac{1}{3}, \ldots$ **22.** $1, \frac{1}{8}, \frac{1}{27}, \frac{1}{64}, \ldots$

Write another expression for the nth term of each sequence.

23. $a_1 = 3; a_n = a_{n-1} + 12$ **24.** $s_1 = 1; s_n = -s_{n-1}$

25. $a_1 = 2; a_n = \frac{2}{3}a_{n-1}$ **26.** $a_1 = 7; a_n = a_{n-1} - 4$

27. Write the first five terms of the sequence defined by $a_n = 3n + 1$. Which term of the sequence is 196?

28. Write the first four terms of the sequence defined by $a_n = n^2 + n$. Which term of the sequence is 132?

29. Write a simple formula to define the sequence $1, 1.1, 1.21, 1.331, \ldots$.

Write the first four terms of each sequence. *What do you notice?*

30. $a_n = 2^{n-1}$ **31.** $a_n = 0.5(n^2 - n + 2)$

For each of the sequences $2, 4, 6, 8, \ldots$ and $3, 7, 11, 15, \ldots$; $a_n - a_{n-1} = a_{n+1} - a_n$. This result shows that the difference between two successive terms is the same as the difference between the next two successive terms. Therefore, the difference between successive terms is constant throughout the sequence. Sequences of this type are called **arithmetic sequences.**

32. Write the common difference for each of the above sequences.

33. Write the common differences for $1, 6, 11, 16, \ldots$ and $70, 53, 36, 19, \ldots$

For each of the sequences $1, 1.1, 1.21, 1.331, \ldots$ and $-1, 1, -1, 1, \ldots$, $\frac{a_{n+1}}{a_n} = \frac{a_n}{a_{n-1}}$. This result shows that each term after the first is obtained by multiplying the previous term by a constant factor. Sequences of this type are called **geometric sequences.**

34. Write the constant factor for each of the above sequences.

35. Write the constant factors for the sequences $4, 6, 9, 13\frac{1}{2}, \ldots$ and $1, -\frac{1}{2}, \frac{1}{4}, -\frac{1}{8}, \ldots$

36. As a reward for service to the king, a wise person was offered the choice of a gift. The request, which the king thought was modest, was "one grain of rice on the first square of a chessboard, two on the second, four on the third, and so on." Each of the 8 rows on a chessboard contains 8 squares. Calculate the number of grains of rice needed for the last square.

Challenge Solve each of the following.

1. Write a simple formula for the sequence 1, 3, 5, ... Find the first three terms of the sequences given by $a_n = n^3 - 6n^2 + 13n - 7$ and $b_n = 2n^3 - 12n^2 + 24n - 13$. Comment on the results.

2. A gumdrop addict unwisely eats a gumdrop one day. Then each day thereafter eats one more gumdrop than on the previous day. Find a formula for the nth term of the sequence which gives the total number of gumdrops eaten by the end of 1, 2, 3, . . . days.

A piece of newspaper 0.005 cm thick is torn in two. The pieces are placed on top of one another. These pieces are then torn in two and the four pieces placed on top of one another.

3. Write the first five terms of the sequence which gives the height of the pile of paper in hundredths of a centimeter after 1, 2, 3, . . . tears.

4. Calculate the height after 8 tears, 10 tears and 50 tears.

13–2   Summations

The wise person in Problem **36** of Section **13–1** made considerable gain through the grain deal. To determine the total number of grains of rice at any given stage, the sum of the grain is needed. For example, when six squares are covered, the total number of grains is $1 + 2 + 4 + 8 + 16 + 32 = 63$. To represent the total number of grains when n squares are covered, the following formula can be written.

$$1 + 2 + 4 + \ldots + 2^{n-1} = S_n$$

The symbol S_n is called the nth sum or the nth *partial sum*. To represent a sum where the addends are the first n terms of a sequence, a special notation Σ (the Greek letter sigma), is introduced. This symbol is called the summation sign in mathematics.

Sigma notation is as follows:
$$\sum_{n=1}^{5} x = 1 + 2 + 3 + 4 + 5 = 15$$

Examples

1.   Using the summation sign, write the sum of six terms of the sequence $\{2n\}$.

$$\sum_{r=1}^{6} 2r = 2 + 4 + 6 + 8 + 10 + 12 = 42$$

2. **Find the sum of the first n terms of the sequence $\left\{\dfrac{1}{2^n}\right\}$.**

$$\sum_{i=1}^{n} \frac{1}{2^i} = \frac{1}{2} + \frac{1}{4} + \cdots + \frac{1}{2^n}$$

The symbol $\displaystyle\sum_{i=1}^{n} \frac{1}{2^i}$ is read, *the sum of $\dfrac{1}{2^i}$ from $i = 1$ to $i = n$.* Notice that r and i are dummy symbols. They can be replaced by any other symbol.

$$\sum_{r=1}^{5} 2r = \sum_{s=1}^{5} 2s = \sum_{t=1}^{5} 2t = 2 + 4 + 6 + 8 + 10 = 30$$

Example

3. **Show that $\displaystyle\sum_{r=1}^{n} r = \frac{1}{2}n(n+1).$**

Since $r = \dfrac{1}{2}[r(r+1) - (r-1)r]$, $\displaystyle\sum_{r=1}^{n} r = \sum_{r=1}^{n} \frac{1}{2}[r(r+1) - (r-1)r].$

$$\tfrac{1}{2}[r(r+1) - (r-1)r] = \tfrac{1}{2}(r^2 + r - r^2 + r) = r$$

Then,

$$\sum_{r=1}^{n} r = \frac{1}{2}\big([(1\cdot2) - (0\cdot1)] + [(2\cdot3) - (1\cdot2)] +$$

$$[(3\cdot4) - (2\cdot3)] + \cdots + [n(n+1) - (n-1)n]\big)$$

$$= \frac{1}{2}[n(n+1) - (0\cdot1)] \qquad \textit{All terms of the sum add in}$$
$$\textit{pairs to zero except} - (0\cdot1),$$
$$= \frac{1}{2}[n(n+1)] \qquad \textit{and } n(n+1).$$

Therefore, $\displaystyle\sum_{r=1}^{n} r = \frac{1}{2}n(n+1).$ This shows that the sum of n terms of the sequence $\{n\}$ is $1 + 2 + 3 + \cdots + n = \dfrac{1}{2}n(n+1).$

Exercises

Exploratory Write each sum in expanded form. Find the sum.

1. $\displaystyle\sum_{n=1}^{4} n$

2. $\displaystyle\sum_{n=1}^{4} 2n + 1$

3. $\displaystyle\sum_{n=1}^{4} n^2$

4. $\displaystyle\sum_{n=1}^{4} n(-1)^n$ **5.** $\displaystyle\sum_{n=1}^{4} \frac{1}{2}n$ **6.** $\displaystyle\sum_{n=1}^{4} 7$

Use sigma Σ notation to write each sum.

7. $1 + 2 + 3 + 4 + 5 + 6$ **8.** $2 + 2^2 + 2^3 + 2^4 + 2^5$

9. $1 + 3 + 5 + 7 + \cdots + 19$ **10.** $\dfrac{2}{3} + \dfrac{2}{4} + \dfrac{2}{5} + \cdots$

Written Write the sum of the first six terms of each sequence. Find the sum.

1. $1, 4, 9, 16, \ldots$ **2.** $5, 10, 20, 40, \ldots$

3. $20, 10, 0, -10, \ldots$ **4.** $\{3n\}$

5. $\left\{\dfrac{n}{2}\right\}$ **6.** $\{2^n - 1\}$

7. Two persons start work at \$5000 per year. One receives a raise of \$500 per year at the end of each year. The other receives a raise of \$1250 at the end of every two years. Use a sum to represent the income of each person at the end of eight years. Find each sum.

Write the partial sums $S_1, S_2, S_3, \ldots$ to see a pattern. Then, find the sum of n terms, S_n.

8. $1 + 1 + 1 + \cdots + 1 + \cdots$ **9.** $-1 - 1 - 1 - \cdots - 1 - \cdots$

10. $1 - 1 + 1 - 1 + \cdots + (-1)^{n-1} + \cdots$

11. $1 + 3 + 5 + 7 + \cdots + (2n - 1) + \cdots$

12. The sum of n terms of the sequence $1, \dfrac{1}{1}, \dfrac{1}{2!}, \dfrac{1}{3!}, \ldots \dfrac{1}{(n-1)!}$ gives an approximation to the irrational number e. Notice that each term of the sequence is found easily from the previous term. Find the sum to seven terms.

13. Show by multiplication that $(1 - r)(1 + r) = 1 - r^2$, $(1 - r) \cdot (1 + r + r^2) = 1 - r^3$, and $(1 - r)(1 + r + r^2 + \cdots + r^{n-2} + r^{n-1}) = 1 - r^n$. If $r \neq 1$, deduce the sum of n terms of the sequence $1, r, r^2, \ldots, r^{n-1}$. What is the sum if $r = 1$?

Write each sum in expanded form.

14. $\displaystyle\sum_{r=1}^{4} 3r$ **15.** $\displaystyle\sum_{r=1}^{5} (r + 2)$ **16.** $\displaystyle\sum_{k=1}^{3} k^3$

17. $\displaystyle\sum_{i=1}^{6} i(i + 1)$ **18.** $\displaystyle\sum_{j=1}^{5} j(j + 1)(j + 2)$ **19.** $\displaystyle\sum_{r=1}^{7} \frac{1}{r(r + 1)}$

Calculate each sum.

20. $\displaystyle\sum_{r=1}^{4} 2r$ **21.** $\displaystyle\sum_{k=1}^{5} (2k + 3)$

22. $\displaystyle\sum_{r=1}^{5} \frac{1}{r}$ **23.** $\displaystyle\sum_{r=1}^{6} (r + 1)(r - 1)$

Use sigma notation to write each sum.

24. $a + 2a + 3a + 4a + 5a + 6a + 7a$

25. $\dfrac{1}{1 \cdot 2} + \dfrac{1}{2 \cdot 3} + \cdots + \dfrac{1}{n(n + 1)}$

26. $1 - 1 + 1 - 1 + 1 - 1 + 1 - 1 + 1$

Challenge Solve each of the following.

1. Show that $\displaystyle\sum_{r=1}^{n} r(r + 1) = \dfrac{1}{3}n(n + 1)(n + 2)$.

(Hint. First, prove that $r(r + 1) = \dfrac{1}{3}$ $[r(r + 1)(r + 2) - (r - 1) \, r(r + 1)]$.)

2. Show that $\displaystyle\sum_{r=1}^{n} r^2 = \dfrac{1}{6} n(n + 1)(2n + 1)$.

(Hint. First, prove that $r^2 = r(r + 1) - r$.)

13–3 Arithmetic Sequences and Sums

A story is told of the great mathematician Carl Friedrich Gauss as a child. The teacher told his elementary class to add the whole numbers from one to one hundred. The teacher hoped to keep the class busy for awhile on the problem. Gauss gave the answer in a few seconds. The method which Gauss used is similar to the one shown in the example.

Example

1. **Find the sum, S_{100}, of the first one hundred natural numbers.**

$$S_{100} = \;\;\; 1 \; + \;\;\; 2 \; + \cdots + \;\;\; 99 + 100$$
$$\text{Also, } S_{100} = 100 + \;\; 99 + \cdots + \;\;\; 2 \; + \;\;\; 1$$
$$\overline{2S_{100} = 101 + 101 + \cdots + 101 + 101} \quad \textit{How many addends are there?}$$
$$2s_{100} = 100 \cdot 101$$
$$S_{100} = 50 \cdot 101$$
$$S_{100} = 5050$$

In an arithmetic sequence, each term after the first can be found by adding a constant, called the *common difference*, to the preceding term.

An arithmetic sequence is a sequence $\{a_n\}$ such that $a_1 = a$, $a_n = a_{n-1} + d$, where d is the common difference.

Definition of Arithmetic Sequence

An arithmetic sequence also may be written as $\{a_n\} = a, a + d$, $a + 2d, \ldots, a + (n - 1)d, \ldots$, where a is the first term, d is the common difference, and $[a + (n - 1)d]$ is the nth term. Using this notation and Gauss' method, a formula for finding the sum of n terms of an arithmetic sequence can be determined.

$$S_n = a + (a + d) + \cdots + [a + (n - 2)d] + [a + (n - 1)d]$$
$$S_n = [a + (n - 1)d] + [a + (n - 2)d] + \cdots + (a + d) + a$$
$$2S_n = [2a + (n - 1)d] + [2a + (n - 1)d] + \cdots + [2a + (n - 1)d] + [2a + (n - 1)d]$$
$$2S_n = n[2a + (n - 1)d]$$
$$S_n = \frac{n}{2}[2a + (n - 1)d]$$

Let $\ell = a + (n - 1)d$ represent the last term to be summed, then $S_n = \frac{n}{2}(a + \ell) = n\left(\frac{a + \ell}{2}\right)$.

$S_n = \frac{n}{2}[2a + (n - 1)d]$ *is more convenient to use when the first term and common difference are known.*

The sum of n terms of an arithmetic sequence is $S_n = n\left(\frac{a + \ell}{2}\right)$, where a is the first term and ℓ is the last term to be summed.

Sum of an Arithmetic Sequence

Thus the sum of an arithmetic sequence to n terms may be found by multiplying the arithmetic average of the first and last terms by n.

The arithmetic average of a and ℓ is $\frac{a + \ell}{2}$.

Examples

2. Find the sum of the first five terms of the arithmetic sequence 0, 7, 14, ...

$$a_1 = 0 \quad a_2 = 7 \quad a_3 = 14 \quad a_4 = 21 \quad a_5 = 28$$
$$S_n = n\left(\frac{a + \ell}{2}\right) \quad \text{Let } n = 5, a = 0, \ell = 28.$$
$$= 5\left(\frac{0 + 28}{2}\right)$$
$$= 70$$

3. Find the sum of the first eleven terms of the arithmetic sequence 7, 5, 3, 1, ...

$$a = 7 \quad d = -2 \quad n = 11$$
$$S_n = \frac{n}{2}[2a + (n - 1)d]$$
$$S_{11} = \frac{11}{2}[2(7) + (11 - 1)(-2)]$$
$$= \frac{11}{2}(-6)$$
$$S_{11} = -33$$

Exercises

Exploratory   The numbers given are the first few terms of an arithmetic sequence. Identify the first term *a* and the common difference *d*. Name the next three terms in the sequence.

1. 19, 25, 31, . . .

2. 1.5, 3, 4.5, . . .

3. −9, −2, 5, . . .

4. 5, −1, −7, . . .

5. 2, 6, 10, . . .

6. 20, 17, 14, . . .

Written   The numbers given are the first few terms of an arithmetic sequence. Identify the first term *a* and the common difference *d* and write the next three terms in the sequence. Then, write the tenth term.

1. 1, 3, 5, . . .

2. $1, \frac{3}{2}, 2, \frac{5}{2}, \ldots$

3. −9, −2, 5, . . .

4. $x, 2x, 3x, \ldots$

5. 5, −4, −13, . . .

6. $b, -b, -3b, \ldots$

Find the two numbers of the sequence between the given two terms of an arithmetic sequence. The terms between any two terms of an arithmetic sequence are called **arithmetic means**.

7. 5, −4

8. 12, 21

9. 7, 16

10. 1, 2

Find the indicated term of each arithmetic sequence.

11. ninth term of 3, 7, 11, . . .

12. seventh term of $\frac{3}{4}, \frac{13}{12}, \frac{17}{12}, \ldots$

13. thirteenth term of $-7\sqrt{2}, -5\sqrt{2}, -3\sqrt{2}, \ldots$

14. eighth term of $a - b, \frac{a - b}{2}, 0, \ldots$

Use Gauss' method to find each sum if the addends are terms in an arithmetic sequence. Show your work.

15. 1 + 3 + 5 + ⋯ + 21

16. 2 + 4 + 6 + ⋯ + 100

17. Find the sum to 40 terms of 14 + 17 + 20 + ⋯.

18. Find the sum of 3 + 8 + 13 + ⋯ + 98.

Challenge   The ancient Greeks were very interested in number patterns. The first five triangular numbers are **1, 3, 6, 10, 15.**

1. What are the next three numbers of the sequence?

2. Is it an arithmetic sequence?

3. Find the twentieth triangular number.

Solve each of the following.

4. Calculate the sum of all natural numbers less than 100 which are exactly divisible by 3.

5. Find *n* if 1 + 2 + ⋯ + *n* = 120.

6. How many terms of 24 + 20 + 16 + ⋯ are needed to give a sum of 72? Interpret your answer.

7. The first term of an arithmetic sequence is −7. The common difference is $\frac{3}{2}$. If the sum of *n* terms is −14, find *n*.

13–4 Geometric Sequences and Sums

A geometric sequence is a sequence such that each term after the first can be found by multiplying the preceding term by a constant called the *common ratio*.

> A geometric sequence is a sequence $\{a_n\}$ such that $a_1 = a$, $a_{n+1} = a_n \cdot r$, where r is the common ratio.

Definition of Geometric Sequence

The sequence depends only on the first term a and the common ratio r. Thus a geometric sequence also can be written as follows.

$$\{a_n\} = a, ar, ar^2, \ldots, ar^{n-1}$$

Examples

1. Show that 1, 2, 4, 8, . . . is a geometric sequence

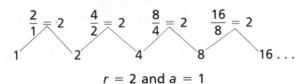

$$\frac{2}{1} = 2 \qquad \frac{4}{2} = 2 \qquad \frac{8}{4} = 2 \qquad \frac{16}{8} = 2$$

1   2   4   8   16 . . .

$$r = 2 \text{ and } a = 1$$

2. Show that 16, 8, 4, 2, . . . is a geometric sequence.

$$\frac{8}{16} = \frac{1}{2} \qquad \frac{4}{8} = \frac{1}{2} \qquad \frac{2}{4} = \frac{1}{2}$$

16   8   4   2 . . .

$$a = 16 \text{ and } r = \frac{1}{2}$$

The sum of the first n terms of a geometric sequence can be represented by S_n.

$$S_n = a + ar + ar^2 + \cdots + ar^{n-1}$$
$$r \cdot S_n = ar + ar^2 + ar^3 + \cdots + ar^{n-1} + ar^n$$
$$S_n - r \cdot S_n = a - ar^n$$
$$S_n(1 - r) = a(1 - r^n)$$
$$S_n = a\left(\frac{1 - r^n}{1 - r}\right), r \neq 1$$

The sum of n terms of a geometric sequence is $S_n = a\left(\dfrac{1 - r^n}{1 - r}\right)$, where $r \neq 1$, a is the first term, and r is the common ratio.

Sum of a Geometric Sequence

Example

3. Given the geometric sequence $16, 8, 4, \ldots, 16 \cdot \dfrac{1}{2}^{n-1}, \ldots$, find the sum to nine terms.

$$a = 16;\ r = \frac{1}{2},\ n = 9$$

$$S_n = a\left(\frac{1 - r^n}{1 - r}\right)$$

$$S_9 = 16\left[\frac{1 - \left(\frac{1}{2}\right)^9}{1 - \frac{1}{2}}\right] = \frac{2^4\left(\frac{2^9 - 1}{2^9}\right)}{\frac{1}{2}}$$

$$= \frac{2^9 - 1}{2^5} \cdot \frac{2}{1} = \frac{2^9 - 1}{2^4}$$

$$S_9 = \frac{511}{16}$$

Exercises

Exploratory The given numbers are the first few terms of a geometric sequence. Identify the common ratio r. Then state the next three terms in the sequence.

1. $1.2, 2.4, 4.8, \ldots$

2. $7, 3.5, 1.75, \ldots$

3. $\dfrac{1}{3}, \dfrac{2}{3}, \dfrac{4}{3}, \ldots$

4. $\dfrac{\sqrt{3}}{2}, \dfrac{\sqrt{3}}{4}, \dfrac{\sqrt{3}}{8}, \ldots$

Write a possible nth term in simplest form for each geometric sequence.

5. $3, 6, 12, 24, \ldots$

6. $4, 20, 100, 500, \ldots$

7. $9, 6, 4, \dfrac{8}{3}, \ldots$

8. $\dfrac{3}{2}, \dfrac{9}{4}, \dfrac{27}{8}, \dfrac{81}{16}, \ldots$

Written The given numbers are the first few terms of a geometric sequence. Identify the common ratio r. Write the next three terms in the sequence. Write a formula for the nth term.

1. $1, \dfrac{3}{2}, \dfrac{9}{4}, \ldots$

2. $-8, -4, -2, -1, \ldots$

3. $15, 5, \dfrac{5}{3}, \ldots$

4. $1, -2, 4, \ldots$

The terms between two given terms of a geometric sequence are called **geometric means**. To find four geometric means between **64** and **2** means to find four numbers $a, b, c,$ and d such that **64**, $a, b, c, d,$ **2** are terms in a geometric sequence. For each of the following find two geometric means between the given terms.

5. 64, 8   6. 81, 24   7. 5, $15\sqrt{3}$ 8. 81, 3

Write a possible nth term in simplest form for each geometric sequence.

9. 1, 2, 4, . . .

10. $\dfrac{1}{2}, \dfrac{1}{4}, \dfrac{1}{8}, \cdots$

11. 4, 2, 1, . . .

12. 2, -6, 18, . . .

13. 9, 3, 1, . . .

14. $a, ar, ar^2, \ldots$

Given the formula for the nth term, write the first, second, and fifth term of the sequence.

15. $a_n = 3^{n-1}$

16. $a_n = 3(-2)^{n-1}$

17. $a_n = 6\left(-\dfrac{1}{2}\right)^{n-1}$

Find $a, r,$ and the fifth term for each geometric sequence.

18. 1, 1.2, 1.44, . . .

19. $\dfrac{1}{3},$ 1, 3, . . .

20. 100, 105, 110.25, . . .

21. the sequence with first term 6 and third term 24

22. the sequence with first term 10 and second term 100

23. the sequence with first term 50 and fourth term 400

24. the sequence with first term 36 and second term -24

Suppose someone buys a savings certificate which has the interest added to the capital at the end of each year. The interest for the next year is calculated on the new capital. This way of calculating interest is called **compound interest**. Suppose the capital is 100 units at the beginning of the year. The rate of interest is 15% per annum, compounded annually.

25. Find the capital at the beginning of the second year.

26. Find the capital at the end of the second year.

27. Find the capital at the end of the third year.

28. Find the capital at the end of the nth year.

29. Write a sequence which shows the capital at the end of each year.

30. Write a sequence which shows the capital at the end of each year, if the interest rate is r% per annum.

Write the values for a and r and use the formula $S_n = a\left(\dfrac{1 - r^n}{1 - r}\right)$ to find each sum.

31. $1 + 2 + 4 + \cdots$ to 8 terms

32. $2 + 6 + 18 + \cdots$ to 7 terms

33. $\dfrac{1}{2} + \dfrac{1}{4} + \dfrac{1}{8} + \cdots$ to 10 terms

34. $2 - 4 + 8 - \cdots$ to 5 terms

35. $2 - \dfrac{2}{3} + \dfrac{2}{9} - \cdots$ to 5 terms

36. $1 + x + x^2 + \cdots$ to n terms

37. Find n if $3 + 3^2 + 3^3 + \cdots + 3^n = 120$.

38. Find the sum of $1 - 1 + 1 - 1 + \cdots$ for n terms.

p. 392 #36

Challenge **Solve each of the following.**

1. Suppose that the height of a plant increases 5% each month. If it is now one meter high, use logarithms or a calculator to give its height after 0, 1, 2, 3, 4, and 5 months. Exhibit the results as a geometric sequence. Approximately how tall is the plant after 10 months? Show the sequence on a graph. (Note: In this sequence, $a_n = (1.05)a_{n-1}$. The number 1.05 is called the growth factor for the sequence.)

2. A neutron can transform spontaneously into a proton and an electron. This transformation is such that given a number of neutrons, about 5% of them have changed by the end of one minute. If you begin with 1,000,000 neutrons, use logarithms or a calculator to compute the number left at the end of 0, 1, 2, 3, and 4 minutes. Write these numbers as a sequence. Then graph the sequence. (Note: In this sequence $a_n = (0.95)a_{n-1}$. The factor 0.95 is called the decay factor for the sequence. The neutrons are said to decay.)

3. Suppose a person pays $100 every year to an insurance company, and the payments earn 5% compounded annually. How much would this person receive on the 60th birthday? The answer depends on several things. For example, at what age the payments start and on such factors as taxes. Disregard the other factors and suppose the first payment was on the 20th birthday. Then this payment has 40 years to grow. The value of this payment on the 60th birthday is $100(1.05)^{40}$. The second payment grows to $100(1.05)^{39}$, and the final payment grows to $100(1.05)$. Show that the total value is $105(1 + 1.05 + 1.05^2 + \cdots + 1.05^{39})$. Calculate the sum of this series to the nearest $100. Use 0.02118 as an approximation for log 1.05.

Excursions in Mathematics

Ambiguity in Sequences

Knowing only the first few terms does not uniquely determine a sequence. For example, the sequence 1, 3, 5, . . . is ambiguous. It may be the arithmetic sequence $\{2n - 1\}$. It may be the sequence formed by one and the odd prime numbers. It also may be this sequence.

$$\{a_n\} : a_n = (n - 1)(n - 2)(n - 3) + (2n - 1)$$

Notice that $(n - 1)(n - 2)(n - 3) = 0$ for $n = 1, 2,$ or 3. The sequence corresponds to $\{2n - 1\}$ in the first three terms. After three terms, $(n - 1)(n - 2)(n - 3) \neq 0$, and the sequence differs from $\{2n - 1\}$. The terms of this sequence are 1, 3, 5, 13, ... The use of expressions such as $(n - 1)(n - 2)$ or $(n - 1)(n - 2)(n - 3)(n - 4)$ results in a sequence that corresponds initially to a given sequence.

A multiple description also can be used to generate a sequence that corresponds to a given sequence in some, but not all, terms. Here are two examples.

$$a_n = \begin{cases} 2^{-1}n \text{ if } 1 \leq n \leq 6 \\ 2n \text{ if } n > 6 \end{cases} \quad \text{or} \quad a_n = \begin{cases} 2n \text{ if } n \text{ is odd} \\ n^2 \text{ if } n \text{ is even} \end{cases}$$

No sequence defined by a formula is ambiguous. The value of the nth term is always known.

13-5   Mathematical Induction

What is the sum of the first n natural numbers? One might approach the problem by making a table like the one below.

Natural Numbers	1	2	3	4	5	6 . . .
Cumulative sums	1	3	6	10	15	21 . . .

Studying this pattern suggests that $\dfrac{n \cdot (n + 1)}{2}$ represents the sum of the first n natural numbers. Such statements are only conjectures based on many observations. Until a statement is proved or disproved, it is only a conjecture.

Statements involving natural numbers are common in mathematics. A method for proving some of these statements is called **Mathematical Induction.** This method is sometimes compared to the domino method. Suppose dominoes are lined up in such a way that each domino will knock over the next. If the first domino falls over, then all the dominoes will fall over.

Let $P(n)$ be a statement involving a natural number $n \in$ N. Then P is true for every natural number n if and only if

a.   P(1) is true and
b.   For any natural number k, if $P(k)$ is true then $P(k + 1)$ is true.

Induction Postulate

Examples

1.   **Prove that the sum of the first n natural numbers is $\dfrac{n(n + 1)}{2}$.**

Let $P(n)$ be the statement $1 + 2 + 3 + \cdots + n = \dfrac{n(n + 1)}{2}$.

a. $\dfrac{1 \cdot (1 + 1)}{2} = 1$. Therefore, $P(1)$ is true.

b.   For $k \in$ N assume that $P(k)$ is true. That is, assume $1 + 2 + 3 + \cdots + k = \dfrac{k(k + 1)}{2}$. Then, show this implies that $P(k + 1)$ is true.

$$1 + 2 + 3 + \cdots + k = \frac{k(k + 1)}{2}$$

$$1 + 2 + 3 + \cdots + k + (k + 1) = \frac{k(k + 1)}{2} + (k + 1)$$

$$= \frac{k(k + 1) + 2(k + 1)}{2}$$

$$= \frac{(k + 1)(k + 2)}{2}$$

Therefore $P(k + 1)$ is true whenever $P(k)$ is true. So, by the Induction Postulate, $P(n)$ is true for every $n \in N$.

2. **Prove that $2n \leq 2^n$ for every $n \in N$. Let $P(n)$ be the statement $2n \leq 2^n$.**

   a. $2 \cdot 1 \leq 2^1$. Therefore $P(1)$ is true.
   b. Assume $2k \leq 2^k$ for some $k \in N$.
       For any $k \in N$, $2 \leq 2^k$.

   $$2k \leq 2^k \quad \text{and} \quad 2 \leq 2^k$$
   $$2k + 2 \quad \leq \quad 2^k + 2^k$$
   $$2(k + 1) \quad \leq \quad 2 \cdot 2^k$$
   $$2(k + 1) \quad \leq \quad 2^{k+1}$$

   Therefore, $P(k + 1)$ is true whenever $P(k)$ is true. So, by the Induction Postulate, $P(n)$ is true for every $n \in N$.

Statements **a** and **b** of the Induction Postulate are equally important in a proof by Mathematical Induction. Both statements must be true to conclude that P is true for every natural number.

Examples

3. **Prove or disprove that $2 + 4 + 6 + \cdots + 2n = n^2 + n + 2$ for every $n \in N$.**

   Let $P(n)$ be the statement $2 + 4 + 6 + \cdots + 2n = n^2 + n + 2$.
   Since $1^2 + 1 + 2 = 4 \neq 2$, $P(1)$ is false. Therefore $P(n)$ is not true for all $n \in N$, and $P(n)$ is said to be false.

4. **Prove or disprove that $n^2 - n + 41$ is a prime number for every $n \in N$.**

   Let $P(n)$ be the statement $n^2 - n + 41$ is a prime number.
   a. $1 - 1 + 41 = 41$ is a prime number. Therefore, $P(1)$ is true.
   b. Suppose $k = 40$. Then $k^2 - k + 41 = (40)^2 - 40 + 41 = 1601$, which is a prime number. But then, $(k + 1)^2 - (k + 1) + 41 = (41)^2 - 41 + 41 = (41)^2$ which is not a prime number. Therefore, $P(n)$ is not true for all on $\in N$.

In Example **1**, it was shown that $P(1)$ is false. The statement $P(1)$ provides a counterexample showing the statement $P(n)$ is not true for every $n \in$ N. In Example **2**, it was shown that $P(41)$ is false. The statement $P(41)$ provides a counterexample showing the statement $P(n)$ is not true for every $n \in$ N. Notice that one could try every natural number less than 41 and not find a counterexample. If one suspects that a statement is false, one should try to find a counterexample. However, if one fails to find a counterexample, and is unable to prove the statement $P(n)$, then one cannot say whether $P(n)$ is true or false.

Exercises

Exploratory Find the $(n + 1)$ th term for each of the following nth terms.

1. $\dfrac{n}{n + 1}$ **2.** $n^2 + n + 1$ **3.** $n(n + 1)$ **4.** $2^n + 1$

Give the value of each expression for $n = 1$.

5. $\dfrac{n}{n + 1}$ **6.** $n^2 + n + 1$ **7.** $n(n + 1)$ **8.** $2^n + 1$

Written Prove or disprove each statement by Mathematical Induction.

1. $1 + 2 + 4 + 8 + \cdots + 2^{n-1} = 2^n - 1$ for every $n \in$ N.

2. $\dfrac{1}{1 \cdot 2} + \dfrac{1}{2 \cdot 3} + \dfrac{1}{3 \cdot 4} + \cdots + \dfrac{1}{n(n + 1)} = \dfrac{n}{n + 1}$ for every $n \in$ N.

3. $1 + 3 + 5 + \cdots + (2n - 1) = n^2 + 3$ for every $n \in$ N.

4. $3 + 6 + 9 + \cdots + 3n = \dfrac{3n(n + 1)}{2}$ for every $n \in$ N.

5. $1^2 + 2^2 + 3^2 + \cdots + n^2 = \dfrac{n(n + 1)(2n + 1)}{6}$ for every $n \in$ N.

6. $5 + 8 + 11 + \cdots + (3n + 2) = \dfrac{n(n + 9)}{2}$ for every $n \in$ N.

7. $(rs)^n = r^n s^n$ for every $n \in$ N. (Assume $a^1 = a$ and $a^{k+1} = a^k \cdot a$ for every $k \in$ N.)

8. $r^m r^n = r^{m+n}$ for every $m, n \in$ N. (Use same assumption as Problem **7.**)

9. $x^n - 1$ is divisible by $(x - 1), x \neq 1, x \in \mathcal{R}$, for every $n \in$ N.

10. $2 \leq 2^n$ for every $n \in$ N.

11. $1 + nx \leq (1 + x)^n, x > 0, x \in \mathcal{R}$, for every $n \in$ N.

12. $\dfrac{n^2}{n!} < 1$ for every $n \geq 4, n \in$ N.

Challenge Prove or disprove each statement by Mathematical Induction.

1. $(\cos \theta + i \sin \theta)^n = \cos n\theta + i \sin n\theta$ for every $n \in$ N. (DeMoivre's Theorem)

2. $\cos n\pi = (-1)^n$ for every $n \in$ N.

3. $a + (a + d) + (a + 2d) + \cdots + [a + (n - 1)d] = \dfrac{n}{2}[2a + (n - 1)d]$ for every $n \in$ N.

4. $(a + b)^n = a^n + \dbinom{n}{1}a^{n-1}b + \dbinom{n}{2}a^{n-2}b^2 + \cdots + \dbinom{n}{n-1}ab^{n-1} + \dbinom{n}{n}b^n$ where $\dbinom{n}{r} = \dfrac{n!}{r!(n - r)!}$,

for every $n \in$ N. (Binomial Theorem)

(Hint: $\dbinom{n}{r} + \dbinom{n}{r-1} = \dbinom{n+1}{r}$ for every $n, r \in$ N.)

13–6 Neighborhoods

Consider the sequence $\left\{1 + (-1)^{n-1} \cdot \dfrac{1}{2^{n-1}}\right\}$. The first six terms of this sequence are $2, \dfrac{1}{2}, \dfrac{5}{4}, \dfrac{7}{8}, \dfrac{17}{16}, \dfrac{31}{32}$. These terms can be located on a number line as shown.

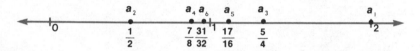

Where are the points corresponding to the rest of the terms? One response might be that they are close to 1. Also one might say that they are in the neighborhood of 1. A definition of a neighborhood of a point is useful in talking about "closeness."

> For any point P on a number line, an open interval with P as its midpoint is called a **neighborhood** of P. The neighborhood of P with radius h units is the set of points between $p - h$ and $p + h$ and is written $\langle p - h, p + h \rangle$.

Definition of Neighborhood

Example

1. The first several terms of the sequence $\left\{\dfrac{n+1}{2n}\right\}$ are $1, \dfrac{3}{4}, \dfrac{4}{6}, \dfrac{5}{8}, \dfrac{6}{10}, \ldots$. Which terms, if any, of this sequence lie within the neighborhood $\langle 0.49, 0.51 \rangle$?

Since a sequence is a function the domain can be graphed along the horizontal axis and the range along the vertical axis.

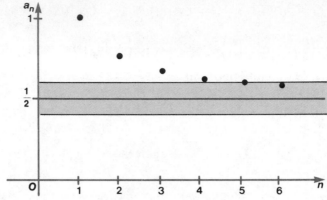

This shaded region shows a neighborhood $\langle 0.4, 0.6 \rangle$ of $\frac{1}{2}$ which has radius $\frac{1}{10}$.

All terms of this sequence are greater than $\frac{1}{2}$.

$$\frac{n+1}{2n} = \frac{n}{2n} + \frac{1}{2n} = \frac{1}{2} + \frac{1}{2n} > \frac{1}{2}$$

Each term is less than the term before it.

$$a_n = \frac{n+1}{2n} = \frac{1}{2} + \frac{1}{2n}$$

$$a_{n+1} = \frac{(n+1)+1}{2(n+1)} = \frac{n+1}{2(n+1)} + \frac{1}{2(n+1)} = \frac{1}{2} + \frac{1}{2n+2}$$

But, $\frac{1}{2} + \frac{1}{2n+2} < \frac{1}{2} + \frac{1}{2n}$ since $\frac{1}{2n+2} < \frac{1}{2n}$

Therefore, $a_{n+1} < a_n$.

Therefore, all terms except the first five lie in a neighborhood of $\frac{1}{2}$ with radius of $\frac{1}{10}$, since the fifth term is $\frac{6}{10}$.

It already has been shown that $0.49 < \frac{n+1}{2n}$ for all $n \in \mathbb{N}$. Therefore, all that is left is to solve the inequation $\frac{n+1}{2n} < 0.51$.

$$\frac{n+1}{2n} < 0.51$$
$$n + 1 < 1.02n$$
$$100n + 100 < 102n$$
$$100 < 2n$$
$$50 < n$$

Therefore, all terms beyond a_{50} lie within the neighborhood of $\frac{1}{2}$ with radius $\frac{1}{100}$, $\langle 0.49, 0.51 \rangle$. That is, exactly 50 terms of the sequence are outside the neighborhood $\langle 0.49, 0.51 \rangle$.

Exercises

Exploratory For each of the following determine the first value of n for which the sequence is inside the given neighborhood.

1. $\left\{\dfrac{n+3}{2n}\right\}, \left\langle\dfrac{1}{2}, 1\right\rangle$ **2.** $\left\{\dfrac{1}{n^2-1}\right\}, \langle 0, 0.01 \rangle$ **3.** $\left\{\dfrac{1}{(-3)^n}\right\}, \langle -0.01, 0.01 \rangle$

Determine which terms of the sequence $\left\{\dfrac{3n-2}{5n}\right\}$ satisfy each condition.

4. <0.6 **5.** >0.6 **6.** inside $\langle 0.5, 0.7 \rangle$

7. inside $\langle 0.55, 0.65 \rangle$ **8.** outside $\langle 0.55, 0.65 \rangle$ **9.** inside $\langle 0.6 - h, 0.6 + h \rangle, h > 0$

Written For each sequence, determine which terms are inside the given neighborhoods. Then determine which are outside.

1. $\left\{\dfrac{2n+5}{3n}\right\}, \left\langle\dfrac{1}{2}, \dfrac{5}{6}\right\rangle$ **2.** $\left\{\dfrac{3n^2+8}{n^2}\right\}, \langle 2.9, 3.1 \rangle$

3. $\left\{\dfrac{3n-1}{n}\right\}, \langle 2.98, 3.02 \rangle$ **4.** $\left\{\dfrac{1}{n^2+n}\right\}, \langle -0.1, 0.1 \rangle$

Suppose h is any positive number. Solve each inequation for n.

5. $\dfrac{3n-2}{2n} < 1.5 + h$ **6.** $1 - h < \dfrac{n^2-5}{n^2}$

7. $\dfrac{n-3}{7n+2} < \dfrac{1}{7} + h$ **8.** $-h < \dfrac{2}{n-3}$

Identify a neighborhood with the given radius that contains all but some finite number of terms of the sequence. Tell how many terms are outside the neighborhood identified.

9. $\left\{\dfrac{1}{n}\right\}, h = \dfrac{1}{5}$ **10.** $\left\{\dfrac{2n-3}{3n}\right\}, h = 0.1$

11. $\left\{\dfrac{n^2+1}{n^2}\right\}, h = .01$ **12.** $\left\{\dfrac{5n}{n+2}\right\}, h = \dfrac{1}{2}$

Graph the first ten ordered pairs of each sequence on centimeter graph paper. Use 1 cm for 1 unit along the n-axis and 2 cm for 1 unit along the a_n-axis. Notice that it appears that there is some lower limit to the terms in each sequence. Name the limit. Then determine the value of n needed in order to be within 10^{-6} of the limit. *As n gets very large, $\dfrac{1}{n}$ gets very small.*

13. the sequence defined by $a_n = 1 + \dfrac{1}{n}$ **14.** the sequence defined by $a_n = 1 - \dfrac{1}{n}$

15. the sequence defined by $a_n = 1 + \dfrac{(-1)^n}{n}$

Challenge Write the first four terms of each sequence. Find the limit of the sequence if it exists. Determine the value of n needed in order to be within 10^{-6} of the limit.

1. the sequence defined by $a_n = 2 + \dfrac{1}{n^2}$ **2.** the sequence defined by $a_n = 5$ for all n

13–7 Limit of a Sequence

The limit of a sequence can be defined in terms of neighborhoods.

Limit of a Sequence

> A number L is the limit of a sequence, $\{a_n\}$, if and only if for each neighborhood of the number L a natural number M can be found such that a_n is in that neighborhood if $n \geq M$.

To denote that the limit of $\{a_n\}$ is L, write $\lim\limits_{n \to \infty} \{a_n\} = L$. If L is the limit of $\{a_n\}$ then each neighborhood of L contains all but a finite number of terms of $\{a_n\}$.

If a sequence $\{a_n\}$ has the limit L, the sequence is said to converge to L. It is written $\{a_n\} \to L$. A sequence which converges is called a **convergent sequence**. A sequence that does not have a limit is said to diverge. It is called a **divergent sequence**.

The process of determining the limit of a sequence may be compared to a game between two players. Suppose the first player examines the sequence $\left\{\dfrac{n-3}{n+3}\right\}$ and says that it converges to 1. (The first several terms are $-\dfrac{1}{2}, -\dfrac{1}{5}, 0, \dfrac{1}{7}, \dfrac{1}{4}, \dfrac{1}{3}, \dfrac{2}{5}, \dfrac{5}{11}, \ldots$) This player argues that beyond some point in the sequence the terms are as close as needed to 1. The second player then chooses a neighborhood of 1, such as $\langle 0.9, 1.1 \rangle$. The first player now must show that beyond a certain term, all terms are inside that neighborhood. The argument is as follows.

$$0.9 < \frac{n-3}{n+3} < 1.1$$

$0.9 < \dfrac{n-3}{n+3}$	$\dfrac{n-3}{n+3} < 1.1$
$9n + 27 < 10n - 30$	$10n - 30 < 11n + 33$
$57 < n$	$-63 < n$
	This is true for all $n \in$ N.

Therefore, all terms beyond the 57th term of the sequence are inside $\langle 0.9, 1.1 \rangle$.

The second player could specify smaller and smaller intervals. Nonetheless the first player always wins because the sequence does converge to 1.

The process suggested by this game is never ending. To avoid this problem, the first player should try to find a general argument that can be used regardless of the specified neighborhood.

Convergence can be observed using a calculator. Try $\{\sqrt{n}\}$ for several values of n.

Example

1. **Suppose ϵ (epsilon) is any positive number, however small. Show that all terms beyond a certain term in the sequence $\left\{\dfrac{n-3}{n+3}\right\}$ are contained in the interval $\langle 1 - \epsilon, 1 + \epsilon \rangle$**

   Show that for some natural number M, if $n > M$, then $1 - \epsilon < \dfrac{n-3}{n+3} < 1 + \epsilon$.

   Solve the inequality.
   $$1 - \epsilon < \frac{n-3}{n+3}$$
   $$(1 - \epsilon)(n + 3) < n - 3$$
   $$n - \epsilon n + 3 - 3\epsilon < n - 3$$
   $$-\epsilon n < 3\epsilon - 6$$
   $$n > -3 + \frac{6}{\epsilon}$$

   Now if $M \geq \dfrac{6}{\epsilon}$, then for $n > M$, the following is true.
   $$n > \frac{6}{\epsilon} > \frac{6}{\epsilon} - 3$$

   Therefore, if $n > M$, $\dfrac{n-3}{n+3} > 1 - \epsilon$. Also $\dfrac{n-3}{n+3} < 1$ for all n, and $0 < \epsilon$, so

   $\dfrac{n-3}{n+3} < 1 + \epsilon$. Therefore, all terms beyond a_M are inside $\langle 1 - \epsilon, 1 + \epsilon \rangle$. Thus,

   $$\lim_{n \to \infty} \left\{\frac{n-3}{n+3}\right\} = 1 \text{ or } \left\{\frac{n-3}{n+3}\right\} \to 1.$$

The general argument above provides a rationale for an alternate definition for the limit of a sequence.

> The number L is the limit of the sequence $\{a_n\}$ if and only if for every $\epsilon > 0$, there is a natural number M such that a_n is in the interval $\langle L - \epsilon, L + \epsilon \rangle$ when $n > M$. The statement a_n is in the interval $\langle L - \epsilon, L + \epsilon \rangle$ also may be written $|a_n - L| < \epsilon$.

Limit of the Sequence

The limit definition does not tell you how to find the number L. It only provides a criterion for deciding whether a specified number is or is not the limit of a given sequence. To find a limit of a sequence, make an educated guess based on examination of the terms or graphs.

Relate this definition to the neighborhood definition and to the general algebraic argument of the example above.

For example, guess that $\left\{\dfrac{1}{n}\right\} \to 0$ as n increases without bound.

In fact, when n appears only in the denominator of a fraction, guess that the limit is 0, for example $\left\{\dfrac{3}{n}\right\} \to 0$ and $\left\{\dfrac{1}{n^2}\right\} \to 0$.

The limit of a sequence of constant terms such as $c, c, c, \ldots$ is that constant term since $|c - c| = 0 < \epsilon$ for every $\epsilon > 0$. The following theorems, which are accepted without proof, will help in finding a candidate for the limit of a sequence.

If $\lim_{n \to \infty} \{a_n\} = A$ and $\lim_{n \to \infty} \{b_n\} = B$, then the following theorems are true.

$$\lim_{n \to \infty} \{a_n + b_n\} = A + B$$

$$\lim_{n \to \infty} \{a_n - b_n\} = A - B$$

$$\lim_{n \to \infty} \{a_n \cdot b_n\} = A \cdot B$$

$$\lim_{n \to \infty} \left\{\frac{a_n}{b_n}\right\} = \frac{A}{B} \text{ providing } B \neq 0, b_n \neq 0$$

$$\lim_{n \to \infty} \{c_n\} = c \text{ where } c_n = c \text{ for each } n$$

Theorem for Limits

Example

2. Find the limit of the sequence $\left\{\dfrac{2n^2 + 3n - 4}{n^2 - 3n}\right\}$.

$$\frac{2n^2 + 3n - 4}{n^2 - 3n} = \frac{2 + \dfrac{3}{n} - \dfrac{4}{n^2}}{1 - \dfrac{3}{n}}$$

$$\frac{2n^2 + 3n - 4}{n^2 - 3n} = \frac{2 + 3\left(\dfrac{1}{n}\right) - 4\left(\dfrac{1}{n}\right)\left(\dfrac{1}{n}\right)}{1 - 3\left(\dfrac{1}{n}\right)}$$

Suppose $\lim_{n \to \infty} \left\{\dfrac{1}{n}\right\} = 0$. The limit can be found by repeated applications of the limit theorems.

$$\lim_{n \to \infty} \left\{\frac{2n^2 + 3n - 4}{n^2 - 3n}\right\} = \lim_{n \to \infty} \left\{\frac{2 + 3\left(\dfrac{1}{n}\right) - 4\left(\dfrac{1}{n}\right)\left(\dfrac{1}{n}\right)}{1 - 3\left(\dfrac{1}{n}\right)}\right\}$$

$$= \frac{2 + 3(0) - 4(0)(0)}{1 - 3(0)}$$

$$\lim_{n \to \infty} \left\{\frac{2n^2 + 3n - 4}{n^2 - 3n}\right\} = 2$$

Exercises

Exploratory Identify the limit as $n \to \infty$, if it exists, of each sequence.

1. $\left\{\dfrac{6 - 2n}{5n}\right\}$

2. $\left\{\dfrac{3n^2 - 5n}{7n - 6}\right\}$

3. $\left\{\dfrac{4 - 3n + n^2}{2n^2 - 3n + 5}\right\}$

4. $\left\{\dfrac{\sqrt{n}}{n + 1}\right\}$

5. $\left\{\dfrac{(n - 1)(n + 1)}{(n + 2)(n + 3)}\right\}$

6. $\left\{\dfrac{n}{(-3)^n}\right\}$

Written Solve the following.

1. Prove that $\lim\limits_{n \to \infty} \left\{\dfrac{1}{n}\right\} = 0$.

Consider the sequence $\left\{\dfrac{n - 2}{n + 2}\right\}$. Determine which terms of the sequence are in each neighborhood. Hint: First solve the inequation $1 - \epsilon < \dfrac{n - 2}{n + 2} < 1 + \epsilon$ for n.

2. $\langle 0.99, 1.01 \rangle$

3. $\langle 0.999, 1.001 \rangle$

4. $\langle 0.9999, 1.0001 \rangle$

Find a natural number M expressed in terms of ϵ to show that each statement is true.

5. $\lim\limits_{n \to \infty} \left\{\dfrac{3n - 2}{5n}\right\} = \dfrac{3}{5}$

6. $\lim\limits_{n \to \infty} \left\{\dfrac{1}{3n + 1}\right\} = 0$

7. $\lim\limits_{n \to \infty} \left\{\dfrac{\sqrt{n}}{n + 1}\right\} = 0$

Consider the sequence defined by $a_n = \dfrac{n(n + 1)}{2}$.

8. Write the first four terms of the sequence.

9. Determine L_1 if there exists such a number.

10. Show that $\dfrac{a_n}{n^2} = \dfrac{1}{2} + \dfrac{1}{2n}$.

11. Determine L_2 for $\dfrac{a_n}{n^2} = \dfrac{1}{2} + \dfrac{1}{2n}$ if there exists such a number.

12. Does $L_2 = \lim\limits_{n \to \infty} \left\{\dfrac{n(n + 1)}{2n^2}\right\}$?

13. Find the limit of $\left\{\dfrac{(n - 1)n}{2n^2}\right\}$.

14. A sequence is defined by $u_1 = 0.1$, $u_{n+1} = u_n(2 - 5u_n)$. Calculate u_2, u_3, and u_4. Compare u_4 with $\dfrac{1}{5}$. To what number does this sequence converge?

Challenge

1. Successive terms of the sequence defined by $u_1 = 1$, $u_{n+1} = \dfrac{1}{2}\left(u_n + \dfrac{3}{u_n}\right)$ are approximations for $\sqrt{3}$. Calculate u_2, u_3, and u_4. If you have a calculator, find u_5.

2. Successive terms of the sequence defined by $u_1 = 0.1$, $u_{n+1} = u_n(2 - 7u_n)$ are approximations of $\dfrac{1}{7}$. Calculate u_2, u_3, and u_4. Check your answer by direct division. Find the next term of the sequence and check that it is correct to eight decimal places.

Using the figure to the right answer each of the following.

3. What fraction of the whole is marked α in the figure?

4. How many cuts must be made before the smallest part is less than one-millionth of the whole?

5. Copy and complete the following sentence $\frac{1}{2} + \frac{1}{4} + \frac{1}{8} + \frac{1}{16} + \cdots = \underline{\quad ? \quad}$.

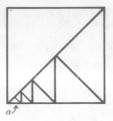

A square is cut consecutively to remove half the area as pictured. Let α represent the remaining area.

13–8 Series

For the sequence $\{a_n\}$, one could represent the sum $a_1 + a_2 + a_3 + \cdots$ as $\sum\limits_{n=1}^{\infty} a_n$. This addition would be impossible to complete since addition has meaning only for a *finite* number of addends.

However, given the sequence $\{a_n\}$ a new sequence $\{S_n\}$ of partial sums can be formed.

$$S_1 = a_1$$
$$S_2 = a_1 + a_2$$
$$S_3 = a_1 + a_2 + a_3$$
$$\cdot$$
$$\cdot$$
$$\cdot$$
$$S_n = a_1 + a_2 + a_3 + \cdots + a_n$$
$$\cdot$$
$$\cdot$$
$$\cdot$$

Written another way, $S_n = \sum\limits_{t=1}^{n} a_t$. The meaning of S_n is *the sum of the first n terms of the sequence* $\{a_n\}$.

The sequence $\{S_n\}$ may converge to a real number S. If it does, then the value of $\sum\limits_{n=1}^{\infty} a_n$ is defined to be a real number S. That is $\sum\limits_{n=1}^{\infty} a_n = S$. Notice that instead of trying to add infinitely many addends, the limit of a sequence is considered.

Examples

1. Find $\displaystyle\sum_{n=1}^{\infty} \frac{1}{3^{n-1}}$.

   The sum is defined $1 + \frac{1}{3} + \frac{1}{9} + \frac{1}{27} + \cdots + \frac{1}{3^{n-1}} + \cdots$.

   $S_1 = 1$

   $S_2 = 1 + \frac{1}{3}$

   $S_3 = 1 + \frac{1}{3} + \frac{1}{9}$
   $\vdots$

   $S_n = 1 + \frac{1}{3} + \frac{1}{9} + \cdots + \frac{1}{3^{n-1}}$

   $\{S_n\} = 1,\ 1\frac{1}{3},\ 1\frac{4}{9},\ 1\frac{13}{27},\ 1\frac{40}{81},\ 1\frac{121}{243},\ \cdots$

   The sequence $\{S_n\}$ seems to converge to $1\frac{1}{2}$. Since the generating sequence $\{a_n\}$ is a geometric sequence with first term 1 and common ratio $\frac{1}{3}$, a formula can be found for S_n.

   $$S_n = \frac{1\left[1 - \left(\frac{1^n}{3}\right)\right]}{1 - \frac{1}{3}} = \frac{1 - \left(\frac{1}{3}\right)^n}{\frac{2}{3}}$$

   $$S_n = \frac{3}{2}\left(1 - \frac{1}{3^n}\right)$$

   As expected $\displaystyle\lim_{n \to \infty} \{S_n\} = \frac{3}{2}(1 - 0) = \frac{3}{2}$. That is, the sequence of partial sums converges to $\frac{3}{2}$. By definition $\displaystyle\sum_{n=1}^{\infty} \frac{1}{3^{n-1}}$ is $\frac{3}{2}$.

2. Find $\displaystyle\sum_{n=1}^{\infty} n$.

   The sum is $1 + 2 + 3 + \cdots + n + \cdots$.
   In this case: $S_1 = 1$
   $\qquad\qquad\quad S_2 = 3$
   $\qquad\qquad\quad S_3 = 6$
   $\qquad\qquad\quad \vdots$
   $\qquad\qquad\quad S_n = \dfrac{n(n+1)}{2}$

   Clearly the sequence $\{S_n\}$ does not converge. In that case $\displaystyle\sum_{n=1}^{\infty} a_n$ is not defined to be a real number.

When an infinite number of addends are given in order, the expression is called a **series**. That is, a series is an expression of form $\sum_{n=1}^{\infty} a_n$, or $a_1 + a_2 + a_3 + \cdots$.

To evaluate a series, look at the sequence $\{S_n\}$ where $S_n = \sum_{t=1}^{n} a_t$. This is called the **sequence of partial sums**. If $\{S_n\}$ converges to a real number S, then the series is called a **convergent series**, and may be written $\sum_{n=1}^{\infty} a_n = S$. If $\{S_n\}$ diverges, then the series is called a **divergent series**, and it is not given a real number value.

The following is a **geometric series**.

$$\sum_{n=1}^{\infty} ar^{n-1} = a + ar + ar^2 + \cdots + ar^{n-1} + \cdots$$

The nth partial sum related to this series is S_n.

$$S_n = \sum_{i=1}^{n} ar^{i-1} = \frac{a(1 - r^n)}{1 - r}$$

If $a = 0$, the sum is 0. If $r = 1$, S_n is undefined. Suppose $a \neq 0$ and $r \neq 1$.

$$S_n = \frac{a(1 - r^n)}{1 - r}$$

$$S_n = \frac{a - ar^n}{1 - r}$$

$$S_n = \frac{a}{1 - r} - \frac{ar^n}{1 - r}$$

$$\lim_{n \to \infty} S_n = \lim_{n \to \infty} \left(\frac{a}{1 - r}\right) - \lim_{n \to \infty} \left(\frac{ar^n}{1 - r}\right)$$

Since $\frac{a}{1 - r}$ is constant, $\lim_{n \to \infty} S_n = \frac{a}{1 - r} - \left(\frac{a}{1 - r}\right) \lim_{n \to \infty} r^n$. If $|r| > 1$, r^n does not have a limit. If $|r| < 1$, then $\lim_{n \to \infty} r^n = 0$ and $\lim_{n \to \infty} S_n = \frac{a}{1 - r}$.

The geometric series $a + ar + ar^2 + \cdots + ar^{n-1} + \cdots$ converges to $\frac{a}{1 - r}$ if $|r| < 1$ and diverges if $|r| \geq 1$.

Example

3. Find the sum for the geometric series $1 + \frac{1}{2} + \frac{1}{4} + \frac{1}{8} + \cdots + \frac{1}{2^{n-1}} + \cdots$.

$$a = 1, \ |r| = \frac{1}{2} < 1$$

$$S = \frac{a}{1-r} = \frac{1}{1 - \frac{1}{2}} = 2$$

Notice that the instructions for the last example stated "find the sum." It is common practice to talk about finding sums for series. However, for series this actually means find the limit of the sequence of partial sums where it exists.

Exercises

Exploratory Identify the common ratio for each geometric series given below. Then, form the first four terms in the sequence of partial sums. Tell if the series has a sum.

1. $1 + \frac{1}{3} + \frac{1}{9} + \cdots$

2. $1 + 3 + 3^2 + \cdots$

3. $4 + 1 + \frac{1}{4} + \frac{1}{16} + \cdots$

4. $2 + \frac{4}{3} + \frac{8}{9} + \cdots$

5. $1 - 5 + 25 - 125 + \cdots$

6. $0.1 + 0.05 + 0.025 + \cdots$

7. $1 + 1 + 1 + 1 + \cdots$

8. $1 - 1 + 1 - 1 + \cdots$

Written Use the formula to find the sum of each series.

1. $\frac{3}{10} + \frac{3}{100} + \frac{3}{1000} + \cdots$

2. $\frac{9}{100} + \frac{9}{10,000} + \frac{9}{1,000,000} + \cdots$

3. Is there a geometric series with first term 6 and sum $\frac{2}{3}$? Give a reason for your answer.

Solve each of the following.

4. A ball rebounds from the ground to a height of 72 cm. It always rebounds $\frac{2}{3}$ of the height from which it falls. Estimate the total distance the ball travels before it stops bouncing. Does it ever come to a rest?

5. Repeat Problem 4 for an initial bounce of 2 m and successive bounces each 0.6 times the height of the preceding one.

The repeating decimal 0.454545... is written $0.\overline{45}$. To express as a common fraction write $S = 0.4545...$ and $100S = 45.4545...$ Then, subtract. Use this method to express each repeating decimal as a common fraction.

6. $0.\overline{09}$ 7. $1.\overline{09}$ 8. $0.\overline{123}$ 9. $0.\overline{142857}$

Challenge Consider the series $\dfrac{1}{1\cdot 2} + \dfrac{1}{2\cdot 3} + \dfrac{1}{3\cdot 4} + \cdots + \dfrac{1}{n(n + 1)} + \cdots$ which is not a geometric series.

1. Write the first four partial sums.

2. Write an expression for the nth partial sum.

3. Find the limit of the series.

4. Prepare an argument to convince your class that a series $a_1 + a_2 + \cdots + a_n + \cdots$ converges only if $\lim_{n\to\infty} \{a_n\} = 0$. Do you believe that the converse of this statement is true? Why?

Chapter Summary

1. A sequence is a function with domain equal to N. A sequence may be defined by a formula or listing the terms of the sequence. (389)

2. The symbol S_n is the nth sum or nth partial sum. The summation sign Σ is used to indicate a sum. (392)

$$\sum_{n=1}^{6} \frac{1}{n} = 1 + \frac{1}{2} + \frac{1}{3} + \frac{1}{4} + \frac{1}{5} + \frac{1}{6} = 2\frac{9}{20}$$

3. An arithmetic sequence is a sequence $\{a_n\}$ such that $a_1 = a$, $a_{n+1} = a_n + d$, where d is the common difference. (395)

4. The sum of n terms of an arithmetic sequence is $n\left(\dfrac{a + \ell}{2}\right)$ where a is the first term and ℓ is the last term to be summed. (396)

5. The terms between any two terms of an arithmetic sequence are called arithmetic means. (397)

6. A geometric sequence is a sequence $\{a_n\}$ such that $a_1 = a$, $a_{n+1} = a_n \cdot r$, where r is the common ratio. (398)

7. The sum of n terms of a geometric sequence is $a \cdot \left(\dfrac{1 - r^n}{1 - r}\right)$, $r \neq 1$ where a is the first term and r is the common ratio. (399)

8. The terms between any two terms of a geometric sequence are called geometric means. (400)

9. Induction Postulate: Let $P(n)$ be a statement involving a natural number $n \in N$. Then P is true for every natural number n if and only if (a) $P(1)$ is true, and (b) For any natural number k, if $P(k)$ is true then $P(k + 1)$ is true. (402)

10. For any point P on a number line, an open interval with P as its midpoint is called a neighborhood of P. The neighborhood of P with radius h units is the set of points between $p - h$ and $p + h$ and is written $\langle p - h, p + h \rangle$. (405)
11. A number L is the limit of a sequence, $\{a_n\}$, if and only if for each neighborhood of the number L a natural number M can be found such that a_n is in that neighborhood if $n \geq M$. (408)
12. A sequence that converges to a limit is called a convergent sequence. (408)
13. A sequence that does not have a limit is a divergent sequence. (408)
14. Limit Theorems (410)

    Given $\lim_{n \to \infty} \{a_n\} = A$, $\lim_{n \to \infty} \{b_n\} = B$.
    $$\lim_{n \to \infty} \{a_n \pm b_n\} = A \pm B$$
    $$\lim_{n \to \infty} \{a_n \cdot b_n\} = A \cdot B$$
    $$\lim_{n \to \infty} \left\{\frac{a_n}{b_n}\right\} = \frac{A}{B}, B \neq 0, b_n \neq 0$$
    $$\lim_{n \to \infty} \{c_n\} = c, \text{ where } c_n = c \text{ for each } n$$

15. A series is an expression of the form $\sum_{n=1}^{\infty} a_n$. (414)

16. The sequence of partial sums is $\{S_n\} = \left\{ \sum_{r=1}^{n} a_r \right\}$. (414)

17. If $\{S_n\}$ converges to a real number S the series is called a convergent series. (414)
18. If $\{S_n\}$ diverges, the series is called a divergent series and it is not given a real number value. (414)
19. The geometric series $a + ar + ar^2 + \cdots + ar^n + \cdots$ converges to $\frac{a}{1 - r}$ if $|r| < 1$ and diverges if $|r| \geq 1$. (414)

Chapter Review

13-1 Write the first four terms of each sequence.

1. $a_n = \dfrac{1}{n^2}$
2. $a_1 = 2, a_{n+1} = a_n + 2$
3. Write a simple rule for the nth term of the sequence 4, 8, 12, 16, . . .

13-2 Write each sum in expanded form and calculate the sum.

4. $\sum_{z=1}^{8} (10 - z)$
5. $\sum_{r=6}^{10} (r + 4)$
6. $\sum_{k=2}^{7} (5 - 2k)$

13–3 **The numbers given are the first few terms of an arithmetic sequence. Identify the first term a and the common difference d. Name the next three terms in the sequence.**

7. $5, 9, 13, \ldots$ **8.** $0, 7, 14, \ldots$ **9.** $-n, 0, n, \ldots$

10.–12. Find the sum in Problems **7, 8,** and **9** for 10 terms.

13–4 **The numbers given are the first few terms of a geometric sequence. Identify the common ratio r. Write the next three terms in the sequence. Write a formula for the nth term.**

13. $4, 2, 1$ **14.** $\sqrt{2}, 2, \sqrt{8}$ **15.** $t^{-2}, t^{-1}, 1$

16. Insert four geometric means between $-\dfrac{2}{3}$ and 162.

Use the formula $S_n = a \dfrac{(1 - r^n)}{(1 - r)}$ to find each sum.

17. $1 + \dfrac{1}{3} + \dfrac{1}{9} + \cdots$ to 5 terms   **18.** $2 - 6 + 18 - 54 + \cdots$ to 7 terms

19. $2 + 3 + 4.5 + \cdots$ to 6 terms   **20.** $0.5 + 1 + 2 + \cdots$ to 9 terms

13–5 **Prove or disprove by Mathematical Induction.**

21. $2 + 7 + 12 + \cdots + (5n - 3) = \dfrac{n}{2}(5n - 1)$ for every $n \in \mathbb{N}$.

22. $a + ar + ar^2 + \cdots + ar^{n-1} = \dfrac{a(1 - r^n)}{1 - r}$ for every $n \in \mathbb{N}$.

23. $\dfrac{1}{2} + \dfrac{1}{2^2} + \dfrac{1}{2^3} + \cdots + \dfrac{1}{2^n} = 1 - \dfrac{1}{2^n}$ for every $n \in \mathbb{N}$.

13–6 **Suppose h is any positive number. Solve each inequation for n.**

24. $\dfrac{3n + 2}{n^2} < h$ for $n, h > 0$ **25.** $\dfrac{5n}{n + 2} < h$ for $n, h > 1$

13–7 **Identify the limit as $n \to \infty$, if it exists, of each sequence.**

26. $\left\{ \dfrac{n^2 + 3}{2n} \right\}$ **27.** $\left\{ \dfrac{4n^3 - 3n}{n^4 - 4n^3} \right\}$

13–8 **Find the sum of each series.**

28. $\dfrac{2}{3} + \dfrac{1}{9} + \dfrac{1}{54} + \dfrac{1}{324} + \cdots$ **29.** $1 + \dfrac{1}{3} + \dfrac{1}{3^2} + \dfrac{1}{3^3} + \cdots$

30. A ball rebounds from the ground to a height of 10 m. It always rebounds 0.75 of the height from which it falls. Estimate the total distance the ball travels before it stops bouncing. Does it ever come to a rest?

Chapter Test

Write the first four terms of each sequence.

1. $a_1 = -13; d = 5$

2. $a_1 = 1.5; a_{n+1} = a_n + 7.5$

3. Write the first four terms of the sequence defined by $a_n = n^2 + 3n$. What term of the sequence is 270?

Calculate the sum.

4. $\displaystyle\sum_{i=1}^{5} i(i + 1)(i + 2)$

5. $\displaystyle\sum_{x=3}^{10} (3x - 2)$

Find the indicated term of each arithmetic sequence.

6. sixth term of 3, 7, 11

7. tenth term of $a - b, \dfrac{a - b}{2}, 0$

Find a, r, and sixth term for each geometric sequence.

8. 8, 12, 18

9. $-3, -2, -1\frac{1}{3}$

Prove or disprove by Mathematical Induction.

10. $(r^m)^n = r^{mn}$ given only that $a^1 = a$ and $a^{k+1} = a^k \cdot a$ for every $k \in$ N.

11. $2 + 6 + 12 + \cdots + n(n + 1) = \dfrac{n(n + 1)(n + 2)}{3}$ for every $n \in$ N.

For each sequence, determine which terms are inside the given neighborhoods.

12. $\left\{\dfrac{1}{n^2 + n}\right\}, \langle -0.5, 0.5 \rangle$

13. $\left\{\dfrac{3n - 1}{n}\right\}, \langle 2.8, 3.1 \rangle$

Identify the limit as $n \to \infty$, if it exists of each sequence.

14. $\left\{\dfrac{7n^3 - 2n}{n^2 + 4n}\right\}$

15. $\left\{\dfrac{2n^3}{4n^5 + 1}\right\}$

Find the sum if it exists for each of the following.

16. $1 + \dfrac{3}{5} + \dfrac{9}{25} + \dfrac{27}{125} + \cdots$

17. $\dfrac{1}{3} + \dfrac{1}{9} + \dfrac{1}{27} + \cdots$

18. The end of a swinging pendulum 90 cm long moves through 50 cm on its first swing. Each succeeding swing is 0.9 of the preceding one. How far will the pendulum travel before coming to rest?

Computers

Consumer Use

Computers are used in banks, supermarkets, department stores, and many other aspects of everyday life.

Banks use computers for the storage of data as well as for keeping an accurate account of daily transactions. When opening a checking account a number is assigned. As deposits are made and withdrawals are completed, the computer keeps a running total by adding or subtracting as necessary. The computer processes this information at such a rate of speed, the time of processing is reduced from weeks to hours. Besides checking accounts, savings accounts, loans, savings clubs, information updating, and daily reporting are all accomplished quickly by using a computer. Computers make 24-hour self service windows possible. In parts of the country, checking account customers are able to make purchases using a special plastic credit card that deducts the amount from the customers checking account.

In supermarkets computers are used for inventory control as well as for check out. The universal product code (UPC) is found on products to identify the product and manufacturer. This code helps to keep a constant inventory and a constant update of the price. The clerk uses a scanning device to "read" the code into the computer. Once read into the computer the cost is recorded at the terminal on the cash register and the item is subtracted from the inventory. Thus, the computer reduces the time of checking out of a supermarket. Computers also keep a more accurate inventory. Inventory was always kept up but the time lapse between the count and the reordering was so great that some items ended up being off the shelf before the

Banks use computers to keep all accounts current.

order came. With computers, inventory is more current and reordering accomplished more quickly. Therefore, the time of reduced inventory has been shortened by use of computers.

Department stores also use computers for inventory control and checkout. Since most department stores use credit cards and laya-

ways, computers do bookkeeping for these accounts, keeping accurate and current records of the accounts. Payroll is another large area of computer use. Any changes for an employee can be input and a correct check can be issued, despite any alterations.

There are many other uses for computers in our everyday life. Some fast food businesses use computer terminals for their cash register. Other restaurants use computers for inventory, bookkeeping, and even some cooking. Computers are being used more and more each day in small and large companies.

Many devices like the one pictured are used to input data to the computer.

Exercises Write programs for each of the following. Let *a* be the first term of an arithmetic sequence, *d* be the common difference, and *n* be a positive integer.

1. Find the *n*th term of the sequence.

2. Find the sum of the first *n* terms of the sequence.

3. Given two real numbers, *a* and *b*, find three arithmetic means between *a* and *b*.

4. Given two real numbers, *a* and *b*, find three geometric means between *a* and *b*.

Let *a* be the first term of a geometric sequence, *r* the common ratio, and *n* a positive integer.

5. Find the *n*th term of the sequence.

6. Find the sum of the first *n* terms of the sequence.

7. Find the least integral value of *n* such that $1 + \frac{1}{2} + \frac{1}{3} + \frac{1}{4} + \ldots \frac{1}{n} > 4$.

8. Find the sum of the series $1 + 2 + 4 + 8 + \ldots + 2^{n-1}$ for any positive integer, *n*.

9. Find $\lim\limits_{n \to \infty} \frac{2}{5n + 3}$.

10. Find the sum of the first ten terms of $1 - \frac{1}{2!} + \frac{1}{4!} - \frac{1}{6!} + \ldots$.

11. Estimate sin *x* for 10 to 40 terms in steps of 2 using the following series.
$$\sin x = x - \frac{x^3}{3!} + \frac{x^5}{5!} - \frac{x^7}{7!} + \ldots$$
(*x* is in radians)

12. Estimate cos *x* for 10 to 40 terms in steps of 2 using the following series.
$$\cos x = 1 - \frac{x^2}{2!} + \frac{x^4}{4!} - \frac{x^6}{6!} + \ldots$$
(*x* is in radians)

Chapter 14

Continuity in design makes the difference between a cluttered room and a well-decorated room. Continuity is as important a concept in working with functions and limits of functions.

Limits of Functions

14–1 Extending the Limit Concept

Sequences are a special class of functions whose domain is the set of natural numbers. In developing the limit concept for sequences the behavior of the range elements for large values of n in the domain was considered. The limit symbolism developed was related to a particular question as follows.

$$\lim_{n \to \infty} \{a_n\} \overset{?}{=} L$$

Question: Do the values of the function (a_n) become arbitrarily close to a given number (L) as the domain elements increase without bound $(n \to \infty)$?

Graphs are helpful in visualizing the limit concept for sequences. Consider this sequence.

$$\{a_n\} = \frac{1}{2}, -\frac{1}{2}, \frac{3}{8}, -\frac{1}{4}, \frac{5}{32}, \frac{-3}{32}, \dots, \frac{(-1)^{n-1} \cdot n}{2^n}, \dots$$

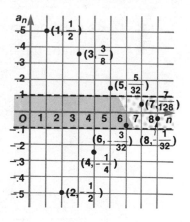

The graph suggests that the sequence converges to 0. The shaded area indicates a neighborhood of zero $\langle -0.1, 0.1 \rangle$ on the a_n-axis. For $n \geq 6$, $|a_n| < 0.1$. Since $|a_{n+1}| < |a_n|$ for all n, all terms after a_5 fall within the shaded area. To prove $\{a_n\} \to 0$, that is $\lim_{n \to \infty} \{a_n\} = 0$, it is necessary to show that whatever neighborhood of 0, $\langle 0 - \epsilon, 0 + \epsilon \rangle$, is chosen there is a natural number M such that $a_n \in \langle 0 - \epsilon, 0 + \epsilon \rangle$ for all $n \geq M$. To extend the limit concept to a function that is not a sequence, consider the function $f(x) = \frac{\sin x}{x}$. For this function, $f(0)$ is undefined. However, it is possible to consider what happens to $f(x)$ as values of x get close to 0.

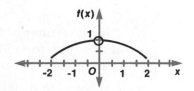

x	-2	-1.5	-1.0	-0.5	-0.1	0.1	0.5	1.0	1.5	2.0
$f(x)$	0.455	0.665	0.841	0.959	0.998	0.998	0.959	0.841	0.665	0.445

From the table and graph it appears that as x gets close to 0, $f(x)$ gets close to 1. Given a measure of closeness for the values of the function, a corresponding measure of closeness in the domain can be found. The symbol $\epsilon > 0$ is usually used when talking about closeness in the range, and $\delta > 0$ is usually used when talking about closeness in the domain. In discussing the two measures of closeness for the function $f(x) = \dfrac{\sin x}{x}$ it is necessary to show that the values of $f(x)$ are in the neighborhood $\langle 1 - \epsilon, 1 + \epsilon \rangle$ when the values of x are in the neighborhood $\langle 0 - \delta, 0 + \delta \rangle$.

ϵ is read epsilon
δ is read delta

Thus, the question to be examined in developing the limit concept in this case is different from the one examined for sequences. Sequences had points falling within a neighborhood on one axis. Now it is necessary to consider neighborhoods on both axes. Again, graphs will be helpful in visualizing this concept.

Examples

1. **Find a neighborhood of 2 such that $2x - 3$ differs from 1 by no more than 0.01.**

    Represent the difference between $2x - 3$ and 1 in terms of absolute value.

    $$|(2x - 3) - 1| = |2x - 4| = 2\,|x - 2|$$

    Now $2\,|x - 2| < 0.01$ when $|x - 2| < 0.005$, so $(2x - 3) \in \langle 0.99, 1.01 \rangle$ when $x \in \langle 1.995, 2.005 \rangle$.

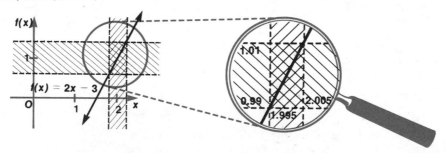

2. **A manufacturer of flooring tile may sell as 9-inch tile only those whose actual area differs from 81 square inches by no more than $\frac{1}{2}$ square inch. Determine the tolerance allowed for the length of a side.**

    Assume that the tiles actually are square. If s is the length of a side, it is required that $s^2 \in \langle 81 - 0.5, 81 + 0.5 \rangle$, or $\langle 80.5, 81.5 \rangle$. This condition can be expressed using absolute value.

    $$|s^2 - 81| < 0.5$$
    $$80.5 < s^2 < 81.5$$
    $$\sqrt{80.5} < s < \sqrt{81.5}$$

    The process of finding neighborhoods relates to quality control methods employed in industry.

Since $\sqrt{80.5} \approx 8.97$ and $\sqrt{81.5} \approx 9.03$, $8.97 < s < 9.03$. Therefore, with suitable adjustment for the limitations of measure-
ment, the manufacturer may instruct his workers to use a tolerance of 0.03 inches. That is, the length of each side s must be
within the neighborhood $\langle 8.97, 9.03 \rangle$. For s in this neighborhood $s^2 \in \langle 80.5, 81.5 \rangle$. The manufacturer could use a more restricted neighborhood, such as $\langle 8.98, 9.02 \rangle$, and still satisfy the
requirement.

3. **Describe the shaded area in the figure.**

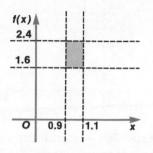

The shaded area in the figure may be described in
three ways.

   a. Neighborhoods: $x \in \langle 0.9, 1.1 \rangle$; $f(x) \in \langle 1.6, 2.4 \rangle$

   b. Inequations: $0.9 < x < 1.1$; $1.6 < f(x) < 2.4$

   c. Absolute value: $|x - 1| < 0.1$; $|f(x) - 2| < 0.4$

Exercises

Exploratory Assume that x is in the indicated neighborhood. Find the smallest neighborhood
that is certain to contain $f(x)$.

1. $x \in \langle 2.9, 3.1 \rangle$, $f(x) = 2x - 1$ 2. $x \in \langle -1.7, -1.3 \rangle$, $f(x) = \dfrac{x}{2}$

For each sentence, write the largest possible domain for x which makes the sentence true.
3. $-0.01 < 6 - 3x < 0.01$ 4. $|x - 2| < 0.05$

Describe the shaded area by **a.** neighborhoods, **b.** inequations, and **c.** absolute values.
5.

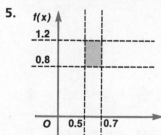

Written Assume that x is in the indicated neighborhood. Find the smallest neighborhood that
is certain to contain $f(x)$.
1. $|x| < 0.1$, $f(x) = x^2 - 2x$ 2. $x \in \langle 2 - a, 2 + a \rangle$, $f(x) = 6 - x$, $a > 0$
3. $|x - 3| < a$, $f(x) = 2x$, $a > 0$

For each sentence, write the largest possible domain for *x* which makes the sentence true.

4. $6.8 < 2x + 3 < 7.2$

5. $3x + 1 \in \langle 3.9, 4.1 \rangle$

6. $\left| \dfrac{x + 1}{2} - 3 \right| < 0.01$

7. $5.9 < x^2 + 3x - 4 < 6.1$

8. $x^2 - 4 \in \langle -0.1, 0.1 \rangle$

Describe each shaded area by a. neighborhoods, b. inequations, and c. absolute values.

9.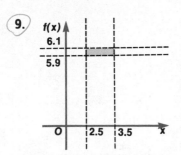

10.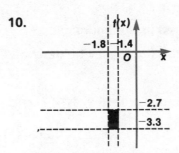

Establish a coordinate system on centimeter graph paper. Shade the smallest area which is sure to contain $(x, f(x))$.

11. $x \in \langle 1.8, 2.2 \rangle; f(x) \in \langle 2.7, 3.3 \rangle$

12. $|x - 1| < 0.3; |f(x) - 2| < 0.5$

13. $x \in \langle 3.3, 3.7 \rangle; |f(x) + 2| < 0.2$

14. $-2.4 < x < -1.6; f(x) \in \langle 2.5, 2.9 \rangle$

15. What tolerance is needed to construct the side of a square if its perimeter may differ from 20 cm by no more than 0.5 cm? Specify the neighborhood within which the side falls.

Challenge The owner of a pizza parlor says money is lost on a medium size pizza, 14 inch diameter, if its area exceeds 176 square inches. Customers complain if the area is less than 132 square inches. What tolerance is allowed for the diameter? Use $\dfrac{22}{7}$ as an approximation for π.

14–2 Limit of a Function

In the preceding section related neighborhoods on the *x*- and $f(x)$-axes were found. Often a general relationship between the neighborhoods can be established.

Examples

1. Find a corresponding neighborhood of x for which $2x - 3 \in \langle 1 - \epsilon, 1 + \epsilon \rangle$. Write this using absolute values.

$$|(2x - 3) - 1| = 2|x - 2| < \epsilon$$

Thus if $|x - 2| < \dfrac{\epsilon}{2}$ then $2x - 3 \in \langle 1 - \epsilon, 1 + \epsilon \rangle$.

Here δ is related to the specified ϵ by the expression $\delta = \frac{\epsilon}{2}$. So, whatever value of ϵ is specified a δ can be found such that

$2x - 3 \in \langle 1 - \epsilon, 1 + \epsilon \rangle$	when $x \in \langle 2 - \delta, 2 + \delta \rangle$
or $\|(2x - 3) - 1\| < \epsilon$	when $\|x - 2\| < \delta$.
So, $\|(2x - 3) - 1\| < 0.1$	when $\|x - 2\| < 0.05$
$\|(2x - 3) - 1\| < 0.01$	when $\|x - 2\| < 0.005$
$\|(2x - 3) - 1\| < 0.0001$	when $\|x - 2\| < 0.0005$.

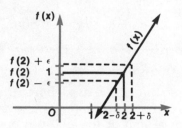

Of course, any smaller value for δ would also meet the requirement.

2. **Consider the function** $f : f(x) = \dfrac{3x^2 - 12}{x - 2}$**. Find a number** L **such that** $\dfrac{3x^2 - 12}{x - 2}$ **is arbitrarily close to** L **for values of** x **sufficiently close to 2.**

The function is not defined for $x = 2$. If $x \neq 2$, then $\dfrac{3x^2 - 12}{x - 2} = 3(x + 2)$.

So, $f(x)$ should be close to 12 when x is close to 2. Now given an $\epsilon > 0$, find a neighborhood of 2 such that for any $x \neq 2$ in that neighborhood $\left| \dfrac{3x^2 - 12}{x - 2} - 12 \right| < \epsilon$. For $x \neq 2$, this argument can be used.

$$\left| \frac{3x^2 - 12}{x - 2} - 12 \right| = |3(x + 2) - 12| = |3x - 6| = 3|x - 2|$$

If $|x - 2| < \dfrac{\epsilon}{3}$, then $3|x - 2| < \epsilon$. Thus, $\dfrac{3x^2 - 12}{x - 2} \in \langle 12 - \epsilon, 12 + \epsilon \rangle$ when $x \in \left\langle 2 - \dfrac{\epsilon}{3}, 2 + \dfrac{\epsilon}{3} \right\rangle$ but $x \neq 2$.

The example shows that it makes sense to talk about $f(x)$ converging to a number L as x approaches a number c, even if $f(c)$ is not defined. This possibility needs to be included in the definition for the limit of a function. For this, the idea of a deleted neighborhood is needed.

A **deleted neighborhood** of the number c is any neighborhood of c with the number c removed. The set of all numbers x such that $0 < |x - c| < h$ is called a deleted neighborhood of c with radius h.

Deleted Neighborhood

Suppose $f(x)$ is defined for all real numbers x in some deleted neighborhood of c. The number L is the limit of $f(x)$ as x approaches c, if and only if to each positive number ϵ there corresponds a positive number δ such that $|f(x) - L| < \epsilon$ when $0 < |x - c| < \delta$.

Limit for Deleted Neighborhoods

This is shown in symbols as $\lim\limits_{x \to c} f(x) = L$. The symbols are read the *limit of* f(x) *as* x *approaches* c *is* L.

Each of the examples above demonstrates that the function has a limit at the point in question. This is done by finding a sufficiently small δ to correspond to the given ϵ. Thus it is possible to say $\lim\limits_{x \to 2} (2x - 3) = 1$ and $\lim\limits_{x \to 2} \dfrac{3x^2 - 12}{x - 2} = 12$.

There are, of course, many functions for which $\lim\limits_{x \to c} f(x)$ does not exist. For example $\lim\limits_{x \to 0} \sin \dfrac{1}{x}$, $\lim\limits_{x \to 0} [x]$, and $\lim\limits_{x \to 0} \dfrac{1}{x}$ all fail to exist, as their graphs suggest.

With limits, the behavior of the function near c is important, not the behavior of the function at c.

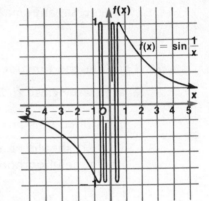

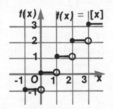

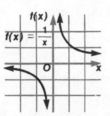

Example

3. **Find the limit of $f(x) = x^3$ as x approaches 2.**

Guess that $\lim\limits_{x \to 2} x^3 = 8$. The problem is to prove it is the limit by using the limit definition. To prove $\lim\limits_{x \to 2} x^3 = 8$, for each $\epsilon > 0$ find a $\delta > 0$ such that $|x^3 - 8| < \epsilon$ when $0 < |x - 2| < \delta$. *Use graphs to show the relationships between ϵ and δ.* Notice that if $|x^3 - 8| = |x - 2| \cdot |x^2 + 2x + 4| < \epsilon$, then $|x - 2| < \dfrac{\epsilon}{|x^2 + 2x + 4|}$.

If $\delta = \dfrac{1}{2}$, then $0 < |x - 2| < \dfrac{1}{2}$ and $x \in \langle 1.5, 2.5 \rangle$. This means $|x^2 + 2x + 4| < |(2.5)^2 + 2(2.5) + 4| = 15.25$. Therefore, if $|x^3 - 8| < \epsilon$ and $x \in \langle 1.5, 2.5 \rangle$, it must be true that $|x - 2| < \dfrac{\epsilon}{15.25}$. So, for each $\epsilon > 0$, choose δ to be smaller than either $\dfrac{1}{2}$ or $\dfrac{\epsilon}{15.25}$.

The $\lim\limits_{x \to 2} x^3 = 8$ because for each $\epsilon > 0$ there corresponds a $\delta > 0$ such that $|x^3 - 8| < \epsilon$ when $0 < |x - 2| < \delta$.

Exercises

Exploratory   Find the limit of each function as x approaches 2. Find a value for δ corresponding to an ϵ of 0.1, to an ϵ of 0.01, and to an ϵ of 0.001.

1. $f(x) = x$

2. $f(x) = x^2$

3. $f(x) = 2x$

4. $f(x) = x + 3$

5. $f(x) = \dfrac{2x - 5}{2}$

6. $f(x) = \dfrac{x^2 - 4}{x - 2}$

Written   Solve the following.

1. What is the limit of $f(x) = 3x - 5$ as x approaches 2? Sketch a graph exhibiting the relation between ϵ and δ. Find a value for δ corresponding to an ϵ of 0.1 and to an ϵ of 0.01.

Given that $\epsilon = 0.01$ find a corresponding δ for each limit. For Problems 4 and 5, initially choose a δ less than $\frac{1}{2}$.

2. $\lim\limits_{x \to -1} (5x + 3) = -2$

3. $\lim\limits_{x \to 2} \dfrac{x^2 - 4}{x - 2} = 4$

4. $\lim\limits_{x \to 1} (x^2 + 2x - 1) = 2$

5. $\lim\limits_{x \to 2} \dfrac{1}{x} = \dfrac{1}{2}$

Prove the following.

6. $\lim\limits_{x \to 3} (2x - 3) = 3$

7. $\lim\limits_{x \to 3} \dfrac{x^2 - 9}{x - 3} = 6$

8. $\lim\limits_{x \to 0} x^2 = 0$

9. Sketch a graph of $f(x) = \dfrac{1}{x}$ in the interval $\langle -1, 1 \rangle$. Explain why the limit of $f(x)$ does not exist at $x = 0$.

10. Consider the function $f(x) = 4$. Explain why any choice of δ will suffice to show that $\lim\limits_{x \to 4} f(x) = 4$.

The definition of limit does not tell how to find the number L. It simply gives a method of confirming that a candidate is, or is not, the limit in question. For the following, indicate what is the most likely candidate.

11. $\lim\limits_{x \to 1} \dfrac{x + 1}{x + 2}$

12. $\lim\limits_{x \to 2} \dfrac{x^2 - 4}{x^3 - 8}$

13. $\lim\limits_{x \to -1} \dfrac{x^3 + 1}{x + 1}$

14. $\lim\limits_{x \to 2} \dfrac{x^2 - x - 2}{x^2 - 4}$

Challenge   Prove each of the following.

1. $\lim\limits_{x \to 2} x^2 = 4$

2. $\lim\limits_{x \to 3} x^3 = 27$

3. $\lim\limits_{x \to 3} \dfrac{2x^2 - 18}{x - 3} = 12$

14-3 Limit Theorems

It is given that $\lim_{x \to c} f(x) = F$ and $\lim_{x \to c} g(x) = G$. Also, a, b, d, and e are positive real numbers. Can a $\delta > 0$ be found such that each of the following is true when $0 < |x - c| < \delta$?

$$|f(x) - F| < a, \ |f(x) - F| < b, \ |g(x) - G| < d, \ |g(x) - G| < e$$

The answer is yes.

1. Pick $\delta_1 > 0$ such that $|f(x) - F| < a$ when $0 < |x - c| < \delta_1$
2. Pick $\delta_2 > 0$ such that $|f(x) - F| < b$ when $0 < |x - c| < \delta_2$
3. Pick $\delta_3 > 0$ such that $|g(x) - G| < d$ when $0 < |x - c| < \delta_3$
4. Pick $\delta_4 > 0$ such that $|g(x) - G| < e$ when $0 < |x - c| < \delta_4$

Now, simply declare δ to be the smallest of δ_1, δ_2, δ_3, and δ_4.

While reading the proof sketches, keep the previous problem in mind. Also keep in mind that if $\epsilon > 0$, then these numbers are all positive.

$$\frac{\epsilon}{2}, \ \frac{\epsilon}{4(|a| + 1)}, \ \frac{G^2 \cdot \epsilon}{2} \text{ if } G \neq 0$$

The theorems hold only when the functions can be defined. For example, $\dfrac{f(x)}{g(x)}$ is defined only at the values for which $g(x) \neq 0$.

$$\lim_{x \to c} x = c$$

Theorem 1

Proof Sketch

Step 1. Choose an $\epsilon > 0$. For that choice, choose $\delta = \epsilon$.
Step 2. For this function, $f(x) = x$. Therefore $0 < |x - c| < \delta$. If $|x - c| < \delta$ then $|f(x) - c| < \delta$. Thus, $|f(x) - c| < \epsilon$.

If $\lim_{x \to c} f(x) = F$ and $\lim_{x \to c} g(x) = G$, then $\lim_{x \to c} [f(x) + g(x)] = F + G$

Theorem 2a

Proof Sketch

Step 1. Choose $\epsilon > 0$. Then choose $\delta > 0$ so that each of the following is true when $0 < |x - c| < \delta$.

$$|f(x) - F| < \frac{\epsilon}{2} \text{ and } |g(x) - G| < \frac{\epsilon}{2}$$

Step 2. For $0 < |x - c| < \delta$, show that $|[f(x) + g(x)] - (F + G)| < \epsilon$. Use the fact that $|[f(x) + g(x)] - (F + G)| \leq |f(x) - F| + |g(x) - G|$.

If $\lim\limits_{x \to c} f(x) = F$ and $k \in \mathcal{R}$, then $\lim\limits_{x \to c} [k \cdot f(x)] = k \cdot F.$

Theorem 2b

Proof Sketch

Step 1. If $k = 0$ then $\lim\limits_{x \to c} [k \cdot f(x)] = \lim\limits_{x \to c} [0 \cdot f(x)] = \lim\limits_{x \to c} 0 = 0.$

Step 2. If $k \neq 0$ then show that for each $\epsilon > 0$ there exists a $\delta > 0$ such that $|kf(x) - kF| < \epsilon$ whenever $0 < |x - c| < \delta$. Since $\lim\limits_{x \to c} f(x) = F$ then for each $\epsilon_1 > 0$ there is a $\delta_1 > 0$ such that $|f(x) - F| < \epsilon_1$ whenever $0 < |x - c| < \delta_1$. Pick $\epsilon_1 = \dfrac{\epsilon}{|k|}$. Then there is a $\delta_1 > 0$ such that $|f(x) - F| < \dfrac{\epsilon}{|k|}$ whenever $0 < |x - c| < \delta_1$. It follows that there exists a $\delta > 0$, namely $\delta = \delta_1$, such that $|kf(x) - kF| < \epsilon$ whenever $0 < |x - c| \; \delta.$

If $\lim\limits_{x \to c} f(x) = F$ and $\lim\limits_{x \to c} g(x) = G$, then $\lim\limits_{x \to c} [f(x) - g(x)] = F - G.$

Theorem 2c

Proof Sketch

Step 1. Define $h(x) = -g(x)$ for all x and show that $\lim\limits_{x \to c} h(x) = -G.$

Step 2. Use Theorem 2a.

$$\lim\limits_{x \to c} [f(x) - g(x)] = \lim\limits_{x \to c} [f(x) + h(x)] = F + (-G)$$
$$= F - G$$

If $\lim\limits_{x \to c} f(x) = F$ and $\lim\limits_{x \to c} g(x) = G$, then $\lim\limits_{x \to c} [f(x) \cdot g(x)] = F \cdot G.$

Theorem 2d

Proof Sketch

Step 1. Show that
$$|f(x)g(x) - FG| \leq |f(x) - F| \cdot |g(x) - G| + |F| \cdot |g(x) - G| + |G| \cdot |f(x) - F|.$$

Step 2. Choose an $\epsilon > 0$. For that choice, choose a corresponding $\delta > 0$ such that when $0 < |x - c| < \delta$ each of the following is true.

$$|f(x) - F| < \frac{\epsilon}{2}, \; |f(x) - F| < \frac{\epsilon}{4(|G| + 1)},$$

$$|g(x) - G| < \frac{\epsilon}{2}, \; |g(x) - G| < \frac{\epsilon}{4(|F| + 1)}$$

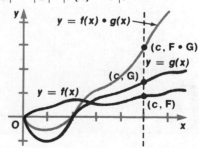

Step 3. Now for x such that $0 < |x - c| < \delta$, the following is true.

$$|f(x)g(x) - FG| \leq |f(x) - F| \cdot |g(x) - G| + |F| \cdot |g(x) - G| + |G| \cdot |f(x) - F|$$

$$< \frac{\epsilon}{2} \cdot \frac{\epsilon}{2} + |F| \cdot \frac{\epsilon}{4(|F| + 1)} + |G| \cdot \frac{\epsilon}{4(|G| + 1)}$$

$$< \frac{\epsilon}{4} + \frac{\epsilon}{4} + \frac{\epsilon}{4}$$

$$< \epsilon \qquad \qquad \text{Since } \epsilon > 0, \frac{3\epsilon}{4} < \epsilon.$$

Using the previous theorems, the following theorems can be proved.

If $\lim\limits_{x \to c} g(x) = G \neq 0$, then $\lim\limits_{x \to c} \dfrac{1}{g(x)} = \dfrac{1}{G}$.　　　　**Theorem 2e**

Below is an example demonstrating the statement of Theorem 2e.

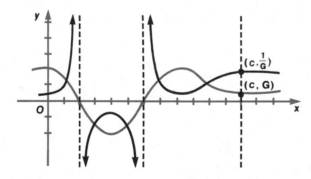

Notice that $\dfrac{1}{g(x)}$ is not a real number when $g(x) = 0$. In other words, points where $g(x) = 0$ are not in the domain of $\dfrac{1}{g}$.

If $\lim\limits_{x \to c} f(x) = F$ and $\lim\limits_{x \to c} g(x) = G \neq 0$, then $\lim\limits_{x \to c} \dfrac{f(x)}{g(x)} = \dfrac{F}{G}$.　　**Theorem 2f**

If $\lim\limits_{x \to c} f(x) = F$, then $\lim\limits_{x \to c} [f(x)]^n = F^n$.　　**Theorem 3a**

If $\lim\limits_{x \to c} f(x) = F$, then $\lim\limits_{x \to c} [f(x)]^{1/n} = F^{1/n}$.　　**Theorem 3b**

Let $f(x) = a_0 x^0 + a_1 x^1 + a_2 x^2 + \cdots + a_n x^n$. Then $\lim\limits_{x \to c} f(x) = f(c)$.　　**Theorem 3c**

Example

1. Use the limit theorems to evaluate $\displaystyle\lim_{x\to 2} \frac{x^2 + x - 5}{3x^2 + 2}$.

$$\lim_{x\to 2} \frac{x^2 + x - 5}{3x^2 + 2} = \frac{\displaystyle\lim_{x\to 2} x^2 + x - 5}{\displaystyle\lim_{x\to 2} 3x^2 + 2}$$

Theorem 2f

$$= \frac{4 + 2 - 5}{12 + 2} \text{ or } \frac{1}{14}$$

Theorems 2a and 2c.

Exercises

Exploratory   Use the limit theorems to evaluate each limit. State which theorems are required.

1. $\displaystyle\lim_{x\to 1} \left(\frac{x - 3}{2x - 4} \right)$

2. $\displaystyle\lim_{x\to 3} (x^2 - 2x - 5)$

3. $\displaystyle\lim_{x\to 1} (x + 2)(x - 3)$

4. $\displaystyle\lim_{x\to -1} \sqrt{x^2 - 1}$

5. $\displaystyle\lim_{x\to 2} \frac{x^3 - 8}{x^2 - 5x + 6}$

6. $\displaystyle\lim_{x\to 0} \frac{x^2 + 5x}{x + 4}$

Written   Use the limit theorems to evaluate each limit.

1. $\displaystyle\lim_{x\to 2} \frac{x^2 - x - 2}{x^2 - 4}$

2. $\displaystyle\lim_{x\to 0} \frac{x^2 - 2x + 3}{3x^2 - 5}$

3. $\displaystyle\lim_{x\to 3} \frac{x^2 - 2x + 1}{x^3}$

4. $\displaystyle\lim_{x\to -1} \sqrt{x^2 - 3x + 4}$

5. $\displaystyle\lim_{x\to 0} \frac{\sqrt{3x^2 + x + 1}}{\sqrt[3]{x^3 - x + 8}}$

6. $\displaystyle\lim_{x\to 1} \frac{x - 1}{x^3 - 1}$

7. Suppose $\epsilon = 0.01$. Use the proof of Theorem 2d to generate a δ so that $\displaystyle\lim_{x\to 2} (3x^2 - 4x - 4)$ $= \displaystyle\lim_{x\to 2} (3x + 2) \cdot \lim_{x\to 2} (x - 2)$ is satisfied for this value of ϵ.

Rewrite the statements for each of the following theorems without specifying limits. This may be done provided each limit exists. Theorem 2a can be written without specifying the limits of the functions as $x \to c$.

$$\lim_{x\to c} [f(x) + g(x)] = [\lim_{x\to c} f(x)] + [\lim_{x\to c} g(x)]$$

8. Theorem 2b

9. Theorem 2c

10. Theorem 2d

11. Theorem 2e

12. Theorem 2f

13. Theorem 3a

Challenge   Prove Theorem 3a if n is a natural number.

14-4   Continuity

The intuitive notion of continuity is simple to explain. A function is continuous if its graph can be drawn without lifting the pencil. Continuity appears to be a property that exists or does not exist over an interval.

However, as with limits, continuity initially is defined for individual points. That is, a function may be continuous at one point, but not continuous (discontinuous) at another.

Remember, there are three conditions that must be met for a function to be continuous at a point. The function must be defined. It must have a limit for the x-value in question. And the value of the function must be equal to the limit of the function at that point.

A function f is continuous at $x = c$ in its domain if and only if f is defined at c and $\lim_{x \to c} f(x) = f(c)$.

A function is everywhere continuous if it is continuous at each value in its domain. A function is continuous on an interval if it is continuous at each interior point of the interval.

Continuous Functions

Theorems like those for limits may be proved for continuity.

A constant function $f(x) = c$ is everywhere continuous.

Theorem 4

If f and g are continuous functions at $x = a$, then $f \pm g$, $f \cdot g$, $\dfrac{f}{g}$, $g(a) \neq 0$ are continuous at a.

Theorem 5

Polynomial functions are everywhere continuous.

Theorem 6

Example

1. Identify points at which $f(x) = \dfrac{x^2 - 4}{x - 4}$ is discontinuous.

   Let $x = 4$ then $f(x) = \dfrac{(4)^2 - 4}{4 - 4} = \dfrac{12}{0}$.

   Thus, $f(x)$ is undefined at 4.

Exercises

Exploratory   Identify points at which each function is discontinuous.

1. $f(x) = 1 - \dfrac{1}{x}$

2. $f(x) = \dfrac{x - 2}{x^2 - 3x + 2}$

3. $f(x) = \sqrt{x^2 - 5x - 6}$

4. $f(x) = \begin{cases} 1 \text{ if } x \text{ is rational} \\ 0 \text{ if } x \text{ is irrational} \end{cases}$

Written Write an example of a function which satisfies each condition.

1. Everywhere continuous

2. Continuous for all values of x except 0

3. Discontinuous only at $x = 3$

4. Discontinuous where x is an even integer

5. Discontinuous at even multiples of π

6. State and illustrate three separate conditions under which a function may be discontinuous.

7. Prove Theorem 4.

Challenge Prove each of the following.

1. If f and g are continuous functions at $x = a$, then $f + g$ is continuous at a.

2. If f and g are continuous functions at $x = a$, then $f \cdot g$ is continuous at a.

3. $f(x) = x$ is everywhere continuous, without using Theorem 6.

14–5 An Application of Continuity

In Chapter **10** zeros of a polynomial were located using the Intermediate Value Theorem and The Location Principle. These tools can be used to find the zeros of other functions continuous on an interval.

> If f is a continuous function and $f(a)$ and $f(b)$ have opposite signs for $a, b, \in \mathcal{R}$, then f has at least one zero between a and b.

Location Principle

There is another way to find or approximate zeros of a function. It is called the **method of false position**. It is a good exercise to do on a computer or calculator.

Example

1. Find a root of $x^3 - 2x^2 - 3x - 4 = 0$. It is possible to use synthetic division to divide $x^3 - 2x^2 - 3x - 4$ by $x - 1$, $x - 2$, and so on.

x	1	-2	-3	-4
1	1	-1	-4	-8
2	1	0	-3	-10
3	1	1	0	-4
4	1	2	5	16

The function $f(x) = x^3 - 2x^2 - 3x - 4$ is continuous on $[3, 4]$ and $f(3)$ and $f(4)$ have opposite signs. So, by the Location Principle, $x^3 - 2x^2 - 3x - 4 = 0$ has a root between 3 and 4. Now, calculate the value of f at the midpoint of this interval, $f\left(\frac{7}{2}\right) = \frac{31}{8}$ so there is a root between 3 and $\frac{7}{2}$. The midpoint of this interval is $\frac{13}{4}$ so calculate $f\left(\frac{13}{4}\right)$. Since $f\left(\frac{13}{4}\right)$ and $f\left(\frac{7}{2}\right)$ have opposite signs, there is a root between $\frac{13}{4}$ and $\frac{7}{2}$. The midpoint of this interval, $\frac{27}{8}$, can be taken as an approximation of the root and the error would be less than $\frac{1}{8}$.

Exercises

Written Use the method of false position to find or approximate within $\frac{1}{8}$ or less a zero for each function in the indicated interval.

1. $f(x) = 2x^3 - 3x^2 - x + 1; [-1, 1]$ 2. $f(x) = x^2 - 4x - 2; [-1, 0]$
3. $f(x) = 4x^3 - x^2 + x + 3; [-1, 1]$ 4. $f(x) = x^3 - 3x + 1; [0, 2]$
5. $f(x) = 4x^4 - x^3 - 4x^2 + 5x - 1; [0, 1]$

Use the Location Principle and the method of false position to determine (or approximate) a value x_0 for which $f(x_0)$ has the given value. Give a rough sketch of the graph. Provide a justification for the method used.

6. $f(x) = 2x^2 - 5x - 1; f(x_0) = -2$ 7. $f(x) = 8x^3 - 5x^2 + 5x - 7; f(x_0) = 4$
8. $f(x) = x^3 - 3x^2 + 3; f(x_0) = 2$

14–6 Finding Other Limits

Consider the following limit.

$$\lim_{x \to \infty} \frac{2x + 3}{3x + 5} = \frac{2}{3}$$

This statement is read "The limit of $\frac{2x + 3}{3x + 5}$ as x tends to infinity is $\frac{2}{3}$." It means that when x is large, $\frac{2x - 3}{3x - 5}$ is close to $\frac{2}{3}$. The limit definition in terms of ϵ and δ neighborhoods does not apply in this case. Instead the limit may be defined as follows.

The statement "tends to infinity" may also be read "increases without bound."

The $\lim\limits_{x \to \infty} f(x) = L$ if and only if to each $\epsilon > 0$ there corresponds a number N such that $|f(x) - L| < \epsilon$ when $x > N$.

Limit

Example

1. Find $\lim\limits_{x \to \infty} \dfrac{3x^2 - 2x + 1}{2x^2 - x + 1}$.

$$\lim\limits_{x \to \infty} \frac{3x^2 - 2x + 1}{2x^2 - x + 1} = \lim\limits_{x \to \infty} \frac{3 - \dfrac{2}{x} + \dfrac{1}{x^2}}{2 - \dfrac{1}{x} + \dfrac{1}{x^2}}$$

$$= \frac{\lim\limits_{x \to \infty} \left(3 - \dfrac{2}{x} + \dfrac{1}{x^2}\right)}{\lim\limits_{x \to \infty} \left(2 - \dfrac{1}{x} + \dfrac{1}{x^2}\right)}$$

$$= \frac{\lim\limits_{x \to \infty} 3 - \lim\limits_{x \to \infty} \dfrac{2}{x} + \lim\limits_{x \to \infty} \dfrac{1}{x^2}}{\lim\limits_{x \to \infty} 2 - \lim\limits_{x \to \infty} \dfrac{1}{x} + \lim\limits_{x \to \infty} \dfrac{1}{x^2}}$$

$$= \frac{3 - 2 \lim\limits_{x \to \infty} \dfrac{1}{x} + \lim\limits_{x \to \infty} \dfrac{1}{x} \cdot \lim\limits_{x \to \infty} \dfrac{1}{x}}{2 - 0 + \lim\limits_{x \to \infty} \dfrac{1}{x} \cdot \lim\limits_{x \to \infty} \dfrac{1}{x}}$$

$$= \frac{3 - 2 \cdot 0 + 0 \cdot 0}{2 - 0 + 0 \cdot 0} = \frac{3}{2}$$

Another way to approach this problem is to let $y = \dfrac{1}{x}$ and consider only $x > 0$. Then $y \to 0$ as $x \to \infty$.

Then, $\lim\limits_{x \to \infty} \dfrac{3x^2 - 2x + 1}{2x^2 - x + 1} = \lim\limits_{x \to \infty} \dfrac{3 - \dfrac{2}{x} + \dfrac{1}{x^2}}{2 - \dfrac{1}{x} + \dfrac{1}{x^2}}$

By transforming variables, the calculation of $\lim\limits_{x \to \infty}$ becomes a calculation of $\lim\limits_{y \to 0}$.

$$= \lim\limits_{y \to 0} \frac{3 - 2y + y^2}{2 - y + y^2} = \frac{3}{2}$$

Exercises

Exploratory   Find the value of each limit.

1. $\lim\limits_{n \to \infty} \dfrac{n + 1}{n}$

2. $\lim\limits_{n \to \infty} \dfrac{3n - 5}{n}$

3. $\lim\limits_{n \to \infty} \dfrac{n^2 + n - 3}{n^2}$

4. $\displaystyle\lim_{n\to\infty}\frac{2n}{n+4}$ **5.** $\displaystyle\lim_{b\to\infty}\frac{5-b}{b-1}$ **6.** $\displaystyle\lim_{x\to\infty}\frac{3}{x^2-2x+1}$

Written

1. Use the definition for $\displaystyle\lim_{x\to\infty}f(x)=L$ to prove that $\displaystyle\lim_{x\to\infty}\frac{2x+5}{3x}=\frac{2}{3}$.

Find the value of each limit.

2. $\displaystyle\lim_{x\to\infty}\frac{3x^2-2x+3}{2x^3-3x-1}$ **3.** $\displaystyle\lim_{x\to\infty}\frac{4x^3-3x^2+x-1}{3x^3+1}$

4. $\displaystyle\lim_{x\to\infty}\frac{2x}{3x^2+x-5}$ **5.** $\displaystyle\lim_{x\to\infty}\frac{2x^2}{3x^2+x-5}$

6. $\displaystyle\lim_{x\to\infty}\sqrt{\frac{2+3x}{3+2x}}$ **7.** $\displaystyle\lim_{x\to\infty}\frac{x^3-2x^2+x-1}{3x^2-2x+1}$

Challenge

1. Guess $\displaystyle\lim_{x\to\infty}x^{1/x}$. Present an argument for your answer.

2. The theorem below is sometimes used as a definition for the limit of a function.
  Theorem: A function f has $\displaystyle\lim_{x\to c}f(x)=L$ if and only if for every sequence of elements
  from the domain of f, $\{x_1, x_2, \ldots, x_n, \ldots\}$, such that $\{x_n\}\to c$ (with $x_n\neq c$), the sequence
  $\{f(x_1), f(x_2), \ldots, f(x_n), \ldots\}$ converges to L, $f(x_n)\to L$.
  Use this theorem to show that the function f does not have a limit at 0 where
  $f(x)=\begin{cases}0, & \text{if } x<0\\ 1, & \text{if } x\geq 0.\end{cases}$

14–7   Limits of Trigonometric Functions

   The values of a function may lie between those of two other functions. Sometimes two such functions can be found having the same limit. In such a case the given function is "caught in the middle." It must have the same limit as the two other functions.

If $f(x)\leq g(x)\leq h(x)$ for each x in some deleted neighborhood of c and $\displaystyle\lim_{x\to c}f(x)=\lim_{x\to c}h(x)=L$, then $\displaystyle\lim_{x\to c}g(x)=L$.   **Theorem 7**

Proof

   Given $\epsilon>0$, then there exist $\delta_0, \delta_1, \delta_2$ such that these statements are true.

$$f(x) \le g(x) \le h(x) \text{ when } 0 < |x - c| < \delta_0$$
$$|f(x) - L| < \epsilon \qquad \text{when } 0 < |x - c| < \delta_1$$
$$|h(x) - L| < \epsilon \qquad \text{when } 0 < |x - c| < \delta_2$$

If δ is the least of $\delta_0, \delta_1, \delta_2$, then all three conditions are satisfied.

$$L - \epsilon < f(x) \le g(x) \le h(x) < L + \epsilon \text{ when } 0 < |x - c| < \delta$$

So, $|g(x) - L| < \epsilon$ when $0 < |x - c| < \delta$.

Theorem 7 is useful for finding a special limit, $\lim_{\theta \to 0} \dfrac{\sin \theta}{\theta}$. This limit permits finding limits of other trigonometric functions.

$$\lim_{\theta \to 0} \frac{\sin \theta}{\theta} = 1 \qquad\qquad \textbf{Theorem 8}$$

Proof

In evaluating the limit, a geometrical argument is used. Interpret θ as the measure in radians of an angle. Since the concern is with θ approaching 0, it is only necessary to consider the behavior of the function in a neighborhood of zero. In particular, suppose that $-\dfrac{\pi}{2} < \theta < \dfrac{\pi}{2}$. The required limit is evaluated by sandwiching $\dfrac{\sin \theta}{\theta}$ between bounds, both having the same limit. First suppose that $0 < \theta < \dfrac{\pi}{2}$. Consider a positive angle AOB whose measure in radians is θ. The segment OA has length 1 unit. The arc AB is part of a circle with center O and radius 1 unit. Also, $\overline{DB}$ is the altitude from B and $\overleftrightarrow{AE}$ is the line through A parallel to $\overline{DB}$.

This theorem establishes a basis for finding limits of trigonometric functions.

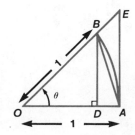

$$\sin \theta = \frac{DB}{OB} = \frac{DB}{1} = DB$$

$$\tan \theta = \frac{AE}{OA} = \frac{AE}{1} = AE$$

This means $\overline{DB}$ has length $\sin \theta$ units and $\overleftrightarrow{AE}$ has length $\tan \theta$ units. Also, area of sector $OAB = \dfrac{\theta}{2\pi} \cdot \pi r^2 = \dfrac{1}{2}(1)^2\theta = \dfrac{1}{2}\theta$. The diagram shows that the area of triangle OAB < area of sector OAB < area of triangle OAE.

This proof relies on geometric intuition.

$$\frac{1}{2} \cdot OA \cdot DB < \frac{1}{2}\theta < \frac{1}{2} \cdot OA \cdot AE$$

$$\frac{1}{2}\sin\theta < \frac{1}{2}\theta < \frac{1}{2}\tan\theta$$

$$\sin\theta < \theta < \tan\theta$$

$$\frac{\sin\theta}{\sin\theta} < \frac{\theta}{\sin\theta} < \frac{\tan\theta}{\sin\theta}$$

$$1 < \frac{\theta}{\sin\theta} < \frac{1}{\cos\theta}$$

Since $\sin\theta > 0$ when

$0 < \theta < \dfrac{\pi}{2}$.

If $1 < \dfrac{\theta}{\sin\theta}$ then $\dfrac{\sin\theta}{\theta} < 1$ and if $\dfrac{\theta}{\sin\theta} < \dfrac{1}{\cos\theta}$ then $\cos\theta < \dfrac{\sin\theta}{\theta}$.

So, $\cos\theta < \dfrac{\sin\theta}{\theta} < 1$ when $0 < \theta < \dfrac{\pi}{2}$. The same result can be

obtained for $-\dfrac{\pi}{2} < \theta < 0$. Thus, for small positive or negative

θ, $\cos\theta < \dfrac{\sin\theta}{\theta} < 1$.

The function $\dfrac{\sin\theta}{\theta}$ is caught between the function $\cos\theta$ and

the constant function 1. As $\theta \to 0$, $OD \to 1$ and $\dfrac{OD}{OB} = \cos\theta \to 1$.

Since $\lim\limits_{\theta \to 0} \cos\theta = 1$ and $\lim\limits_{\theta \to 0} 1 = 1$, Theorem 8 applies. Thus,

$$\lim\limits_{\theta \to 0} \frac{\sin\theta}{\theta} = 1.$$

Examples

1. Find $\lim\limits_{x \to 0} \dfrac{\tan x}{x}$.

$$\lim\limits_{x \to 0} \frac{\tan x}{x} = \lim\limits_{x \to 0}\left(\frac{\sin x}{x} \cdot \frac{1}{\cos x}\right)$$
$$= \lim\limits_{x \to 0}\left(\frac{\sin x}{x}\right) \cdot \lim\limits_{x \to 0}\left(\frac{1}{\cos x}\right)$$
$$= 1 \cdot 1 = 1$$

2. Find $\lim\limits_{x \to \infty} x \sin \dfrac{1}{x}$ when $x \neq 0$.

$$\lim\limits_{x \to \infty} x \sin \frac{1}{x} = \lim\limits_{x \to \infty}\left(\frac{\sin \dfrac{1}{x}}{\dfrac{1}{x}}\right)$$
$$= \lim\limits_{z \to 0} \frac{\sin z}{z} \text{ for } z = \frac{1}{x}$$
$$= 1$$

Exercises

Written   Solve each of the following.

1. Show that $\lim\limits_{\theta \to 0} \sin \theta = 0$.

2. Suppose θ is measured in degrees rather than radians. How would this affect $\lim\limits_{\theta \to 0} \dfrac{\sin \theta}{\theta}$?

Find the value of each limit.

3. $\lim\limits_{\theta \to 0} \dfrac{\sin^2 \theta}{\theta}$

4. $\lim\limits_{x \to 0} \dfrac{\sin 2x}{x}$

5. $\lim\limits_{x \to \infty} \dfrac{\sin 3x}{5x}$

6. $\lim\limits_{\theta \to 0} \dfrac{1 - \cos \theta}{\theta^2}$ (Hint: Multiply and divide by $1 + \cos \theta$.)

7. $\lim\limits_{\theta \to 0} \dfrac{1 - \cos \theta}{\theta}$

8. $\lim\limits_{\theta \to 0} \dfrac{\theta \cos \theta - \sin \theta}{\theta \cos \theta}$

Chapter Summary

1. A deleted neighborhood of the number c is any neighborhood with the number c removed. The set of all numbers x such that $0 < |x - c| < h$ is called a deleted neighborhood of c with radius h units.   (427)

2. If $f(x)$ is defined for all real numbers x in some deleted neighborhood of c, the number L is the limit of $f(x)$ as x approaches c, if and only if to each positive number ϵ there corresponds a positive number δ such that $|f(x) - L| < \epsilon$ when $0 < |x - c| < \delta$.   (428)

3. The following theorems are given for $\lim\limits_{x \to c} f(x) = F$ and $\lim\limits_{x \to c} g(x) = G$ and real numbers c, k, and n a positive number.   (430)

   1. $\lim\limits_{x \to c} x = c$

   2a. $\lim\limits_{x \to c} [f(x) + g(x)] = F + G$

   2b. $\lim\limits_{x \to c} [k \cdot f(x)] = k \cdot F$

   2c. $\lim\limits_{x \to c} [f(x) - g(x)] = F - G$

   2d. $\lim\limits_{x \to c} [f(x) \cdot g(x)] = F \cdot G$

   2e. $\lim\limits_{x \to c} \dfrac{1}{g(x)} = \dfrac{1}{G}$ if $G \neq 0$

   2f. $\lim\limits_{x \to c} \dfrac{f(x)}{g(x)} = \dfrac{F}{G}$ if $G \neq 0$

   3a. $\lim\limits_{x \to c} f(x)^n = F^n$

   3b. $\lim\limits_{x \to c} f(x)^{1/n} = F^{1/n}$

   3c. If $f(x) = a_0 x^0 + a_1 x^1 + a_2 x^2 + \cdots + a_n x^n$ then $\lim\limits_{x \to c} f(x) = f(c)$.

4. A function f is continuous at $x = c$ in its domain if and only if f is defined at c and $\lim_{x \to c} f(x) = f(c)$. (434)

5. A function is everywhere continuous if it is continuous at each value in its domain. A function is continuous on an interval if it is continuous at each interior point of the interval. (434)

6. A constant function $f(x) = c$ is everywhere continuous. (434)

7. If f and g are continuous functions at $x = a$, then $f \pm g$, $f \cdot g, \dfrac{f}{g}, g(a) \neq 0$ are continuous at a. (434)

8. Polynomial functions are everywhere continuous. (434)

9. If f is a continuous function and $f(a)$ and $f(b)$ have opposite signs for $a, b \in \mathscr{R}$, then f has at least one zero between a and b. (435)

10. The $\lim_{x \to \infty} f(x) = L$ if and only if to each $\epsilon > 0$ there corresponds a number N such that $|f(x) - L| < \epsilon$ when $x > N$. (437)

Chapter Review

14–1 **Assume that x is in the indicated neighborhood, find the smallest neighborhood that contains $f(x)$.**

1. $|x - 1| < 0.05, f(x) = 3x + 2$
2. $|x - c| < \delta, f(x) = 3x - 1$

14–2 **Given that $\epsilon = 0.01$ find a corresponding δ for each limit.**

3. $\lim_{x \to 1} (5x + 3) = 8$
4. $\lim_{x \to 2} (x^2 + 2x - 1) = 7$

14–3 **Use the limit theorem to evaluate each limit.**

5. $\lim_{x \to 2} \dfrac{x^2 - 4}{x - 2}$
6. $\lim_{x \to 1} \dfrac{x - 3}{2x - 4}$

7. $\lim_{x \to 3} (2x^2 + 3x + 4)$
8. $\lim_{x \to -1} x^2 - 3x + 4$

14–4 **Identify points at which each function is discontinuous.**

9. $f(x) = \dfrac{1}{(x - 3)^2}$
10. $f(x) = \begin{cases} 1, x > 0 \\ 0, x = 0 \\ -1, x < 0 \end{cases}$

14–5 **Use the method of false position to find or approximate within $\frac{1}{8}$, a zero for each function in the indicated interval.**

11. $f(x) = 3x^3 - 2x^2 + x + 3; [-1, 0]$
12. $f(x) = x^3 - 4x^2 - 2x + 1; [-2, 0]$

14–6 **Find the value of each limit**
14–7

13. $\lim_{x \to \infty} \dfrac{5x^3 - 2x^2 + 2x - 1}{7x^3 + 40x^2 + 2}$
14. $\lim_{x \to \infty} \sqrt{\dfrac{4x - 1}{2x + 3}}$

15. $\lim_{x \to 0} \dfrac{\sin 3x}{x}$
16. $\lim_{x \to \infty} x \tan \dfrac{1}{x}$

Chapter Test

For each sentence, write the largest possible domain for x, which makes the sentence true.

1. $4.8 < 2x + 3 < 5.2$

2. $x^2 - 4 \in \langle -0.2, 0.2 \rangle$

Given that $\epsilon = 0.001$ find a corresponding δ for each limit.

3. $\lim\limits_{x \to 1} (5x + 3) = 8$

4. $\lim\limits_{x \to 2} (x^2 + 2x - 1) = 7$

5. $\lim\limits_{x \to 3} \dfrac{1}{x} = \dfrac{1}{3}$

Evaluate each limit.

6. $\lim\limits_{x \to 2} \dfrac{x^2 - 1}{x^2 + 1}$

7. $\lim\limits_{x \to 0} \dfrac{3x^3 - 2x}{2x^2 - 3x}$

8. $\lim\limits_{x \to 1} [x^{1/3}(x + 3)^{1/2}(3x + 4)]$

9. Write an example of a function that is discontinuous where x is an odd integer.

Use the method of false position to find or approximate within $\frac{1}{8}$, a zero for each function in the indicated interval.

10. $f(x) = x^3 + 2x^2 - 5;\ [1, 2]$

11. $f(x) = x^3 - 2x^2 - 1;\ [2, 3]$

Find the value of each limit.

12. $\lim\limits_{x \to 3} \dfrac{x^2 - 2x + 1}{x^3}$

13. $\lim\limits_{x \to 1} \dfrac{x - 1}{x^3 - 1}$

14. $\lim\limits_{x \to 0} \dfrac{\sin^2 x}{x}$

15. $\lim\limits_{x \to 0} \dfrac{1 - \cos x}{x^2}$

Computers

Medicine

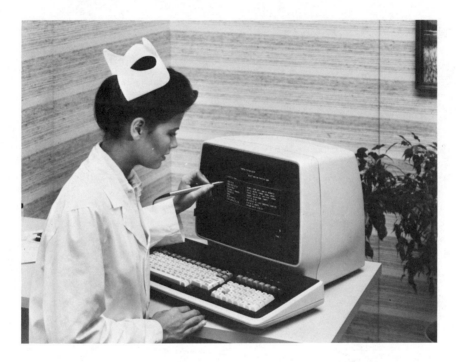

In a hospital, a computer keeps account of patients' rooms and appointments.

Medicine is facing the problem of information overload. People in the medical profession are overwhelmed by the large amount of information processed as a result of research. The computer has begun to aid the medical profession. Through modern information storage, indexing, and retrieval systems, computers can be used by doctors to keep up on the important advances in the field, thus helping to improve the quality of medical care. Computers help to extend the frontiers of medicine and may help medical research conquer some diseases.

Within the hospital many uses for computers exist. The most common functions are business oriented such as accounting, payroll, billing, and inventory control. Computers now perform several other functions for the hospitals. One function is to help doctors in the diagnosis process. A physician can type in a few symptoms and the computer will print out a list of possible diseases. The physician then can have the computer explain the reason for listing a particular disease. Searching a data center like this a doctor can logically examine many possibilities and achieve a diagnosis more quickly.

Another function with which computers are assisting is monitoring patients. This takes place in the operating room, the recovery room, and the patient's room. Usually an alarm with sound and lights will signal a variable exceeding high or low limits. Temperature, heart action, and respiratory problems are the main functions monitored.

An electrocardiogram (EKG) is a method of monitoring using a computer. Computers analyze EKG waveforms for normal and abnormal conditions. The computer performs an analysis, characterizes the waveforms from each of the leads of a scalar electrocardiogram, calculates rate, and produces an interpretation of the status of the heart. The analysis is then printed on a teletypewriter for assessment by the physician.

In several hospitals, computers are already being used to administer preliminary interviews of patients. The questions are put on a screen and the patient inputs the response. After patients have completed the interview with the computer, their medical histories are printed out for use by doctors.

A properly designed computer system can monitor laboratory instruments, analyze data to provide continuous control of quality, and relay error messages to the technologists in the event that potentially erroneous data are transmitted. Many laboratory procedures also require computations to convert raw data obtained by analytical instruments into meaningful, clinically useful information.

Radiology has benefited from the use of computers. The system can examine X-rays, compare the images to known standards, and prepare a list of likely causes in the order of probability. Computers are able to help in the studies concerning long term effects of radiation on human heredity. Computers can . be linked to optical scanning devices to determine the presence of abnormal cells.

Research and model simulation are other areas of medicine that use computers. Research is a common use of computers, since calculations of statistics are quickly performed on a computer. Model simulation is another way computers are used. In one school of medicine, students are given situations and then asked to respond in much the way a doctor would during an office visit. They ask the patient about his or her medical history, present conditions, or other areas that may help the doctor determine the nature of the person's condition. The computer, in playing the patient, responds as a patient would to the questions of the physician. The physical examination is in terms of a report. This type of simulation helps the student to become a better diagnostician.

Exercises   **Write programs for each of the following.**

1. Determine the limit of $\frac{x^2 - 4}{x - 2}$ as x approaches 2 by finding $\frac{x^2 - 4}{x - 2}$ for $x = 1, 1.5, 1.75, 1.875, \ldots$ until the difference between successive values is less than 0.0001.

2. Determine the limit of $\frac{\sin x}{x}$ as x approaches zero by finding $\frac{\sin x}{x}$ for $x = 1$, 0.5, 0.25, $\ldots$ until the difference between successive values is less than 0.0005.

Use the method of false position to find or approximate within $\frac{1}{8}$, a zero for each function in the indicated interval.

3. $f(x) = 3x^3 - 2x^2 + x + 3; [-1, 0]$

4. $f(x) = x^3 - 2x^2 - 1; [2, 3]$

5. The owner of a pizza parlor loses money on a pizza with an x inch diameter if the area exceeds y square inches. Customers complain if the area is less than z square inches. What tolerance is allowed for the diameter?

Chapter 15

The strength of a rectangular beam is directly proportional to the product of the width and the square of the depth. Derivatives help to determine the dimensions of the strongest beam that can be cut from a circular log with a given dimension.

Rates of Change

15–1   Distance with Respect to Time

Suppose a rocket starts from rest at a point O and is at a distance s feet from O along a straight path at the end of t seconds. If the distance s feet at the time t seconds is given by the equation $s = 10t^2$, a function with domain $\mathcal{R}$ and range the set of nonnegative real numbers is found. Of course, the physical situation would determine the meaningful domain and range of the function.

Using $f: t \rightarrow 10t^2$ to denote the function associated with $s = 10t^2$, gives $f(t) = 10t^2$ where $f(t)$ is the distance traveled in time t from $t = 0$.

$f(1) = 10(1)^2 = 10$ 10 ft is the distance traveled
                                   from $t = 0$ to $t = 1$.

$f(2) = 10(2)^2 = 40$ 40 ft is the distance traveled
                                   from $t = 0$ to $t = 2$.

The average speed over the time interval from $t = 1$ to $t = 2$ is $\dfrac{\text{change in distance}}{\text{change in time}}$.

$$\frac{f(2) - f(1)}{2 - 1} = \frac{40 - 10}{1} = 30$$

The average speed over this interval is 30 ft/s. In the same way, the average speed from $t = 1$ to $t = 1.5$ can be determined.

$$\frac{f(1.5) - f(1)}{1.5 - 1} = \frac{10(1.5)^2 - 10(1)^2}{0.5} = \frac{22.5 - 10}{0.5} = 25$$

The average speed on this interval is 25 ft/s. The figure gives a graphical representation.

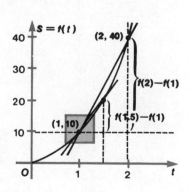

What is the speed at $t = 1$? An answer for this question could be obtained by tabulating average speeds over short time intervals from $t = 1$ to $t = 1 + h$ for smaller and smaller positive values of h.

$$\frac{f(1 + h) - f(1)}{(1 + h) - 1} = \frac{f(1 + h) - f(1)}{h}$$

h	0.2	0.1	0.05	0.01	0.001
$\dfrac{f(1 + h) - f(1)}{h}$	22	21	20.5	20.1	20.01

The figure illustrates the ratio formed to calculate average speed over the interval $\langle 1, 1 + h \rangle$. It seems clear that the average speed over the interval from $t = 1$ to $t = 1 + h$ is very close to 20 ft/s for small positive values of h. (Average speeds for small negative values of h reveal a pattern which seems to converge to 20 from the other direction.) The ratio can be made as close as desired to 20 by taking h sufficiently small, $h \neq 0$. This fact can be proved.

$$f(t) = 10t^2$$

$$\frac{f(1 + h) - f(1)}{h} = \frac{10(1 + h)^2 - 10(1)^2}{h}$$

$$= \frac{10 + 20h + 10h^2 - 10}{h}$$

$$= 20 + 10h, h \neq 0$$

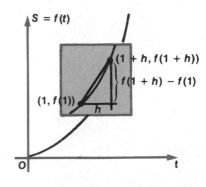

Thus, $\dfrac{f(1 + h) - f(1)}{h}$ can be made arbitrarily close to 20 by taking h sufficiently small.

$$\lim_{h \to 0} \frac{f(1 + h) - f(1)}{h} = 20$$

This limit provides the answer to the question "What is the speed of the rocket at $t = 1$?" Therefore, speed at an instant, sometimes called *instantaneous velocity*, may be defined by a limit. The speed at $t = 1$ then is 20 ft/s.

Speed is a scalar. Velocity is a vector.

Example

1. **Find the speed of the rocket at $t = 5$ if its distance s at time t is given by $s = 10t^2$.**

The speed at $t = 5$ is given by $\lim\limits_{h \to 0} \dfrac{f(5 + h) - f(t)}{h}$ where $f(t) = 10t^2$.

$$\lim_{h \to 0} \frac{f(5 + h) - f(5)}{h} = \lim_{h \to 0} \frac{10(5 + h)^2 - 10(5)^2}{h}$$

$$= \lim_{h \to 0} \frac{10(25 + 10h + h^2) - 10(25)}{h}$$

$$= \lim_{h \to 0} \frac{250 + 100h + 10h^2 - 250}{h}$$

$$= \lim_{h \to 0} (100 + 10h)$$

$$\lim_{h \to 0} \frac{f(5 + h) - f(5)}{h} = 100$$

At $t = 5$, the speed is 100 ft/s.

Exercises

Written **Given $f(t) = 10t^2$, calculate the average speed for the given intervals for t by evaluating $\dfrac{f(t + h) - f(t)}{h}$.**

1. $t = 2$ to $t = 2.5$
2. $t = 2$ to $t = 2.1$
3. $t = 2$ to $t = 2 + h$
4. $t = 4$ to $t = 4.5$
5. $t = 4$ to $t = 4.1$
6. $t = 4$ to $t = 4 + h$
7. Deduce the speed at $t = 2$.
8. Deduce the speed at $t = 4$.
9. Using the results of Problems **1–8**, copy and complete the table for instantaneous speeds (v).

t	0	1	2	3	4	5
v	0	20	?	?	?	100

10. Write a formula expressing v as a function of t. Find $\lim\limits_{h \to 0} \dfrac{f(t + h) - f(t)}{h}$ where $f(t) = 10t^2$.

Solve each of the following.

11. Suppose a rocket accelerates from rest under the condition $s = 10t^2$. Let s be the number of feet the rocket travels in t seconds. At what instant is the rocket going 60 miles per hour?

12. Suppose an astronaut drops a rock from a cliff on the moon. If $s = 5.5t^2$ where s is the number of feet the rock travels in t seconds, at what instant is the rock going 55 miles per hour?

Suppose a marble initially at rest rolls down an inclined plane. Let s be the number of inches the marble rolls in t seconds where s is related to t by the equation $s = 3t^2$. Find the average rate of change of s with respect to t over the indicated interval.

13. $t = 2$ to $l = 3$ **14.** $t = 2$ to $t = 2.5$ **15.** $t = 2$ to $t = 2.1$

16. Evaluate $\dfrac{f(2 + h) - f(2)}{h}$ to find the average rate of change of s with respect to t from $t = 2$ to $t = 2 + h$. Deduce the instantaneous speed at $t = 2$.

17. Calculate the speed at $t = 3$ by evaluating $\displaystyle\lim_{h \to 0} \dfrac{f(3 + h) - f(3)}{h}$.

Challenge A ball is thrown vertically upward with an initial velocity of 80 ft/s. If the ball is released 6 feet above the ground, its height in feet s at the end of t seconds is given by the formula $s = -16t^2 + 80t + 6$.

1. Tabulate several ordered pairs that belong to the function defined by this equation. Sketch a graph of the function for nonnegative values of t.

2. Find the instantaneous velocity of the ball at the end of 0, 1, 2, and 3 seconds. Derive a formula for v that fits this data.

3. Estimate from the graph the maximum height reached by the ball and the time at which that height is reached. What is the velocity of the ball at that instant? Try to find the exact coordinates of the highest point on your graph.

15–2 Difference Ratio

To express speed at a given instant, the average speed over a time interval was considered. This process involved the ratio $\dfrac{\text{change in value of the function}}{\text{change in value of } t}$.

The average rate of change in the value of the function f with respect to x can be expressed by the following.

$$\frac{\text{change in value of function}}{\text{change in variable}} = \frac{f(a + h) - f(a)}{(a + h) - a}$$
$$= \frac{f(a + h) - f(a)}{h}, h \neq 0$$

The graph shows the changes in the variable and in the value of the function over an interval $a \leq x \leq a + h$.

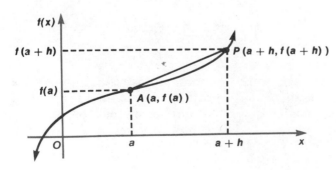

Note that the graph exhibits $h > 0$, while $\displaystyle\lim_{h \to 0}$ includes both $h > 0$ and $h < 0$.

Using the limiting process, the ratio of differences can be used to find the rate of change of f at $x = a$.

$$\lim_{h \to 0} \frac{f(a + h) - f(a)}{h}$$

Rate of change of f at $x = a$

The ratio $\dfrac{f(a + h) - f(a)}{h}$ is called the **difference quotient** (or difference ratio). It is the ratio of differences in function values to differences in values of the independent variable. The limit as $h \to 0$ of the difference quotient is called the derivative of f at $x = a$ and is denoted $f'(a)$.

$$f'(a) = \lim_{h \to 0} \frac{f(a + h) - f(a)}{h}$$

Derivative of f at $x = a$

A function is **differentiable** if the derivative of the function exists at each value in its domain. A function is **differentiable on an interval** if the derivative of the function exists at each point of the interval.

The following examples extend difference ratios and derivatives to situations other than those involving time and distance.

Examples

1. **Blow up a balloon. If the radius of the spherical balloon is r cm, the volume V cm³ enclosed by the balloon is given by the equation $V = \frac{4}{3}\pi r^3$. When r changes, the volume V changes. Find the rate at which V is changing with respect to r when $r = 2$.**

$$\frac{\text{change in volume}}{\text{change in radius}} = \frac{f(2 + h) - f(2)}{h}$$

$$\frac{f(2 + h) - f(2)}{h} = \frac{\frac{4}{3}\pi(2 + h)^3 - \frac{4}{3}\pi(2)^3}{h}$$

$$= \frac{\frac{4}{3}\pi(8 + 12h + 6h^2 + h^3) - \frac{4}{3}\pi(8)}{h}$$

$$= \frac{\frac{4}{3}\pi(12h + 6h^2 + h^3)}{h}$$

$$= 16\pi + 8\pi h + \frac{4}{3}\pi h^2; \, h \neq 0$$

$$\lim_{h \to 0} \frac{f(2 + h) - f(2)}{h} = 16\pi$$

The ratio gives the average rate of change of volume with respect to the radius during the interval $r = 2$ to $r = 2 + h$. Therefore, the rate of change at $r = 2$ is defined to be

$$\lim_{h \to 0} \frac{f(2 + h) - f(2)}{h},$$

if it exists.

Hence, the volume is changing at the rate of 16π cm³/cm at $r = 2$.

2. **A farmer estimates that if he harvests his crop now he will get 50 bushels per acre which he can sell for $1.00 per bushel. Past experience suggests that his crop will increase at the rate of 5 bushels per week, but the price probably will decline at the rate of 5¢ per bushel per week. However, he can wait no longer than 6 weeks or his crop may be endangered. When should he harvest his crop so that he gets the maximum amount?**

The amount A is controlled by the following equation, where w represents the number of weeks he should wait before harvesting his crop.

$$A = (50 + 5w)(1 - 0.05w) = \tfrac{1}{4}(200 + 10w - w^2)$$

The graph of the function defined by this equation is a parabola. The amount the farmer receives increases to the vertex of the parabola and then begins to decrease. The rate of change of the function is positive to the left of the vertex and negative to the right. The farmer should harvest and sell his crop when the function reaches its highest point, where $f'(w)$ is 0.

$$f'(w) = \lim_{h \to 0} \frac{f(w + h) - f(w)}{h}$$

$$= \lim_{h \to 0} \frac{\tfrac{1}{4}[(200 + 10(w + h) - (w + h)^2)] - \tfrac{1}{4}[200 + 10w - w^2]}{h}$$

$$= \lim_{h \to 0} \frac{\tfrac{1}{4}(10h - 2wh - h^2)}{h} \qquad \lim_{h \to 0} \frac{10 - 2w - h}{4}$$

$$f'(w) = \frac{10 - 2w}{4}$$

$$f'(w) = 0 \text{ when } w = 5$$

Thus, the farmer should wait 5 weeks to harvest and sell the crop.

3. **Find $f'(0)$ where $f:x \to |x|$.**

The function is defined on $\mathcal{R}$. Its graph consists of two branches, each a ray.

$$f(0) = 0$$
$$f(0 + h) = f(h) = h$$
$$f(0 + h) = \begin{cases} h, h > 0 \\ -h, h < 0 \end{cases}$$
$$\frac{f(0 + h) - f(0)}{h} = \frac{h}{h} = 1, h > 0$$
$$\frac{f(0 + h) - f(0)}{h} = \frac{-h}{h} = -1, h < 0$$

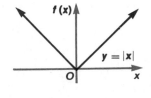

Clearly there is no fixed number L such that the difference ratio is as close as desired to L for $|h|$ small enough. The ratio is 1 for all small positive h and -1 for all small negative h. Hence $f'(0)$ does not exist. Notice that geometrically the graph of f has no unique tangent at $x = 0$.

Exercises

Exploratory   Find the difference quotient for each function at the given value of x and simplify.

1. $f(x) = x^2$ at $x = 1$
2. $f(x) = 2x$ at $x = 5$
3. $f(x) = 2x + 1$ at $x = 4$
4. $f(x) = x^2 + 1$ at $x = 3$
5. $f(x) = 4x^2$ at $x = 2$
6. $f(x) - x^2 + x$ at $x = 7$

Written   Find the derivative of each function at the given value of x.

1. $f(x) = x^2$ at $x = 1$
2. $f(x) = 2x$ at $x = 5$
3. $f(x) = 2x + 1$ at $x = 4$
4. $f(x) = x^2 + 1$ at $x = 3$
5. $f(x) = 4x^2$ at $x = 2$
6. $f(x) = x^2 + x$ at $x = 7$
7. If $g(x) = x^2 + 4x$, find $g'(2)$
8. If $h(x) = 2x^2 + 1$, find $h'(1)$.

Solve each of the following.

9. Find the rate of change of the circumference of a circle with respect to the radius when the radius is 3 cm.

10. Find the rate of change of the area of a square with respect to the length of a side, when the side is 5 cm.

11. Find the rate of change of the volume of a cube with respect to the length of an edge, when the edge is 2 mm.

12. For a marble rolling in a track the distance s cm from one end at time t seconds is given by $s = 5t - t^2$. Find the speed of the marble when $t = 2$.

Challenge   Solve each of the following.

1. Find the rate of change of the total surface area of a cylinder of height 8 cm with respect to the radius of the base, when the radius is 2 cm. (Hint: If A is the surface area and r the radius, $A = 2\pi r^2 + 16\pi r$. Find $f'(2)$ for the function $f:r \rightarrow 2\pi r^2 + 16\pi r$.)

2. A ball thrown vertically upward with a speed of 30 m/s moves according to the equation $h = 30t - 5t^2$, where h is the height in meters above the starting point and t is the time in seconds after it is thrown. Find its speed after 2 seconds.

15–3   Differentiation

The process of finding derivatives, which are defined as limits of difference quotients, is called **differentiation**. The function f is differentiated to obtain f'.

Using the definition to find the derivative is sometimes referred to as "taking the derivative from first principles."

$$f'(x) = \lim_{h \to 0} \frac{f(x + h) - f(h)}{h}$$

Definition of Derivative

The function $f'(x)$ has the same domain as f if $f'(x)$ exists for each x in the domain of f.

Example

1. Find the derivative of the function f defined by $f(x) = x^3$.

$$\frac{f(x+h) - f(x)}{h} = \frac{(x-h)^3 - x^3}{h}$$

$$= \frac{x^3 + 3x^2h + 3xh^2 + h^3 - x^3}{h}$$

$$= \frac{h(3x^2 + 3xh + h^2)}{h}$$

$$= 3x^2 + 3xh + h^2, h \neq 0$$

$$f'(x) = \lim_{h \to 0} \frac{f(x+h) - f(x)}{h}$$

$$f'(x) = \lim_{h \to 0} (3x^2 + 3xh + h^2)$$

$$f'(x) = 3x^2$$

To avoid repeated application of the definition, formulas are developed that can be used to write certain derivatives easily.

If $f(x) = c$, where c is a constant, then

$$f'(x) = \lim_{h \to 0} \frac{f(x+h) - f(x)}{h} = \lim_{h \to 0} \frac{c - c}{h} = 0.$$

The derivative of a constant function, $f(x) = c$, is zero.
$f'(x) = 0$ for all x in the domain of f

Derivative of a Constant Function

The derivatives of x^n for $n = 1, 2, 3$ have previously been found.

$f(x)$	x	x^2	x^3
$f'(x)$	1	$2x$	$3x^2$

The above pattern suggests the derivatives for x^4, x^5, ... The Binomial Theorem may be used to show the expected result.

If $f(x) = x^n (n \in N)$, then $f(x + h) = (x + h)^n$.

$$(x + h)^n = x^n + nx^{n-1}h + \frac{n(n-1)}{2!}x^{n-2}h^2 + \cdots + h^n$$

$$f'(x) = \lim_{h \to 0} \frac{x^n + nx^{n-1}h + \frac{n(n-1)}{2!}x^{n-2}h^2 + \cdots + h^n - x^n}{h}$$

$$f'(x) = \lim_{h \to 0} \left(nx^{n-1} + \frac{n(n-1)}{2!}x^{n-2}h + \cdots + h^{n-1}\right)$$

Since each term after the first contains h as a factor, $f'(x) = nx^{n-1} + 0 + 0 + \cdots + 0 = nx^{n-1}$.

If $f(x) = x^n (n \in N)$, then $f'(x) = nx^{n-1}$.

Derivative for $f(x) = x^n$

Example

2. **Find the derivative of $f(x) = x^6$.**

$$f'(x) = nx^{n-1}.$$
$$= 6x^{6-1} = 6x^5$$

The derivative of a constant c times a function f is the constant times the derivative of the function, $c \cdot f'(x)$, for all values of x for which $f'(x)$ exists. Thus, if $g(x) = c \cdot f(x)$, then $g'(x) = c \cdot f'(x)$.

Derivative for $g(x) = c \cdot f(x)$

Let $g(x) = c \cdot f(x)$ where $f'(x)$ exists.

$$g'(x) = \lim_{h \to 0} \frac{c \cdot f(x + h) - c \cdot f(x)}{h}$$
$$= \lim_{h \to 0} \frac{c[f(x + h) - f(x)]}{h}$$
$$= c \lim_{h \to 0} \frac{f(x + h) - f(x)}{h}$$
$$g'(x) = c \cdot f'(x)$$

A formula also may be found for the sum of a finite number of differentiable functions.

Let $f(x) = f_1(x) + f_2(x) + \cdots + f_n(x)$ where each of the $f_1, f_2, \ldots, f_n$ is differentiable.

$$f'(x) = \lim_{h \to 0} \frac{f(x + h) - f(x)}{h}$$
$$= \lim_{h \to 0} \frac{f(x + h)}{h} - \lim_{h \to 0} \frac{f(x)}{h}$$
$$= \lim_{h \to 0} \left[\frac{f_1(x + h) + f_2(x + h) + \cdots + f_n(x + h)}{h} \right] - \lim_{h \to 0} \left[\frac{f_1(x) + f_2(x) + \cdots + f_n(x)}{h} \right]$$
$$= \lim_{h \to 0} \frac{f_1(x + h) - f_1(x)}{h} + \lim_{h \to 0} \frac{f_2(x + h) - f_2(x)}{h} + \cdots + \lim_{h \to 0} \frac{f_n(x + h) - f_n(x)}{h}$$
$$f'(x) = f_1'(x) + f_2'(x) + \cdots + f_n'(x)$$

$$\lim_{h \to 0} \left[\frac{f(x + h)}{h} - \frac{f(x)}{h} \right]$$

> The derivative of the sum of a finite number of differentiable functions is the sum of their derivatives.

Derivative of Sums

These few results may be used to write the derivative for any polynomial function.

Examples

3. **Given $f(x) = x^3 - 2x + 6$, find $f'(x)$ and $f'(-1)$.**

$$f(x) = x^3 - 2x + 6$$
$$f'(x) = f'(x^3) + f'(-2x) + f'(6)$$
$$f'(x) = 3x^2 - 2(1) + 0$$
$$f'(x) = 3x^2 - 2$$
$$f'(-1) = 3(-1)^2 - 2 = 2 - 2 = 1$$

4. **Given $f(x) = (x^2 - 3)^2$, find $f'(x)$ and the rate of change of f at $x = 2$.**

Since the theorems you have deal only with expressions of the form ax^n, first expand $(x^2 - 3)^2$.

$$f(x) = (x^2 - 3)^2 = x^4 - 6x^2 + 9$$
$$f'(x) = 4x^3 - 12x$$

The rate of change of f at $x = 2$ is $f'(2)$.

$$f'(2) = 4(2)^3 - 12(2) = 32 - 24 = 8$$

Exercises

Exploratory Find the derivative of each function.

1. $f(x) = x^6$
2. $f(x) = 4x^3$
3. $f(x) = \frac{1}{2}x^2$
4. $f(x) = -2x^5$
5. $f(x) = ax^3$
6. $f(x) = 5$
7. $f(x) = 5x$
8. $f(x) = 3x + 4x^2$
9. $f(x) = x^2 + 2x + 5$

Written Find the derivative of each function.

1. $f(x) = (x + 3)^2$
2. $f(x) = (x + 3)(2x - 1)$
3. $f(x) = 6 - 4x^5 + 2x^9$
4. $f(x) = ax^2 + bx + c$
5. $f(x) = (x^2 - 3x)^2$
6. $f(x) = (x + 1)(x - 2)^2$
7. $f(x) = (x + 3)(x - 3)(2x + 5)$
8. $f(x) = 1 + 2x - 3x^2 + 4x^3$
9. Given $f(x) = 3 + x - x^2$, find the values of $f'(0)$, $f'\left(\frac{1}{2}\right)$, $f'(1)$, $f'(-10)$.

Find the derived function f' for each function. Sketch the graphs of f and f'.

10. $f{:}x \rightarrow 5x$
11. $f{:}x \rightarrow x^2$
12. $f{:}x \rightarrow x^3$

If $f(x) = \frac{1}{3}x^3 + \frac{1}{2}x^2 - 6x$, find x to make each sentence true.

13. $f'(x) = 0$ **14.** $f'(x) = -4$ **15.** $f'(x) < 0$

16. Given the function $f:x \rightarrow (x^3 - 2)^2$, find the derived function f' and the rate of change of f at $x = -1$ and at $x = 2$.

Solve each of the following.

17. Show that the rate of change of the area of a circle with respect to the radius is equal to the circumference.

18. Show that the rate of change of the volume of a sphere with respect to the radius is equal to the surface area. $(V = \frac{4}{3}\pi r^3; A = 4\pi r^2)$

Challenge One of the results of this section states the derivative of a sum is the sum of the derivatives. Are there comparable results for products and quotients? Consider that $x^5 = x^2 \cdot x^3$ and that $x^2 = \dfrac{x^5}{x^3}$. Present an argument for or against the statement "The derivative of a product (quotient) is the product (quotient) of the derivatives."

15–4 Geometric Interpretation

From the graph of a function f, it is possible to obtain a geometric meaning for $\lim\limits_{h \to 0} \dfrac{f(a + h) - f(a)}{h}$.

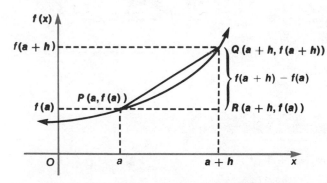

The graph depicts $h > 0$. For the derivative to exist $\lim\limits_{h \to 0^-}$ must be the same as $\lim\limits_{h \to 0^+}$.

Consider the difference quotient $\dfrac{f(a + h) - f(a)}{(a + h) - a}$. This ratio defines the slope of the secant line (or chord) $\overline{PQ}$ since it represents $\dfrac{\text{change in y-coordinate}}{\text{change in x-coordinate}}$.

Suppose that point P is fixed and point Q moves along the curve toward P. At each point Q, the difference quotient defines the slope of $\overline{PQ}$. As Q becomes close to P, h approaches 0 and this suggests considering the derivative of a,

$$\lim\limits_{h \to 0} \dfrac{f(a + h) - f(a)}{h}.$$

By taking h sufficiently small, the slope of $\overline{PQ}$ can be made as close as desired to the slope of the tangent at P. So, if $\lim\limits_{h \to 0} \dfrac{f(a + h) - f(a)}{h}$ exists, the derivative when $x = a$ may be interpreted as defining the slope of the tangent to the curve at $x = a$. Therefore, the value of the derivative at $x = a$ may be called the slope of the curve at $x = a$. If the derivative does not exist when $x = a$, then the slope of the curve is not defined when $x = a$. For example, the slope of $f(x) = |x|$ is not defined at $x = 0$.

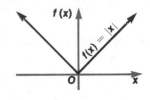

Many applications of calculus deal with a change in some variable. To show this, the symbol h often is replaced by Δx. It is read *delta x*. Thus Δx is equal to the change, or increment, in x. The corresponding change in the value of y is denoted Δy. If $y = f(x)$, then $\Delta y = f(x + \Delta x) - f(x)$. The delta notation then may be used for the derivative.

$$f'(x) = \lim_{\Delta x \to 0} \frac{f(x + \Delta x) - f(x)}{\Delta x} = \lim_{\Delta x \to 0} \frac{\Delta y}{\Delta x}$$

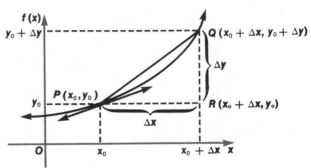

Leibniz introduced alternative symbols for the derivative: $f'(x) = \dfrac{dy}{dx}$. The notation $\dfrac{dy}{dx}$, called **differential notation,** was one of the original notations used for derivative. It is still widely used. Since dy and dx can be given individual meaning, differential notation makes certain formulas easy to use and remember.

Examples

1. **Find the slope of the curve $y = \frac{1}{2}x^2 + 1$ at $x = 2$.**

$$\frac{f(2 + \Delta x) - f(2)}{\Delta x} = \frac{[\frac{1}{2}(2 + \Delta x)^2 + 1 - (\frac{1}{2}(2)^2 + 1)]}{\Delta x}$$

$$= \frac{\{\frac{1}{2}(4 + 4\Delta x + (\Delta x)^2) + 1\} - (2 + 1)}{\Delta x}$$

$$= \frac{4\Delta x + (\Delta x)^2}{2\Delta x}$$

$$\frac{f(2 + \Delta x) - f(2)}{\Delta x} = 2 + \frac{1}{2}\Delta x$$

$$\frac{dy}{dx} = \lim_{\Delta x \to 0} (2 + \frac{1}{2}\Delta x) = 2$$

The slope of the curve, or slope of the tangent to the curve, at $x = 2$ is 2.

2. Find the slope and the equation of the tangent to the parabola $y = 3x^2 + 4x - 5$ at $(1, 2)$.

$$y = 3x^2 + 4x - 5$$
$$f'(x) = \frac{dy}{dx} = 6x + 4$$
$$f'(1) = 6(1) + 4 = 10$$

The slope of the tangent at $(1, 2)$ is 10.
By the point-slope formula, the equation of the tangent line is $y - 2 = 10(x - 1)$ or $y = 10x - 8$.

Exercises

Exploratory Find the slope of each curve at the given point.
1. $y = x^2$ at $(3, 9)$
2. $y = 5x$ at $(-1, -5)$
3. $y = 2x^2 - 3$ at $(2, 5)$
4. $y = x^3 - 3x^2 + 2$ at $(1, 0)$
5. $y = x^3$ at $x = -2$
6. $y = x^2 - 3x + 2$ at $x = 1$

Written Find the slope and the equation of the tangent to each curve at the given point.
1. $y = 2x^4$ at $x = -1$
2. $y = (2x + 3)(x - 1)$ at $x = 3$
3. $y = 2x^5$ at $x = 1$
4. $y = 1 - x^2$ at $x = 0$
5. $y = 5$ at $x = 2$
6. $y = x$ at $x = -1$

Solve each of the following.

7. Find the equation of the tangent to the curve $y = \frac{1}{4}x^2$ at the point given by $x = 2$. Show that if the tangent has intercepts at P and Q, the midpoint of $\overline{PQ}$ is $\left(\frac{1}{2}, -\frac{1}{2}\right)$.

8. Find the equations of the tangents to the curve $y = 2x^2$ at the points given by $x = 1$ and $x = -1$. Find the point of intersection of these tangents.

9. Show that there is one tangent to the curve $y = x^2 + 5$ which has slope 4. Find its equation.

10. Find the coordinates of the point on the curve $y = x^2 + 4x + 6$ at which the tangent has slope 12.

11. Find the equation of the tangent to the curve $y = x^3$ at the point given by $x = 1$. Find the point at which this tangent meets the curve again. (Hint: Show the tangent has equation $y = 3x - 2$ and meets the curve where $x^3 = 3x - 2$.

12. Find the equation of the tangent to the curve $y = x^3$ at the point given by $x = 2$. Find the point at which this tangent meets the curve again.

13. Find the equations of the tangents to the parabola $y = x^2 + 2$ at the points with x-coordinates -1 and 2. Show that the tangents intersect at a point on the x-axis.

14. The tangent to the parabola $y = (x - 2)^2$ at the point $(4, 4)$ crosses the x-axis at P and the y-axis at Q. Find the length of $\overline{PQ}$.

15. The tangent at a point P on the curve $4y = x^2 + 4x - 16$ is parallel to the line $6x - 2y = 5$. Find the coordinates of P.

16. A curve has equation $y = x^2 + ax + b$ where a and b are constants. If the line $y = 2x$ is tangent to the curve at $(2, 4)$, find a and b.

15–5 Extending Differentiation Techniques

This section extends differentiation techniques to negative and rational powers of x.

Example

1. **If $f(x) = x^{-1}$ and $g(x) = x^{-2}$, find $f'(x)$ and $g'(x)$.**

$$\frac{f(x + h) - f(x)}{h} = \frac{\frac{1}{x + h} - \frac{1}{x}}{h} = \frac{x - (x + h)}{h} \cdot \frac{1}{x(x + h)}$$

$$\frac{f(x + h) - f(x)}{h} = (-1)\frac{1}{x(x + h)} \quad (h \neq 0)$$

Hence, $f'(x) = (-1)\dfrac{1}{x \cdot x} = \dfrac{1}{x^2} = -x^{-2}$

$$\frac{g(x + h) - g(x)}{h} = \frac{\frac{1}{(x + h)^2} - \frac{1}{x^2}}{h}$$

$$= \frac{x^2 - (x + h)^2}{h} \cdot \frac{1}{x^2(x + h)^2}$$

$$= \frac{-2x - h}{1} \cdot \frac{1}{x^2(x + h)^2} \quad (h \neq 0)$$

$$\frac{g(x + h) - g(x)}{h} = \frac{-2x}{x^2(x + h)^2} + \frac{-h}{x^2(x + h)^2}$$

Hence, $g'(x) = \dfrac{-2x}{x^2 \cdot x^2} = -\dfrac{2}{x^3} = -2x^{-3}$.

It can be shown that if $f(x) = x^{-n}$ ($x \neq 0$ and n a positive integer), then $f'(x) = -n \cdot x^{-n-1} = -\dfrac{n}{x^{n+1}}$.

$$\frac{f(x + h) - f(x)}{h} = \frac{\frac{1}{(x + h)^n} - \frac{1}{x^n}}{h} = \frac{x^n - (x + h)^n}{h} \cdot \frac{1}{x^n(x + h)^n} \quad (h \neq 0)$$

$$-\frac{x^n - \left[x^n + nx^{n-1}h + \dfrac{n(n-1)}{2!}x^{n-2}h^2 + \cdots + nxh^{n-1} + h^n\right]}{h} \cdot \frac{1}{x^n(x+h)^n}$$

$$= \frac{-nx^{n-1} - h\left[\dfrac{n(n-1)}{2!}x^{n-2} + \cdots + nxh^{n-3} + h^{n-2}\right]}{x^n(x+h)^n}$$

Hence, $f'(x) = \lim\limits_{h \to 0} \dfrac{f(x+h) - f(x)}{h} = \dfrac{-nx^{n-1} - 0}{x^n(x+0)^n} = \dfrac{-n}{x^{n+1}}.$

> If $f(x) = x^n$, then $f'(x) = nx^{n-1}$ for all $n \in Z$, provided $x \neq 0$ when n is negative.

Differentiation for Negative Exponents

Extending to fractional exponents is a more difficult step. For now, accept that the differentiation formula $f'(x^n) = nx^{n-1}$ holds for any rational number n.

Examples

2. If $f(x) = x^{1/2}$, $x \geq 0$, find $f'(x)$.

$$f'(x) = \frac{1}{2}x^{-1/2} \quad (x > 0)$$

3. If $f(x) = \dfrac{1}{3x^2}$, find $f'(x)$.

$$f(x) = \frac{1}{3x^2} = \frac{1}{3}x^{-2}$$

$$f'(x) = \frac{-2}{3}x^{-3} = \frac{-2}{3x^3}$$

4. If $f(x) = \left(2x + \dfrac{1}{2x}\right)^2$, find $f'(x)$.

$$f(x) = 4x^2 + 2 + \frac{1}{4x^2} = 4x^2 + 2 + \frac{1}{4}x^{-2}$$

$$f'(x) = 8x + 0 + \left(-\frac{1}{2}\right)x^{-3} = 8x - \frac{1}{2x^3}$$

5. If $f(x) = \dfrac{x+1}{\sqrt{x}}$, find $f'(x)$.   *Express all radicals as fractional exponents.*

$$f(x) = \frac{x+1}{\sqrt{x}} = \frac{x}{\sqrt{x}} + \frac{1}{\sqrt{x}} = \frac{x}{x^{1/2}} + \frac{1}{x^{1/2}} = x^{1/2} + x^{-1/2}$$

$$f'(x) = \frac{1}{2}x^{-1/2} + \left(-\frac{1}{2}\right)x^{-3/2} = \frac{1}{2x^{1/2}} - \frac{1}{2x^{3/2}}$$

Exercises

Exploratory Find the derivative.

1. $x^{3/2}$

2. $x^{5/2}$

3. $x^{1/2}$

4. x^{-1}

5. $2x^{-3}$

6. $\frac{1}{2}x^{-4}$

7. $\sqrt{x}$

8. $\sqrt[3]{x}$

9. $\sqrt[3]{x^2}$

Written Find the derivative of each of the following.

1. $\frac{1}{x^4}$

2. $\frac{1}{\sqrt{x}}$

3. $\frac{2}{x^3}$

4. $\frac{1}{2x^{1/2}}$

5. $\frac{2}{3x^2}$

6. $\frac{4}{3x^3}$

7. $\frac{1}{5x^4}$

8. $\frac{1}{2\sqrt{x}}$

9. $\frac{2}{x}$

Write each expression as a sum of terms of the form ax^n. Then find the derivative.

10. $\sqrt{x} + \frac{1}{\sqrt{x}}$

11. $2x^2 - \frac{1}{4x^2}$

12. $\frac{x}{5} + \frac{5}{x}$

13. $8x^{3/4} - \frac{6}{x^{2/3}}$

14. $x^2(1 + \sqrt{x})$

15. $\left(x^2 - \frac{1}{x^2}\right)^2$

16. $\left(\sqrt{x} - \frac{1}{\sqrt{x}}\right)^2$

17. $\frac{2x^3 - 3x^2 + 4}{x^3}$

Solve each of the following.

18. If $f(x) = 4x^{3/2}$, find the values of $f'(0)$, $f'(1)$, $f'(4)$, and $f'\left(\frac{1}{9}\right)$.

19. If $f(x) = \left(x + 1 + \frac{1}{x}\right)\left(x + 1 - \frac{1}{x}\right)$, find $f'(x)$.

20. Calculate the rate of change of the function $f{:}x \rightarrow \sqrt[3]{x} + \frac{1}{\sqrt[3]{x}}$ at $x = 8$.

21. Given $f(x) = x^{1/2}\left(x + \frac{1}{x}\right)\left(x - \frac{1}{x}\right)$, show that $f'(x) = \frac{5x^4 + 3}{2x^{5/2}}$.

Verify for the following expressions that if $f(x) = g(x) \cdot h(x)$, then $f'(x) = g(x) \cdot h'(x) + h(x) \cdot g'(x)$.

22. $f(x) = x^2(1 + \sqrt{x})$

23. $f(x) = \left(x^2 - \frac{1}{x^2}\right)^2$

Verify for the following expressions that if $f(x) = \frac{g(x)}{h(x)}$, then $f'(x) = \frac{h(x) \cdot g'(x) - g(x) \cdot h'(x)}{[h(x)]^2}$.

24. $f(x) = \frac{2x^3 - 3x^2 - 4}{x^3}$

25. $f(x) = \frac{1}{x^2}(1 + \sqrt{x})$

Solve each of the following.

26. Find the equation of the tangent to the curve $y = x - \dfrac{1}{x^2}$ at the point where the curve crosses the x-axis.

27. Find the equation of the tangent to the curve $y = (x - 3)\sqrt{x}$ at the point where $x = 1$.

28. Show that the slope of the tangent at each point of the curve $y = \dfrac{1}{x}$ is negative.

Find the equation of the tangent at $x = \dfrac{1}{2}$

29. Prove that the slope of the tangent to the curve with equation $y = x^3 - 6x^2 + 12x + 1$ is never negative. Find the point on the curve where the slope is zero.

30. The curve $y = \left(a + \dfrac{b}{x}\right)\sqrt{x}$ passes through $(4, 8)$. The slope of the tangent at $(4, 8)$ is 2. Find a and b.

31. A curve has equation $y = 8\sqrt{x}$. Show that the tangent to the curve at the point where $x = 4$ crosses the y-axis at $(0, 8)$.

15–6   Increasing and Decreasing Functions

Information about the derivative helps in sketching the graph of a function. For example, the sign of the derivative indicates whether the function is increasing or decreasing at a point. This is because the derivative represents the instantaneous rate of change as well as the slope of the tangent line.

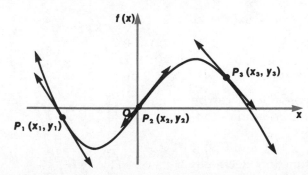

In the figure, the slope of the tangent line (the derivative) is negative at P_1 and P_3. At those points the tangent line is falling as one moves to the right, and the function is decreasing. At P_2, the tangent line is rising (the derivative is positive), and the function is increasing.

If $f'(x) > 0$ for every x in an interval, $a < x < b$, then the function is increasing in that interval. If $f'(x) < 0$ for every $x \in \langle a, b \rangle$, then $f(x)$ is decreasing on $\langle a, b \rangle$.

Increasing and Decreasing Functions

Example

1. For what values of x is the function $f(x) = 2x^3 - 9x^2 - 24x + 13$ decreasing?

$$f'(x) = 6x^2 - 18x - 24$$
$$f'(x) = 6(x^2 - 3x - 4)$$
$$f'(x) = 6(x - 4)(x + 1)$$
So, $f'(x) < 0$ when $6(x - 4)(x + 1) < 0$.

Therefore, $f(x)$ is decreasing on the interval $\langle -1, 4 \rangle$.

In the above example $f'(x) > 0$ if $x < -1$ or $x > 4$, so the function is increasing on those intervals. When $x = -1$ or $x = 4$, then $f'(x) = 0$, and the function is neither increasing nor decreasing. At $x = -1$ the function changes from decreasing to increasing. These points are among those called **critical points** on the graph of $f(x)$.

Example

2. Find the intervals for which the function $f(x) = x^3 - 3x^2 + 2$ is (1) increasing, and (2) decreasing. Then, find (3) the critical points on the graph of the function.

$$f(x) = x^3 - 3x^2 + 2$$
$$f'(x) = 3x^2 - 6x = 3x(x - 2)$$

(1) $f'(x) > 0$
$3x(x - 2) > 0$
$x < 0$ or $x > 2$

(2) $f'(x) < 0$
$3x(x - 2) < 0$
$0 < x < 2$

(3) $f'(x) = 0$
$3x(x - 2) = 0$
$x = 0$ or $x = 2$

The relation between the functions f and f' can be seen by graphing both in the same coordinate system.

Notice that $f(x)$ is increasing for $x < 0$, and $f'(x)$ is positive on that interval. The function decreases from $x = 0$ to $x = 2$, and $f'(x)$ is negative on that interval. Finally, $f(x)$ increases for $x > 2$, and $f'(x)$ again is positive for those values of x.

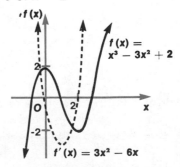

Exercises

Exploratory Determine if the function is (1) increasing or (2) decreasing at the given point.

1. $f(x) = x^2$ at $x = 2$
2. $f(x) = x^2 - 2x$ at $x = 0$
3. $f(x) = x^2 + 6x - 6$ at $x = -5$

4. $f(x) = x + \dfrac{1}{x}$ at $x = 5$ **5.** $f(x) = x^2 + 6x - 6$ at $x = -1$ **6.** $f(x) = x^3 - 3x$ at $x - 0$

Written   Determine the intervals in which each function is **(1)** increasing, and **(2)** decreasing.

1. $f(x) = x^2$

2. $f(x) = x^2 - 2x$

3. $f(x) = x - x^2$

4. $f(x) = x^2 + 6x - 6$

5. $f(x) = x^3 - 3x$

6. $f(x) = 2x^3 - 9x^2 + 12x$

7. $f(x) = \dfrac{1}{3}x^3 - x^2 - 3x + 3$

8. $f(x) = x(x - 2)^2$

9. $f(x) = \dfrac{1}{4}x^4 - \dfrac{9}{2}x^2$

10. $f(x) = x^3(4 - x)$

11. $f(x) = x^3 - x^2 - 8x - 15$

12. $f(x) = x + \dfrac{1}{x}$

Challenge   Solve each of the following.

1. Show that for all real numbers x the function $f{:}x \rightarrow x^3 + x + 2$ is increasing. Find the equation of the tangent to the curve at the point $(-1, 0)$. Determine the coordinates of the point where the tangent intersects the curve again.

2. A hyperbola has equation $y = \dfrac{c^2}{x}, x \neq 0$ and c a constant. Show that the slope of the tangent to the hyperbola always is negative. Find the equation of the tangent at the point $A(c, c)$. Show that if this tangent crosses the axes at M and N, then A is the midpoint of $\overline{MN}$.

15–7   Stationary Values

The graph of $f(x) = 5x^3 - 3x^5$ is shown in the figure. The function $f'(x) = 15x^2 - 15x^4 = 15x^2(1 - x^2)$. At the points $A, O,$ and B, where x is 1, 0, and -1, respectively, $f'(x) = 0$. The tangents to the curve are parallel to the x-axis. At these points f is neither increasing nor decreasing and is said to have **stationary values.**

The nature of stationary values can be examined by considering the sign of $f'(x)$ in the neighborhood of the critical points.

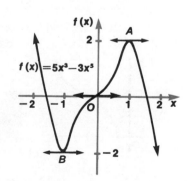

1. The stationary value at A:

$\left.\begin{array}{l} \text{If } x < 1, f'(x) > 0 \\ \text{If } x = 1, f'(x) = 0 \\ \text{If } x > 1, f'(x) < 0 \end{array}\right\}$ for values of x in a small neighborhood of 1

Since $f'(x)$ changes sign from positive through zero to negative, f is said to have a *maximum stationary* (or *turning*) *value*, $f(1) = 2$, at $x = 1$.

2. The stationary value at B:

$$\left.\begin{array}{l} \text{If } x < -1, f'(x) < 0 \\ \text{If } x = -1, f'(x) = 0 \\ \text{If } x > -1, f'(x) > 0 \end{array}\right\}$$ for values of x in a small neighborhood of -1

A maximum or minimum stationary value is a local property. Functions may have several stationary values.

Since $f'(x)$ changes from negative through zero to positive, f is said to have a *minimum stationary* (or turning) *value*, $f(-1) = -2$, at $x = -1$.

3. The stationary value at O:

$$\left.\begin{array}{l} \text{If } x < 0, f'(x) > 0 \\ \text{If } x = 0, f'(x) = 0 \\ \text{If } x > 0, f'(x) > 0 \end{array}\right\}$$ for values of x in a small neighborhood of 0

Notice $f'(x)$ does not change sign through zero, and $f'(x) = 0$ at $x = 0$. When this occurs, the graph has a *point of inflection* at $x = 0$.

A point of inflection can occur without the slope of the tangent being zero. Whenever, a curve "stops bending to the left and starts bending to the right," or vice versa as x increases from left to right, there is a point of inflection.

Suppose $f'(a) = 0$ and $f'(x)$ exists at every point in some neighborhood of a. Then near $x = a$ there are four possibilities for the graph of f.

A method for identifying other kinds of inflection points will be developed later.

In the tables, a^- and a^+ should be read as "a little less than a" and "a little more than a," respectively.

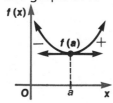

x	a^-	a	a^+
f'(x)	−	0	+

The value $f(a)$ is a minimum stationary value of f.

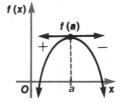

x	a^-	a	a^+
f'(x)	+	0	−

The value $f(a)$ is a maximum stationary value of f.

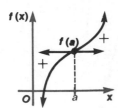

x	a^-	a	a^+
f'(x)	+	0	+

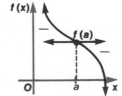

x	a^-	a	a^+
f'(x)	−	0	−

The point $(a, f(a))$ is a point of inflection on the graph of f.

   Maximum or minimum stationary values often are called **relative maximum values** or **relative minimum values**. These are local properties of a function. They refer only to the behavior of a function in the neighborhood of a critical point. The terms **absolute maximum** and **absolute minimum** refer to the greatest or least value assumed by a function throughout its domain of definition.

Example

1.   **Find the stationary values of the function f defined by $f(x) = x^3(x - 4)$. Determine the nature of each.**

$$f(x) = x^4 - 4x^3$$
$$f'(x) = 4x^3 - 12x^2 = 4x^2(x - 3)$$

Let $f'(x) = 0$, then $4x^2(x - 3) = 0$.

$$x = 0 \quad \text{or} \quad x = 3$$

Thus, f has stationary values $f(0) = 0$ at $x = 0$ and $f(3) = -27$ at $x = 3$.

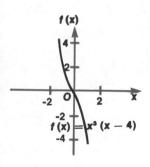

x	0^-	0	0^+
$4x^2$	$+$	0	$+$
$x - 3$	$-$	$-$	$-$
$f'(x)$	$-$	0	$-$
Behavior of f	decreasing	$f(0) = 0$	decreasing

Thus, $x = 0$ gives a point of inflection $(0, 0)$.

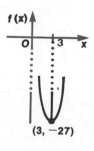

x	3^-	3	3^+
$4x^2$	$+$	$+$	$+$
$x - 3$	$-$	0	$+$
$f'(x)$	$-$	0	$+$
Behavior of f	decreasing	$f(3) = -27$	increasing

Thus, $x = 3$ gives a minimum stationary value of f, $f(3) = -27$.

Exercises
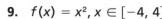

Exploratory Name the critical points for $f(x)$.

1. $f(x) = x^2$

2. $f(x) = x^2 - 2x$

3. $f(x) = x - x^2$

4. $f(x) = x^3$

5. $f(x) = x^3 - 3x$

6. $f(x) = 7x - 2x^3$

7–12. Determine the nature of the stationary values of each function.

Written Find and determine the nature of the stationary values of each function.

1. $f(x) = 2x^3 - 9x^2 + 12x$

2. $f(x) = x(x - 2)^2$

3. $f(x) = \frac{1}{4}x^4 - \frac{9}{2}x^2$

4. $f(x) = x^3(4 - x)$

5. $f(x) = x + \frac{1}{x}$

6. $f(x) = \sqrt{x}$

7. $f(x) = x^3 - 12x + 3$

8. $f(x) = 2x^4 - 2x^2$

Find the maximum and minimum values for each function on the given interval. Maximum and minimum points need not occur at turning points. They could occur at the endpoints of the interval.

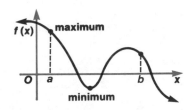

9. $f(x) = x^2, x \in [-4, 4]$

10. $f(x) = x^2 - 9, x \in [-6, 6]$

11. $f(x) = 2x^3, x \in [-3, 3]$

12. $f(x) = x^3 - 6x^2, x \in [-1, 3]$

Challenge The derivative of a polynomial function f also is a polynomial function f'. Find the derivative of f'. It is symbolized as f''. Since f'' is the derivative of f', its value tells whether the derivative (f') is increasing or decreasing at a point. Using this information and considering that the first derivative changes sign from left to right of a relative maximum or minimum point, develop a "second derivative test for relative maxima and minima." Illustrate the test by giving two examples of its application to polynomial functions. What does the value of the second derivative indicate about the curve at a given point?

15–8 Curve Sketching

This section emphasizes the graph of a function. The language, therefore, becomes geometric, and terms such as stationary points will be used.

In sketching the graph of a differentiable function f, some or all of these steps may be helpful.

1. The value of f at $x = 0$
2. The points on the graph where $f(x) = 0$, if found easily
3. Symmetry about a line or about the origin, if any
4. The behavior of the function for large positive and large negative x
5. Stationary points
6. Table of signs for $f'(x)$

One more step may be helpful in some cases. This is to find the derivative of the derived function of f. It is called the **second derivative** and is written f''. The sign of the second derivative indicates whether the slope of the curve is increasing or decreasing. The sign of the second derivative thus indicates the direction of concavity of the curve.

In the interval $\langle a, b \rangle$ the slope of the tangent line is decreasing. Since $f'(x)$ is decreasing, its derivative $f''(x)$ must be negative on this interval. At b, the slope of the tangent line, $f'(x)$, changes from decreasing to increasing. Therefore, $f''(b) = 0$. On the interval $\langle b, c \rangle$, $f'(x)$ is increasing. Its derivative $f''(x)$ is positive. The curve is concave downward where $f''(x) < 0$. It is concave upward where $f''(x) > 0$. At $f''(x) = 0$ there may be a point of inflection. Thus, there is more information to help sketch the graph of a function.

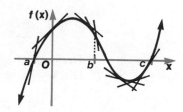

7. Table of signs for $f''(x)$

Example

1. **Sketch the graph of the function f given by $f(x) = x(x - 3)^2$.**

    1. $f(0) = 0$

    2. Let $f(x) = 0$

        Thus, $x(x - 3)^2 = 0$.

        So, $x = 0$ or $x = 3$.

    3. No symmetry

    4. For large positive x, $f(x)$ is positive. When $|x|$ is large and $x < 0$, $f(x)$ is negative.

    5. $f(x) = x(x^2 - 6x + 9) = x^3 - 6x^2 + 9x$
        $f'(x) = 3x^2 - 12x + 9 = 3(x^2 - 4x + 3) = 3(x - 3)(x - 1)$
        Stationary points are $(1, 4)$ and $(3, 0)$.

    6.

x	1^-	1	1^+
$3(x - 1)$	$-$	0	$+$
$(x - 3)$	$-$	$-$	$-$
$f'(x)$	$+$	0	$-$
f	inc.	$f(1) = 4$	dec.

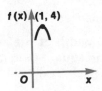

x	3^-	3	3^+
$3(x - 1)$	$+$	$+$	$+$
$x - 3$	$-$	0	$+$
$f'(x)$	$-$	0	$+$
f	dec.	$f(3) = 0$	inc.

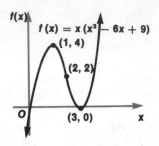

$$f(x) = x(x^2 - 6x + 9)$$
(1, 4)
(2, 2)
O   (3, 0)   x

Thus, $x = 1$ gives a maximum stationary point $(1, 4)$, and $x = 3$ gives a minimum stationary point $(3, 0)$.

7. $f'(x) = 3x^2 - 12x + 9$
$f''(x) = 6x - 12 = 6(x - 2)$

$f''(x) < 0$	$f''(x) = 0$	$f''(x) > 0$
$x < 2$	$x = 2$	$x > 2$
f is concave downward ($\cap$) for $x < 2$.	f has an inflection point at $x = 2$.	f is concave upward ($\cup$) for $x > 2$.

Exercises

Written   Sketch the graph of each function.

1. $f(x) = x^2$
2. $f(x) = x^2 - 2x$
3. $f(x) = x - x^2$
4. $f(x) = x^3$
5. $f(x) = x^3 - 3x$
6. $f(x) = 2x^3 - 9x^2 + 12x$
7. $f(x) = x(x - 2)^2$
8. $f(x) = \dfrac{1}{4}x^4 - \dfrac{9}{2}x^2$
9. $f(x) = x^3(4 - x)$
10. $f(x) = x + \dfrac{1}{x}$

15–9   Maxima and Minima Problems

Differentiation techniques can be used to find maximum and minimum solutions for many application problems.

Example

1.   **Suppose an area of farmland along a straight stone wall is to be fenced. There are 400 m of fencing available. What is the greatest rectangular area that can be enclosed?**

If the width of the enclosure is x m, the length is $(400 - 2x)$ m, as shown. The area in square meters is $A = x(400 - 2x) = 400x - 2x^2$. This defines a function f for which $f(x) = 400x - 2x^2$. For this problem, $x \geq 0$ and $400 - 2x \geq 0$, or $0 \leq x \leq 200$.

$$f(x) = 400x - 2x^2$$
$$f'(x) - 400 - 4x = 4(100 - x)$$
$$\text{So, } f'(x) = 0 \text{ when } x = 100$$

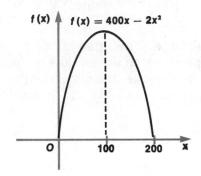

x	100^-	100	100^+
$4(100 - x)$	+	0	−
$f'(x)$	+	0	−
f	inc.	$f(100) = 20{,}000$	dec.

Thus, $x = 100$ gives maximum stationary value $f(100) = 20{,}000$. Also, $f(0) = 0$ and $f(200) = 0$. Thus, the required maximum area is 20,000 m². This occurs when the width is 100 m and the length is 200 m.

Exercises

Written   Solve each of the following.

1. Suppose an area of farmland along a straight stone wall is to be fenced. There are 600 m of fencing available. What is the greatest rectangular area that can be enclosed?

2. The sum of two nonnegative integers is 28. What is the largest possible value for their product? What is the smallest possible value?

3. Squares of side x cm are cut from the corners of a cardboard square of side 6 cm. The flaps are bent up and taped to form a tray. Sketch the tray. Show that its volume V cm³ is given by $V = 4x(3 - x)^2$. Find the maximum volume that the tray can have.

4. A right triangle is formed by the x-axis, the y-axis, and the line with equation $y = 4 - 2x$. What is the area of the largest rectangle that can be fitted inside this triangle so that one vertex is at the origin?

5. The height of a projectile above its point of projection after t seconds is given by the formula $h(t) = 20t - 5t^2$. Calculate the time it takes to reach its maximum height. Find the maximum height.

6. A circle of radius r units has a sector with area 25 cm². The perimeter of the sector is given by the formula $P = 2\left(r + \dfrac{25}{r}\right)$. Find the minimum value of P.

7. The perimeter of a rectangular enclosure is 100 m. Show that for maximum area the enclosure should be square.

8. Suppose a cylindrical can is to be made to hold 16π in³. What should be the radius r and height h of the can to minimize the amount of aluminum used? Assume uniform thickness at all points.

9. A wing piece drops from an airplane after breaking apart. If it drops from 14,400 ft, the formula $s(t) = 14,400 - 16t^2$ gives the height in feet above the ground at the end of t seconds (neglecting air resistance). When and with what velocity in mph does the piece hit the ground?

10. A rectangular box with a square base of side x cm and height h cm is open at the top. Show that if its volume is 32 cm³, its surface area A is given by $A = x^2 + \dfrac{128}{x}$. Determine the dimensions of the box so that it has a minimum surface area.

Challenge The strength of a rectangular beam is directly proportional to the product of the width and the square of the depth. What are the dimensions of the strongest beam that can be cut from a circular log 20 inches in diameter?

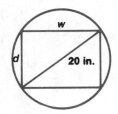

Chapter Summary

1. The rate of change of the function f at $x = a$ is as follows. (451)
$$f'(a) = \lim_{h \to 0} \frac{f(a + h) - f(a)}{h}$$

2. The derivative of a constant function, $f(x) = c$, is zero
$$f'(x) = 0 \text{ for all } x \text{ in the domain of } f. \quad (454)$$

3. If $f(x) = x^n$, then $f'(x) = nx^{n-1}$ for any rational number n. (455)

4. The derivative of a constant c times a function f is the constant times the derivative of the function, $c \cdot f'(x)$, for all values of x for which $f'(x)$ exists. Thus, if $g(x) = c \cdot f(x)$, then $g'(x) = c \cdot f'(x)$. (455)

5. The derivative of the sum of a finite number of differentiable functions is the sum of their derivatives. (456)

6. The slope of the tangent to the curve $y = f(x)$ at the point (x, y) is denoted by $\dfrac{dy}{dx}$ where $\dfrac{dy}{dx} = f'(x)$. (458)

7. If $f'(x) > 0$ for every x in an interval, $a < x < b$, then the function is increasing in that interval. If $f'(x) < 0$ for every $x \in \langle a, b \rangle$, then $f(x)$ is decreasing on $\langle a, b \rangle$. (463)

8. If $f'(x) = 0$, then $f(a)$ is a stationary value of f at $x = a$. (465)

9. The nature of a stationary value depends on the sign of $f'(x)$ in a small neighborhood of $x = a$. (465)

10. Maximum and minimum values of a function in a closed interval occur at stationary values or at the endpoints of the interval. (465)

11. To sketch a curve, investigate: (468)
    a. the points where the curve intersects the x-axis and y-axis.
    b. the location and nature of stationary points.
    c. the behavior of the function for large values of $|x|$.
    d. symmetry.
12. The sign of f'' indicates the direction of concavity of the curve.
    a. If $f''(x) < 0$, the curve is concave downward.
    b. If $f''(x) > 0$, the curve is concave upward.

Chapter Review

15–1 **Given $f(t) = 20t^2$, calculate the average speed for the given intervals of t by evaluating $\dfrac{f(t + h) - f(t)}{h}$.**

1. $t = 2$ to $t = 3.5$
2. $t = 3$ to $t = 3.1$

3. Deduce the speed at $t = 3$ by evaluating $\displaystyle\lim_{h \to 0} \dfrac{f(3 + h) - f(3)}{h}$ for the function $f(t) = 20t^2$.

15–2 **Find the derivative of each function at the given value of x by direct use of the definition.**

4. $f(x) = 2x + 3$ at $x = 3$
5. $g(x) = x^2 + 2x$ at $x = 5$

6. Find the rate of change of the area of an equilateral triangle with respect to the length of a side, when the side is 5 cm.

15–3 **Find the derivative for each function.**

7. $f(x) = \dfrac{1}{3}x^6$
8. $f(x) = 5x^4 + 2x^3 + 1$

9. Given $f(x) = 2x^3 - 4x + 5$, find $f'(x)$ and $f'(-1)$.

15–4 **Solve each of the following.**

10. Find the equation of the tangent to the curve $y = x^2 - 4x + 3$ when $x = 2$.

11. Find the equation of the tangent to the curve $y = x^2 + 2x$ when $x = 4$.

12. Show that the tangents to the curve $y = x^3$ at the points where $x = 1$ and $x = -1$ are parallel. Find the coordinates of the points where these tangents cross the x- and y-axes.

13. Find the coordinates of the points on the curve $y = x^2(x - 3)$ at which the slope of the tangent is 9. Find the equation of the tangents at these points.

15–5 **Find each derivative.**

14. $x^{4/3}$ **15.** $x^{1/3}$ **16.** x^{-6}

17. $\dfrac{1}{x^3}$ **18.** $\dfrac{2}{x}$ **19.** $\dfrac{1}{\sqrt[3]{x}}$

Given $f(x) = \dfrac{1}{x^2}$, find each value.

20. $f'(1)$ **21.** $f'(-1)$ **22.** $f'(2)$

23. Find the point on the curve $y = 2x^2 - 3x + 1$ at which the tangent makes an angle of 45° with the x-axis.

15–6 **Determine the interval in which each function is (a) increasing, and (b) decreasing.**

24. $f(x) = x^2 - 3$ **25.** $f(x) = x - \dfrac{1}{x}$

15–7 **Find and determine the nature of the stationary values of each function.**

26. $f(x) = \dfrac{1}{3}x^2$ **27.** $f(x) = x + \dfrac{4}{x}$

28. Find the maximum and minimum value for $f(x) = 2x^2 - 3x + 1$ on the interval $x \in [-2, 3]$.

15–8 **Sketch the graph for each function.**

29. $f(x) = x^3 - 2x$ **30.** $f(x) = x^4 - 2x^2 + 2$

15–9 **Solve each of the following.**

31. $PQRS$ is a rectangle 10 cm by 6 cm enclosing quadrilateral $WXYZ$ as shown. $PW = QX = RY = SZ = x$ cm. Find the minimum area of $WXYZ$.

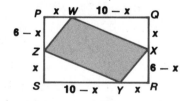

32. A solid circular cylinder is to be machined from a solid metal sphere of radius R mm. The radius of the cylinder is x mm. The height is $2y$ mm. Find the formula that gives the volume of the cylinder. What is the maximum cylinder that can be obtained? What is the ratio of the volume of this cylinder to the volume of the sphere?

Chapter Test

Given $f(t) = 5t^2$, calculate the average speed for the given intervals for t by evaluating $\dfrac{f(t + h) - f(t)}{h}$.

1. $t = 1$ to $t = 1.5$

2. $t = 1$ to $t = 1.1$

3. Deduce the speed at $t = 1$ by evaluating $\lim\limits_{h \to 0} \dfrac{f(1 + h) - f(1)}{h}$ for the function $f(t) = 5t^2$.

Find the derivative for each function at the given value at x.

4. $f(x) = x^2 + x$ at $x = 3$

5. $f(x) = 4x^2 + x$ at $x = 2$

Solve each of the following.

6. Find the rate of change of the volume of a cube with respect to the length of an edge, when the edge is 3 cm.

7. For a marble rolling in a track the distance s cm from one end at time t seconds is given by $s = 3t - t^2$. Find the speed of the marble when $t = 3$.

Find each derivative.

8. $\dfrac{1}{4x^5}$

9. $x^{-1/2}$

10. $x^{-2/3}$

11. $\dfrac{3}{x^2}$

12. $\sqrt[3]{x}$

13. $\dfrac{x^2}{2}$

14. Find the point on the curve $y = 2x^2 - 3x + 1$ at which the tangent is parallel to the line $y = 3x$.

Determine the interval in which each function is (a) increasing, and (b) decreasing.

15. $f(x) = \dfrac{1}{3}x^3 - x^2 - 3x - 1$

16. $f(x) = 2x - \dfrac{1}{x}$

Find and determine the nature of the stationary values of each function.

17. $f(x) = x^3 - 2x$

18. $f(x) \; x^4 - 2x^2 + 2$

19. Find the maximum value for $f(x) = x^2 - 4$ on the interval $x \in [-3, 4]$.

20. Sketch the graph for $f(x) = x^2 - 2x$.

21. Squares of side x cm are cut from the corners of a cardboard square of side 12 cm. The flaps are bent up and taped to form a tray. Calculate the maximum volume of the tray.

Computers

Careers in the Computer Center

Many positions have been created as a result of the computer. The titles vary from company to company, but the positions exist in most data processing centers. The manager of information processing heads the computer division. This individual coordinates and directs the overall efforts of the entire department. Such a position requires considerable experience, good management skills, and, in most companies, a college degree.

A systems analyst is involved with collecting facts regarding the information requirement of a computer user as well as analyzing those facts. Systems analysts plan the most efficient means for achieving the distribution of the data. The person performing the analysis must

Teams of systems analysts and programmers examine data produced by the computer.

be able to understand the problem and to interpret it correctly. An analyst must formulate a mathematical model of a management problem and use it to provide a basis for making decisions. Many companies require a degree in mathematics, physics, or an appropriate engineering science plus two or more years of programming experience.

After the solution has been designed for a problem, a programmer devises a detailed plan called a program. This program is a set of instructions that uses a computer language to interpret a plan for the computer. The programmer must check the program to make sure it works in every detail. Sometimes a project will take from several months to a year. Usually programmers work in teams, with each member of the team responsible for different levels of the program. A degree in computer science is helpful but not necessary for many companies.

Computer operators are the people that actually run the computers. They read through the program and set the computer to run. If a program stops running, it is these people that must decide where the problem lies. If the problem is in the equipment, a maintenance engineer is called. If the problem is in the program, it is sent back to the programming department. Usually computer operators serve an apprenticeship during which they help the operators. Employers require high school education and many prefer some college. A college degree will help if the operator plans on advancing.

Many other positions have been created as a result of computers. Clerical jobs, such as maintaining libraries of magnetic tapes, operating schedules, and logs of operation are very important. These jobs provide on-the-job training for high school graduates who would like to learn about computers. Another position requiring a high school education and two or three weeks of training is a keypunch operator. These people punch data onto many different types of recording devices such as cards, tapes, and discs.

An information processing center is significant in the overall organization because of its role as a service department that accepts input data, performs processing and storage, and provides information. If the function is not well managed, it can seriously impair the activities of the entire organization. For this reason, managers are extremely concerned about the security of the departments. Computer personnel will probably be carefully interviewed before employment. Companies want dependable people who are honest.

Exercises   Write programs for each of the following.

1. Given a polynomial P, find the first derivative for P.

2. Find the slope of the tangent to the curve $y = Ax^2 + Bx + C$ when $x = a$.

3. Given a polynomial of the form $Ax^3 + Bx^2 + Cx + D$, find the critical point(s) (if any) and determine whether each is a maximum or minimum.

4. Squares of side x cm are cut from the corners of a cardboard square of side y cm. The flaps are bent up and taped to form a tray. Calculate the maximum volume of the tray.

5. Newton's Method to approximate irrational zeros of a polynomial function is based on the iteration formula given below.

$$x_{n + 1} = x_n - \frac{f(x_n)}{f'(x_n)} \text{ for } n = 1, 2, 3, \ldots$$

Given two consecutive integers between which a root lies, approximate the root using this method.

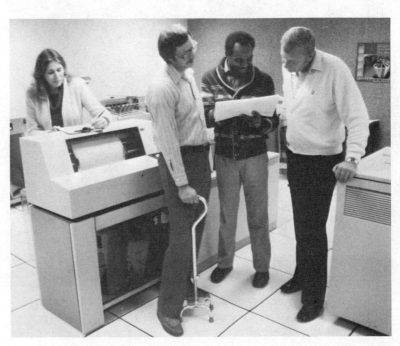

Computer operators are responsible for the running of the programs developed by the programmers.

Chapter 16

*In construction it is important to find the point at which a beam
or other structure balances its weight. Integration can be used
to find this point as well as areas of irregular shaped regions.*

Integrals

16–1 Approximating Areas

This chapter introduces a part of calculus called **integration**. The limit concept again is important in the development.

The easiest application of integration to visualize concerns area. The closed curve C in Figure **1** surrounds a region of the plane. What is the area S of this region? Approximations to the area S can be found by placing a grid of unit squares over the region. From Figure 2, $S > 41$ and $S < 66$, or $41 < S < 66$.

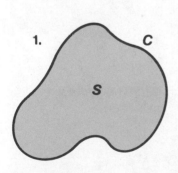

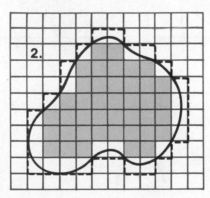

By taking a finer mesh of squares a better approximation for S could be obtained. However, integration enables the evaluation of the area exactly and the solving of problems concerning volumes, masses, and other mathematical and physical topics. Since integration problems often can be interpreted as the calculation of an area, this topic will be covered first. The exercises will help to develop a feeling for the basis of the integration process.

Exercises

Written Solve each of the following.

1. Count squares to approximate the area of the region enclosed by the curve. Use inequations to express the answer.

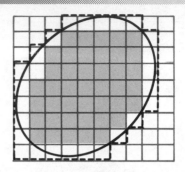

2. Calculate the sum of the areas of the shaded rectangles in Figure **a** and then Figure **b**. Use your answers to write inequations which approximate the area S of triangle OAB.

3. Repeat Problem **2** for the case where $\overline{OA}$ is divided into ten congruent parts. Compare your answers to those in Problem **2**. How could you otbain better approximations for the area of triangle OAB?

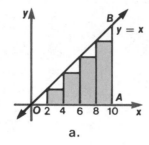

a.

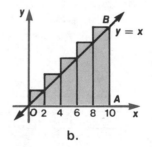

b.

4. Write inequations to approximate the area bounded by the curve $y = x^2$, the x-axis, and the line $x = 10$.

5. Repeat Problem **4** for the curve $y = x^3$.

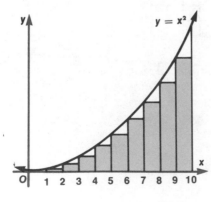

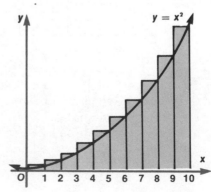

Solve each of the following using the region bounded above by $y = f(x)$, to the left by the line $x = a$, to the right by the line $x = b$, and below by the x-axis as shown.

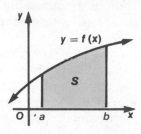

6. Use the figure below to show that S lies between $f(a) \cdot (b - a)$ and $f(b) \cdot (b - a)$.

7. In the figure below, M_1 is the midpoint of $\overline{AB}$. Using rectangles write lower and upper approximations to the area of the region.

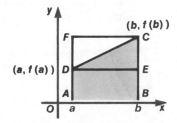

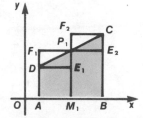

8. Divide $\overline{AB}$ into three congruent parts. Repeat Problem **7.**

9. As the number of parts into which $\overline{AB}$ is divided is increased, what happens to these lower and upper approximations?

10. If $\overline{AB}$ is divided into n parts, what is the length of each?

11. Repeat Problem **7** for the following figure.

12. As n becomes greater and greater, what happens to the approximations?

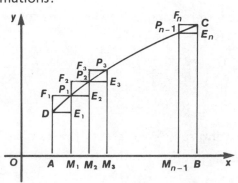

16–2 Upper and Lower Sums

The process suggested in the previous exercises can be used to interpret area using limits. First consider a region located above the x-axis. Suppose the area is nested between the areas of two sets of rectangles. These areas give upper and lower approximations for the area of the region. By increasing the number of rectangles, these approximations would tend to "creep in" toward the area of the region.

If the lower approximations can be made arbitrarily close to some number L, then S cannot be less than this number L. Why not? Thus, $S \geq L$. In the same way, if the upper approximations have limit L', then $S \leq L'$. If both the sequence of upper approximations and the sequence of lower approximations have the same limit L, then $L \leq S \leq L$ and $S = L$.

Before going on, recall the following results which were previously proved.

$$\sum_{r=1}^{n} r = 1 + 2 + 3 + \cdots + n = \frac{1}{2}n(n + 1)$$

These results were established by mathematical induction.

$$\sum_{r=1}^{n} r^2 = 1^2 + 2^2 + 3^2 + \cdots + n^2 = \frac{1}{6}n(n + 1)(2n + 1)$$

$$\sum_{r=1}^{n} r^3 = 1^3 + 2^3 + 3^3 + \cdots + n^3 = \frac{1}{4}n^2(n + 1)^2$$

Example

1. **Find the area S of the region bounded by the curve $y = x^2$, the x-axis, $x = 0$ and $x = 1$.**

   Divide the interval $x = 0$ to $x = 1$ into n congruent intervals. The length of each interval is $\frac{1}{n}$. The lower approximating sum $\sum_1$ of areas of rectangles is given by the following equation which has $(n - 1)$ terms.

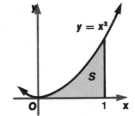

   $$\sum_1 = 0^2 \cdot \frac{1}{n} + \left(\frac{1}{n}\right)^2 \cdot \frac{1}{n} + \left(\frac{2}{n}\right)^2 \cdot \frac{1}{n} + \cdots + \left(\frac{n-1}{n}\right)^2 \cdot \frac{1}{n}$$

   $$\sum_1 = \frac{1}{n^3}(1^2 + 2^2 + 3^2 + \cdots + (n - 1)^2)$$

   The upper approximating sum $\sum_2$ of areas of rectangles is given by the following equation which has n terms.

   $$\sum_2 = \left(\frac{1}{n}\right)^2 \cdot \frac{1}{n} + \left(\frac{2}{n}\right)^2 \cdot \frac{1}{n} + \cdots + \left(\frac{n}{n}\right)^2 \cdot \frac{1}{n}$$

   $$= \frac{1}{n^3}(1^2 + 2^2 + 3^2 + \cdots + n^2)$$

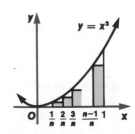

   $$\sum_1 \leq S \leq \sum_2$$

$$\frac{1}{n^3}\left[1^2 + 2^2 + \cdots + (n-1)^2\right] \le S \le \frac{1}{n^3}\left(1^2 + 2^2 + \cdots + n^2\right)$$

$$\left(\frac{1}{n^3}\right)\sum_{r=1}^{n-1} r^2 \le S \le \left(\frac{1}{n^3}\right)\sum_{r=1}^{n} r^2$$

$$\left(\frac{1}{n^3}\right)\frac{1}{6}(n-1)(n)(2n-1) \le S \le \left(\frac{1}{n^3}\right)\frac{1}{6}(n)(n+1)(2n+1)$$

$$\frac{1}{3} - \frac{1}{2n} + \frac{1}{6n^2} \le S \le \frac{1}{3} + \frac{1}{2n} + \frac{1}{6n^2}$$

$$\lim_{n \to \infty}\left(\frac{1}{3} - \frac{1}{2n} + \frac{1}{6n^2}\right) = \frac{1}{3} \quad \text{and} \quad \lim_{n \to \infty}\left(\frac{1}{3} + \frac{1}{2n} + \frac{1}{6n^2}\right) = \frac{1}{3}$$

Therefore, $S = \frac{1}{3}$.

By Theorem 8 in Section 14–7

In summary, here is a method for obtaining an area S.
1. Divide the interval into n congruent parts.
2. Find the lower approximating sum of areas of rectangles, $\sum_1$.
3. Find the upper approximating sum of areas of rectangles, $\sum_2$.
4. Evaluate the finite sums $\sum_1$ and $\sum_2$.
5. Simplify the inequations $\sum_1 \le S \le \sum_2$.
6. Calculate S by finding the limits of $\sum_1$ and $\sum_2$ as n increases without bound.

In step 4 evaluate means to give a general simplified expression for $\sum_1$ and $\sum_2$.

Example

2. Calculate the area bounded by the curve $y = x^3$ and the x-axis from $x = 0$ to $x = 2$.

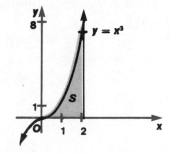 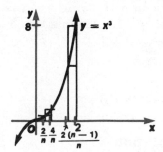

1. The points of division of the interval $x = 0$ to $x = 2$ into n congruent parts, including endpoints, are:

$$x = 0, \frac{2}{n}, \frac{4}{n}, \frac{6}{n}, \ldots, \frac{2(n-1)}{n}, \frac{2n}{n} = 2$$

2. $\sum_1 = 0^3 \cdot \dfrac{2}{n} + \left(\dfrac{2}{n}\right)^3 \cdot \dfrac{2}{n} + \left(\dfrac{4}{n}\right)^3 \cdot \dfrac{2}{n} + \left(\dfrac{6}{n}\right)^3 \cdot \dfrac{2}{n} + \cdots + \left[\dfrac{2(n-1)}{n}\right]^3 \cdot \dfrac{2}{n}$

Thus, $\sum_1 = \dfrac{16}{n^4}[1^3 + 2^3 + 3^3 + \cdots + (n-1)^3]$

Step 2 gives the lower approximating sum.

3. $\sum_2 = \left(\dfrac{2}{n}\right)^3 \cdot \dfrac{2}{n} + \left(\dfrac{4}{n}\right)^3 \cdot \dfrac{2}{n} + \left(\dfrac{6}{n}\right)^3 \cdot \dfrac{2}{n} + \cdots + \left(\dfrac{2n}{n}\right)^3 \cdot \dfrac{2}{n}$

Step 3 gives the upper approximating sum.

Thus, $\sum_2 = \dfrac{16}{n^4}[1^3 + 2^3 + 3^3 + \cdots + n^3]$

4. $\sum_1 = \left(\dfrac{16}{n^4}\right)\displaystyle\sum_{r=1}^{n-1} r^3 = \dfrac{16}{n^4} \cdot \dfrac{(n-1)^2(n)^2}{4} = 4\left(1 - \dfrac{2}{n} + \dfrac{1}{n^2}\right)$

$\sum_2 = \left(\dfrac{16}{n^4}\right)\displaystyle\sum_{r=1}^{n} r^3 = \dfrac{16}{n^4} \cdot \dfrac{n^2(n+1)^2}{4} = 4\left(1 + \dfrac{2}{n} + \dfrac{1}{n^2}\right)$

5. $4\left(1 - \dfrac{2}{n} + \dfrac{1}{n^2}\right) \le S \le 4\left(1 + \dfrac{2}{n} + \dfrac{1}{n^2}\right)$

6. $\displaystyle\lim_{n\to\infty} 4\left(1 - \dfrac{2}{n} + \dfrac{1}{n^2}\right) = 4 = \lim_{n\to\infty} 4\left(1 + \dfrac{2}{n} + \dfrac{1}{n^2}\right)$

Therefore, $S = 4$.

Exercises

Written   Calculate the area of the region between each curve and the x-axis over the given interval. Notice that all the regions lie above the x-axis. In Problems 2 and 6, $b > 0$.

1. $y = x$ from $x = 0$ to $x = 3$

2. $y = x$ from $x = 0$ to $x = b$

3. $y = x^2$ from $x = 0$ to $x = 3$

4. $y = x^2$ from $x = 0$ to $x = b$

5. $y = x^3$ from $x = 0$ to $x = 3$

6. $y = x^3$ from $x = 0$ to $x = b$

Write the areas between each curve and the x-axis over the given interval in Problems 7–9. Guess the area in Problem 10. Assume that $a > 0$ and $b > a$.

7. $y = x$ from $x = a$ to $x = b$

8. $y = x^2$ from $x = a$ to $x = b$

9. $y = x^3$ from $x = a$ to $x = b$

10. $y = x^4$ from $x = a$ to $x = b$

16–3 Integral Notation

The area S of the region bounded by the curve $y = f(x)$, the x-axis, and the lines $x = a$ and $x = b$ is shown. Suppose that the interval $[a, b]$ is separated into n small intervals of lengths Δx_1, $\Delta x_2, \ldots, \Delta x_n$, not necessarily equal.

Within each small interval choose an x_i. The rectangle of width Δx_i has height $f(x_i)$. The area of the rectangle is $f(x) \cdot \Delta x_i$. This area approximates the area under the curve $y = f(x)$ on the interval of width Δx_i.

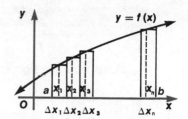

The area of the first rectangle is $f(x_1)\Delta x_1$.
The area of the second rectangle is $f(x_2)\Delta x_2$.
The area of the third rectangle is $f(x_3)\Delta x_3$.
$\vdots$
The area of the nth rectangle is $f(x_n)\Delta x_n$.

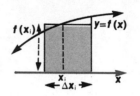

The sum of the areas of the rectangles is $\sum_{i=1}^{n} f(x_i)\Delta x_i$.

$$S \approx \sum_{i=1}^{n} f(x_i)\Delta x_i$$

If the interval $[a, b]$ is divided into smaller subintervals, then the sum of the rectangle areas will give a better approximation to S. For continuous functions $\left| S - \sum_{i=1}^{n} f(x_i)\Delta x_i \right|$ can be made as small as desired by taking n sufficiently large and each Δx_i sufficiently small.

Note that the Δx_i's are not necessarily equal. This requires that the maximum Δx_i converge to 0 in the limit. This guarantees that all Δx_i will converge to 0.

$$S = \lim_{n \to \infty} \sum_{i=1}^{n} f(x_i)\Delta x_i$$
(and each $\Delta x_i \to 0$)

The formal notation for $\lim_{\substack{n \to \infty \\ \Delta x_i \to 0}} \left(\sum_{i=1}^{n} f(x_i)\Delta x_i \right)$ is $\int_a^b f(x)dx$ and is read, *the integral of $f(x)dx$ from a to b.*

For S to be the numerical value of the area, f must be continuous and non-negative on $[a, b]$.

$$S = \int_a^b f(x)dx$$

Thus, the area S is equal to the integral of $f(x)$ from a to b.

The symbol $\int$ is an elongated S. It suggests that a summing process is involved.

Examples

1. Show the area given by $\displaystyle\int_1^3 x\, dx$ by shading in a sketch.

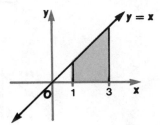

2. Show the area given by $\displaystyle\int_0^1 x^3\, dx$ by shading in a sketch.

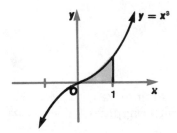

3. Show the area given by $\displaystyle\int_0^{\pi/2} \cos x\, dx$ by shading in a sketch.

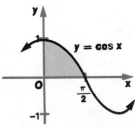

Exercises

Exploratory Use integral notation to express the areas of the regions between each curve and the x-axis on the given interval. In Problems **2, 4, 5** and **6** assume $b > a > 0$.

1. $y = x$ from $x = 0$ to $x = 1$
2. $y = x$ from $x = 0$ to $x = b$
3. $y = x^2$ from $x = 0$ to $x = 1$
4. $y = x^2$ from $x = 0$ to $x = b$
5. $y = x^2$ from $x = a$ to $x = b$
6. $y = x^4$ from $x = a$ to $x = b$

Written Consider the first example in Section 16–2 (page 482). Suppose the given curve is replaced by the curve with equation $y = 4x^2$. Describe what happens to each of the following.

1. the height of each rectangle
2. the lower and upper approximations
3. the area of the region under the curve
4. Generalize findings from Problems 1–3 to the curve with equation $y = ax^2$.

Use the answers to the previous exercises to evaluate each integral.

5. $\int_0^4 3x^2 \, dx$

6. $\int_1^4 3x^2 \, dx$

7. Sketch the curve $y = 2x^2$. Calculate the area of the region bounded by this curve, the x-axis, $x = 1$, and $x = 2$.

Shade sketches to show the area given by each integral.

8. $\int_0^4 x \, dx$

9. $\int_0^1 2x \, dx$

10. $\int_0^2 x^3 \, dx$

11. $\int_1^4 (x + 2) \, dx$

Describe in words the area given by each integral.

12. $\int_2^4 \sqrt{x} \, dx$

13. $\int_0^3 \sqrt{9 - x^2} \, dx$

14. $\int_0^{\pi/2} \sin x \, dx$

15. $\int_0^1 x^2(1 - x) \, dx$

Use the figures to explain similarities and differences between each pair of integrals.

16. $\int_0^1 x \, dx$ and $\int_{-1}^0 x \, dx$

17. $\int_{-1}^0 (x^3 - x) \, dx$ and $\int_0^1 (x^3 - x) \, dx$

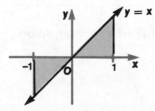

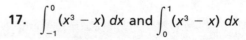

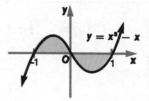

Write an integral to represent each shaded region.

18.

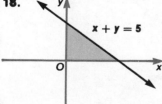

$x + y = 5$

19.

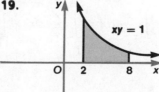

$xy = 1$

20.

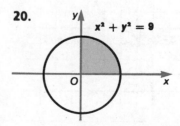

$x^2 + y^2 = 9$

16–4 Negative Integrals

Suppose a function f is negative on the interval $[a, b]$. In this case, the curve $y = f(x)$ lies below the x-axis. To find $\int_a^b f(x)\, dx$, consider the approximating sum $\sum_{i=1}^{n} f(x_i)\Delta x_i$. For each term $f(x_i) \cdot \Delta x_i$ the number $f(x_i)$ is negative and the number Δx_i is positive. Thus, $\sum_{i=1}^{n} f(x_i)\Delta x_i$ is negative. The integral $\int_a^b f(x)\, dx$ is the *negative* of the area of the shaded region. The numerical value of the area is $\left| \int_a^b f(x)\, dx \right|$, which equals $-\int_a^b f(x)\, dx$.

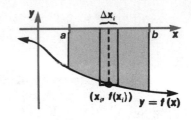

The integrals $\int_a^c f(x)\, dx$ and $\int_d^b f(x)\, dx$ are positive. The integral $\int_c^d f(x)\, dx$ is negative. It is possible to show that $\int_a^b f(x)\, dx$ can be expressed in the following way.

$$\int_a^b f(x)\, dx = \int_a^c f(x)\, dx + \int_c^d f(x)\, dx + \int_d^b f(x)\, dx$$

Thus, $\int_a^b f(x)\, dx$ does not represent the area of the region between the curve $y = f(x)$ and the x-axis on the interval $[a, b]$. Integrals can express the numerical value of the area as follows.

$$\text{Area of } [a, b] = \int_a^c f(x)\, dx - \int_c^d f(x)\, dx + \int_d^b f(x)\, dx$$

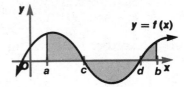

In the figure, the function f sometimes has positive values and sometimes has negative values in the interval $[a, b]$.

By theorem 2a in Chapter 14, if $\lim\limits_{x \to c} f(x) = F$ and $\lim\limits_{x \to c} g(x) = G$, then $\lim\limits_{x \to c} [f(x) + g(x)] = F + G$.

Example

1. Sketch the graph of $f(x) = \dfrac{x^3}{2}$. Find the value of the integral on $[-2, 2]$.

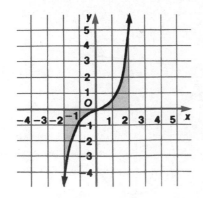

$$\int_{-2}^{2} \frac{x^3}{2}\, dx = \int_{-2}^{0} \frac{x^3}{2}\, dx + \int_{0}^{2} \frac{x^3}{2}\, dx$$
$$= 0$$

Exercises

Exploratory State the integrals to represent the area of the shaded regions on each of the following graphs.

1.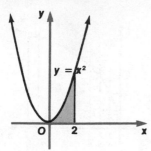

2.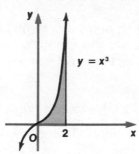

3.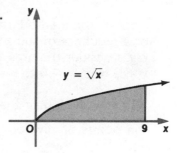

4.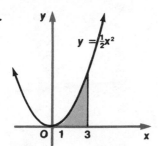

5.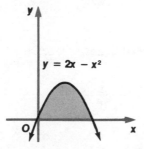

6.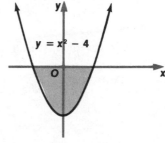

Written Use sketches to interpret each integral as an area.

1. $\left| \int_0^3 (x^2 - 9)\, dx \right|$

2. $\left| \int_{-3}^3 (x^2 - 9)\, dx \right|$

3. $\left| \int_3^4 (x^2 - 9)\, dx \right|$

4. State the relation between the areas given in Problems **1** and **2**. Determine the value $\int_{-3}^3 (x^2 - 9)\, dx$.

5. State the relation between $\int_{-2}^2 (x^4 - 2x^2 - 8)\, dx$ and $\int_0^2 (x^4 - 2x^2 - 8)\, dx$. Determine the value of $\int_{-2}^2 (8 - 2x^2 - x^4)\, dx$.

Sketch the graph of each function to be integrated. Determine the value of each integral.

6. $\int_{-1}^1 x\, dx$

7. $\int_{-2}^2 x^3\, dx$

8. $\int_{-\pi}^{\pi} \sin x\, dx$

9. Describe a property which the curves in Problem **6** through **8** have in common. Write two other integrals which illustrate the same idea.

Solve each of the following.

10. Use the graph of the sine function to find constants a and b, $a \neq 0$ and $b \neq \frac{\pi}{2}$, for which $\int_a^b \sin x\, dx = \int_{\pi/2}^0 \sin x\, dx$.

11. Use the graphs of the sine and cosine functions to find constants c and d for which $\int_c^d \cos x\, dx = \int_0^{\pi/2} \sin x\, dx$.

Excursions in mathematics

Limitations of Summation Method

So far the method used in finding areas was to find the limit of a sequence of sums. In many cases this cannot be done simply. Consider the area bounded by the curve $y = \sqrt{x}$ and the x-axis from $x = 0$ to $x = 1$.

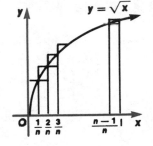

In the division of the interval $[0, 1]$ into n congruent parts, the points of division, including endpoints are $x = 0, \dfrac{1}{n}, \dfrac{2}{n}, \dfrac{3}{n}, \ldots, \dfrac{n-1}{n}, \dfrac{n}{n}$.

The lower approximating sum of areas of rectangles is $\sum_1$.

$$\sum_1 = \sqrt{0} \cdot \frac{1}{n} + \sqrt{\frac{1}{n}} \cdot \frac{1}{n} + \sqrt{\frac{2}{n}} \cdot \frac{1}{n} \cdots + \sqrt{\frac{n-1}{n}} \cdot \frac{1}{n}$$

$$\sum_1 = \frac{1}{n^{3/2}} (\sqrt{1} + \sqrt{2} + \sqrt{3} + \cdots + \sqrt{n-1})$$

The upper approximating sum of areas of rectangles is $\sum_2$.

$$\sum_2 = \sqrt{\frac{1}{n}} \cdot \frac{1}{n} + \sqrt{\frac{2}{n}} \cdot \frac{1}{n} + \sqrt{\frac{3}{n}} \cdot \frac{1}{n} + \cdots + \sqrt{\frac{n}{n}} \cdot \frac{1}{n}$$

$$\sum_2 = \frac{1}{n^{3/2}} (\sqrt{1} + \sqrt{2} + \sqrt{3} + \cdots + \sqrt{n})$$

$$\frac{1}{n^{3/2}} (\sqrt{1} + \sqrt{2} + \sqrt{3} + \cdots + \sqrt{n-1}) \le S \le \frac{1}{n^{3/2}} (\sqrt{1} + \sqrt{2} + \sqrt{3} + \cdots + \sqrt{n})$$

What is $\displaystyle\sum_{r=1}^{n} \sqrt{r}$? Calculators or computers can be used to obtain good approximations. Unfortunately, an expression for this sum cannot be found in a simple way.

This example illustrates a severe limitation in the limit of sums method to evaluate areas. The sums which arise are difficult to evaluate in many cases. However, by taking n sufficiently large, the method always provides as close an approximation to an area as desired. The method is appropriate for use on a computer.

16–5 The Fundamental Theorem of Calculus

Evaluating integrals by the **limit of sums method** is a difficult procedure. This section establishes a significant result that provides the basis for an easier method. The easier method shows that, in a sense, differentiation and integration are inverse processes. The theorem establishing this important result is called the *Fundamental Theorem of Calculus*.

The figure shows a function f which is continuous over $[a, b]$. A second function S is defined in the following way.

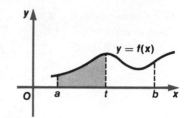

$$S(t) = \int_a^t f(x)\,dx \text{ when } t \in [a, b]$$

The value $S(t)$ is the area of the region bounded by $x = a, x = t$, $y = 0$, and $y = f(x)$.

The function S has the extremely important property that $S'(t) = f(t)$ when t is between a and b.

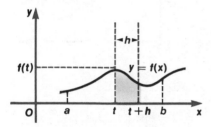 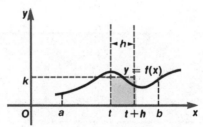

Assume the shaded regions of both figures have the same area. The region shown in Figure **a** has area $S(t + h) - S(t)$. The region shown in Figure **b** has area $k \cdot h$.

$$k = \frac{S(t + h) - S(t)}{h} \text{ when } h \neq 0$$

The two are equal by the Intermediate Value Theorem.

Since f is continuous, a sufficiently small value of h can be chosen so that $f(x)$ is as close as desired to $f(t)$ for all $x \in [t, t + h]$. For some x in the interval, k must equal $f(x)$. Therefore, h can be chosen so that k and $f(t)$ are also as close as desired. In other words,

Notice that the line $y = k$ must intersect the graph of f between the lines $x = t$ and $x = t + h$ if the two areas are to be the same.

$$\lim_{\substack{h \to 0 \\ (h > 0)}} \frac{S(t + h) - S(t)}{h} = f(t)$$

This argument works equally well for $h < 0$. It also works for continuous functions that do not stay above the x-axis. In summary, $S'(t) = f(t)$ for any t between a and b.

The graphs for f and S are shown on the same plane. If a formula for S were known, it would be easy to find $\int_a^b f(x)\,dx$ by simply computing $S(b)$.

Suppose F is any function differentiable on $[a, b]$ such that $F'(t) = f(t)$ for all t between a and b. This would mean that $F'(t) = S'(t)$ for all such t. That is, at each t in the interval $[a, b]$, these particular functions S and F have the same slope. Intuitively, the graphs are parallel and the difference between $F(t)$ and $S(t)$ is constant for all $t \in [a, b]$. *(See figure at the bottom of the page.)*

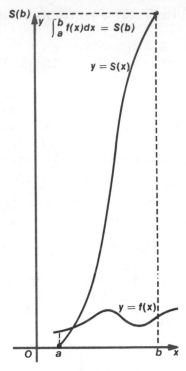

> Let f be a function continuous on $[a, b,]$. Let F and S be functions differentiable on $[a, b]$ such that $S'(x) = f(x)$ for all $x \in [a, b]$. Then $F'(x) = f(x)$ for all $x \in [a, b]$ if and only if for some real constant C, $F(x) = S(x) + C$ for all $x \in [a, b]$.

Definition of $F(x)$

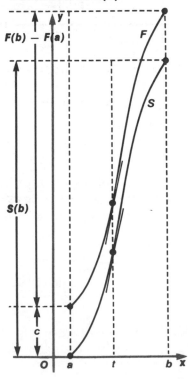

Proof Sketch

I. Suppose $F(x) = S(x) + C$ for all $x \in [a, b]$ where C is some real constant. Then $F'(x) = S'(x) + 0 = S'(x)$ and, since $S'(x) = f(x)$, $F'(x) = f(x)$ for all $x \in [a, b]$.

II. Suppose $F'(x) = f(x)$ for all $x \in [a, b]$. Then, since $S'(x) = f(x)$, $F'(x) = S'(x)$ for all $x \in [a, b]$. The function defined by $F(x) - S(x)$ has derivative $F'(x) - S'(x) = 0$ for all x. It can be proved that only a constant function has this property. Therefore, for some real number C, $F(x) = S(x) + C$ for all $x \in [a, b]$.

Since the functions S and F differ by a constant, $F(a) = S(a) + C$ and $F(b) = S(b) + C$. Thus, it would be easy to find $\int_a^b f(x)\,dx$ if a formula for F were available.

$$\int_a^b f(x)\,dx = S(b)$$
$$= S(b) - S(a) \text{ since } S(a) = 0$$
$$= [F(b) - C] - [F(a) - C]$$
$$= F(b) - F(a)$$

If f is a function continuous on $[a, b]$ and F is a function differentiable on $[a, b]$, and $F'(x) = f(x)$ for all $x \in [a, b]$, then

$$\int_a^b f(x)\,dx = F(b) - F(a).$$

The Fundamental Theorem of Calculus

The Fundamental Theorem of Calculus provides a simple method for evaluating integrals, such as $\int_a^b f(x)\,dx$. The method requires finding an equation that defines a function F with the property $F'(x) = f(x)$ for all x in $[a, b]$.

Let f be a continuous function and F be a differentiable function with the same domain as f. If $F'(x) = f(x)$ for all x in that domain, then F is called an **antiderivative** of f.

Definition of Antiderivative

Example

1. Let $f(x) = 3x^2 + 1$ for all real x. Find an antiderivative of f.

$F_1(x) = x^3 + x$ for all $x \in R$
$F_2(x) = x^3 + x - 27$ for all $x \in R$
$F_3(x) = x^3 + x + 12$ for all $x \in R$

All antiderivatives for a given function differ by a constant.

Many different antiderivatives of a function can be formed by simply varying the constant term. The symbol $\int f(x)\,dx$ may be used to stand for *any particular* antiderivative of f. If F is an antiderivative of f, it is acceptable to write $\int f(x)\,dx = F(x)$. However, as a reminder that F is not unique, it is customary to write $\int f(x)\,dx = F(x) + C$ with the understanding that C may represent any constant.

In the sentence $\int f(x)\,dx = F(x) + C$, the expression $\int f(x)\,dx$ is called an *indefinite integral*. The function f is called the *integrand* and C is called the *constant of integration*.

The following theorems are very useful tools for finding antiderivatives.

$$\int x^n \, dx = \frac{x^{n+1}}{n+1} + C \text{ for } n \neq -1, \text{ and all real } x.$$

$$\int k \, f(x) \, dx = k \int f(x) \, dx \text{ for real constant } k.$$

$$\int [f(x) \pm g(x) \pm \cdots \pm h(x)] \, dx$$

$$= \int f(x) \, dx \pm \int g(x) \, dx \pm \cdots \pm \int h(x) \, dx$$

provided antiderivatives exist for each function.

Theorems for Antiderivatives

The proofs follow from the derivative theorems.

Examples

2. Integrate $\int (x + 1)^2 \, dx$.

$$\int (x + 1)^2 \, dx = \int (x^2 + 2x + 1) \, dx$$

$$= \int x^2 \, dx + 2 \int x \, dx + \int 1 \, dx$$

$$= \frac{x^3}{3} + x^2 + x + C$$

3. Integrate $\int \left(\sqrt{x} + \frac{1}{\sqrt{x}} \right) dx$

$$\int \left(\sqrt{x} + \frac{1}{\sqrt{x}} \right) dx = \int x^{1/2} \, dx + \int x^{-1/2} \, dx$$

$$= \frac{x^{3/2}}{\frac{3}{2}} + \frac{x^{1/2}}{\frac{1}{2}} + C$$

$$= \frac{2}{3} x^{3/2} + 2x^{1/2} + C$$

4. Given $F'(x) = 4x - 1$ and $F(3) = 20$, find F.

$$F'(x) = 4x - 1 \qquad \text{Therefore, } F(x) = \int (4x - 1) \, dx = 2x^2 - x + C$$

$$F(3) = 2(3)^2 - 3 + C$$

$$5 = C$$

Therefore, $F(x) = 2x^2 - x + 5$.

Exercises

Written Integrate each of the following.

1. $\displaystyle\int (3x^2 + 4x + 7)\, dx$

2. $\displaystyle\int (x - 3)^2\, dx$

3. $\displaystyle\int (6x^2 - 1)\, dx$

4. $\displaystyle\int (10x^4 + 3x^2)\, dx$

5. $\displaystyle\int (1 - x)\, dx$

6. $\displaystyle\int (x^2 - 4)\, dx$

7. $\displaystyle\int x(x + 1)(x - 2)\, dx$

8. $\displaystyle\int \left(x^3 + \frac{1}{x^2}\right) dx$

9. $\displaystyle\int \left(x - \frac{1}{x}\right)^2 dx$

10. $\displaystyle\int \frac{x^4 + 1}{x^2}\, dx$

11. $\displaystyle\int \frac{(x^2 + 1)^2}{x^2}\, dx$

12. $\displaystyle\int \left(\sqrt{x} - \frac{1}{x}\right)^2 dx$

13. $\displaystyle\int (4x^{1/3} - x^{-1/3})\, dx$

14. $\displaystyle\int (x^{1/2} - 2x^{-1/2})\, dx$

15. $\displaystyle\int [x^{-1/4}(2x + 1)]\, dx$

16. $\displaystyle\int [x^{-2/3}(1 - x)^2]\, dx$

Find the function F in each case.

17. $F'(x) = 2x$ and $F(4) = 10$

18. $F'(x) = 1 - 2x$ and $F(3) = 4$

19. $F'(x) = 6x^2$ and $F(0) = 0$

20. $F'(x) = x - \dfrac{2}{x^2}$ and $F(2) = 9$

21. $F'(x) = 1 - \dfrac{1}{\sqrt{x}}$ and $F(4) = 1$

22. $F'(x) = 3(x^2 - 3)$ and $F(1) = 12$

Challenge Integrate each of the following.

1. $\displaystyle\int \left[\frac{1}{\sqrt{x}}(1 + \sqrt{x})^2\right] dx$

2. $\displaystyle\int \frac{1 + \sqrt{x}}{x^2}\, dx$

16–6 Applications

Suppose the slope of the tangent at each point (x, y) on a curve $y = f(x)$ is x. The following statements are true.

$$f'(x) = x \text{ and } f(x) = \int x\, dx$$

$$f(x) = \frac{1}{2}x^2 + C, \text{ where } C \in \mathcal{R}$$

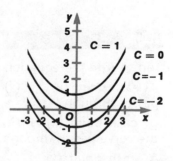

The equation $y = \dfrac{1}{2}x^2 + C$, $C \in \mathcal{R}$ is the equation for a family of parabolas. Some of the members of this family are shown in the interval $[-3, 3]$.

The given information in this case is not sufficient to identify a single member of the family. If, in addition, it is known that the curve passes through the point (2, 3), then it is possible to find the member of the family which satisfies the given conditions.

1. Find the particular member of the family of curves $f(x) = \frac{1}{2}x^2 + C$ that passes through (2, 3).

$$f(x) = \frac{1}{2}x^2 + C$$

$$f(2) = \frac{1}{2}(2)^2 + C = 3$$

$$\frac{1}{2}(4) + C = 3$$

$$2 + C = 3$$

$$C = 1$$

Therefore, $f(x) = \frac{1}{2}x^2 + 1$.

2. The slope of a family of straight lines is 2. Write the equation of the family. Find the equation of its member that passes through (−2, 1).

$$f'(x) = 2 \quad \text{Therefore, } f(x) = \int 2\, dx \quad f(x) = 2x + C, \text{ where } C \in \mathcal{R}$$

$$f(-2) = 2(-2) + C = 1$$

$$-4 + C = 1$$

$$C = 5$$

Therefore, $f(x) = 2x + 5$.

Exercises

Written Write the equation of the curve which satisfies each set of given conditions.

1. At each point (x, y), $f'(x) = 4x$; the curve passes through (1, 3).

2. At each point (x, y), $f'(x) = 2x - 1$; the curve passes through (2, 8).

3. At each point (x, y), $f'(x) = 3x^2 - 10x$; the curve passes through (−1, 0).

4. At each point (x, y), $f'(x) = 6x^2 - 6x + 3$; the curve passes through (0, 0).

5. At each point (x, y), $f'(x) = 3x(2 - x)$; the curve passes through the point (−1, 10).

6. At each point (x, y) of a curve, $f'(x) = 1 - \frac{4}{x^2}$; the curve passes through the point (2, 5).

Solve each of the following.

7. The slope of a curve at each point (x, y) is given by $f'(x) = 3x^2 - 8x + 5$. If the curve passes through the point $(2, 0)$, show that it also passes through the point $(3, 4)$.

8. The slope of a curve at each point (x, y) is given by $f'(x) = 1 - 2x$. If the maximum value of f is $6\frac{1}{4}$, find the equation of the curve.

9. The velocity v in meters per second of a body after t seconds is given by $v = -\int 10\ dt$ and $v = 15$ when $t = 0$. Find a formula for v in terms of t.

10. Given that $v = \dfrac{ds}{dt}$, where s meters is the distance covered (or displacement) at time t seconds, and that $s = 0$ when $t = 0$, find an equation for s in terms of t. Use the results of Problem **9**.

11. The velocity v in meters per second of a body starting from rest is given by $v = \int (t^2 + 2t)\ dt$, where t seconds is the time from rest. Find a formula for v in terms of t. Use the formula to find the velocity of the body after 3 seconds.

12. Use Problem **11** to find the displacement in meters at the end of 3 seconds, given that $v = \dfrac{ds}{dt}$.

Challenge **Solve each of the following.**

1. If $\dfrac{dM}{dx} = \dfrac{1}{2}wl - wx$ where w and l are positive constants, find M in terms of w, l, and x, given that $M = 0$ when $x = 0$. What is the maximum value of M?

2. The velocity-time graph of a body moving with velocity v at time t is a straight line with equation $v = 5 - 2t$. Given that $v = \dfrac{ds}{dt}$ and $s = 0$ when $t = 0$, use integration to find a formula for the displacement s at time t.

16–7 Definite Integrals

The Fundamental Theorem of Calculus provides a way to evaluate the **definite integral** $\displaystyle\int_{a}^{b} f(x)\ dx$ if an antiderivative F can be found. Using square bracket notation $\left[F(x)\right]_{a}^{b}$ for $F(b) - F(a)$ the principal statement of the theorem may be written in the following way.

For convenience choose $c = 0$. The constant C drops out in calculations.

$$\int_{a}^{b} f(x)\ dx = \left[F(x)\right]_{a}^{b}$$
$$= F(b) - F(a)$$

If f has one antiderivative, it has many. Thus, there are many choices for F and any one may be used in the Fundamental Theorem of Calculus.

Examples

1. Evaluate $\displaystyle\int_1^3 x\, dx$.

$$\int_1^3 x\, dx = \left[\frac{x^2}{2}\right]_1^3$$
$$= \frac{9}{2} - \frac{1}{2}$$
$$= 4$$

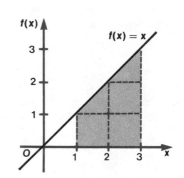

2. Evaluate $\displaystyle\int_1^2 (1 - 2x)^2\, dx$.

$$\int_1^2 (1 - 2x)^2\, dx = \int_1^2 (1 - 4x + 4x^2)\, dx$$
$$= \left[x - 2x^2 + \frac{4}{3}x^3\right]_1^2$$
$$= \left(2 - 2\cdot 2^2 + \frac{4}{3}\cdot 2^3\right) - \left(1 - 2\cdot 1^2 + \frac{4}{3}\cdot 1^3\right)$$
$$\int_1^2 (1 - 2x)^2\, dx = 4\frac{1}{3}$$

Exercises

Exploratory Evaluate each of the following.

1. $\displaystyle\int_0^1 (2x + 3)\, dx$

2. $\displaystyle\int_0^4 (7 - x)\, dx$

3. $\displaystyle\int_0^1 x^2\, dx$

4. $\displaystyle\int_1^2 3x^2\, dx$

5. $\displaystyle\int_{-1}^1 (x^2 + 2x + 1)\, dx$

6. $\displaystyle\int_0^2 \frac{1}{2}x^2\, dx$

Written Evaluate each definite integral.

1. $\displaystyle\int_0^1 (3x^2 + 6x + 1)\, dx$

2. $\displaystyle\int_1^2 (x - 1)(2x - 1)(3x - 1)\, dx$

3. $\displaystyle\int_{-1}^1 (4x^3 + 3x^2)\, dx$

4. $\displaystyle\int_1^4 \left(t^2 + \frac{2}{t^2}\right) dt$

5. $\displaystyle\int_{-1}^2 (3x - 1)^2\, dx$

6. $\displaystyle\int_{-1}^1 12x(x + 1)(x - 1)\, dx$

7. $\int_{-1}^{2} (1 + 2u - 3u^2)\, du$

8. $\int_{2}^{4} \frac{1 + \sqrt{x}}{x^2}\, dx$

9. $\int_{2}^{6} \left(5x^2 - \frac{3}{x^2}\right) dx$

10. $\int_{0}^{a} (t^3 - 2t)\, dt,\ a > 0$

11. $\int_{0}^{p} (u^{1/2} + 1)^2\, du$

12. Verify that $\int_{1}^{2} (1 - 3x^2)\, dx + \int_{2}^{3} (1 - 3x^2)\, dx = \int_{1}^{3} (1 - 3x^2)\, dx$

For $a > b$, $\int_{a}^{b} f(x)\, dx$ is defined to mean $-\int_{b}^{a} f(x)\, dx$.

13. Find $\int_{3}^{-1} (10x^4 + 2x)\, dx$

14. If g is an antiderivative of $f{:}x \to 10x^4 + 2x$, does $\int_{3}^{-1} (10x^4 + 2x)\, dx = g(-1) - g(3)$?

Find a for each of the following.

15. $\int_{0}^{a} x(1 - x)\, dx = 0$

16. $\int_{0}^{a} x^{1/2}\, dx = 42$

17. $\int_{0}^{a} x^{1/2}\, dx = 18$

Evaluate each definite integral.

18. $\int_{1}^{2} 6x^2\, dx$

19. $\int_{0}^{4} x^{1/2}\, dx$

20. $\int_{1}^{2} \left(6u^2 - \frac{2}{u^2}\right) du$

Solve the following to demonstrate that in general $\int_{a}^{c} f(x)\, dx = \int_{a}^{b} f(x)\, dx + \int_{b}^{c} f(x)\, dx$.

21. $\int_{1}^{2} 4x^3\, dx + \int_{2}^{3} 4x^3\, dx = \int_{1}^{3} 4x^3\, dx$

22. $\int_{2}^{c} (2x + 3)\, dx = \int_{2}^{10} (2x + 3)\, dx + \int_{10}^{4} (2x + 3)\, dx$

23. $\int_{3}^{5} (x - 2)\, dx + \int_{5}^{3} (x - 2)\, dx = \int_{3}^{3} (x - 2)\, dx$ Note: $\int_{a}^{a} f(x)\, dx$ is defined to have value zero.

Challenge **Solve each of the following.**

1. The pressure p and volume v of a gas are related by the equation $pv^{1.5} = 128$. Evaluate $\int_{1}^{4} p\, dv$. (Hint: Solve the equation for p.)

2. If the function f is defined as follows on the interval $[0, 4]$, find the area of the enclosed region.
$$f(x) = x^2 \text{ for } 0 \le x \le 1$$
$$f(x) = 1 \text{ for } 1 \le x \le 3$$
$$f(x) = 2 - \frac{x}{3} \text{ for } 3 \le x \le 4$$

16–8 The Trapezoid Rule

If a continuous function f has an antiderivative F, then $\int_{a}^{b} f(x)\, dx = F(b) - F(a)$. Unfortunately, not every continuous function has an antiderivative that can be expressed in terms of simple functions. For example, for the functions given by

$f(x) = \dfrac{1}{\sqrt{1 + x^3}}$, $f(x) = \sin x^2$, $f(x) = \sqrt{1 + 2\sin^2 x}$, $f(x) = \dfrac{\cos x}{\sqrt{x}}$,
and many others, there is no simple function F such that $F'(x) = f(x)$. The limit of sums process, dividing the interval of integration into n congruent parts, makes it possible to obtain a

close approximation to $\displaystyle\int_a^b f(x)\, dx$. The approximation is made

using approximating rectangles.

Other methods are known to obtain better approximations for the same number n of small intervals. The study of these methods is the part of numerical analysis called numerical integration or approximate integration. One such method is called the **Trapezoid Rule**.

The interval $x = a$ to $x = b$ is divided into n congruent parts. The x-coordinates of the points of subdivision are denoted by $a = x_0, x_1, x_2, \ldots, x_n = b$. If h is the length of each subinterval, then $h = \dfrac{1}{n}(b - a)$.

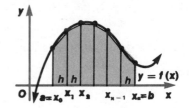

The total area is $\displaystyle\int_a^b f(x)\, dx$ which is approximately equal to the

sum of the areas of the n trapezoids under the curve $y = f(x)$.

The sum of the areas of the trapezoids is $\dfrac{1}{2}h[f(x_0) + f(x_1)] +$

$\dfrac{1}{2}h[f(x_1) + f(x_2)] + \dfrac{1}{2}h[f(x_2) + f(x_3)] + \cdots + \dfrac{1}{2}h[f(x_{n-2}) + f(x_{n-1})]$

$+ \dfrac{1}{2}h[f(x_{n-1}) + f(x_n)]$.

$$\int_a^b f(x)\, dx = \frac{1}{2}h[f(x_0) + 2f(x_1) + \cdots + 2f(x_{n-1}) + f(x_n)].$$ **Trapezoid Rule**

Example

1. Use the Trapezoid Rule with $n = 5$ to estimate $\displaystyle\int_0^1 \frac{1}{1 + x^2}\, dx$.

    Work to four decimal places and write an answer that is correct to three decimal places. Compare the estimate with $\dfrac{1}{4}\pi$, the exact answer.

    $$f(x) = \frac{1}{1 + x^2}, \, a = 0, b = 1, n = 5 \qquad h = \frac{b - a}{n} = \frac{1}{5}$$

$$x_0 = a = 0, x_1 = \frac{1}{5}, x_2 = \frac{2}{5}, x_3 = \frac{3}{5}, x_4 = \frac{4}{5}, x_5 = b = 1$$

$$\int_0^1 \frac{dx}{1 + x^2} \approx \frac{1}{10}\left[f(0) + 2f\left(\frac{1}{5}\right) + 2f\left(\frac{2}{5}\right) + 2f\left(\frac{3}{5}\right) + 2f\left(\frac{4}{5}\right) + f(1)\right]$$

$$\approx \frac{1}{10}\left[1 + 2 \cdot \frac{25}{26} + 2 \cdot \frac{25}{29} + 2 \cdot \frac{25}{34} + 2 \cdot \frac{25}{41} + \frac{1}{2}\right]$$

$$\approx \frac{1}{10}(1.0000 + 1.9231 + 1.7241$$

$$+ 1.4706 + 1.2195 + 0.5000)$$

$$\approx \frac{1}{10}(7.8373)$$

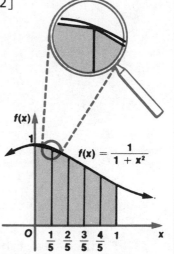

$$\int_0^1 \frac{1}{1 + x^2}\, dx \approx 0.784 \text{ and } \frac{1}{4}\pi \approx 0.785$$

Exercises

Written   Use the Trapezoid Rule to approximate each definite integral. Use the given value for *n*. Work to the number of decimal places indicated, and round to one less place.

1. $\int_1^2 \frac{1}{x}\, dx$, $n = 5$, four decimal places

2. $\int_0^{\pi/2} \sin x\, dx$, $n = 10$, four decimal places

3. $\int_0^1 \frac{1}{\sqrt{1 + x^2}}\, dx$, $n = 5$, four decimal places

4. $\int_0^{1/2} \frac{1}{\sqrt{1 - x^2}}\, dx$, $n = 5$, four decimal places

Use the Trapezoid Rule to approximate each definite integral. Compare the approximation to the value found in evaluating each definite integral.

5. $\int_0^2 (x^2 + 2)\, dx$, $n = 4$

6. $\int_0^3 3x^2\, dx$, $n = 6$

16–9   Areas

The areas of many types of regions can be found using integrals. The following example shows how to manage functions that may have graphs completely or in part below the *x*-axis.

Examples

1. **Find the area of the region between the curve and the x-axis from $x = 0$ to $x = 2$.**

   The graph of the function $f(x) = x(x - 1)(x - 2)$ is shown. The areas of the regions above and below the x-axis are represented by A_1 and A_2

   $A_1 = \left| \int_0^1 x(x - 1)(x - 2) \, dx \right|$ $\quad A_2 = \left| \int_1^2 x(x - 1)(x - 2) \, dx \right|$

   $\quad = \left| \int_0^1 (x^3 - 3x^2 + 2x) \, dx \right|$ $\quad = \left| \int_1^2 (x^3 - 3x^2 + 2x) \, dx \right|$

   $\quad = \left| \left[\frac{1}{4}x^4 - x^3 + x^2 \right]_0^1 \right|$ $\quad = \left| \left[\frac{1}{4}x^4 - x^3 + x^2 \right]_1^2 \right|$

   $A_1 = \dfrac{1}{4}$ $\qquad\qquad A_2 = \dfrac{1}{4}$ $\quad$ *Without absolute values, the answer would be zero.*

   The total area of the region between the curve and the x-axis is $\dfrac{1}{4} + \dfrac{1}{4} = \dfrac{1}{2}$.

2. **Find the area of the region between the curve $y = 4 - x^2$ and the straight line $y = 3x$.**

   The parabola and line intersect where $4 - x^2 = 3x$; that is, at $x = -4$ and at $x = 1$.

   In Figure **a** the area of a strip of width Δx is approximately $[(4 - x^2) - 3x]\Delta x$. Hence, the approximating sum for the area of the shaded region is $\displaystyle\sum_{x=0}^{1} (4 - x^2 - 3x)\Delta x$.

   $A_a = \displaystyle\int_0^1 (4 - x^2 - 3x) \, dx = \left[4x - \frac{x^3}{3} - \frac{3x^2}{2} \right]_0^1 = 2\frac{1}{6}$

   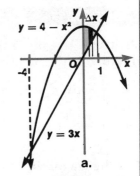

   a.

   In Figure **b**, the area of the strip of width Δx is also $[(4 - x^2) - 3x]\Delta x$.

   $A_b = \displaystyle\int_{-4}^1 (4 - x^2 - 3x) \, dx = \left[4x - \frac{x^3}{3} - \frac{3x^2}{2} \right]_{-4}^1 = 20\frac{5}{6}$

   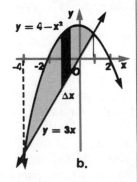

   b.

Suppose an enclosed region lies completely below the *x*-axis. An approximation to the area of the strip of width Δx is found by forming a difference. Show that this is correct by considering the region enclosed by the curve $y = x^2$ and the line $y = 2x$. In general, the results of this section may be expressed as follows.

> The area of the region enclosed by the lines $x = a$, $x = b$, and the curves $y = f(x)$ and $y = g(x)$ where $f(x) \geq g(x)$ for all x in $[a, b]$ is given by $\int_{a}^{b} [f(x) - g(x)]\, dx$.

Area Between Curves

In calculating area, it may be necessary to separate the interval into several parts.

Exercises

Exploratory Express each area as a definite integral and evaluate the integral.

1.
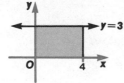

2.
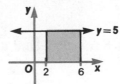

3.
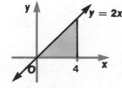

4.
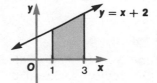

Find the area of each region described.

5. Bounded by the lines $x = 1$, $x = 2$, $y = 6x$ and the parabola $y = 2x^2$

6. Bounded by the line $y = x$ and the curve $y = x^3$

7. Bounded by the line $y = \frac{1}{2}x$ and the curve $y = \sqrt{x}$

8. Bounded by the curves $y = x^2$ and $y = x^4$

9. Bounded by the curves $y = x^4$ and $y = x^3$, and the y-axis.

10. Bounded by the curves $y = x^4$ and $y = x^3$ and the lines $x = 2$ and $y = 0$.

Written   Use integration to find the area of each shaded region.

1.
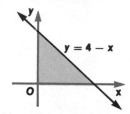

$y = 4 - x$

2.
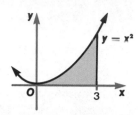

$y = x^2$

3
3.
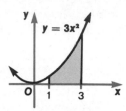

$y = 3x^2$

1   3

4.
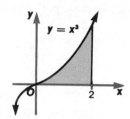

$y = x^3$

2

5.
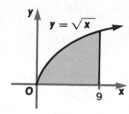

$y = \sqrt{x}$

9

6.
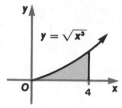

$y = \sqrt{x^3}$

4

7.
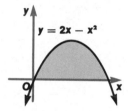

$y = 2x - x^2$

8.
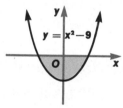

$y = x^2 - 9$

Sketch the graph of each function. Find the area of the region cut off below the x-axis.

9. $f(x) = x (4 - x)$

10. $f(x) = x^2 - 3x + 2$

Sketch the graphs for each pair of equations. Find the area of the region enclosed between them.

11. $f(x) = x^2; g(x) = 4x$ 12. $f(x) = x^2 - 5x + 8; g(x) = 2$ 13. $f(x) = x^3; g(x) = 4x(x \geq 0)$

Solve each of the following.

14. Sketch the curve $y = (x - 2)^2$. Calculate the area of the region enclosed by the curve, the x-axis, and the y-axis.

15. The rectangle formed by the coordinate axes and the lines $x = 3$ and $y = 9$ is separated into two parts by the parabola $y = x^2$. Make a sketch and find the area of each part.

16. The distance a body falls in a vacuum in 2 seconds starting from rest is s meters where $s = \int_0^2 10t \; dt$. Make a graph and find out how far the body falls in 2 seconds.

17. Find the area of the region bounded by the parabola $y^2 = x$ and the line $y = x - 2$. (The upper half of the parabola is the graph of the function defined by $y = \sqrt{x}$. The lower half is that of the function defined by $y = -\sqrt{x}$.)

Find the coordinates of A, B, and C in each figure. Calculate the total area of the shaded part.

18.

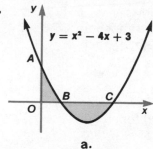

$y = x^2 - 4x + 3$

a.

19.

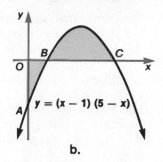

$y = (x - 1)(5 - x)$

b.

Challenge   Solve each of the following.

1. Show that the area of the region bounded by the parabola $y = (x + 2)$ $(x - 4)$ and the x-axis is separated by the y-axis in the ratio 7:20.

2. Sketch the curve $y = \dfrac{1}{x^2}$ in the interval from $x = 1$ to $x = 4$. Find the area of the region enclosed by the curve, the x-axis, and the ordinates at $x = 1$ and $x = 4$. Then, find the real number k such that the line $x = k$ separates this region into two parts having equal area.

Excursions in mathematics

Multiple Integration

The process of integration produces a function. As a result this process can be repeated. The integral of an integral can be found.

Example   Find the integral of $\displaystyle\int_1^3 \left(\int_1^x x^2\, dx \right) dx.$

$$\int_1^3 \left(\int_1^x x^2\, dx \right) dx = \int_1^3 \left[\frac{x^3}{3} \right]_1^x dx$$

$$= \int_1^3 \left(\frac{x^3}{3} - \frac{1}{3} \right) dx$$

$$= \left[\frac{x^4}{12} - \frac{1}{3}x \right]_1^3$$

$$= \left(\frac{81}{12} - \frac{3}{3} \right) - \left(\frac{1}{12} - \frac{1}{3} \right)$$

$$= \frac{80}{12} - \frac{2}{3} = 6$$

Chapter Summary

1. The Fundamental Theorem of Calculus is as follows.
    If f is a function continuous on $[a, b]$ and F is a function differentiable on $[a,b]$, and $F'(x) = f(x)$ for all $x \subset [a,b]$, then

    $$\int_a^b f(x)\, dx = F(b) - F(a). \quad (493)$$

2. Let f be a continuous function and F be a differentiable function with the same domain as f. If $F'(x) = f(x)$ for all x in that domain, then F is called an antiderivative of f. (493)

3. In the sentence $\int f(x)\, dx = F(x) + C$, the expression $\int f(x)\, dx$ is called an indefinite integral. The function f is called the integrand and C is called the constant of integration. (493)

4. $\int x^n dx = \dfrac{x^{n+1}}{n+1} + C$ for $n \neq -1$, and all real x. (494)

5. $\int k\, f(x) = k \int f(x)\, dx$ for real constant k. (494)

6. $\int [f(x) \pm g(x) \pm \cdots \pm h(x)]\, dx = \int f(x)\, dx \pm \int g(x)\, dx \pm \cdots \pm$ $\int h(x)\, dx$ provided antiderivatives exist for each function. (494)

7. The expression $\int_a^b f(x)\, dx$ is a definite integral. The lower limit of integration is a. The upper limit of integration is b. The interval of integration is the interval from $x = a$ to $x = b$. (497)

8. The numerical value of the area of the shaded region is $\int_a^b f(x)\, dx$. In Figure **a** the integral is positive. In Figure **b** the integral is negative. (503)

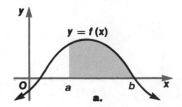

a.

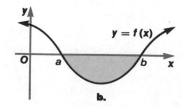

b.

9. The area of the region enclosed by the lines $x = a$, $x = b$, and the curves $y = f(x)$ and $y = g(x)$ where $f(x) \geq g(x)$

for all x in $[a, b]$ is given by $\displaystyle\int_{a}^{b} [f(x) - g(x)]\, dx$. (503)

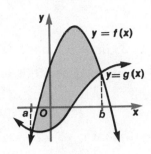

Chapter Review

16–1
16–2 Calculate the area of the region between each curve and the x-axis over the given interval using the limit of sums process.

   1. $y = 2x$ from $x = 0$ to $x = 1$ **2.** $y = x^2$ from $x = 0$ to $x = b$

16–3   **3.** Sketch the curve with equation $y = 3x^2$. Calculate the area of the region bounded by this curve, the x-axis, $x = 0$, and $x = 2$.

16–4 Evaluate each integral.

   4. $\displaystyle\int_{0}^{2} (x^2 + 1)\, dx$ **5.** $\displaystyle\int_{-2}^{0} (x^2 - 4x + 2)\, dx$

16–5 Find each indefinite integral.

16–6   **6.** $\displaystyle\int (x^2 + x + 1)\, dx$ **7.** $\displaystyle\int (x - 1)(3x - 5)\, dx$

   8. $\displaystyle\int x(x - 2)(x + 2)\, dx$ **9.** $\displaystyle\int x^{1/3}(x^{2/3} - x^{-1/3})\, dx$

   10. $\displaystyle\int \frac{x^{1/2} + x^{-1/2}}{x}\, dx$

Find the function F in each case.

   11. $F'(x) = 8x - 3$ and $F(-1) = 10$ **12.** $F'(x) = x^2 - \dfrac{1}{x^2}$ and $F(1) = \dfrac{1}{3}$

Find each indefinite integral.

13. $\int \left(3x^2 + \dfrac{2}{x^3}\right) dx$

14. $\int \left(\dfrac{1}{4x^2} + \dfrac{4}{x^3}\right) dx$

15. $\int (2\sqrt{x} - 1)^2 \, dx$

16. $\int \dfrac{3x^2 + 4x - 5}{\sqrt{x}} \, dx$

16-7 **17.** The slope of the tangent to a curve at a point (x, y) is given by $\dfrac{dy}{dx} = 4x - \dfrac{4}{x^2}$. If the curve passes through the point $(2, 11)$, find its equation.

16-8 Evaluate each definite integral.

18. $\int_0^1 (9x^2 + 1) \, dx$

19. $\int_{-1}^0 (2 - 2x) \, dx$

20. $\int_1^4 \left(\sqrt{x} - \dfrac{1}{\sqrt{x}}\right) dx$

Find a, given the following.

21. $\int_{-1}^a (2x + 4) \, dx = 4$

22. $\int_{-1}^{2a} \dfrac{1}{x^2} \, dx = \dfrac{1}{2}$

16-9 **Show by shading in sketches the areas given by the following, and then calculate the areas.**

23. $\int_{-1}^2 (2x + 4) \, dx$

24. $\int_{-6}^6 x^2 \, dx$

Find the area of the region enclosed between each of these curves and the x-axis.

25. $y = (x - 1)(x + 2)$

26. $y = (2 - x)(4 + x)$

Sketch the following pairs of curves. Find their points of intersection. Calculate the area of the region enclosed by the curves in each case.

27. $y = x^2$ and $y = 9$

28. $y = 5 + 2x - x^2$ and $y = 1 - x$

29. $y = 10 - x^2$ and $y = (x - 2)^2$

30. The tangents at the points $A(0, 1)$ and $B(2, 5)$ on the parabola $y = x^2 + 1$ meet at C. Calculate the area of the region between the tangents and the arc AB of the parabola.

Chapter Test

Calculate the area of the region between each curve and the *x*-axis over the given interval using the limit of sums process.

1. $y = 2x$ from $x = 1$ to $x = 2$

2. $y = x^2$ from $x = 1$ to $x = b$

Evaluate each integral.

3. $\displaystyle\int_{-1}^{1} 2x\, dx$

4. $\displaystyle\int_{0}^{2} 7x^2\, dx$

Find each indefinite integral.

5. $\displaystyle\int (3 - 2x - 6x^2)\, dx$

6. $\displaystyle\int (3x + 4)^2\, dx$

7. $\displaystyle\int (x^{1/2} - x^{-1/2})\, dx$

8. $\displaystyle\int \left(\frac{1}{x^2} - \frac{1}{x^3}\right) dx$

9. $\displaystyle\int \left(3x^{1/2} + \frac{1}{3x^{1/3}}\right) dx$

10. $\displaystyle\int \left(3x + \frac{1}{x^3}\right)^2 dx$

Evaluate each definite integral.

11. $\displaystyle\int_{1}^{2} (3x^2 + 4x - 5)\, dx$

12. $\displaystyle\int_{0}^{1} (x + 1)^3\, dx$

13. $\displaystyle\int_{1}^{4} \left(3\sqrt{x} + \frac{1}{3\sqrt{x}}\right) dx$

14. Find the area of the region enclosed between the curve $y = x(x - 2)(2x - 1)$ and the *x*-axis.

15. Find the area of the region enclosed by the *x*-axis, the parabola $y = x^2$ and the line $x = 4$.

Sketch the following pairs of curves. Find their points of intersection. Calculate the area of the region enclosed by the curves in each case.

16. $y = x^2$ and $y = 2 - x^2$

17. $y = x(x - 3)$ and $y = 2x(3 - x)$

18. $y = 9 - x^2$ and $y = x^2(x^2 - 9)$

Computers

Number System

The concept of number and the process of counting were developed long before the time of recorded history. Systems of counting were developed to serve a purpose. As nations developed mathematical systems, refinements of the number systems were needed.

As the different types of mathematics were developed different number bases were used. Each system had a base number which indicated the grouping of the numbers. Modern mankind uses base ten for many calculations. As computers were developed, base ten proved to be difficult with which to work. Therefore, the developers of computers began to rely on the binary system.

Machine languages use only two digits - 0 and 1. These digits (bits) are used in a base two, or binary number system.

In the binary system, each place-value position is a power of two. To find the equivalent base ten numeral for a binary numeral like $(101011)_2$ multiply the bit in each place-value position by the corresponding power of two, and add.

$$
\begin{aligned}
(101011)_2 &= (1 \times 2^5) + (0 \times 2^4) + (1 \times 2^3) + \\
&\quad (0 \times 2^2) + (1 \times 2^1) + (1 \times 2^0) \\
&= (1 \times 32) + 0 + (1 \times 8) + 0 + \\
&\quad (1 \times 2) + (1 \times 1) \\
&= 32 + 8 + 2 + 1 \\
&= 43
\end{aligned}
$$

Thus, the binary numeral $(101011)_2$ is the same as 43 in base ten.

Bits are the alphabet of machine language. To see how a computer uses this language, a simple analogy will help. Imagine that a light bulb is used to represent a bit. When the bulb is on (current is flowing), it represents zero. If several bulbs are arranged in a row, then each bulb can stand for a place-value position. In this way, the row of bulbs is used to represent different numbers.

This rather simple concept is the basis of modern computers. Of course, a computer does not contain rows of light bulbs. But it does contain a large number of tiny electronic switches.

Other number systems used in working with computers are the hexadecimal and octal. The hexadecimal system is the number system for base 16. It uses the symbols 0, 1, 2, 3, 4, 5, 6, 7, 8, 9, A, B, C, D, E, and F. The octal system is the number system for base 8. It uses the digits 0, 1, 2, 3, 4, 5, 6, and 7. These other systems can easily be converted to binary numbers but they offer smaller representatives with which to work.

Hexadecimal numerals and octal numerals are converted to decimal numerals in the same way as binary numerals keeping in mind the base.

$$
\begin{aligned}
(1\ 4\ A)_{16} &= (1 \times 16^2) + (4 \times 16^1) + \\
&\quad (10 \times 16^0) \\
&= 256 + 64 + 10 \\
&= 330
\end{aligned}
$$

$$
\begin{aligned}
(7\ 4\ 3)_8 &= (7 \times 8^2) + (4 \times 8^1) + \\
&\quad (3 \times 8^0) \\
&= 448 + 32 + 3 \\
&= 483
\end{aligned}
$$

To convert a hexadecimal numeral to a binary numeral, substitute the corresponding group of four binary digits for each hexadecimal digit

$$
\begin{aligned}
(1\ 4\ A)_{16} &= \quad 1 \qquad 4 \qquad\quad A \\
&= 0001 \quad 0100 \quad 1010 \\
&= (101001010)_2
\end{aligned}
$$

Decimal, binary, hexadecimal, and octal notation

Decimal	Binary	Hexadecimal	Octal
0	00000	0	0
1	00001	1	1
2	00010	2	2
3	00011	3	3
4	00100	4	4
5	00101	5	5
6	00110	6	6
7	00111	7	7
8	01000	8	10
9	01001	9	11
10	01010	A	12
11	01011	B	13
12	01100	C	14
13	01101	D	15
14	01110	E	16
15	01111	F	17
16	10000	10	20
17	10001	11	21
18	10010	12	22
19	10011	13	23
20	10100	14	24
21	10101	15	25
22	10110	16	26
23	10111	17	27
24	11000	18	30
25	11001	19	31
26	11010	1A	32
27	11011	1B	33
.	.	.	.
.	.	.	.
.	.	.	.

$$(743)_8 = \quad 7 \qquad 4 \qquad 3$$
$$= 0111 \quad 0100 \quad 0011$$
$$= (11101000011)_2$$

Octal numerals are grouped in threes to convert to the binary numeral.

The reverse process (binary to either hexadecimal or octal) is done in a similar way.

Exercises Write programs for each of the following.

1. Find the area under the curve $y = x^2$ from $x = 0$ to $x = 1$ by finding the limit of the area of n rectangles under the curve.

2. Find the area under the curve $y = x^2$ from $x = 0$ to $x = 1$ by using the trapezoid rule with n intervals.

3. Given a year (past, present, or future), print the calendar for that year.

Appendix

A-1   Standardized Testing

Scholastic Aptitude Test

In order to be admitted to most colleges, students need to take standardized tests. These tests provide colleges with a means of evaluating the knowledge of the students. One test frequently taken by high school juniors and seniors is the SAT (Scholastic Aptitude Test). This test is designed to evaluate the general background of the students as well as their verbal and mathematical abilities. The test is administered several times each year and consists of six sections. Each section takes approximately thirty minutes to complete. There are two sections that evaluate verbal skills, two sections that evaluate mathematical skills, and one section that evaluates writing skills. The final section is non-graded and evaluates skills in a specific area. The last section is designed to provide input for future tests.

The mathematical sections of the SAT have questions that require basic knowledge of algebra and geometry. The questions involve solving linear equations, finding roots of quadratic equations, finding areas, and locating points on a grid. Also, there are questions which emphasize quantitative comparisons involving relationships and estimations. Multiple-choice questions make up approximately two-thirds of the test. The remaining third consists of quantitative comparison questions.

Sample questions of the SAT are provided below to show the types of questions found on previous tests. The questions and instructional material are published by the *Educational Testing Service* and the *College Entrance Examination Board* and reprinted with permission. Answers are provided at the end of the sample questions.

The SAT questions are from SAT Form Code 8G071. College Entrance Examination Board, 1980. Reprinted by permission of Educational Testing Service, copyright owner of the test questions.

Permission to reprint the above SAT material does not constitute review or endorsement by Educational Testing Service or the College Board of this publication as a whole or of any other sample questions or testing information it may contain.

Multiple-Choice Questions

In this section solve each problem, using any available space on the page for scratchwork. Then indicate the <u>one</u> correct answer in the appropriate space on the answer sheet.

The following information is for your reference in solving some of the problems.

Circle of radius r: Area = πr^2; Circumference = $2\pi r$
   The number of degrees of arc in a circle is 360.
The measure in degrees of a straight angle is 180.

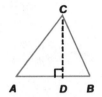

Triangle: The sum of the measures in degrees of the angles of a triangle is 180.
If $\angle CDA$ is a right angle, then
   (1) area of $\triangle ABC = \dfrac{AB \times CD}{2}$
   (2) $AC^2 = AD^2 + DC^2$

Definitions of symbols:
=	is equal to	≤	is less than or equal to
≠	is unequal to	≥	is greater than or equal to
<	is less than	‖	is parallel to
>	is greater than	⊥	is perpendicular to

<u>Note:</u> Figures which accompany problems in this test are intended to provide information useful in solving the problems. They are drawn as accurately as possible EXCEPT when it is stated in a specific problem that its figure is not drawn to scale. All figures lie in a plane unless otherwise indicated. All numbers used are real numbers.

---

1. In a certain dart game, Don scored 25 per cent more points than Craig. If Craig scored 100 points, how many points did Don score?

   (A) 225   **(B)** 125   **(C)** 100   **(D)** 80   **(E)** 75

2. For which of the following blocks could the top face viewed from the top look like the front face viewed from the front?

(A) P   **(B)** O   **(C)** Y   **(D)** T   **(E)** J

3. A polygon is NOT a triangle if it has exactly

   (A) three sides   **(B)** three angles
   (C) one angle which mea- **(D)** two perpendicular
        sures 135°   sides
   (E) two parallel sides

4. $2\frac{1}{2} - \left(\frac{1}{4} + \frac{1}{4} + \frac{1}{4} - \frac{1}{3}\right) =$

   (A) $1\frac{5}{6}$ **(B)** 2 **(C)** $2\frac{1}{12}$ **(D)** $2\frac{1}{6}$ **(E)** $2\frac{5}{12}$

5. If the freshman class has 28 students of whom $\frac{1}{2}$ are women and the sophomore class has 24 students of whom $\frac{2}{3}$ are women, which of the following gives the total number of women in both classes?

   (A) $\left(\frac{1}{2}\right) + \left(\frac{2}{3}\right)\left(\frac{24 + 28}{2}\right)$ **(B)** $2\left(\frac{1}{2} + \frac{2}{3}\right)(24 + 28)$

   (C) $\left(\frac{1}{2}\right)\left(\frac{2}{3}\right)(24 + 28)$ **(D)** $\frac{2}{3}(28) + \frac{1}{2}(24)$

   (E) $\frac{1}{2}(28) + \frac{2}{3}(24)$

6. A roll of plastic 250 meters long costs $26. If it takes a length of $2\frac{1}{2}$ meters of this plastic to cover a certain machine, how much will it cost to buy the exact length of plastic needed to cover 600 such machines?

   (A) $62 **(B)** $65 **(C)** $156 **(D)** $1,550 **(E)** $1,560

7. The clock above is accurate, but the minute, hour, and second hands are drawn the same length. If the time shown is between 2:45 and 3:00, which of the three lettered hands could be the <u>second</u> hand?
   (A) A only   **(B)** B only
   (C) C only   **(D)** Either A or C
   (E) Either B or C

8. If the two middle digits of 4,579 are interchanged the resulting number is

(A) 18 less than 4,579   (B) 180 less than 4,579
(C) equal to 4,579   (D) 18 more than 4,579
(E) 180 more than 4,579

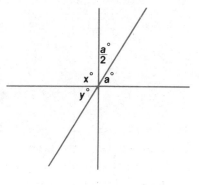

9. If three lines intersect in a point to form the angles shown above, then $x + y =$

(A) $\dfrac{a}{2} - 180$ (B) $180 - \dfrac{a}{2}$ (C) $180 - \dfrac{5a}{2}$

(D) $180 - a$ (E) $a - 180$

10. If $x^2 = 1$, then x^3 is equal to

(A) -3 (B) -1 *only*   (C) 1 only
(D) 3   (E) -1 *or* 1

Quantitative Comparison Questions

Questions 11–15 each consist of two quantities, one in Column **A** and one in Column **B**. You are to compare the two quantities and on the answer sheet blacken space

A if the quantity in Column **A** is greater;
B if the quantity in Column **B** is greater;
C if the two quantities are equal;
D if the relationship cannot be determined from the information given.

Notes: 1. In certain questions, information concerning one or both of the quantities to be compared is centered above the two columns.
2. A symbol that appears in both columns represents the same thing in Column **A** as it does in Column **B**.
3. Letters such as x, n, and k stand for real numbers.
4. Since there are only four choices NEVER MARK **(E)**

Column **A**   Column **B**

11. Area of a circle with radius 1   Area of a square with side 1

1 skedallion = 4.6 skippers
2 phantoms = 9.3 skippers

12. Value of one skedallion   Value of one phantom

$$x^2 + 8x + 15 = 0$$

13. | $x^2 + 8x$ | | 15 |

A point Q to be placed on the grid has x-coordinate of 6.

14. | Distance OP | | Distance OQ |

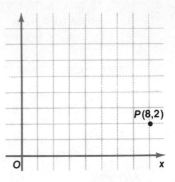

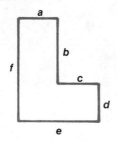

In the figure above, all segments intersect at right angles and the segments have lengths a, b, c, d, e, and f as shown.

15. | $a + b + c + d$ | | $e + f$ |

Answers to Multiple-Choice Questions

1. Craig's score = 100
Don's score = 25% + Craig's score
Don's score = 125

The correct answer is **(B)**.

2. The correct answer is **(C)**.

3. If a figure has two parallel sides, the figure must have at least four sides.

The correct answer is **(E)**.

4. $2\frac{1}{2} - \left(\frac{1}{4} + \frac{1}{4} + \frac{1}{4} - \frac{1}{3}\right) = 2\frac{1}{2} - \left(\frac{3}{4} - \frac{1}{3}\right)$

$$= 2\frac{1}{2} - \left(\frac{9}{12} - \frac{4}{12}\right)$$

$$= 2\frac{1}{2} - \left(\frac{5}{12}\right)$$

$$= 2\frac{1}{12}$$

The correct answer is **(C)**.

5. $\frac{1}{2}(28) + \frac{2}{3}(24)$

   The correct answer is (**E**).

6. 250 m costs $26.

   x = number of meters needed

   $x = 2\frac{1}{2} \times 600 = 1500$ m

   $\text{cost} = \frac{1500}{250} \times 26 = \$156$

   The correct answer is (**C**).

7. The hour hand must be between the 2 and the 3. The minute hand must be between the 9 and the 12. Thus, the only hand that could be the second hand is **C**.

   The correct answer is (**C**).

8. $4759 - 4579 = 180$

   The correct answer is (**E**).

9. From the figure we can form the following equation.

   $$x + y + \frac{a}{2} = 180$$
   $$\text{So, } x + y = 180 - \frac{a}{2}$$

   The correct answer is (**B**).

10. If $x^2 = 1$, $x = 1$ or $x = -1$. So, $x^3 = 1$ or -1.

    The correct answer is (**E**).

Answers to Quantitative Comparison Questions

	Column **A**	Column **B**
11.	Area = π	Area = 1

   The correct choice is (**A**).

12. 1 skedallion = 4.6 skippers   1 phantom = $\frac{9.3}{2}$ skippers

    The correct answer is (**B**).

13. $x^2 + 8x = -15$ 15

    The correct answer is (**B**).

14. $OP = \sqrt{64 + 4}$ $\qquad\qquad OQ = \sqrt{36 + y^2}$

The correct answer is **(D)**.

15. $a + b + c + d = (a + c) + (b + d)$ $\qquad e + f$

The correct answer is **(C)**.

Achievement Tests

The Educational Testing Service also provides Achievement Tests. These tests are designed to evaluate the knowledge of students in particular areas such as biology, world history, various foreign languages, and mathematics. There are two levels of mathematics Achievement Tests. The first level provides an evaluation of basic topics usually covered in a three-year college preparatory sequence of mathematics. The topics would include basic topics from algebra as well as plane Euclidean geometry. Also included are topics from coordinate and solid geometry, trigonometry, and functions. Level II is a test to evaluate students with a stronger mathematic background. This level includes more advanced topics usually included in a 3½-to 4-year sequence of mathematics. This test requires a more sophisticated, deeper understanding of mathematics.

Provided below are sample questions for both Level I and Level II Achievement Tests. The answers follow the testing material.

The sample Achievement test questions are from *About the Achievement Tests*. College Entrance Examination Board, 1981. Reprinted by permission of Educational Testing Service, copyright owner of the sample test questions.

Permission to reprint the above sample test material does not constitute review or endorsement by Educational Testing Service or the College Board of this publication as a whole or of any other sample questions or testing information it may contain.

Mathematics Level I

DIRECTIONS: For each of the following problems, decide which is the best of the choices given. Then blacken the corresponding space on the answer sheet.

Notes: **(1)** Figures that accompany problems in this test are intended to provide information useful in solving the problems. They are drawn as accurately as possible EXCEPT when it is stated in a specific problem that its figure is not drawn to scale. All figures lie in a plane unless otherwise indicated. **(2)** Unless otherwise specified, the domain of a function f is assumed to be the set of all real numbers x for which $f(x)$ is a real number.

1. If $x = bc$ and $y = bd$, then $y - x =$
   (A) $bc(1 - d)$ **(B)** $bd(1 - c)$ **(C)** $d(b - c)$
   (D) $b(d - c)$ **(E)** $c(b - d)$

2. Each of c cases contains b boxes, and each box contains k items. What is the total number of items in the c cases?
   (A) $b + c + k$ **(B)** $\dfrac{bc}{k}$ **(C)** $\dfrac{ck}{b}$

   (D) $\dfrac{bk}{c}$ **(E)** bck

3. If $x + 2 = y$, what is the value of $|x - y| + |y - x|$?
   (A) -4 **(B)** 0 **(C)** 2 **(D)** 4

   (E) It cannot be determined from the information given.

4. The graph of the equation $3x - 2y = 4$ intersects the y-axis at
   (A) $(0, -4)$ **(B)** $(0, -2)$ **(C)** $(0, 2)$ **(D)** $(0, 4)$ **(E)** $(2, 0)$

5. If $f(x) = 3x + 6$ and $g(x) = 5x - 4$, what is the real number r such that $f(r) = g(r)$?
   (A) -2 **(B)** 0 **(C)** $\dfrac{1}{4}$ **(D)** $\dfrac{4}{5}$ **(E)** 5

Figure 1

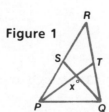

6. In $\triangle PQR$ in Figure **1**, the degree measure of $\angle QPR$ is 60 and the degree measure of $\angle RQP$ is 80. If QS bisects $\angle RQP$ and PT bisects $\angle QPR$, then $x =$
   (A) 40   **(B)** 100   **(C)** 110   **(D)** 120   **(E)** 140

7. Which of the lines in Figure 2 is the graph of $x = 3$?

    (A) m **(B)** n **(C)** p **(D)** q **(E)** r Figure 2

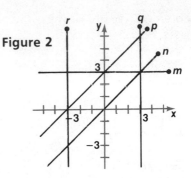

Answers to Mathematics Level I Questions

1. If $x = bc$ and $y = bd$, then $y - x = bd - bc$ or $b(d - c)$.

   The correct answer is **(D)**.

2. Total $= c(b)\,(k)$

   The correct answer is **(E)**.

3. Let $y = x + 2$

   $|x - y| = |x - (x + 2)| = |x - x - 2| = 2$
   $|y - x| = |x + 2 - x| \quad = |x + 2 - x| = 2$
   $|x - y| + |y - x| = 4$

   The correct answer is **(D)**.

4. $3x - 2y = 4$

   Let $x = 0$, $3(0) - 2y = 4$
   $ - 2y = 4$
   $ y = -2$

   The correct answer is **(B)**.

5. $3x + 6 = 5x - 4$
   $10 = 2x$
   $5 = x$

   The correct answer is **(E)**.

6. $m \angle QPR = 60°$ $m \angle RQP = 80°$
   $m \angle TPQ = 30°$ since $\overline{PT}$ bisects $\angle QPR$ $m \angle PQS = 40°$ since $\overline{QS}$ bisects $\angle RQP$

           $m \angle TPQ + m \angle SQP + x = 180°$
                       $30° + 40° + x = 180°$
                               $x = 180° - 70°$
                               $x = 110°$

   The correct answer is **(C)**.

7. The correct answer is **(D)**.

Directions: For each of the following problems, decide which is the best of the choices given. Then blacken the corresponding space on the answer sheet.

Notes: **(1)** Figures that accompany problems in this test are intended to provide information useful in solving the problems. They are drawn as accurately as possible EXCEPT when it is stated in a specific problem that its figure is not drawn to scale. All figures lie in a plane unless otherwise indicated. **(2)**   Unless otherwise specified, the domain of a function f is assumed to be the set of all real numbers x for which $f(x)$ is a real number.

1.   If $f(x) = x^2 - x^3$, then $f(-1)=$

(A) 2   (B) 1   (C) 0   (D) -1 (E) -2

2.   If $\sin x = 2 \cos x$, what is $\tan x$?

(A) $\dfrac{1}{2}$ (B) $\dfrac{\sqrt{2}}{2}$ (C) $\sqrt{2}$ (D) 2

(E)   It cannot be determined from the information given.

3.   For all positive real numbers, $a * b$ is defined by $a * b = \dfrac{ab}{a + b}$. If $2 * x = 3 * 4$, then $x =$

(A) 12   (B) 8   (C) 6   (D) 4   (E) 3

4.   For what real numbers x is $y = 2^{-x}$ a negative number?

(A)   All real x (B) $x > 0$ only
(C) $x \geqq 0$ only   (D) $x < 0$ only
(E)   No real x

5.   Given the two complex numbers, $Z = p + qi$ and $\bar{Z} = p - qi$ where p and q are real numbers. Which of the following statements involving Z and $\bar{Z}$ is true?

(A) $Z = -\bar{Z}$ (B) $(\bar{Z})^2$ is a real number.
(C) $Z \cdot Z$ is a real number.   (D) $(\bar{Z})^2 = Z^2$
(E) $Z^2 = -(\bar{Z})^2$

6.   If $0 < y < x < \dfrac{\pi}{2}$, which of the following are true?

      I. $\sin y < \sin x$
     II. $\cos y < \cos x$
    III. $\tan y < \tan x$

(A) None   (B) I and II only
(C) I and III only   (D) II and III only
(E) I, II, and III

7. The base of an equilateral triangle lies on the x-axis. What is the sum of the slopes of the three sides?

   (A) -1 **(B)** 0 **(C)** 1 **(D)** $2\sqrt{3}$ **(E)** $1 + 2\sqrt{3}$

Answers to Mathematics Level II Questions

1. $f(-1) = (-1)^2 - (-1)^3$
   $= 1 + 1$
   $= 2$

   The correct answer is **(A)**.

2. $\sin x = 2 \cos x$
   $\tan x = \dfrac{\sin x}{\cos x} = \dfrac{2 \cos x}{\cos x} = 2$

   The correct answer is **(D)**.

3. $a * b = \dfrac{ab}{a + b}$

   $2 * x = \dfrac{2x}{2 + x}$

   $3 * 4 = \dfrac{12}{7}$

   $\dfrac{2x}{2 + x} = \dfrac{12}{7}$
   $14x = 24 + 12x$
   $2x = 24$
   $x = 12$

   The correct answer is **(A)**.

4. $y = 2^{-x}$ can never be negative.

   The correct answer is **(E)**.

5. $Z \cdot \bar{Z} = (p + qi)(p - qi) = p^2 - q^2 i^2 = p^2 - q^2$

   The correct answer is **(C)**.

6. If $0 < y < x < \dfrac{\pi}{2}$, then $\sin y < \sin x$, $\cos y > \cos x$, and $\tan y < \tan x$.
   The correct answer is **(C)**.

7. The slope of the base is 0. The slope of the equal sides are equal but with opposite signs. Thus, the sum is 0.

   The correct answer is **(B)**.

Scoring Tests

Most standardized tests are scored by machines. The machine-scoring method of the SAT is done in three steps.

1. The answer sheet is "read" by a scanning machine and the oval filled in for each question is recorded on a computer tape.

2. The computer compares the oval filled in for each question with the correct response. Each correct answer receives one point; omitted questions do not count toward the score. For each wrong answer, a fraction of a point is subtracted to correct for random guessing. For questions with five answer choices, one-fourth of a point is subtracted for each wrong response; for questions with four answer choices, one-third of a point is subtracted for each wrong response. The result of these calculations is the raw score. Obtaining raw scores frequently involves the rounding of fractional numbers to the nearest whole number.

3. Raw test scores are then placed on the College Board scale of 200 to 800 points through a process that adjusts scores to account for minor differences in difficulty between different editions of the test. This process, known as equating, is performed so that the student's reported score is not affected by the edition of the test taken or by the abilities of the group with whom the student takes the test. As a result of placing SAT scores on the College Board scale, scores earned by students at different times can be compared.

When planning to take any standardized test, speak with a teacher or a guidance counselor for help in deciding which test should be taken and when it should be taken. Also, check with the College Admission office for the tests required for admission. Once a decision has been made to take a certain test, write for materials as soon as possible and complete the registration as quickly as possible. The testing service will provide information as well as sample problems. Read the material thoroughly and work the sample problems so that you will be as prepared as possible for the test.

A-2 Matrices

Matrices and Determinants

A **matrix** is any rectangular array of terms called **elements**. The elements of a matrix are arranged in rows and columns and are usually enclosed by brackets. A matrix with m rows and n columns is an **m × n matrix** (read "m by n"). The **dimensions** of the matrix are m and n.

$$\begin{bmatrix} 5 & -7 \\ 10 & 2 \end{bmatrix} \qquad \begin{bmatrix} 1 & -4 \\ 0 & 8 \\ 9 & 6 \end{bmatrix}$$

Large parentheses are sometimes used instead of brackets.

2 × 2 Matrix   **3 × 2 Matrix**

A **square matrix** has the same number of rows as columns. A matrix of **nth order** has n rows and n columns.

Each square matrix has a **determinant**. The determinant of $\begin{bmatrix} 8 & 7 \\ 4 & 5 \end{bmatrix}$ is denoted by det $\begin{bmatrix} 8 & 7 \\ 4 & 5 \end{bmatrix}$ or $\begin{vmatrix} 8 & 7 \\ 4 & 5 \end{vmatrix}$. The value of a second order determinant is defined as follows.

> The value of det $\begin{bmatrix} a_1 & b_1 \\ a_2 & b_2 \end{bmatrix}$ or $\begin{vmatrix} a_1 & b_1 \\ a_2 & b_2 \end{vmatrix} = a_1 b_2 - a_2 b_1.$

Second Order Determinant

Example

1. Find the value of $\begin{vmatrix} 7 & 9 \\ 3 & 6 \end{vmatrix}$.

$$\begin{vmatrix} 7 & 9 \\ 3 & 6 \end{vmatrix} = 7(6) - 3(9)$$
$$= 42 - 27$$
$$= 15$$

To evaluate a determinant of the nth order, expand the determinant by minors, using the elements in the first row. The **minor** of an element is a determinant of $(n - 1)$th order. This minor can be found by deleting the row and column containing the element. The expansion of a third order determinant is shown below. Notice that the signs of the terms alternate, with the first term being positive.

$$\begin{vmatrix} a_1 & b_1 & c_1 \\ a_2 & b_2 & c_2 \\ a_3 & b_3 & c_3 \end{vmatrix} = a_1 \begin{vmatrix} b_2 & c_2 \\ b_3 & c_3 \end{vmatrix} - b_1 \begin{vmatrix} a_2 & c_2 \\ a_3 & c_3 \end{vmatrix} + c_1 \begin{vmatrix} a_2 & b_2 \\ a_3 & b_3 \end{vmatrix}$$

**Third Order
Determinant**

Determinants can be used to solve systems of linear equations. If a system of two equations in two variables is given, the solution set, if it exists as a single ordered pair, can be found by using Cramer's rule.

Notice the positions of the constants, c_1 and c_2, in the top determinants.

The solution to $\begin{aligned} a_1x + b_1y &= c_1 \\ a_2x + b_2y &= c_2 \end{aligned}$ is (x, y) where

Cramer's Rule

$$x = \frac{\begin{vmatrix} c_1 & b_1 \\ c_2 & b_2 \end{vmatrix}}{\begin{vmatrix} a_1 & b_1 \\ a_2 & b_2 \end{vmatrix}} \text{ and } y = \frac{\begin{vmatrix} a_1 & c_1 \\ a_2 & c_2 \end{vmatrix}}{\begin{vmatrix} a_1 & b_1 \\ a_2 & b_2 \end{vmatrix}} \text{ and } \begin{vmatrix} a_1 & b_1 \\ a_2 & b_2 \end{vmatrix} \neq 0.$$

Example

2. Use Cramer's rule to solve the following system of equations.
$$2x - 3y = 12$$
$$5x + 9y = 63$$

$$x = \frac{\begin{vmatrix} 12 & -3 \\ 63 & 9 \end{vmatrix}}{\begin{vmatrix} 2 & -3 \\ 5 & 9 \end{vmatrix}} \qquad y = \frac{\begin{vmatrix} 2 & 12 \\ 5 & 63 \end{vmatrix}}{\begin{vmatrix} 2 & -3 \\ 5 & 9 \end{vmatrix}}$$

$$= \frac{297}{33} \qquad\qquad = \frac{66}{33}$$

$$= 9 \qquad\qquad\qquad = 2$$

The solution is $(9, 2)$.

This method can be extended to solve a system of n linear equations in n variables. The determinant in each denominator contains the coefficients of the variables arranged in order and is called the **determinant of the system**. If the determinant of the system is equal to zero, there is no unique common solution.

Exercises

Written Find the value of each determinant using expansion by minors.

1. $\begin{vmatrix} 7 & 1 & 6 \\ 3 & -1 & 4 \\ -2 & 3 & 0 \end{vmatrix}$

2. $\begin{vmatrix} 2 & 3 & 4 \\ 5 & 6 & 7 \\ 8 & 9 & 10 \end{vmatrix}$

3. $\begin{vmatrix} 6 & 7 & 4 \\ -2 & -4 & 3 \\ 1 & 1 & 1 \end{vmatrix}$

4. $\begin{vmatrix} 2 & 4 & 6 \\ 1 & 2 & 3 \\ 3 & -1 & 4 \end{vmatrix}$

5. $\begin{vmatrix} 3 & 0 & 2 \\ 0 & -1 & 5 \\ 6 & 7 & 0 \end{vmatrix}$

6. $\begin{vmatrix} 4 & 2 & -3 \\ 5 & 1 & 0 \\ -2 & 1 & 11 \end{vmatrix}$

Solve each system of equations using Cramer's rule.

7. $5x - y = 16$
   $2x + 3y = 3$

8. $-7x + y = 19$
   $2x - y = -9$

9. $2x + 5y = 23$
   $3x - 2y = 6$

10. $2x + y = 13$
    $x - 5y = 1$

11. $x - y = 8$
    $3x + 2y = 4$

12. $7x + 8y = -5$
    $4x + 9y = 6$

13. $x + 6y = 6$
    $3x - 2y = 8$

14. $3x - y = 3$
    $6x + 5y = -1$

15. $5x + y = 0$
    $10x - 3y = -15$

Addition of Matrices

Many of the properties and operations of real numbers also apply to matrices. For example, two matrices are equal if and only if they have the same dimensions and are identical, element by element.

Example

1. Find the values of x and y for which the following equation is true.

$$\begin{bmatrix} y - 3 \\ y \end{bmatrix} = \begin{bmatrix} x \\ 2x \end{bmatrix}$$

Since corresponding elements are equal, the following equations are true.

$y - 3 = x$
$y = 2x$

Solve the system of equations.

$2x - 3 = x$
$x = 3$
$y = 2(3) \text{ or } 6$

The matrices are equal if $x = 3$ and $y = 6$.

The elements of an $m \times n$ matrix can be represented using double subscript notation.

$$\begin{bmatrix} a_{11} & a_{12} & a_{13} & \cdot & \cdot & \cdot & a_{1n} \\ a_{21} & a_{22} & a_{23} & \cdot & \cdot & \cdot & a_{2n} \\ \cdots\cdots\cdots\cdots\cdots\cdots\cdots\cdots \\ a_{m1} & a_{m2} & a_{m3} & \cdot & \cdot & \cdot & a_{mn} \end{bmatrix}$$

a_{ij} would be the element in the i th row and the j th column.

Matrices with the same dimensions can be added. The *ij*th element of the sum of *A* and *B* is $a_{ij} + b_{ij}$. Addition is not defined for matrices with different dimensions.

The sum of two *m* × *n* matrices is an *m* × *n* matrix in which the elements are the sum of the corresponding elements of the given matrices.

Addition of Matrices

Examples

2. Find the sum of *A* and *B* if $A = \begin{bmatrix} 2 & 1 & -3 \\ 1 & 4 & 0 \end{bmatrix}$ and $B = \begin{bmatrix} -2 & 3 & 2 \\ 7 & 5 & -6 \end{bmatrix}$.

$$\begin{aligned} A + B &= \begin{bmatrix} 2 & 1 & -3 \\ 1 & 4 & 0 \end{bmatrix} + \begin{bmatrix} -2 & 3 & 2 \\ 7 & 5 & -6 \end{bmatrix} \\ &= \begin{bmatrix} 2 + -2 & 1 + 3 & -3 + 2 \\ 1 + 7 & 4 + 5 & 0 + -6 \end{bmatrix} \\ &= \begin{bmatrix} 0 & 4 & -1 \\ 8 & 9 & -6 \end{bmatrix} \end{aligned}$$

3. Show that $A + B = B + A$ where $A = \begin{bmatrix} a_{11} & a_{12} \\ a_{21} & a_{22} \end{bmatrix}$ and $B = \begin{bmatrix} b_{11} & b_{12} \\ b_{21} & b_{22} \end{bmatrix}$.

$$\begin{aligned} A + B &= \begin{bmatrix} a_{11} + b_{11} & a_{12} + b_{12} \\ a_{21} + b_{21} & a_{22} + b_{22} \end{bmatrix} \\ &= \begin{bmatrix} b_{11} + a_{11} & b_{12} + a_{12} \\ b_{21} + a_{21} & b_{22} + a_{22} \end{bmatrix} \\ &= B + A \end{aligned}$$

Therefore, $A + B = B + A$.

Matrices, like real numbers, have identity elements. For every matrix *A*, another matrix can be found such that their sum is *A*. For example, if $A = \begin{bmatrix} a_{11} & a_{12} \\ a_{21} & a_{22} \end{bmatrix}$, then $\begin{bmatrix} a_{11} & a_{12} \\ a_{21} & a_{22} \end{bmatrix} + \begin{bmatrix} 0 & 0 \\ 0 & 0 \end{bmatrix} = \begin{bmatrix} a_{11} & a_{12} \\ a_{21} & a_{22} \end{bmatrix}$. The matrix $\begin{bmatrix} 0 & 0 \\ 0 & 0 \end{bmatrix}$ is called a **zero matrix**. Thus, the **identity matrix under addition** for any *m* × *n* matrix is an *m* × *n* zero matrix.

Matrices also have **additive inverses**. If $A = \begin{bmatrix} a_{11} & a_{12} \\ a_{21} & a_{22} \end{bmatrix}$, the matrix which must be added to A to obtain a zero matrix is $\begin{bmatrix} -a_{11} & -a_{12} \\ -a_{21} & -a_{22} \end{bmatrix}$ or $-A$. Therefore $-A$ is the additive inverse of A. The additive inverse is used when subtracting matrices.

Exercises

Written Use matrices A, B, and C to find each sum or difference.

$$A = \begin{bmatrix} 1 & 5 & 7 \\ 5 & 2 & -6 \\ 3 & 0 & -2 \end{bmatrix} \qquad B = \begin{bmatrix} -3 & 6 & -9 \\ 4 & -3 & 0 \\ 8 & -2 & 3 \end{bmatrix} \qquad C = \begin{bmatrix} 6 & 9 & -4 \\ -11 & 13 & -8 \\ 20 & 4 & -2 \end{bmatrix}$$

1. $A + B$
2. $A + C$
3. $B + C$
4. $(A + B) + C$
5. $B + -A$
6. $C - B$
7. $B - C$
8. $C - A$

Multiplication of Matrices

A matrix can be multiplied by a constant called a **scalar**. The product of a scalar k and a matrix A is defined as follows.

> The product of an $m \times n$ matrix A and a scalar k is an $m \times n$ matrix kA. Each element of kA is equal to k times the corresponding element of A.

Scalar Product

Example

1. Multiply the matrix $\begin{bmatrix} 4 & 3 & -2 \\ -2 & 7 & -9 \end{bmatrix}$ by 6.

$$6 \begin{bmatrix} 4 & 3 & -2 \\ -2 & 7 & -9 \end{bmatrix} = \begin{bmatrix} 6(4) & 6(3) & 6(-2) \\ 6(-2) & 6(7) & 6(-9) \end{bmatrix} = \begin{bmatrix} 24 & 18 & -12 \\ -12 & 42 & -54 \end{bmatrix}$$

A matrix can also be multiplied by another matrix, provided that the first matrix has the same number of columns as the second matrix has rows. The product of the two matrices is found by multiplying rows and columns. The product of a row $[a\ b\ c]$ and a column $\begin{bmatrix} x \\ y \\ z \end{bmatrix}$ is the real number $ax + by + cz$.

The row and column must have the same number of elements.

Suppose $A = \begin{bmatrix} a_1 & b_1 \\ a_2 & b_2 \end{bmatrix}$ and $X = \begin{bmatrix} x_1 & y_1 \\ x_2 & y_2 \end{bmatrix}$. Each element of matrix AX is the product of one row of matrix A and one column of matrix X.

$$AX = \begin{bmatrix} a_1 & b_1 \\ a_2 & b_2 \end{bmatrix} \begin{bmatrix} x_1 & y_1 \\ x_2 & y_2 \end{bmatrix} = \begin{bmatrix} a_1x_1 + b_1x_2 & a_1y_1 + b_1y_2 \\ a_2x_1 + b_2x_2 & a_2y_1 + b_2y_2 \end{bmatrix}$$

The product of an $m \times n$ matrix A and an $n \times r$ matrix B is an $m \times r$ matrix AB. The ijth element of AB is the product of the ith row of A and the jth column of B.

Product of Matrices

Example

2. Find the product of A and B if $A = \begin{bmatrix} 4 & 3 \\ 1 & 0 \end{bmatrix}$ and $B = \begin{bmatrix} 1 & 7 \\ 8 & 1 \end{bmatrix}$.

$$AB = \begin{bmatrix} 4(1) + 3(8) & 4(7) + 3(1) \\ 1(1) + 0(8) & 1(7) + 0(1) \end{bmatrix}$$

$$= \begin{bmatrix} 28 & 31 \\ 1 & 7 \end{bmatrix}$$

Exercises

Written   Use matrices A, B, and C to find each product.

$$A = \begin{bmatrix} 7 & 0 \\ 5 & 3 \end{bmatrix} \qquad B = \begin{bmatrix} 2 & 4 \\ 8 & -4 \\ -2 & 6 \end{bmatrix} \qquad C = \begin{bmatrix} 3 & -3 & 6 \\ 5 & 4 & -2 \end{bmatrix}$$

1. $3A$
2. $4B$
3. $2C$
4. $-5A$
5. BA
6. BC
7. CB
8. AC
9. AA
10. $(CB)A$
11. $B(AC)$
12. $-4BC$

Inverses of Matrices

The identity matrix under multiplication for any matrix A is the matrix I, such that $IA = A$ and $AI = A$. A second order matrix can be represented by $\begin{bmatrix} a_1 & b_1 \\ a_2 & b_2 \end{bmatrix}$. Since $\begin{bmatrix} a_1 & b_1 \\ a_2 & b_2 \end{bmatrix} \begin{bmatrix} 1 & 0 \\ 0 & 1 \end{bmatrix} =$ $\begin{bmatrix} a_1 & b_1 \\ a_2 & b_2 \end{bmatrix}$, the matrix $\begin{bmatrix} 1 & 0 \\ 0 & 1 \end{bmatrix}$ is the identity matrix under multiplication.

> **The identity matrix of nth order, I_n, is the square matrix whose elements in the main diagonal, from upper left to lower right, are 1's, while all other elements are 0's.**

Identity Matrix

Multiplicative inverses also exist for some matrices. Suppose A is equal to $\begin{bmatrix} a_1 & b_1 \\ a_2 & b_2 \end{bmatrix}$, a non-zero matrix of second order. The product of a matrix A and its inverse matrix A^{-1}, designated $\begin{bmatrix} x_1 & y_1 \\ x_2 & y_2 \end{bmatrix}$, must equal the identity matrix for multiplication.

$$\begin{bmatrix} a_1 & b_1 \\ a_2 & b_2 \end{bmatrix} \begin{bmatrix} x_1 & y_1 \\ x_2 & y_2 \end{bmatrix} = \begin{bmatrix} 1 & 0 \\ 0 & 1 \end{bmatrix}$$

$$\begin{bmatrix} a_1x_1 + b_1x_2 & a_1y_1 + b_1y_2 \\ a_2x_1 + b_2x_2 & a_2y_1 + b_2y_2 \end{bmatrix} = \begin{bmatrix} 1 & 0 \\ 0 & 1 \end{bmatrix}$$

From the previous matrix equation, write two systems of linear equations.

$$a_1x_1 + b_1x_2 = 1 \qquad a_1y_1 + b_1y_2 = 0$$
$$a_2x_1 + b_2x_2 = 0 \qquad a_2y_1 + b_2y_2 = 1$$

By solving each pair of equations simultaneously, you can obtain values for x_1, x_2, y_1, and y_2.

$$x_1 = \frac{b_2}{a_1b_2 - a_2b_1} \qquad y_1 = \frac{-b_1}{a_1b_2 - a_2b_1}$$

$$x_2 = \frac{-a_2}{a_1b_2 - a_2b_1} \qquad y_2 = \frac{a_1}{a_1b_2 - a_2b_1}$$

The denominator $a_1b_2 - a_2b_1$ is equal to the determinant of A. If the determinant of $A \neq 0$, the inverse exists and can be defined.

> If $A = \begin{bmatrix} a_1 & b_1 \\ a_2 & b_2 \end{bmatrix}$ and $\begin{vmatrix} a_1 & b_1 \\ a_2 & b_2 \end{vmatrix} \neq 0$, then
>
> $$A^{-1} = \frac{1}{\begin{vmatrix} a_1 & b_1 \\ a_2 & b_2 \end{vmatrix}} \begin{bmatrix} b_2 & -b_1 \\ -a_2 & a_1 \end{bmatrix}$$

Inverse of a Second-Order Matrix

Example

1. Find the inverse under multiplication of the matrix $\begin{bmatrix} 3 & -1 \\ 4 & 2 \end{bmatrix}$.

$\begin{vmatrix} 3 & -1 \\ 4 & 2 \end{vmatrix} = 3(2) - 4(-1) = 10$ The inverse is $\frac{1}{10}\begin{bmatrix} 2 & 1 \\ -4 & 3 \end{bmatrix}$ or $\begin{bmatrix} \frac{1}{5} & \frac{1}{10} \\ -\frac{2}{5} & \frac{3}{10} \end{bmatrix}$

Matrix equations can be solved using inverse matrices.

Example

2. Find matrix M if $\begin{bmatrix} 2 & 1 \\ -3 & 2 \end{bmatrix} M = \begin{bmatrix} 8 & -9 \\ 5 & -3 \end{bmatrix}$.

$\dfrac{1}{\begin{vmatrix} 2 & 1 \\ -3 & 2 \end{vmatrix}} \begin{bmatrix} 2 & -1 \\ 3 & 2 \end{bmatrix} \begin{bmatrix} 2 & 1 \\ -3 & 2 \end{bmatrix} M = \dfrac{1}{\begin{vmatrix} 2 & 1 \\ -3 & 2 \end{vmatrix}} \begin{bmatrix} 2 & -1 \\ 3 & 2 \end{bmatrix} \begin{bmatrix} 8 & -9 \\ 5 & -3 \end{bmatrix}$

$\dfrac{1}{7}\begin{bmatrix} 7 & 0 \\ 0 & 7 \end{bmatrix} M = \dfrac{1}{7}\begin{bmatrix} 11 & -15 \\ 34 & -33 \end{bmatrix}$

$M = \begin{bmatrix} \frac{11}{7} & \frac{-15}{7} \\ \frac{34}{7} & \frac{-33}{7} \end{bmatrix}$

Notice that the inverse is written at the left of both sides of the equation. This is necessary since multiplication of matrices is not commutative.

Exercises

Written Find the inverse of each matrix if it exists.

1. $\begin{bmatrix} 1 & 3 \\ 2 & 5 \end{bmatrix}$ 2. $\begin{bmatrix} -1 & -2 \\ 3 & -6 \end{bmatrix}$ 3. $\begin{bmatrix} 4 & 3 \\ 8 & 6 \end{bmatrix}$ 4. $\begin{bmatrix} 7 & 40 \\ 2 & 12 \end{bmatrix}$

5. $\begin{bmatrix} 5 & 9 \\ 7 & -3 \end{bmatrix}$ 6. $\begin{bmatrix} 4 & 1 \\ -6 & 2 \end{bmatrix}$ 7. $\begin{bmatrix} -9 & 3 \\ 14 & -3 \end{bmatrix}$ 8. $\begin{bmatrix} 29 & -32 \\ 16 & -12 \end{bmatrix}$

Find matrix X for each of the following.

9. $\begin{bmatrix} 2 & -1 \\ 3 & 5 \end{bmatrix} X = \begin{bmatrix} 4 & 3 \\ 1 & -2 \end{bmatrix}$ 10. $\begin{bmatrix} 5 & 1 \\ -2 & 2 \end{bmatrix} X + \begin{bmatrix} 3 & -2 \\ 4 & 6 \end{bmatrix} = \begin{bmatrix} 4 & 3 \\ 10 & 2 \end{bmatrix}$

Matrix Solutions

When considering the algebraic solution of a system of equations, once the variables equal signs and constants have been arranged similarly in the equations, the remaining work involves only the coefficients. The array of numbers can be considered a matrix.

So matrices can be used to solve systems of linear equations. The coefficients and constants of the system of equations shown below can be written in the form of a 3 × 4 **augmented matrix.**

System of Equations

$$x - 2y + z = 7$$
$$3x + y - z = 2$$
$$2x + 3y + 2z = 7$$

Augmented Matrix

$$\begin{bmatrix} 1 & -2 & 1 & 7 \\ 3 & 1 & -1 & 2 \\ 2 & 3 & 2 & 7 \end{bmatrix}$$

An augmented matrix is an array of the coefficients and constants of a system of equations.

This matrix can be modified by transforming rows since each row represents an equation. Each change of the matrix represents a corresponding change of the system. Any operation which results in an equivalent system of equations is permitted for the matrix.

Combinations of the steps can also be used. Therefore the operations of subtraction and division can be used.

Any of the following row operations can be used to transform an augmented matrix.

1. **Interchange any two rows.**
2. **Replace any row with a non-zero multiple of that row.**
3. **Replace any row with the sum of that row and another row.**

Row Operations on Matrices

Example

1. **Solve the system of equations by using row operations.**

$$x - 2y + z = 7$$
$$3x + y - z = 2$$
$$2x + 3y + 2z = 7$$

First, write the augmented matrix.

$$\begin{bmatrix} 1 & -2 & 1 & 7 \\ 3 & 1 & -1 & 2 \\ 2 & 3 & 2 & 7 \end{bmatrix}$$

The objective is to get as many zeros in the matrix as possible.

Multiply row one by −3 and add the result to row two.

$$\begin{bmatrix} 1 & -2 & 1 & 7 \\ 0 & 7 & -4 & -19 \\ 2 & 3 & 2 & 7 \end{bmatrix}$$

A zero is obtained in the a_{21} position.

Multiply row one by −2 and add the result to row three.

$$\begin{bmatrix} 1 & -2 & 1 & 7 \\ 0 & 7 & -4 & -19 \\ 0 & 7 & 0 & -7 \end{bmatrix}$$

A zero is obtained in the a_{31} position.

Multiply row two by −1 and add the result to row three.

$$\begin{bmatrix} 1 & -2 & 1 & 7 \\ 0 & 7 & -4 & -19 \\ 0 & 0 & 4 & 12 \end{bmatrix}$$

Add row three to row two.

$$\begin{bmatrix} 1 & -2 & 1 & 7 \\ 0 & 7 & 0 & -7 \\ 0 & 0 & 4 & 12 \end{bmatrix}$$

Multiply row three by $\frac{1}{4}$.

$$\begin{bmatrix} 1 & -2 & 1 & 7 \\ 0 & 7 & 0 & -7 \\ 0 & 0 & 1 & 3 \end{bmatrix}$$

The system of equations which this matrix represents could be easily solved by substitution.

$$x - 2y + z = 7$$
$$7y = -7$$
$$z = 3$$

Multiply row three by -1 and add the result to row one.

$$\begin{bmatrix} 1 & -2 & 0 & 4 \\ 0 & 7 & 0 & -7 \\ 0 & 0 & 1 & 3 \end{bmatrix}$$

Multiply row two by $\frac{1}{7}$.

$$\begin{bmatrix} 1 & -2 & 0 & 4 \\ 0 & 1 & 0 & -1 \\ 0 & 0 & 1 & 3 \end{bmatrix}$$

Multiply row two by 2 and add the result to row one.

$$\begin{bmatrix} 1 & 0 & 0 & 2 \\ 0 & 1 & 0 & -1 \\ 0 & 0 & 1 & 3 \end{bmatrix}$$

Notice the positions of the 1's and 0's.

Thus, $x = 2$, $y = -1$, and $z = 3$.

Exercises

Written   Solve each system of equations using augmented matrices.

1. $3x + 5y = 7$
   $6x - y = -8$

2. $4x - 7y = -2$
   $x + 2y = 7$

3. $3x + 3y = -9$
   $-2x + y = -4$

4. $x - y + z = 3$
   $2y - z = 1$
   $2y - x + 1 = 0$

5. $x + y + z = -2$
   $2x - 3y + z = -11$
   $-x + 2y - z = 8$

6. $2x + 6y + 8z = 5$
   $-2x + 9y - 12z = -1$
   $4x + 6y - 4z = 3$

Homogeneous Systems and Systems Without Unique Solutions

Matrix methods can also be applied to homogeneous systems.

Homogeneous systems are systems of equations in which each equation is set equal to zero.

Examples

1. Solve the homogeneous system $\begin{cases} 2x + y + 3z = 0 \\ x + 2y \quad\;\;\, = 0. \\ y + z \quad\;\;\, = 0 \end{cases}$

Write the matrix for the system.

$$\begin{bmatrix} 2 & 1 & 3 & 0 \\ 1 & 2 & 0 & 0 \\ 0 & 1 & 1 & 0 \end{bmatrix}$$

Exchange row one and row two.

$$\begin{bmatrix} 1 & 2 & 0 & 0 \\ 2 & 1 & 3 & 0 \\ 0 & 1 & 1 & 0 \end{bmatrix}$$

Multiply row one by -2 and add the results to row 2.

$$\begin{bmatrix} 1 & 2 & 0 & 0 \\ 0 & -3 & 3 & 0 \\ 0 & 1 & 1 & 0 \end{bmatrix}$$

Divide row two by -3.

$$\begin{bmatrix} 1 & 2 & 0 & 0 \\ 0 & 1 & -1 & 0 \\ 0 & 1 & 1 & 0 \end{bmatrix}$$

Subtract row two from row three.

$$\begin{bmatrix} 1 & 2 & 0 & 0 \\ 0 & 1 & -1 & 0 \\ 0 & 0 & 2 & 0 \end{bmatrix}$$

Divide row three by two.

$$\begin{bmatrix} 1 & 2 & 0 & 0 \\ 0 & 1 & -1 & 0 \\ 0 & 0 & 1 & 0 \end{bmatrix}$$

Add row three to row two.

$$\begin{bmatrix} 1 & 2 & 0 & 0 \\ 0 & 1 & 0 & 0 \\ 0 & 0 & 1 & 0 \end{bmatrix}$$

Multiply row two by -2 and add the results to row one.

$$\begin{bmatrix} 1 & 0 & 0 & 0 \\ 0 & 1 & 0 & 0 \\ 0 & 0 & 1 & 0 \end{bmatrix}$$

This matrix is equivalent to the system of equations $\begin{cases} x = 0 \\ y = 0 \\ z = 0 \end{cases}$ so the solution is the trivial solution.

2. **Solve the homogeneous system** $\begin{cases} 3x - 2y + 6z = 0 \\ 3x + 2y - 6z = 0 \end{cases}$.

Write the matrix for the system.

$$\begin{bmatrix} 3 & -2 & 6 & 0 \\ 3 & 2 & -6 & 0 \\ 0 & 0 & 0 & 0 \end{bmatrix}$$

Subtract row one from row two.

$$\begin{bmatrix} 3 & -2 & 6 & 0 \\ 0 & 4 & -12 & 0 \\ 0 & 0 & 0 & 0 \end{bmatrix}$$

Divide row two by 4.

$$\begin{bmatrix} 3 & -2 & 6 & 0 \\ 0 & 1 & -3 & 0 \\ 0 & 0 & 0 & 0 \end{bmatrix}$$

Multiply row two by 2 and add the results to row one.

$$\begin{bmatrix} 3 & 0 & 0 & 0 \\ 0 & 1 & -3 & 0 \\ 0 & 0 & 0 & 0 \end{bmatrix}$$

The equivalent algebraic system is $\begin{cases} 3x = 0 \\ y - 3z = 0 \\ 0z = 0 \end{cases}$.

The final row of zeros indicates that z may take on any value, say k. Then $y = 3k$ and $x = 0$, so the general solution is $(0, 3k, k)$, that is, there are an infinite number of solutions to the system.

For non-homogeneous equations it is possible for the solution set to contain *no* values or *an infinite number* of values. What happens when each of these situations is treated by matrix methods?

Examples

3. Solve the system $\begin{cases} x + 2y - 2z = 6 \\ -2x - 3y + 5z = -7 \\ 3x + 6y - 6z = 19 \end{cases}$.

Write the matrix for the system.

$$\begin{bmatrix} 1 & 2 & -2 & 6 \\ -2 & -3 & 5 & -7 \\ 3 & 6 & -6 & 19 \end{bmatrix}$$

Multiply row one by 2 and add the results to row two. Multiply row one by -3 and add the results to row three.

$$\begin{bmatrix} 1 & 2 & -2 & 6 \\ 0 & 1 & 1 & 5 \\ 0 & 0 & 0 & 1 \end{bmatrix}$$

From the last row it is clearly seen that there is no solution possible.

4. Solve the system $\begin{cases} x + 3y - 2z = -6 \\ -x + 2y + 3z = -4 \\ -2x - 6y + 4z = 12 \end{cases}$.

Write the matrix for the system.

$$\begin{bmatrix} 1 & 3 & -2 & -6 \\ -1 & 2 & 3 & -4 \\ -2 & -6 & 4 & 12 \end{bmatrix}$$

Add row one to row two. Multiply row one by 2 and add to row three.

$$\begin{bmatrix} 1 & 3 & -2 & -6 \\ 0 & 5 & 1 & -10 \\ 0 & 0 & 0 & 0 \end{bmatrix}$$

Divide row two by 5. Multiply row two by -3 and add to row one.

$$\begin{bmatrix} 1 & 0 & -\dfrac{13}{5} & 0 \\ 0 & 1 & \dfrac{1}{5} & -2 \\ 0 & 0 & 0 & 0 \end{bmatrix}$$

The equivalent system of equations is $\begin{cases} x - \dfrac{13}{5}z = 0 \\ y + \dfrac{1}{5}z = 2 \\ 0z = 0 \end{cases}$.

The general solution is given by $x = \dfrac{13}{5}k$, $y = 2 - \dfrac{1}{5}k$, and $z = k$.

Exercises

Written Solve each system of equations using matrix methods.

1. $\begin{cases} x - 3y + 2z = 0 \\ x - 2y - z = 0 \\ 2x - y + 3z = 0 \end{cases}$

2. $\begin{cases} x - 3y - z = 0 \\ 3x + y - 2z = 0 \\ 4x + 2y - z = 0 \end{cases}$

3. $\begin{cases} x - 2y + 3z = 3 \\ 2x + 5y - 3z = 2 \\ 2x + 5y - 3z = 2 \end{cases}$

4. $\begin{cases} x + 2y - 3z = 5 \\ 2x + 4y - 6z = -10 \\ y + 5z = 2 \end{cases}$

5. $\begin{cases} x + 6z - 2w = 5 \\ x + y + 3z = 3 \\ 2x + 13z - 3w = 12 \end{cases}$

6. $\begin{cases} x + 6y - 3z = 0 \\ 3x + 10y - z = 0 \end{cases}$

7. $\begin{cases} x - y - z = 0 \\ 3x - y + 3z = 0 \\ 4x - 3y - z = 0 \end{cases}$

8. $\begin{cases} 2x - y + 3z = 4 \\ 3x + 2y - z = 5 \\ 5x + 8y - 9z = 9 \end{cases}$

9. $\begin{cases} x + y + z = 1 \\ 2x + y + z = 2 \\ x + 2y + 2z = 1 \end{cases}$

10. $\begin{cases} 6x - y + 2z = 0 \\ -x + 3y - z = 0 \\ 2x + 7y = 0 \end{cases}$

11. $\begin{cases} x + 3y + z = 0 \\ x + y = z \\ x = 2y + 4z \end{cases}$

12. $\begin{cases} 4x = 6y - 2z + 9 \\ 5 - 5z + 4y = -x \\ 3z - 3 = 5x - 2y \end{cases}$

Summary

1. A matrix is a rectangular array of elements. It has dimensions $m \times n$ if it contains m rows and n columns. (524)

2. The value of det $\begin{bmatrix} a_1 & b_1 \\ a_2 & b_2 \end{bmatrix}$ or $\begin{vmatrix} a_1 & b_1 \\ a_2 & b_2 \end{vmatrix} = a_1 b_2 - a_2 b_1$. (524)

3. Cramer's Rule: The solution to $\begin{aligned} a_1 x + b_1 y = c_1 \\ a_2 x + b_2 y = c_2 \end{aligned}$ is (x, y)

   where $x = \dfrac{\begin{vmatrix} c_1 & b_1 \\ c_2 & b_2 \end{vmatrix}}{\begin{vmatrix} a_1 & b_1 \\ a_2 & b_2 \end{vmatrix}}$ and $y = \dfrac{\begin{vmatrix} a_1 & c_1 \\ a_2 & c_2 \end{vmatrix}}{\begin{vmatrix} a_1 & b_1 \\ a_2 & b_2 \end{vmatrix}}$ and $\begin{vmatrix} a_1 & b_1 \\ a_2 & b_2 \end{vmatrix} \neq 0$.

   (525)

4. The sum of two $m \times n$ matrices is an $m \times n$ matrix in which the elements are the sum of the corresponding elements of the given matrices. (527)

5. The product of an $m \times n$ matrix A and a scalar k is an $m \times n$ matrix kA. Each element of kA is equal to k times the corresponding element of A. (528)

6. The product of an $m \times n$ matrix A and an $n \times r$ matrix B is an $m \times r$ matrix AB. The ijth element of AB is the product of the ith row of A and the jth column of B. (529)

7. The identity matrix of nth order, I_n, is the square matrix whose elements in the main diagonal, from upper left to lower right, are 1's, while all other elements are 0's. (530)

8. The inverse of a second-order matrix can be defined as follows. (530)

   If $A = \begin{bmatrix} a_1 & b_1 \\ a_2 & b_2 \end{bmatrix}$ and $\begin{vmatrix} a_1 & b_1 \\ a_2 & b_2 \end{vmatrix} \neq 0$, then

   $$A^{-1} = \frac{1}{\begin{vmatrix} a_1 & b_1 \\ a_2 & b_2 \end{vmatrix}} \begin{bmatrix} b_2 & -b_1 \\ -a_2 & a_1 \end{bmatrix}.$$

9. Any of the following row operations can be used to transpose an augmented matrix. (532)

   1. Interchange any two rows.
   2. Replace any row with a non-zero multiple of that row.
   3. Replace any row with the sum of that row and another row.

VALUES OF TRIGONOMETRIC FUNCTIONS

Angle	Radians r	sin r	csc r	tan r	cot r	sec r	cos r		
0° 00′	0.0000	0.0000	Undefined	0.0000	Undefined	1.000	1.0000	1.5708	90° 00′
10′	.0029	.0029	343.8	.0029	343.8	1.000	1.0000	1.5679	50′
20′	.0058	.0058	171.9	.0058	171.9	1.000	1.0000	1.5650	40′
30′	.0087	.0087	114.6	.0087	114.6	1.000	1.0000	1.5621	30′
40′	.0116	.0116	85.95	.0116	85.94	1.000	0.9999	1.5592	20′
50′	.0145	.0145	68.76	.0145	68.75	1.000	.9999	1.5563	10′
1° 00′	.0175	.0175	57.30	.0175	57.29	1.000	.9998	1.5533	89° 00′
10′	.0204	.0204	49.11	.0204	49.10	1.000	.9998	1.5504	50′
20′	.0233	.0233	42.98	.0233	42.96	1.000	.9997	1.5475	40′
30′	.0262	.0262	38.20	.0262	38.19	1.000	.9997	1.5446	30′
40′	.0291	.0291	34.38	.0291	34.37	1.000	.9996	1.5417	20′
50′	.0320	.0320	31.26	.0320	31.24	1.001	.9995	1.5388	10′
2° 00′	.0349	.0349	28.65	.0349	28.64	1.001	.9994	1.5359	88° 00′
10′	.0378	.0378	26.45	.0378	26.43	1.001	.9993	1.5330	50′
20′	.0407	.0407	24.56	.0407	24.54	1.001	.9992	1.5301	40′
30′	.0436	.0436	22.93	.0437	22.90	1.001	.9990	1.5272	30′
40′	.0465	.0465	21.49	.0466	21.47	1.001	.9989	1.5243	20′
50′	.0495	.0494	20.23	.0495	20.21	1.001	.9988	1.5213	10′
3° 00′	.0524	.0523	19.11	.0524	19.08	1.001	.9986	1.5184	87° 00′
10′	.0553	.0552	18.10	.0553	18.07	1.002	.9985	1.5155	50′
20′	.0582	.0581	17.20	.0582	17.17	1.002	.9983	1.5126	40′
30′	.0611	.0610	16.38	.0612	16.35	1.002	.9981	1.5097	30′
40′	.0640	.0640	15.64	.0641	15.60	1.002	.9980	1.5068	20′
50′	.0669	.0669	14.96	.0670	14.92	1.002	.9978	1.5039	10′
4° 00′	.0698	.0698	14.34	.0699	14.30	1.002	.9976	1.5010	86° 00′
10′	.0727	.0727	13.76	.0729	13.73	1.003	.9974	1.4981	50′
20′	.0756	.0756	13.23	.0758	13.20	1.003	.9971	1.4952	40′
30′	.0785	.0785	12.75	.0787	12.71	1.003	.9969	1.4923	30′
40′	.0814	.0814	12.29	.0816	12.25	1.003	.9967	1.4893	20′
50′	.0844	.0843	11.87	.0846	11.83	1.004	.9964	1.4864	10′
5° 00′	.0873	.0872	11.47	.0875	11.43	1.004	.9962	1.4835	85° 00′
10′	.0902	.0901	11.10	.0904	11.06	1.004	.9959	1.4806	50′
20′	.0931	.0929	10.76	.0934	10.71	1.004	.9957	1.4777	40′
30′	.0960	.0958	10.43	.0963	10.39	1.005	.9954	1.4748	30′
40′	.0989	.0987	10.13	.0992	10.08	1.005	.9951	1.4719	20′
50′	.1018	.1016	9.839	.1022	9.788	1.005	.9948	1.4690	10′
6° 00′	.1047	.1045	9.567	.1051	9.514	1.006	.9945	1.4661	84° 00′
10′	.1076	.1074	9.309	.1080	9.255	1.006	.9942	1.4632	50′
20′	.1105	.1103	9.065	.1110	9.010	1.006	.9939	1.4603	40′
30′	.1134	.1132	8.834	.1139	8.777	1.006	.9936	1.4573	30′
40′	.1164	.1161	8.614	.1169	8.556	1.007	.9932	1.4544	20′
50′	.1193	.1190	8.405	.1198	8.345	1.007	.9929	1.4515	10′
7° 00′	.1222	.1219	8.206	.1228	8.144	1.008	.9925	1.4486	83° 00′
10′	.1251	.1248	8.016	.1257	7.953	1.008	.9922	1.4457	50′
20′	.1280	.1276	7.834	.1287	7.770	1.008	.9918	1.4428	40′
30′	.1309	.1305	7.661	.1317	7.596	1.009	.9914	1.4399	30′
40′	.1338	.1334	7.496	.1346	7.429	1.009	.9911	1.4370	20′
50′	.1367	.1363	7.337	.1376	7.269	1.009	.9907	1.4341	10′
8° 00′	.1396	.1392	7.185	.1405	7.115	1.010	.9903	1.4312	82° 00′
10′	.1425	.1421	7.040	.1435	6.968	1.010	.9899	1.4283	50′
20′	.1454	.1449	6.900	.1465	6.827	1.011	.9894	1.4254	40′
30′	.1484	.1478	6.765	.1495	6.691	1.011	.9890	1.4224	30′
40′	.1513	.1507	6.636	.1524	6.561	1.012	.9886	1.4195	20′
50′	.1542	.1536	6.512	.1554	6.435	1.012	.9881	1.4166	10′
9° 00′	.1571	.1564	6.392	.1584	6.314	1.012	.9877	1.4137	81° 00′
		cos r	sec r	cot r	tan r	csc r	sin r	Radians r	Angle

VALUES OF TRIGONOMETRIC FUNCTIONS

Angle	Radians r	sin r	csc r	tan r	cot r	sec r	cos r		
9° 00′	0.1571	0.1564	6.392	0.1584	6.314	1.012	0.9877	1.4137	81° 00′
10′	.1600	.1593	6.277	.1614	6.197	1.013	.9872	1.4108	50′
20′	.1629	.1622	6.166	.1644	6.084	1.013	.9868	1.4079	40′
30′	.1658	.1650	6.059	.1673	5.976	1.014	.9863	1.4050	30′
40′	.1687	.1679	5.955	.1703	5.871	1.014	.9858	1.4021	20′
50′	.1716	.1708	5.855	.1733	5.769	1.015	.9853	1.3992	10′
10° 00′	.1745	.1736	5.759	.1763	5.671	1.015	.9848	1.3963	80° 00′
10′	.1774	.1765	5.665	.1793	5.576	1.016	.9843	1.3934	50′
20′	.1804	.1794	5.575	.1823	5.485	1.016	.9838	1.3904	40′
30′	.1833	.1822	5.487	.1853	5.396	1.017	.9833	1.3875	30′
40′	.1862	.1851	5.403	.1883	5.309	1.018	.9827	1.3846	20′
50′	.1891	.1880	5.320	.1914	5.226	1.018	.9822	1.3817	10′
11° 00′	.1920	.1908	5.241	.1944	5.145	1.019	.9816	1.3788	79° 00′
10′	.1949	.1937	5.164	.1974	5.066	1.019	.9811	1.3759	50′
20′	.1978	.1965	5.089	.2004	4.989	1.020	.9805	1.3730	40′
30′	.2007	.1994	5.016	.2035	4.915	1.020	.9799	1.3701	30′
40′	.2036	.2022	4.945	.2065	4.843	1.021	.9793	1.3672	20′
50′	.2065	.2051	4.876	.2095	4.773	1.022	.9787	1.3643	10′
12° 00′	.2094	.2079	4.810	.2126	4.705	1.022	.9781	1.3614	78° 00′
10′	.2123	.2108	4.745	.2156	4.638	1.023	.9775	1.3584	50′
20′	.2153	.2136	4.682	.2186	4.574	1.024	.9769	1.3555	40′
30′	.2182	.2164	4.620	.2217	4.511	1.024	.9763	1.3526	30′
40′	.2211	.2193	4.560	.2247	4.449	1.025	.9757	1.3497	20′
50′	.2240	.2221	4.502	.2278	4.390	1.026	.9750	1.3468	10′
13° 00′	.2269	.2250	4.445	.2309	4.331	1.026	.9744	1.3439	77° 00′
10′	.2298	.2278	4.390	.2339	4.275	1.027	.9737	1.3410	50′
20′	.2327	.2306	4.336	.2370	4.219	1.028	.9730	1.3381	40′
30′	.2356	.2334	4.284	.2401	4.165	1.028	.9724	1.3352	30′
40′	.2385	.2363	4.232	.2432	4.113	1.029	.9717	1.3323	20′
50′	.2414	.2391	4.182	.2462	4.061	1.030	.9710	1.3294	10′
14° 00′	.2443	.2419	4.134	.2493	4.011	1.031	.9703	1.3265	76° 00′
10′	.2473	.2447	4.086	.2524	3.962	1.031	.9696	1.3235	50′
20′	.2502	.2476	4.039	.2555	3.914	1.032	.9689	1.3206	40′
30′	.2531	.2504	3.994	.2586	3.867	1.033	.9681	1.3177	30′
40′	.2560	.2532	3.950	.2617	3.821	1.034	.9674	1.3148	20′
50′	.2589	.2560	3.906	.2648	3.776	1.034	.9667	1.3119	10′
15° 00′	.2618	.2588	3.864	.2679	3.732	1.035	.9659	1.3090	75° 00′
10′	.2647	.2616	3.822	.2711	3.689	1.036	.9652	1.3061	50′
20′	.2676	.2644	3.782	.2742	3.647	1.037	.9644	1.3032	40′
30′	.2705	.2672	3.742	.2773	3.606	1.038	.9636	1.3003	30′
40′	.2734	.2700	3.703	.2805	3.566	1.039	.9628	1.2974	20′
50′	.2763	.2728	3.665	.2836	3.526	1.039	.9621	1.2945	10′
16° 00′	.2793	.2756	3.628	.2867	3.487	1.040	.9613	1.2915	74° 00′
10′	.2822	.2784	3.592	.2899	3.450	1.041	.9605	1.2886	50′
20′	.2851	.2812	3.556	.2931	3.412	1.042	.9596	1.2857	40′
30′	.2880	.2840	3.521	.2962	3.376	1.043	.9588	1.2828	30′
40′	.2909	.2868	3.487	.2994	3.340	1.044	.9580	1.2799	20′
50′	.2938	.2896	3.453	.3026	3.305	1.045	.9572	1.2770	10′
17° 00′	.2967	.2924	3.420	.3057	3.271	1.046	.9563	1.2741	73° 00′
10′	.2996	.2952	3.388	.3089	3.237	1.047	.9555	1.2712	50′
20′	.3025	.2979	3.357	.3121	3.204	1.048	.9546	1.2683	40′
30′	.3054	.3007	3.326	.3153	3.172	1.049	.9537	1.2654	30′
40′	.3083	.3035	3.295	.3185	3.140	1.049	.9528	1.2625	20′
50′	.3113	.3062	3.265	.3217	3.108	1.050	.9520	1.2595	10′
18° 00′	.3142	.3090	3.236	.3249	3.078	1.051	.9511	1.2566	72° 00′
		cos r	sec r	cot r	tan r	csc r	sin r	Radians	Angle

VALUES OF TRIGONOMETRIC FUNCTIONS

Angle	Radians r	sin r	csc r	tan r	cot r	sec r	cos r		
18° 00′	0.3142	0.3090	3.236	0.3249	3.078	1.051	0.9511	1.2566	72° 00′
10′	.3171	.3118	3.207	.3281	3.047	1.052	.9502	1.2537	50′
20′	.3200	.3145	3.179	.3314	3.018	1.053	.9492	1.2508	40′
30′	.3229	.3173	3.152	.3346	2.989	1.054	.9483	1.2479	30′
40′	.3258	.3201	3.124	.3378	2.960	1.056	.9474	1.2450	20′
50′	.3287	.3228	3.098	.3411	2.932	1.057	.9465	1.2421	10′
19° 00′	.3316	.3256	3.072	.3443	2.904	1.058	.9455	1.2392	71° 00′
10′	.3345	.3283	3.046	.3476	2.877	1.059	.9446	1.2363	50′
20′	.3374	.3311	3.021	.3508	2.850	1.060	.9436	1.2334	40′
30′	.3403	.3338	2.996	.3541	2.824	1.061	.9426	1.2305	30′
40′	.3432	.3365	2.971	.3574	2.798	1.062	.9417	1.2275	20′
50′	.3462	.3393	2.947	.3607	2.773	1.063	.9407	1.2246	10′
20° 00′	.3491	.3420	2.924	.3640	2.747	1.064	.9397	1.2217	70° 00′
10′	.3520	.3448	2.901	.3673	2.723	1.065	.9387	1.2188	50′
20′	.3549	.3475	2.878	.3706	2.699	1.066	.9377	1.2159	40′
30′	.3578	.3502	2.855	.3739	2.675	1.068	.9367	1.2130	30′
40′	.3607	.3529	2.833	.3772	2.651	1.069	.9356	1.2101	20′
50′	.3636	.3557	2.812	.3805	2.628	1.070	.9346	1.2072	10′
21° 00′	.3665	.3584	2.790	.3839	2.605	1.071	.9336	1.2043	69° 00′
10′	.3694	.3611	2.769	.3872	2.583	1.072	.9325	1.2014	50′
20′	.3723	.3638	2.749	.3906	2.560	1.074	.9315	1.1985	40′
30′	.3752	.3665	2.729	.3939	2.539	1.075	.9304	1.1956	30′
40′	.3782	.3692	2.709	.3973	2.517	1.076	.9293	1.1926	20′
50′	.3811	.3719	2.689	.4006	2.496	1.077	.9283	1.1897	10′
22° 00′	.3840	.3746	2.669	.4040	2.475	1.079	.9272	1.1868	68° 00′
10′	.3869	.3773	2.650	.4074	2.455	1.080	.9261	1.1839	50′
20′	.3898	.3800	2.632	.4108	2.434	1.081	.9250	1.1810	40′
30′	.3927	.3827	2.613	.4142	2.414	1.082	.9239	1.1781	30′
40′	.3956	.3854	2.595	.4176	2.394	1.084	.9228	1.1752	20′
50′	.3985	.3881	2.577	.4210	2.375	1.085	.9216	1.1723	10′
23° 00′	.4014	.3907	2.559	.4245	2.356	1.086	.9205	1.1694	67° 00′
10′	.4043	.3934	2.542	.4279	2.337	1.088	.9194	1.1665	50′
20′	.4072	.3961	2.525	.4314	2.318	1.089	.9182	1.1636	40′
30′	.4102	.3987	2.508	.4348	2.300	1.090	.9171	1.1606	30′
40′	.4131	.4014	2.491	.4383	2.282	1.092	.9159	1.1577	20′
50′	.4160	.4041	2.475	.4417	2.264	1.093	.9147	1.1548	10′
24° 00′	.4189	.4067	2.459	.4452	2.246	1.095	.9135	1.1519	66° 00′
10′	.4218	.4094	2.443	.4487	2.229	1.096	.9124	1.1490	50′
20′	.4247	.4120	2.427	.4522	2.211	1.097	.9112	1.1461	40′
30′	.4276	.4147	2.411	.4557	2.194	1.099	.9100	1.1432	30′
40′	.4305	.4173	2.396	.4592	2.177	1.100	.9088	1.1403	20′
50′	.4334	.4200	2.381	.4628	2.161	1.102	.9075	1.1374	10′
25° 00′	.4363	.4226	2.366	.4663	2.145	1.103	.9063	1.1345	65° 00′
10′	.4392	.4253	2.352	.4699	2.128	1.105	.9051	1.1316	50′
20′	.4422	.4279	2.337	.4734	2.112	1.106	.9038	1.1286	40′
30′	.4451	.4305	2.323	.4770	2.097	1.108	.9026	1.1257	30′
40′	.4480	.4331	2.309	.4806	2.081	1.109	.9013	1.1228	20′
50′	.4509	.4358	2.295	.4841	2.066	1.111	.9001	1.1199	10′
26° 00′	.4538	.4384	2.281	.4877	2.050	1.113	.8988	1.1170	64° 00′
10′	.4567	.4410	2.268	.4913	2.035	1.114	.8975	1.1141	50′
20′	.4596	.4436	2.254	.4950	2.020	1.116	.8962	1.1112	40′
30′	.4625	.4462	2.241	.4986	2.006	1.117	.8949	1.1083	30′
40′	.4654	.4488	2.228	.5022	1.991	1.119	.8936	1.1054	20′
50′	.4683	.4514	2.215	.5059	1.977	1.121	.8923	1.1025	10′
27° 00′	.4712	.4540	2.203	.5095	1.963	1.122	.8910	1.0996	63° 00′
		cos r	sec r	cot r	tan r	csc r	sin r	Radians r	Angle

VALUES OF TRIGONOMETRIC FUNCTIONS

Angle	Radians r	sin r	csc r	tan r	cot r	sec r	cos r		
27° 00′	0.1712	0.4540	2.203	0.5095	1.963	1.122	0.8910	1.0996	63° 00′
10′	.4741	.4566	2.190	.5132	1.949	1.124	.8897	1.0966	50′
20′	.4771	.4592	2.178	.5169	1.935	1.126	.8884	1.0937	40′
30′	.4800	.4617	2.166	.5206	1.921	1.127	.8870	1.0908	30′
40′	.4829	.4643	2.154	.5243	1.907	1.129	.8857	1.0879	20′
50′	.4858	.4669	2.142	.5280	1.894	1.131	.8843	1.0850	10′
28° 00′	.4887	.4695	2.130	.5317	1.881	1.133	.8829	1.0821	62° 00′
10′	.4916	.4720	2.118	.5354	1.868	1.134	.8816	1.0792	50′
20′	.4945	.4746	2.107	.5392	1.855	1.136	.8802	1.0763	40′
30′	.4974	.4772	2.096	.5430	1.842	1.138	.8788	1.0734	30′
40′	.5003	.4797	2.085	.5467	1.829	1.140	.8774	1.0705	20′
50′	.5032	.4823	2.074	.5505	1.816	1.142	.8760	1.0676	10′
29° 00′	.5061	.4848	2.063	.5543	1.804	1.143	.8746	1.0647	61° 00′
10′	.5091	.4874	2.052	.5581	1.792	1.145	.8732	1.0617	50′
20′	.5120	.4899	2.041	.5619	1.780	1.147	.8718	1.0588	40′
30′	.5149	.4924	2.031	.5658	1.767	1.149	.8704	1.0559	30′
40′	.5178	.4950	2.020	.5696	1.756	1.151	.8689	1.0530	20′
50′	.5207	.4975	2.010	.5735	1.744	1.153	.8675	1.0501	10′
30° 00′	.5236	.5000	2.000	.5774	1.732	1.155	.8660	1.0472	60° 00′
10′	.5265	.5025	1.990	.5812	1.720	1.157	.8646	1.0443	50′
20′	.5294	.5050	1.980	.5851	1.709	1.159	.8631	1.0414	40′
30′	.5323	.5075	1.970	.5890	1.698	1.161	.8616	1.0385	30′
40′	.5352	.5100	1.961	.5930	1.686	1.163	.8601	1.0356	20′
50′	.5381	.5125	1.951	.5969	1.675	1.165	.8587	1.0327	10′
31° 00′	.5411	.5150	1.942	.6009	1.664	1.167	.8572	1.0297	59° 00′
10′	.5440	.5175	1.932	.6048	1.653	1.169	.8557	1.0268	50′
20′	.5469	.5200	1.923	.6088	1.643	1.171	.8542	1.0239	40′
30′	.5498	.5225	1.914	.6128	1.632	1.173	.8526	1.0210	30′
40′	.5527	.5250	1.905	.6168	1.621	1.175	.8511	1.0181	20′
50′	.5556	.5275	1.896	.6208	1.611	1.177	.8496	1.0152	10′
32° 00′	.5585	.5299	1.887	.6249	1.600	1.179	.8480	1.0123	58° 00′
10′	.5614	.5324	1.878	.6289	1.590	1.181	.8465	1.0094	50′
20′	.5643	.5348	1.870	.6330	1.580	1.184	.8450	1.0065	40′
30′	.5672	.5373	1.861	.6371	1.570	1.186	.8434	1.0036	30′
40′	.5701	.5398	1.853	.6412	1.560	1.188	.8418	1.0007	20′
50′	.5730	.5422	1.844	.6453	1.550	1.190	.8403	0.9977	10′
33° 00′	.5760	.5446	1.836	.6494	1.540	1.192	.8387	.9948	57° 00′
10′	.5789	.5471	1.828	.6536	1.530	1.195	.8371	.9919	50′
20′	.5818	.5495	1.820	.6577	1.520	1.197	.8355	.9890	40′
30′	.5847	.5519	1.812	.6619	1.511	1.199	.8339	.9861	30′
40′	.5876	.5544	1.804	.6661	1.501	1.202	.8323	.9832	20′
50′	.5905	.5568	1.796	.6703	1.492	1.204	.8307	.9803	10′
34° 00′	.5934	.5592	1.788	.6745	1.483	1.206	.8290	.9774	56° 00′
10′	.5963	.5616	1.781	.6787	1.473	1.209	.8274	.9745	50′
20′	.5992	.5640	1.773	.6830	1.464	1.211	.8258	.9716	40′
30′	.6021	.5664	1.766	.6873	1.455	1.213	.8241	.9687	30′
40′	.6050	.5688	1.758	.6916	1.446	1.216	.8225	.9657	20′
50′	.6080	.5712	1.751	.6959	1.437	1.218	.8208	.9628	10′
35° 00′	.6109	.5736	1.743	.7002	1.428	1.221	.8192	.9599	55° 00′
10′	.6138	.5760	1.736	.7046	1.419	1.223	.8175	.9570	50′
20′	.6167	.5783	1.729	.7089	1.411	1.226	.8158	.9541	40′
30′	.6196	.5807	1.722	.7133	1.402	1.228	.8141	.9512	30′
40′	.6225	.5831	1.715	.7177	1.393	1.231	.8124	.9483	20′
50′	.6254	.5854	1.708	.7221	1.385	1.233	.8107	.9454	10′
36° 00′	.6283	.5878	1.701	.7265	1.376	1.236	.8090	.9425	54° 00′
		cos r	sec r	cot r	tan r	csc r	sin r	Radians r	Angle

VALUES OF TRIGONOMETRIC FUNCTIONS

Angle	Radians r	sin r	csc r	tan r	cot r	sec r	cos r		
36° 00′	.6283	.5878	1.701	.7265	1.376	1.236	.8090	.9425	54° 00′
10′	.6312	.5901	1.695	.7310	1.368	1.239	.8073	.9396	50′
20′	.6341	.5925	1.688	.7355	1.360	1.241	.8056	.9367	40′
30′	.6370	.5948	1.681	.7400	1.351	1.244	.8039	.9338	30′
40′	.6400	.5972	1.675	.7445	1.343	1.247	.8021	.9308	20′
50′	.6429	.5995	1.668	.7490	1.335	1.249	.8004	.9279	10′
37° 00′	.6458	.6018	1.662	.7536	1.327	1.252	.7986	.9250	53° 00′
10′	.6487	.6041	1.655	.7581	1.319	1.255	.7969	.9221	50′
20′	.6516	.6065	1.649	.7627	1.311	1.258	.7951	.9192	40′
30′	.6545	.6088	1.643	.7673	1.303	1.260	.7934	.9163	30′
40′	.6574	.6111	1.636	.7720	1.295	1.263	.7916	.9134	20′
50′	.6603	.6134	1.630	.7766	1.288	1.266	.7898	.9105	10′
38° 00′	.6632	.6157	1.624	.7813	1.280	1.269	.7880	.9076	52° 00′
10′	.6661	.6180	1.618	.7860	1.272	1.272	.7862	.9047	50′
20′	.6690	.6202	1.612	.7907	1.265	1.275	.7844	.9018	40′
30′	.6720	.6225	1.606	.7954	1.257	1.278	.7826	.8988	30′
40′	.6749	.6248	1.601	.8002	1.250	1.281	.7808	.8959	20′
50′	.6778	.6271	1.595	.8050	1.242	1.284	.7790	.8930	10′
39° 00′	.6807	.6293	1.589	.8098	1.235	1.287	.7771	.8901	51° 00′
10′	.6836	.6316	1.583	.8146	1.228	1.290	.7753	.8872	50′
20′	.6865	.6338	1.578	.8195	1.220	1.293	.7735	.8843	40′
30′	.6894	.6361	1.572	.8243	1.213	1.296	.7716	.8814	30′
40′	.6923	.6383	1.567	.8292	1.206	1.299	.7698	.8785	20′
50′	.6952	.6406	1.561	.8342	1.199	1.302	.7679	.8756	10′
40° 00′	.6981	.6428	1.556	.8391	1.192	1.305	.7660	.8727	50° 00′
10′	.7010	.6450	1.550	.8441	1.185	1.309	.7642	.8698	50′
20′	.7039	.6472	1.545	.8491	1.178	1.312	.7623	.8668	40′
30′	.7069	.6494	1.540	.8541	1.171	1.315	.7604	.8639	30′
40′	.7098	.6517	1.535	.8591	1.164	1.318	.7585	.8610	20′
50′	.7127	.6539	1.529	.8642	1.157	1.322	.7566	.8581	10′
41° 00′	.7156	.6561	1.524	.8693	1.150	1.325	.7547	.8552	49° 00′
10′	.7185	.6583	1.519	.8744	1.144	1.328	.7528	.8523	50′
20′	.7214	.6604	1.514	.8796	1.137	1.332	.7509	.8494	40′
30′	.7243	.6626	1.509	.8847	1.130	1.335	.7490	.8465	30′
40′	.7272	.6648	1.504	.8899	1.124	1.339	.7470	.8436	20′
50′	.7301	.6670	1.499	.8952	1.117	1.342	.7451	.8407	10′
42° 00′	.7330	.6691	1.494	.9004	1.111	1.346	.7431	.8378	48° 00′
10′	.7359	.6713	1.490	.9057	1.104	1.349	.7412	.8348	50′
20′	.7389	.6734	1.485	.9110	1.098	1.353	.7392	.8319	40′
30′	.7418	.6756	1.480	.9163	1.091	1.356	.7373	.8290	30′
40′	.7447	.6777	1.476	.9217	1.085	1.360	.7353	.8261	20′
50′	.7476	.6799	1.471	.9271	1.079	1.364	.7333	.8232	10′
43° 00′	.7505	.6820	1.466	.9325	1.072	1.367	.7314	.8203	47° 00′
10′	.7534	.6841	1.462	.9380	1.066	1.371	.7294	.8174	50′
20′	.7563	.6862	1.457	.9435	1.060	1.375	.7274	.8145	40′
30′	.7592	.6884	1.453	.9490	1.054	1.379	.7254	.8116	30′
40′	.7621	.6905	1.448	.9545	1.048	1.382	.7234	.8087	20′
50′	.7650	.6926	1.444	.9601	1.042	1.386	.7214	.8058	10′
44° 00′	.7679	.6947	1.440	.9657	1.036	1.390	.7193	.8029	46° 00′
10′	.7709	.6967	1.435	.9713	1.030	1.394	.7173	.7999	50′
20′	.7738	.6988	1.431	.9770	1.024	1.398	.7153	.7970	40′
30′	.7767	.7009	1.427	.9827	1.018	1.402	.7133	.7941	30′
40′	.7796	.7030	1.423	.9884	1.012	1.406	.7112	.7912	20′
50′	.7825	.7050	1.418	.9942	1.006	1.410	.7092	.7883	10′
45° 00′	.7854	.7071	1.414	1.000	1.000	1.414	.7071	.7854	45° 00′
		cos r	sec r	cot r	tan r	csc r	sin r	Radians r	Angle

SQUARES AND APPROXIMATE SQUARE ROOTS

N	N^2	$\sqrt{N}$	N	N^2	$\sqrt{N}$
1	1	1.000	51	2601	7.141
2	4	1.414	52	2704	7.211
3	9	1.732	53	2809	7.280
4	16	2.000	54	2916	7.348
5	25	2.236	55	3025	7.416
6	36	2.449	56	3136	7.483
7	49	2.646	57	3249	7.550
8	64	2.828	58	3364	7.616
9	81	3.000	59	3481	7.681
10	100	3.162	60	3600	7.746
11	121	3.317	61	3721	7.810
12	144	3.464	62	3844	7.874
13	169	3.606	63	3969	7.937
14	196	3.742	64	4096	8.000
15	225	3.873	65	4225	8.062
16	256	4.000	66	4356	8.124
17	289	4.123	67	4489	8.185
18	324	4.243	68	4624	8.246
19	361	4.359	69	4761	8.307
20	400	4.472	70	4900	8.367
21	441	4.583	71	5041	8.426
22	484	4.690	72	5184	8.485
23	529	4.796	73	5329	8.544
24	576	4.899	74	5476	8.602
25	625	5.000	75	5625	8.660
26	676	5.099	76	5776	8.718
27	729	5.196	77	5929	8.775
28	784	5.292	78	6084	8.832
29	841	5.385	79	6241	8.888
30	900	5.477	80	6400	8.944
31	961	5.568	81	6561	9.000
32	1024	5.657	82	6724	9.055
33	1089	5.745	83	6889	9.110
34	1156	5.831	84	7056	9.165
35	1225	5.916	85	7225	9.220
36	1296	6.000	86	7396	9.274
37	1369	6.083	87	7569	9.327
38	1444	6.164	88	7744	9.381
39	1521	6.245	89	7921	9.434
40	1600	6.325	90	8100	9.487
41	1681	6.403	91	8281	9.539
42	1764	6.481	92	8464	9.592
43	1849	6.557	93	8649	9.644
44	1936	6.633	94	8836	9.695
45	2025	6.708	95	9025	9.747
46	2116	6.782	96	9216	9.798
47	2209	6.856	97	9409	9.849
48	2304	6.928	98	9604	9.899
49	2401	7.000	99	9801	9.950
50	2500	7.071	100	10000	10.000

COMMON LOGARITHMS OF NUMBERS

x	0	1	2	3	4	5	6	7	8	9
1.0	.0000	.0043	.0086	.0128	.0170	.0212	.0253	.0294	.0334	.0374
1.1	.0414	.0453	.0492	.0531	.0569	.0607	.0645	.0682	.0719	.0755
1.2	.0792	.0828	.0864	.0899	.0934	.0969	.1004	.1038	.1072	.1106
1.3	.1139	.1173	.1206	.1239	.1271	.1303	.1335	.1367	.1399	.1430
1.4	.1461	.1492	.1523	.1553	.1584	.1614	.1644	.1673	.1703	.1732
1.5	.1761	.1790	.1818	.1847	.1875	.1903	.1931	.1959	.1987	.2014
1.6	.2041	.2068	.2095	.2122	.2148	.2175	.2201	.2227	.2253	.2279
1.7	.2304	.2330	.2355	.2380	.2405	.2430	.2455	.2480	.2504	.2529
1.8	.2553	.2577	.2601	.2625	.2648	.2672	.2695	.2718	.2742	.2765
1.9	.2788	.2810	.2833	.2856	.2878	.2900	.2923	.2945	.2967	.2989
2.0	.3010	.3032	.3054	.3075	.3096	.3118	.3139	.3160	.3181	.3201
2.1	.3222	.3243	.3263	.3284	.3304	.3324	.3345	.3365	.3385	.3404
2.2	.3424	.3444	.3464	.3483	.3502	.3522	.3541	.3560	.3579	.3598
2.3	.3617	.3636	.3655	.3674	.3692	.3711	.3729	.3747	.3766	.3784
2.4	.3802	.3820	.3838	.3856	.3874	.3892	.3909	.3927	.3945	.3962
2.5	.3979	.3997	.4014	.4031	.4048	.4065	.4082	.4099	.4116	.4133
2.6	.4150	.4166	.4183	.4200	.4216	.4232	.4249	.4265	.4281	.4298
2.7	.4314	.4330	.4346	.4362	.4378	.4393	.4409	.4425	.4440	.4456
2.8	.4472	.4487	.4502	.4518	.4533	.4548	.4564	.4579	.4594	.4609
2.9	.4624	.4639	.4654	.4669	.4683	.4698	.4713	.4728	.4742	.4757
3.0	.4771	.4786	.4800	.4814	.4829	.4843	.4857	.4871	.4886	.4900
3.1	.4914	.4928	.4942	.4955	.4969	.4983	.4997	.5011	.5024	.5038
3.2	.5051	.5065	.5079	.5092	.5105	.5119	.5132	.5145	.5159	.5172
3.3	.5185	.5198	.5211	.5224	.5237	.5250	.5263	.5276	.5289	.5302
3.4	.5315	.5328	.5340	.5353	.5366	.5378	.5391	.5403	.5416	.5428
3.5	.5441	.5453	.5465	.5478	.5490	.5502	.5514	.5527	.5539	.5551
3.6	.5563	.5575	.5587	.5599	.5611	.5623	.5635	.5647	.5658	.5670
3.7	.5682	.5694	.5705	.5717	.5729	.5740	.5752	.5763	.5775	.5786
3.8	.5798	.5809	.5821	.5832	.5843	.5855	.5866	.5877	.5888	.5899
3.9	.5911	.5922	.5933	.5944	.5955	.5966	.5977	.5988	.5999	.6010
4.0	.6021	.6031	.6042	.6053	.6064	.6075	.6085	.6096	.6107	.6117
4.1	.6128	.6138	.6149	.6160	.6170	.6180	.6191	.6201	.6212	.6222
4.2	.6232	.6243	.6253	.6263	.6274	.6284	.6294	.6304	.6314	.6325
4.3	.6335	.6345	.6355	.6365	.6375	.6385	.6395	.6405	.6415	.6425
4.4	.6435	.6444	.6454	.6464	.6474	.6484	.6493	.6503	.6513	.6522
4.5	.6532	.6542	.6551	.6561	.6571	.6580	.6590	.6599	.6609	.6618
4.6	.6628	.6637	.6646	.6656	.6665	.6675	.6684	.6693	.6702	.6712
4.7	.6721	.6730	.6739	.6749	.6758	.6767	.6776	.6785	.6794	.6803
4.8	.6812	.6821	.6830	.6839	.6848	.6857	.6866	.6875	.6884	.6893
4.9	.6902	.6911	.6920	.6928	.6937	.6946	.6955	.6964	.6972	.6981

COMMON LOGARITHMS OF NUMBERS

x	0	1	2	3	4	5	6	7	8	9
5.0	.6990	.6998	.7007	.7016	.7024	.7033	.7042	.7050	.7059	.7067
5.1	.7076	.7084	.7093	.7101	.7110	.7118	.7126	.7135	.7143	.7152
5.2	.7160	.7168	.7177	.7185	.7193	.7202	.7210	.7218	.7226	.7235
5.3	.7243	.7251	.7259	.7267	.7275	.7284	.7292	.7300	.7308	.7316
5.4	.7324	.7332	.7340	.7348	.7356	.7364	.7372	.7380	.7388	.7396
5.5	.7404	.7412	.7419	.7427	.7435	.7443	.7451	.7459	.7466	.7474
5.6	.7482	.7490	.7497	.7505	.7513	.7520	.7528	.7536	.7543	.7551
5.7	.7559	.7566	.7574	.7582	.7589	.7597	.7604	.7612	.7619	.7627
5.8	.7634	.7642	.7649	.7657	.7664	.7672	.7679	.7686	.7694	.7701
5.9	.7709	.7716	.7723	.7731	.7738	.7745	.7752	.7760	.7767	.7774
6.0	.7782	.7789	.7796	.7803	.7810	.7818	.7825	.7832	.7839	.7846
6.1	.7853	.7860	.7868	.7875	.7882	.7889	.7896	.7903	.7910	.7917
6.2	.7924	.7931	.7938	.7945	.7952	.7959	.7966	.7973	.7980	.7987
6.3	.7993	.8000	.8007	.8014	.8021	.8028	.8035	.8041	.8048	.8055
6.4	.8062	.8069	.8075	.8082	.8089	.8096	.8102	.8109	.8116	.8122
6.5	.8129	.8136	.8142	.8149	.8156	.8162	.8169	.8176	.8182	.8189
6.6	.8195	.8202	.8209	.8215	.8222	.8228	.8235	.8241	.8248	.8254
6.7	.8261	.8267	.8274	.8280	.8287	.8293	.8299	.8306	.8312	.8319
6.8	.8325	.8331	.8338	.8344	.8351	.8357	.8363	.8370	.8376	.8382
6.9	.8388	.8395	.8401	.8407	.8414	.8420	.8426	.8432	.8439	.8445
7.0	.8451	.8457	.8463	.8470	.8476	.8482	.8488	.8494	.8500	.8506
7.1	.8513	.8519	.8525	.8531	.8537	.8543	.8549	.8555	.8561	.8567
7.2	.8573	.8579	.8585	.8591	.8597	.8603	.8609	.8615	.8621	.8627
7.3	.8633	.8639	.8645	.8651	.8657	.8663	.8669	.8675	.8681	.8686
7.4	.8692	.8698	.8704	.8710	.8716	.8722	.8727	.8733	.8739	.8745
7.5	.8751	.8756	.8762	.8768	.8774	.8779	.8785	.8791	.8797	.8802
7.6	.8808	.8814	.8820	.8825	.8831	.8837	.8842	.8848	.8854	.8859
7.7	.8865	.8871	.8876	.8882	.8887	.8893	.8899	.8904	.8910	.8915
7.8	.8921	.8927	.8932	.8938	.8943	.8949	.8954	.8960	.8965	.8971
7.9	.8976	.8982	.8987	.8993	.8998	.9004	.9009	.9015	.9020	.9025
8.0	.9031	.9036	.9042	.9047	.9053	.9058	.9063	.9069	.9074	.9079
8.1	.9085	.9090	.9096	.9101	.9106	.9112	.9117	.9122	.9128	.9133
8.2	.9138	.9143	.9149	.9154	.9159	.9165	.9170	.9175	.9180	.9186
8.3	.9191	.9196	.9201	.9206	.9212	.9217	.9222	.9227	.9232	.9238
8.4	.9243	.9248	.9253	.9258	.9263	.9269	.9274	.9279	.9284	.9289
8.5	.9294	.9299	.9304	.9309	.9315	.9320	.9325	.9330	.9335	.9340
8.6	.9345	.9350	.9355	.9360	.9365	.9370	.9375	.9380	.9385	.9390
8.7	.9395	.9400	.9405	.9410	.9415	.9420	.9425	.9430	.9435	.9440
8.8	.9445	.9450	.9455	.9460	.9465	.9469	.9474	.9479	.9484	.9489
8.9	.9494	.9499	.9504	.9509	.9513	.9518	.9523	.9528	.9533	.9538

COMMON LOGARITHMS OF NUMBERS

x	0	1	2	3	4	5	6	7	8	9
9.0	.9542	.9547	.9552	.9557	.9562	.9566	.9571	.9576	.9581	.9586
9.1	.9590	.9595	.9600	.9605	.9609	.9614	.9619	.9624	.9628	.9633
9.2	.9638	.9643	.9647	.9652	.9657	.9661	.9666	.9671	.9675	.9680
9.3	.9685	.9689	.9694	.9699	.9703	.9708	.9713	.9717	.9722	.9727
9.4	.9731	.9736	.9741	.9745	.9750	.9754	.9759	.9763	.9768	.9773
9.5	.9777	.9782	.9786	.9791	.9795	.9800	.9805	.9809	.9814	.9818
9.6	.9823	.9827	.9832	.9836	.9841	.9845	.9850	.9854	.9859	.9863
9.7	.9868	.9872	.9877	.9881	.9886	.9890	.9894	.9899	.9903	.9908
9.8	.9912	.9917	.9921	.9926	.9930	.9934	.9939	.9943	.9948	.9952
9.9	.9956	.9961	.9965	.9969	.9974	.9978	.9983	.9987	.9991	.9996

EXPONENTIAL FUNCTIONS

x	e^x	e^{-x}	x	e^x	e^{-x}
0.00	1.0000	1.0000	1.5	4.4817	0.2231
.01	1.0101	0.9901	1.6	4.9530	.2019
.02	1.0202	.9802	1.7	5.4739	.1827
.03	1.0305	.9705	1.8	6.0496	.1653
.04	1.0408	.9608	1.9	6.6859	.1496
.05	1.0513	.9512	2.0	7.3891	.1353
.06	1.0618	.9418	2.1	8.1662	.1225
.07	1.0725	.9324	2.2	9.0250	.1108
.08	1.0833	.9331	2.3	9.9742	.1003
.09	1.0942	.9139	2.4	11.023	.0907
.10	1.1052	.9048	2.5	12.182	.0821
.11	1.1163	.8958	2.6	13.464	.0743
.12	1.1275	.8869	2.7	14.880	.0672
.13	1.1388	.8781	2.8	16.445	.0608
.14	1.1503	.8694	2.9	18.174	.0550
.15	1.1618	.8607	3.0	20.086	.0498
.16	1.1735	.8521	3.1	22.198	.0450
.17	1.1853	.8437	3.2	24.533	.0408
.18	1.1972	.8353	3.3	27.113	.0369
.19	1.2092	.8270	3.4	29.964	.0334
.20	1.2214	.8187	3.5	33.115	.0302
.21	1.2337	.8106	3.6	36.598	.0273
.22	1.2461	.8025	3.7	40.447	.0247
.23	1.2586	.7945	3.8	44.701	.0224
.24	1.2712	.7866	3.9	49.402	.0202
.25	1.2840	.7788	4.0	54.598	.0183
.30	1.3499	.7408	4.1	60.340	.0166
.35	1.4191	.7047	4.2	66.686	.0150
.40	1.4918	.6703	4.3	73.700	.0136
.45	1.5683	.6376	4.4	81.451	.0123
.50	1.6487	.6065	4.5	90.017	.0111
.55	1.7333	.5769	4.6	99.484	.0101
.60	1.8221	.5488	4.7	109.95	.0091
.65	1.9155	.5220	4.8	121.51	.0082
.70	2.0138	.4966	4.9	134.29	.0074
.75	2.1170	.4724	5.0	148.41	.0067
.80	2.2255	.4493	5.5	244.69	.0041
.85	2.3396	.4274	6.0	403.43	.0025
.90	2.4596	.4066	6.5	665.14	.0015
.95	2.5857	.3867	7.0	1096.6	.0009
1.0	2.7183	.3679	7.5	1808.0	.0006
1.1	3.0042	.3329	8.0	2981.0	.0003
1.2	3.3201	.3012	8.5	4914.8	.0002
1.3	3.6693	.2725	9.0	8103.1	.0001
1.4	4.0552	.2466	10.0	22026	.00005

NATURAL LOGARITHMS

Use ln 10 = 2.30259 to find logarithms of numbers greater than 10 or less than 1.

N	0	1	2	3	4	5	6	7	8	9
1.0	0.0000	0100	0198	0296	0392	0488	0583	0677	0770	0862
1.1	0953	1044	1133	1222	1310	1398	1484	1570	1655	1740
1.2	1823	1906	1989	2070	2151	2231	2311	2390	2469	2546
1.3	2624	2700	2776	2852	2927	3001	3075	3148	3221	3293
1.4	3365	3436	3507	3577	3646	3716	3784	3853	3920	3988
1.5	0.4055	4121	4187	4253	4318	4383	4447	4511	4574	4637
1.6	4700	4762	4824	4886	4947	5008	5068	5128	5188	5247
1.7	5306	5365	5423	5481	5539	5596	5653	5710	5766	5822
1.8	5878	5933	5988	6043	6098	6152	6206	6259	6313	6366
1.9	6419	6471	6523	6575	6627	6678	6729	6780	6831	6881
2.0	0.6932	6981	7031	7080	7130	7178	7227	7276	7324	7372
2.1	7419	7467	7514	7561	7608	7655	7701	7747	7793	7839
2.2	7885	7930	7975	8020	8065	8109	8154	8198	8242	8286
2.3	8329	8373	8416	8459	8502	8544	8587	8629	8671	8713
2.4	8755	8796	8838	8879	8920	8961	9002	9042	9083	9123
2.5	0.9163	9203	9243	9282	9322	9361	9400	9439	9478	9517
2.6	9555	9594	9632	9670	9708	9746	9783	9821	9858	9895
2.7	9933	9970	*0006	*0043	*0080	*0116	*0152	*0189	*0225	*0260
2.8	1.0296	0332	0367	0403	0438	0473	0508	0543	0578	0613
2.9	0647	0682	0716	0750	0784	0818	0852	0886	0919	0953
3.0	1.0986	1019	1053	1086	1119	1151	1184	1217	1249	1282
3.1	1314	1346	1378	1410	1442	1474	1506	1537	1569	1600
3.2	1632	1663	1694	1725	1756	1787	1817	1848	1878	1909
3.3	1939	1970	2000	2030	2060	2090	2119	2149	2179	2208
3.4	2238	2267	2296	2326	2355	2384	2413	2442	2470	2499
3.5	1.2528	2556	2585	2613	2641	2670	2698	2726	2754	2782
3.6	2809	2837	2865	2892	2920	2947	2975	3002	3029	3056
3.7	3083	3110	3137·	3164	3191	3218	3244	3271	3297	3324
3.8	3350	3376	3403	3429	3455	3481	3507	3533	3558	3584
3.9	3610	3635	3661	3686	3712	3737	3762	3788	3813	3838
4.0	1.3863	3883	3913	3938	3962	3987	4012	4036	4061	4085
4.1	4110	4134	4159	4183	4207	4231	4255	4279	4303	4327
4.2	4351	4375	4398	4422	4446	4469	4493	4516	4540	4563
4.3	4586	4609	4633	4656	4679	4702	4725	4748	4771	4793
4.4	4816	4839	4861	4884	4907	4929	4952	4974	4996	5019
4.5	1.5041	5063	5085	5107	5129	5151	5173	5195	5217	5239
4.6	5261	5282	5304	5326	5347	5369	5390	5412	5433	5454
4.7	5476	5497	5518	5539	5560	5581	5603	5624	5644	5665
4.8	5686	5707	5728	5749	5769	5790	5810	5831	5852	5872
4.9	5892	5913	5933	5953	5974	5994	6014	6034	6054	6074
5.0	1.6094	6114	6134	6154	6174	6194	6214	6233	6253	6273
5.1	6292	6312	6332	6351	6371	6390	6409	6429	6448	6467
5.2	6487	6506	6525	6544	6563	6582	6601	6620	6639	6658
5.3	6677	6696	6715	6734	6752	6771	6790	6808	6827	6846
5.4	6864	6883	6901	6919	6938	6956	6975	6993	7011	7029

*An asterisk indicates the point at which the whole number value changes.

NATURAL LOGARITHMS

Example. ln 220 = ln 2.2 + 2 ln 10 = 0.7885 + 2(2.30259) = 5.3937

N	0	1	2	3	4	5	6	7	8	9
5.5	1.7048	7066	7084	7102	7120	7138	7156	7174	7192	7210
5.6	7228	7246	7263	7281	7299	7317	7334	7352	7370	7387
5.7	7405	7422	7440	7457	7475	7492	7509	7527	7544	7561
5.8	7579	7596	7613	7630	7647	7664	7682	7699	7716	7733
5.9	7750	7767	7783	7800	7817	7834	7851	7868	7884	7901
6.0	1.7918	7934	7951	7968	7984	8001	8017	8034	8050	8067
6.1	8083	8099	8116	8132	8148	8165	8181	8197	8213	8229
6.2	8246	8262	8278	8294	8310	8326	8342	8358	8374	8390
6.3	8406	8421	8437	8453	8469	8485	8500	8516	8532	8547
6.4	8563	8579	8594	8610	8625	8641	8656	8672	8687	8703
6.5	1.8718	8733	8749	8764	8779	8795	8810	8825	8840	8856
6.6	8871	8886	8901	8916	8931	8946	8961	8976	8991	9006
6.7	9021	9036	9051	9066	9081	9095	9110	9125	9140	9155
6.8	9169	9184	9199	9213	9228	9243	9257	9272	9286	9301
6.9	9315	9330	9344	9359	9373	9387	9402	9416	9431	9445
7.0	1.9459	9473	9488	9502	9516	9530	9545	9559	9573	9587
7.1	9601	9615	9629	9643	9657	9671	9685	9699	9713	9727
7.2	9741	9755	9769	9782	9796	9810	9824	9838	9851	9865
7.3	9879	9892	9906	9920	9933	9947	9961	9974	9988	*0001
7.4	2.0015	0028	0042	0055	0069	0082	0096	0109	0122	0136
7.5	2.0149	0162	0176	0189	0202	0216	0229	0242	0255	0268
7.6	0282	0295	0308	0321	0334	0347	0360	0373	0386	0399
7.7	0412	0425	0438	0451	0464	0477	0490	0503	0516	0528
7.8	0541	0554	0567	0580	0592	0605	0618	0631	0643	0656
7.9	0669	0681	0694	0707	0719	0732	0744	0757	0769	0782
8.0	2.0794	0807	0819	0832	0844	0857	0869	0882	0894	0906
8.1	0919	0931	0943	0956	0968	0980	0992	1005	1017	1029
8.2	1041	1054	1066	1078	1090	1102	1114	1126	1138	1151
8.3	1163	1175	1187	1199	1211	1223	1235	1247	1259	1270
8.4	1282	1294	1306	1318	1330	1342	1354	1365	1377	1389
8.5	2.1401	1412	1424	1436	1448	1459	1471	1483	1494	1506
8.6	1518	1529	1541	1552	1564	1576	1587	1599	1610	1622
8.7	1633	1645	1656	1668	1679	1691	1702	1713	1725	1736
8.8	1748	1759	1770	1782	1793	1804	1816	1827	1838	1849
8.9	1861	1872	1883	1894	1905	1917	1928	1939	1950	1961
9.0	2.1972	1983	1994	2006	2017	2028	2039	2050	2061	2072
9.1	2083	2094	2105	2116	2127	2138	2149	2159	2170	2181
9.2	2192	2203	2214	2225	2235	2246	2257	2268	2279	2289
9.3	2300	2311	2322	2332	2343	2354	2365	2375	2386	2397
9.4	2407	2418	2428	2439	2450	2460	2471	2481	2492	2502
9.5	2.2513	2523	2534	2544	2555	2565	2576	2586	2597	2607
9.6	2618	2628	2638	2649	2659	2670	2680	2690	2701	2711
9.7	2721	2732	2742	2752	2762	2773	2783	2793	2803	2814
9.8	2824	2834	2844	2854	2865	2875	2885	2895	2905	2915
9.9	2925	2935	2946	2956	2966	2976	2986	2996	3006	3016

Glossary

abscissa The x-coordinate of a point is called the abscissa. (33)

absolute maximum or minimum values Absolute maximum or minimum values are the greatest or least values, respectively, assumed by a function throughout its domain of definition. (467)

absolute value The absolute value of x, symbolized $|x|$, is defined to be x if $x \geq 0$ and $-x$ if $x < 0$. (9)

absolute value function The absolute value function can be defined as follows. (73)

$$f(x) = |x| = \begin{cases} x, x \geq 0 \\ -x, x < 0 \end{cases}$$

additive identity If a is an element of F, then there is an element $-a$ in F such that $a + (-a) = (-a) + a = 0$. (11)

additive identity for vectors The additive identity for vectors is $0 + 0i$. (57)

additive inverse There is an element 0 of F such that for every element in F, $a * 0 = 0 * a = a$. (11)

additive inverse for vectors Two arrows which are in opposite directions and have the same length are called additive inverses. (57)

amplitude If a periodic function has a maximum M and a minimum m, the amplitude is defined as $A = \dfrac{M - m}{2}.$ (133)

antiderivative Let f be a continuous function and F be a differentiable function with the same domain as f. If $F'(x) = f(x)$ for all x in that domain, then F' is called an antiderivative of f. (493)

antilogarithm If $\ln x = b$, then x is called the antilogarithm of b, abbreviated $\text{antiln } b = x$. (343)

Arccosine function The Arccosine function is the inverse of the cosine function. (153)

Arcsine function The Arcsine function is the inverse for the sine function. (153)

Arctangent function The Arctangent function is the inverse of tangent function. (153)

arithmetic means The terms between any two terms of an arithmetic sequence are called arithmetic means. (397)

arithmetic sequence (1) An arithmetic sequence is a sequence in which the difference between successive terms is constant throughout the sequence. (391) **(2)** An arithmetic sequence is a sequence $\{a_n\}$ such that $a_1 = a, a_n = a_{n-1} + d$, where d is the common difference. (395)

associative property If a, b, and c are elements of F, then $a * (b * c) = (a * b) * c$ where $*$ is a binary operation defined on F. (11)

asymptotes (1) Asymptotes are lines which a curve approaches. (108) **(2)** The equations of the asymptotes of a hyperbola with a horizontal transverse axis are $y - k = \pm \dfrac{b}{a}(x - h)$. If the transverse axis is vertical, the equations are $y - k = \pm \dfrac{a}{b}(x - h)$. (278)

BASIC BASIC, an abbreviation for *Beginner's*

*A*ll-purpose *S*ymbolic *I*nstruction *C*ode, is a computer language. (236)

BASIC function A BASIC function is a subprogram, stored in the computer. Some common BASIC functions are ABS(X), SQR(X), INT(X), SIN(X), COS(X), TAN(X), LOG(X), and RND(X). (292)

basis vectors Any pair of nonzero, nonparallel vectors forms a basis for a vector space. That is, any vector $\bar{v}$ can be written as a linear combination of any two specific vectors $\bar{u}$ and $\bar{w}$ as long as they do not have the same or opposite direction. (221)

cardioid A cardioid is a limaçon where $|a| = |b|$ so the equations for the curve are $r = a + a\cos\theta$ or $r = a + a\sin\theta$. (380)

Cartesian coordinate system The set of points in the plane and the associated set of ordered pairs of real numbers are called the Cartesian coordinate system. (34)

Cartesian product (cross product) The set of all ordered pairs of real numbers (x, y) is indicated by $\mathcal{R} \times \mathcal{R}$ and is called the Cartesian product. (35)

$$\{(x, y) \mid x, y \in \mathcal{R}\}$$

circle A circle is the locus of points in a plane at a given distance, called the radius, from a given point, called the center. The standard form of the equation of a circle with center (h, k) and radius r is $(x - h)^2 + (y - k)^2 = r^2$. (269)

circular functions The functions sine, cosine, and tangent are related to a circle and are called circular functions. (130)

closed interval A closed interval $\{x \mid a \le x \le b\}$ is represented as $[a, b]$. (18)

closure If a and b are elements of a field then a and b combined by using a binary operation yields an element of F. (11)

common logarithms Base ten logarithms are called common logarithms. (343)

commutative property If a and b are elements of F, then $a * b = b * a$. (11)

completeness property There is exactly one real number (point) common to all the intervals $\{I_n\}$ such that each interval contains its successor and the length of the interval approaches 0 as n increases without bound. (22)

complex conjugates The quadratic formula generates two complex conjugates of the form $a \pm bi$, where $a, b \in \mathcal{R}$. The sum of such conjugates is a real number, $2a$. Their product is a real number $a^2 + b^2$. (316)

complex number A complex number is written in the form $a + bi$, where a and b are real numbers. The symbol i is defined so that $i^2 = -1$. (56)

composition of functions If f and g denote functions, then their composition, denoted $f \circ g$, is the function such that $(f \circ g)(x) = f(g(x))$. Its domain $D(f \circ g) = \{x \mid x \in D(g) \text{ and } g(x) \in D(f)\}$. (78)

compound interest law The compound interest law is

$$A = Pe^{it}. \quad (349)$$

conic sections (1) A conic section is the intersection of a plane with a cone. The general equation for a conic section is $Ax^2 + Bxy + Cy^2 + Dx + Ey + F = 0$. (281) **(2)** A conic section is the locus of points such that the ratio of the distance from a point called a focus to the distance from a line called a directrix is a constant. (281)

conjugate axis The conjugate axis is the line segment perpendicular to the transverse axis at its midpoint. (278)

constant function A constant function is a function which assigns the same real numbers to every element of the domain. (72)

continuous function (1) A function is continuous on an interval if it is continuous at all interior points of the interval.

(119) (2) A function f is continuous at $x = c$ in its domain if and only if f is defined at c and line $f(x) = f(c)$. **(434)**

convergent sequence A convergent sequence is a sequence with a limit to which it converges. **(408)**

convergent series A convergent series is a series $\{S_n\}$ which converges to a real number S. **(414)**

coordinates A coordinate is the number on a line with an established scale which corresponds to a point. **(8)**

coordinate planes The planes determined by each pair of coordinate axes are the coordinate planes. **(239)**

coordinate system A coordinate system is an entire scale on the line. **(8)**

cosecant function The cosecant function is defined as follows. **(137)**

$$\left\{ (x,y) \mid y = \csc x = \frac{1}{\sin x} \right\}$$

cotangent function The cotangent function is defined as follows. **(137)**

$$\left\{ (x,y) \mid y = \cot x = \frac{1}{\tan x} = \frac{\cos x}{\sin x} \right\}$$

coterminal Angles in standard position which have the same terminal side are called coterminal. **(166)**

critical points (1) Critical points are points at which the linear factors are equal to zero. **(20) (2)** Critical points are points for which the derivative of a function equals zero. **(464)**

cross product (1) The cross product of $\mathcal{R}$ with $\mathcal{R}$ is the set of all ordered pairs of real numbers. **(35) (2)** The cross product of two vectors $\vec{v} = \begin{pmatrix} v_1 \\ v_2 \\ v_3 \end{pmatrix}$ and $\vec{w} = \begin{pmatrix} w_1 \\ w_2 \\ w_3 \end{pmatrix}$ is

$$\vec{v} \times \vec{w} = \begin{pmatrix} v_2 w_3 - v_3 w_2 \\ v_3 w_1 - v_1 w_3 \\ v_1 w_2 - v_2 w_1 \end{pmatrix}. \quad \textbf{(250)}$$

cycle The portion of a function included in one period is called a cycle. **(133)**

DATA statement A DATA statement is a BASIC statement which lists information to be used in a computer program. **(236)**

decreasing function (1) A function is decreasing if for $x_1, x_2 \in D(f)$ and $x_1 < x_2$, then $f(x_1) > f(x_2)$. **(87) (2)** If $f'(x) < 0$ for every $x \in \langle a, b \rangle$, then $f(x)$ is decreasing on $\langle a, b \rangle$. **(463)**

Dedekind cuts Suppose all real numbers are separated into two collections, denoted L and R, such that each of the following is true.

  I. Every number is either in L or in R.

  II. Both L and R are nonempty.

  III. If $a \in L$ and $b \in R$, then $a < b$.

Then, there is a real number c such that all numbers less than c are in L. All numbers greater than c are in R. The number c, the cut number, may belong to L or R, but not to both. **(26)**

definite integral The expression $\displaystyle\int_a^b f(x)\, dx$ is a definite integral. The lower limit of integration is a. The upper limit of integration is b. The interval of integration is the interval from $x = a$ to $x = b$. **(497)**

degenerate The degenerate cases when a plane passes through the vertex of the conical surface are a point, a line, and two intersecting lines. **(281)**

degree The degree of a polynomial is the exponent of the highest power of x. **(295)**

deleted neighborhood A deleted neighborhood of the number c is any neighborhood of c with the number c removed. The set of all numbers x such that $0 < |x - c| < h$ is called a deleted neighborhood of c with radius h. **(427)**

DeMoivre's theorem For all real numbers r, n and θ $[r (\cos \theta + i \sin \theta)]^n$

$$= r^n (\cos n\, \theta + i \sin n\, \theta). \quad \textbf{(187)}$$

derivative A derivative is the limit of a difference quotient. **(453)**

derivative of sums The derivative of the sum of a finite number of differentiable functions is the sum of their derivatives. (456)

difference quotient (difference ratio) The ratio $\dfrac{f(a+h)-f(a)}{h}$ is called the difference quotient (or difference ratio). (451)

differentiable function A function is differentiable if the deviation of the function exists at each value in its domain. (451)

differentiation The process of finding derivatives, which are defined as limits of difference quotients, is called differentiation. (453)

dilation A dilation is a transformation brought about by scalar multiplication. If the scalar k is such that $k > 1$, then stretching occurs. If k is such that $0 < k < 1$, then shrinking occurs. (117)

DIM statement A DIM statement is a BASIC statement which assigns storage space in the computer for subscripted variables. (292)

directed distance If $\overline{AB}$ is an arrow, A is the point $(x_1,\ y_1)$, and B is the point $(x_2,\ y_2)$, then the directed distance of $\overline{AB}$ is associated with $\begin{pmatrix} x_2 - x_1 \\ y_2 - y_1 \end{pmatrix}$. (197)

direction angles The angles α, β, γ, formed by the position vectors with each axis are called the direction angles. The cosines of these angles are called the direction cosines. (248)

discriminant The discriminant of a second degree equation in the expression $B^2 - 4AC$. (283)

distance formula The distance between $P(x_1, y_1)$ and $Q(x_2, y_2)$ is
$$PQ = \sqrt{(x_2 - x_1)^2 + (y_2 - y_1)^2}.\quad (36)$$

distance from a point to a line The distance, d, between the line with equation $Ax + By + C = 0$ and point (x_0, y_0) is given by
$$d = \frac{|Ax_0 + By_0 + C|}{\sqrt{A^2 + B^2}}$$

when at least one of A and B is nonzero. (51)

distance from a point to a plane The distance from a point with coordinates (x', y', z') to a plane with the equation $Ax' + By' + Cz' + D = 0$ is
$$d = \frac{|Ax' + By' + Cz' + D|}{\sqrt{A^2 + B^2 + C^2}}.\quad (259)$$

distributive property If a, b, and c are elements of F, then $a \cdot (b + c) = (a \cdot b) + (a \cdot c)$. (12)

divergent sequence A sequence that does not have a limit is called divergent. (408)

divergent series A divergent series is a series $\{S_n\}$ which diverges and is not given a real number value. (414)

domain The domain of a relation is the set of all first elements. (65)

dot product The scalar or dot product of two nonzero vectors $\vec{v}$ and $\vec{u}$ is $\vec{v} \cdot \vec{u} = \|\vec{v}\|\,\|\vec{u}\|\cos\theta$ where θ is the angle between $\vec{v}$ and $\vec{u}$. (226)

double-intercept form If a line passes through $(a, 0)$ and $(0, b)$ and a and $b \neq 0$, then the double-intercept form can be written $\dfrac{x}{a} + \dfrac{y}{b} = 1$. (46)

e The number e can be defined as follows. (336)
$$e = \lim_{n \to \infty} (1 + \frac{1}{n})^n \approx 2.71828$$

eccentricity The eccentricity e of a conic is defined as $e = \dfrac{c}{a}$. (1) For an ellipse, $e < 1$. (275) (2) For an hyperbola, $e > 1$. (278) (3) For a parabola, $e = 1$. (284)

ellipse An ellipse is the locus of points in a plane such that the sum of the distance from two fixed points called foci is a constant. The standard forms of the equations of an ellipse with center (h, k) and sum of the distances to the foci $2a$ are as follows. (274)

$$\frac{(x-h)^2}{a^2} + \frac{(y-k)^2}{b^2} = 1 \begin{cases} \text{if segment joining} \\ \text{the foci is parallel} \\ \text{to the } x\text{-axis} \end{cases}$$

$$\frac{(y-k)^2}{a^2} + \frac{(x-h)^2}{b^2} = 1 \begin{cases} \text{if segment joining} \\ \text{the foci is parallel} \\ \text{to the } y\text{-axis} \end{cases}$$

equal vectors Two vectors are equal if and only if they contain the same set of arrows. (199)

equations of rotation The equations of rotation are two sets of transformational equations that give the relationships between the coordinates of a given point in the xy-plane and the $x'y'$-plane under a rotation through an angle θ. (114)

equivalence class of arrows The complete family of arrows that have the same magnitude and the same direction are called the equivalence class of arrows. (198)

Euler's Formula Euler's formula is as follows. (339)

$$e^{i\theta} = \cos\theta + i\sin\theta$$

even relations Even relations are relations which are symmetric with respect to the y-axis. (100)

excluded regions Intervals of a polynominal function's domain which do not contain any part of the graph are called excluded regions. (104)

exponential function An exponential function $y = a^t, a > 1$, has domain $\mathcal{R}$; for each $x_i \in \mathcal{R}$, the corresponding real number y_i in the range is the least upper bound $S = \{y \,|\, y = a^t, t$ is a rational number, and $t < x_i\}$. (333)

factor theorem The complex number c is a zero of a polynomial P if and only if $x - c$ is a factor of P. (305)

field A field (F) is a mathematical system which consists of a nonempty set F with an equivalence relation $(=)$ and two binary operations, addition $(+)$ and multiplication $(\cdot)$. These operations are defined on F and satisfy the properties of closure, associativity, identity, inverses, commutativity for both binary operations. The property of distributivity of multiplication over addition also exists. Also the equivalence relations of reflexivity, symmetry, and transitivity hold. (11)

FOR-NEXT loops FOR-NEXT loops are used in a BASIC computer program to repeat a portion of the program a certain number of times. (267)

function A function is a relation such that for each first element there corresponds a unique second element. (68)

Fundamental Theorem of Algebra Every polynomial function over the field of complex numbers has at least one zero. (305)

Fundamental Theorem of Calculus If f is a function continuous on $[a, b]$ and F is a function differentiable on $[a, b]$ and $F'(x) = f(x)$ for all $x \in [a, b]$, then

$$\int_a^b f(x)\, dx = F(b) - F(a). \quad (49)$$

general form **(1)** The equation $Ax + By + C = 0$, where A and B are not both zero, is called the general form of the equation of the line. (43) **(2)** The equation $Ax + By + Cz + D = 0$ is called the general or scalar form for the equation of a plane. (258)

general polar equation of a circle The general polar equation of a circle is

$$a^2 = r^2 + c^2 - 2rc\cos(\theta - \phi). \quad (367)$$

general polar form of a line The general polar form of a line is

$$r\cos(\theta - \omega) = \rho. \quad (367)$$

geometric means The terms between two given terms of a geometric sequence are called geometric means. (400)

geometric sequence (1) A geometric sequence is a sequence in which each term after the first is obtained by multiplying the previous term by a constant factor. (391) (2) A geometric sequence is a sequence $\{a_n\}$ such that $a_1 = a$, $a_{n+1} = a_n \cdot r$, where r is the common ratio. (398)

geometric series The geometric series $a + ar + ar^2 + \ldots + ar^{n-1} + \ldots$ converges to $\dfrac{a}{1-r}$ if $|r| < 1$ and diverges if $|r| \geq 1$. (414)

GOTO statement A GOTO statement is a BASIC statement which returns the computer to a particular step in a program. (239)

greatest integer function The greatest integer function is a step function f such that $f(x) = [x]$, where $[x]$ is the greatest integer not greater than x. (73)

growth formula The growth formula may be expressed by the function $y = y_0 2^{t/h}$ where h is the growth rate factor of time doubling. (348)

half-angles formulas The half-angles formulas are as follows. (178)

$$\left.\begin{array}{l} \tan \frac{1}{2}A = \dfrac{r}{s-a} \\[2mm] \tan \frac{1}{2}B = \dfrac{r}{s-b} \\[2mm] \tan \frac{1}{2}C = \dfrac{r}{s-c} \end{array}\right\} \quad \text{where} \quad r = \dfrac{\sqrt{(s-a)(s-b)(s-c)}}{s} \quad \text{and} \quad s > \dfrac{a+b+c}{2}$$

half-life formula The half-life formula

$$y = y_0 \cdot \left(\frac{1}{2}\right)^{t/T} \text{ or } y = y_0 \cdot 2^{-t/T}$$

where T is the half-life of a substance. (349)

Hero's formula Hero's formula is a way to find the area of $\triangle ABC$ when the lengths of the three sides are known. (181)

$$a = \sqrt{s(s-a)(s-b)(s-c)}$$

horizontal unit vector The horizontal unit vector is $\vec{i} = \begin{pmatrix} 1 \\ 0 \end{pmatrix}$ for two-dimensional vectors. (217)

hyperbola A hyperbola is the locus of points in a plane such that the difference of the distances from two fixed points called foci is a constant. The standard forms of the equations of a hyperbola with center at (h, k) and difference of the distance from the foci $2a$ are as follows. (277)

$$\dfrac{(x-h)^2}{a^2} - \dfrac{(y-k)^2}{b^2} = 1 \begin{cases} \text{If the transverse} \\ \text{axis is} \\ \text{horizontal} \end{cases}$$

$$\dfrac{(y-k)^2}{a^2} - \dfrac{(x-h)^2}{b^2} = 1 \begin{cases} \text{If the transverse} \\ \text{axis is vertical} \end{cases}$$

identity (1) There is an element A' in F such that $a * A' = A' * a = a$ where $*$ is a binary operation defined on F. (11) (2) An identity is an equation which is true for all permissible values of the variables. (140)

identity function The identity function maps each element of the domain into itself. (72)

IF-THEN statements The IF-THEN statement is a BASIC statement which makes a comparison of two numbers and then tells the computer what to do based on this comparison. (266)

imaginary part The imaginary part of a complex number, $a + bi$, is b. (56)

inclination The angle α which a line makes with a positively directed ray on the x-axis is called the inclination of the line. (40)

increasing function (1) A function f is increasing if for $x_1, x_2 \in D(f)$ and $x_1 < x_2$, $f(x_1) < f(x_2)$. (87) (2) If $f(x) > 0$ for every x in an interval, $a < x < b$, then the function is increasing in that interval. (463)

indefinite integral   In the sentence $\int f(x)\,dx = F(x) + C$, the expression $\int f(x)\,dx$ is called an indefinite integral, the function f is called the integrand, and C is called the constant of integration.   (494)

induction postulate   Let $P(n)$ be a statement involving a natural number $n \in N$. Then P is true for every natural number if and only if **(a)** $P(1)$ is true and **(b)** For any natural number k, if $P(k)$ is true then $P(k + 1)$ is true.   (402)

initial side   The initial side of an angle is the starting position of a ray used to generate an angle by rotation.   (165)

Integer Zero theorem   If a polynomial $P(x) = 1 \cdot x^n + a_{n-1} x^{n-1} + \ldots + a_1 x + a_0$ has a leading coefficient 1, integral coefficients, and $a_0 \neq 0$, then any rational zeros are integers and divide a_0.   (313)

inverse function   The functions of f and g are inverse functions if $f(g(x)) = x$ for every $x \in D\,(g)$ and $g(f(y)) = y$ for every $y \in D(f)$.   (83)

inverse property   If a is an element of F, then there is an element a' in F such that $a * a'$ is equal to the identity element for the binary operation defined.   (12)

latus rectum   The latus rectum of a conic is a line segment through a focus perpendicular to the axis with endpoints on the conic.   **(1)** The length of the latus rectum for a parabola is $|4p|$ where $|p|$ is the distance from the focus to the vertex.   (273)   **(2)** The length of the latus rectum of an ellipse or a hyperbola is $\dfrac{2b^2}{a}$.   (276, 279)

Law of Cosines   The Laws of Cosines can be stated as follows.   (175)

$$a^2 = b^2 + c^2 - 2bc \cos A$$
$$b^2 = a^2 + c^2 - 2ac \cos B$$
$$c^2 = a^2 + b^2 - 2ab \cos C$$

Law of Sines   The Law of Sines can be stated as follows.   (175)

$$\frac{\sin A}{a} = \frac{\sin B}{b} = \frac{\sin C}{c}$$

Law of Tangents   The law of Tangents can be stated as follows.   (178)

$$\frac{a - b}{a + b} = \frac{\tan \frac{1}{2}(A - B)}{\tan \frac{1}{2}(A + B)}$$

lemniscate   A lemniscate is a curve with equation of the form $r^2 = a^2 \cos 2\,\theta$ or $r^2 = a^2 \sin 2\,\theta$.   (379)

LET statement   A LET statement is a BASIC statement which assigns specific values to indicated variables.   (236)

limacon   A limaçon is a curve with equations of the form $r = a + b \cos \theta$ or $r = a + b \sin \theta$.   (380)

limit   The $\lim\limits_{x \to \infty} f(x) = L$ if and only if to each $\epsilon > 0$ there corresponds a number N such that $|f(x) - L| < \epsilon$ when $x > N$.   (437)

limit of a sequence   A number L is the limit of a sequence, $\{a_n\}$, if and only if for each neighborhood of the number L a natural number M can be found such that a_n is in that neighborhood if $n \geq M$.   (408)

linear equations   Linear equations are equations of lines whose graphs are straight lines.   (44)

linear function   A linear function is a function of the form $f(x) = mx + b$ for $m, b \in \mathcal{R}$ and $x \in D(f)$.   (73)

location principle   If f is a continuous function and $f(a)$ and $f(b)$ have opposite signs for a, $b \in \mathcal{R}$, then f has at least one zero between a and b.   (311, 435)

locus   A locus is the set of all points, and only those points, which satisfy a given set of conditions.   (54)

logarithmic function   The logarithmic function $y = \log_a x$, $a > 0$ and $a \neq 1$, is the inverse of the function $y = a^x$.   (340)

lower bound A real number I such that no zero of a function f is less than I is called a lower bound for the zeros of f. (312)

magnitude The length of the arrow, called the magnitude of the arrow, is $\sqrt{a^2 + b^2}$. (57)

major axis The major axis of an ellipse is the segment with endpoints at the vertices of the ellipse. (274)

mapping A mathematical relation makes a correspondence between the elements of its domain and range. This relationship is called a mapping. (66)

mathematical induction Mathematical induction is a method for proving statements involving natural numbers. (462)

method of false position The method of false position is a way to find or approximate zeros of a function. (435)

minor axis The minor axis of an ellipse is the segment perpendicular to the major axis at the center, with endpoints on the ellipse (274)

Mollweide's equation Molleweide's equation can be stated as follows. (178)

$$\frac{a - b}{c} = \frac{\sin \frac{1}{2}(A - B)}{\cos \frac{1}{2}C}$$

monotonic functions (1) Monotonic functions are functions which are either nondecreasing or nonincreasing. (88) (2) If a function f is monotonic over a closed interval $[a, b]$, then f reaches its maximum and minimum values at its endpoints. (89)

multiplicity A zero z of a polynomial P of degree $n > 0$ has multiplicity k if P can be factored as

$$P(x) = (x - 2)^k Q(x)$$

where $Q(x)$ is a polynomial of degree $n - k$ and z is not a zero of $Q(x)$. (308)

natural logarithms Base e logarithms are called natural logarithms. (342)

neighborhood For any point P on a number line, an open interval with P as its midpoint is called a neighborhood of P. The neighborhood of P with radius h units is the set of points between $p - h$ and $p + h$ and is written $\langle p - h, p + h \rangle$. (405)

nested intervals There is exactly one real number (point) common to all the intervals in an infinite sequence of closed intervals $\{l_n\}$ such that each interval contains its successor and the length of the interval approaches 0 as n increases without bound. (23)

nondecreasing function A function f is nondecreasing if whenever $x_1, x_2 \in D(f)$ and $x_1 < x_2$, then $f(x_1) \le f(x_2)$. (88)

nonincreasing function A function f is nonincreasing if whenever $x_1, x_2 \in D(f)$ and $x_1 < x_2$, then $f(x_1) > f(x_2)$. (88)

normal form The equation $x \cos \alpha + y \cos \beta + z \cos \gamma = \rho$ is the normal form for the equation of a plane. (257)

norm of a vector The magnitude of a vector is called the norm of the vector and is denoted $\|\bar{v}\|$, $\|\bar{v}\| = \sqrt{a^2 + b^2 + c^2}$. (247)

Number Line Postulate (NLP) There is a one-to-one correspondence between the points on a line and the real numbers. This correspondence is such that if the points A and B correspond to the real numbers a and b, then the distance between A and B is $|a - b|$. (8)

octants Three mutually perpendicular axes separate space into eight parts called octants which are named by the signs of the coordinates of points in the octant. (240)

odd relation An odd relation is a relation

which is symmetric with respect to the origin. (100)

open interval An open interval $\{x \mid a < x < b\}$ is represented as $\langle a, b \rangle$. (18)

opposite vectors The opposite of a vector $\bar{v}$ (written $-\bar{v}$) is the vector consisting of the class of arrows having the same slope and length as the arrows of $\bar{v}$, but with the opposite direction. (199)

order relation An order relation $(<)$ is defined on a field F has the properties of trichotomy (0_1) and transitivity (0_2). The relation also has the following two properties: If $a, b,$ and c are elements of F with $a < b$ then $(a + c) < (b + c)$. (0_3) If $a, b,$ and c are elements of F with $a < b$ and $0 < c$ then $a \cdot c < b \cdot c$. Also, if $a < b$ and $c < 0$, then $b \cdot c < a \cdot c$. (0_4) (17)

ordered fields The real numbers and rational numbers which satisfy the field and order properties are called ordered fields. (22)

ordinate The y-coordinate of a point is called the ordinate. (33)

origin The point of intersection of two numbers lines, the zero point on each line, is called the origin. (3)

orthogonal vectors (1) Two vectors are orthogonal if their position vectors lie on lines which are perpendicular. (212) (2) Two nonzero vectors are orthogonal if and only if their dot product is zero. (226)

parabola A parabola is the locus of points in a plane which are equidistant from a given point called the focus and a given line called the directrix. The standard form for equations of a parabola with vertex at (h, k), where $|p|$ is the distance from the focus to the vertex are as follows. (271)

$$(y - k)^2 = 4p\ (x - h) \begin{cases} \text{If the axis} \\ \text{of the parabola} \\ \text{is parallel to} \\ \text{the } x\text{-axis.} \end{cases}$$

$$(x - h)^2 = 4p\ (y - k) \begin{cases} \text{If the axis} \\ \text{of the parabola} \\ \text{is parallel to} \\ \text{the } y\text{-axis.} \end{cases}$$

parallel lines Two distinct nonvertical lines ℓ_1 and ℓ_2 with slopes m_1 and m_2, respectively, are parallel if and only if $m_1 = m_2$. (47)

parallel vectors (1) Two vectors are parallel if and only if they have the same or opposite direction. (200) (2) If two vectors $\bar{v}$ and $\bar{w}$ are parallel, then $\bar{v} \times \bar{w} = \bar{0}$. (252)

parameter A parameter, t, in some third variable used to express x and y. (44, 223)

parametric equations Points in a plane can be represented by expressing x and y in terms of some third variable t. Equations used as $3 - 2t = x$ and $t + 5 = y$ are called parametric equations. (44, 254)

period If p is the least constant for which $f(x) = f(x + p)$ then p is called the period. (127)

periodic function A function f such that $f(x) = f(x + p)$ is a periodic function. (74)

perpendicular lines Two nonvertical lines ℓ_1 and ℓ_2 with slopes m_1 and m_2, respectively, are perpendicular if and only if $m_1\ m_2 = -1$. (48)

phase shift The graph of $y = \sin\left(2x - \dfrac{\pi}{3}\right)$ is the same as that of $y = \sin 2x$ shifted $\dfrac{\pi}{6}$ units to the right. This difference is called a phase shift. (135)

point-slope form If the point (x_1, y_1) lies on a line having slope, m, the point-slope form of the equation of the lines is as follows. (42)

$$y - y_1 = m\ (x - x_1)$$

polar axis The polar axis is a fixed ray drawn usually in a horizontal direction from a point known as the pole. (359)

polar coordinates   If $0 \le \theta < 360°$ and θ is in standard position, then every point (x, y) in the plane can be described by (r, θ), where $x = r \cos \theta, y = r \sin \theta$, and $\theta = $ arctan $\frac{y}{x}$.   (167)

polar distance formula   The polar distance formula for the distance between $P_1 (r_1, \theta_1)$ and $P_2 (r_2, \theta_2)$ is $(P_2 P_1)^2 = r_2{}^2 + r_1{}^2 - 2 r_2 r_1 \cos (\theta_2 - \theta_1)$.   (362)

polar graph   The pole graph of a given relation is the set of all points which have at least one pair of polar coordinates that satisfy a given condition.   (363)

pole   The pole is a fixed point 0 in the plane.   (359)

polynomial functions   A polynomial function, P, is one which may be expressed as $P(x) = a_n x^n + a_{n-1} x^{n-1} + a_{n-2} x^{n-2} + \ldots + a_1 x + a_0$ where $n \in W, a_n \ne 0$.   (295)

position vector   An arrow drawn from the origin to a point (a, b) is called a position vector.   (199)

principal value   Principal values of trigonometric functions are the values in the domain of the functions sine, cosine, and tangent.   (154)

projection of a vector   The projection of a vector $\bar{v}$ on a line ℓ is a vector $\bar{v}_l$, determined by drawing perpendiculars from the endpoints of $\bar{v}$ to the line.   (213)

pure imaginary numbers   Any number which can be written in the form $0 + bi$ is called a pure imaginary number.   (56)

Pythagorean Theorem   The Pythagorean Theorem is $a^2 + b^2 = c^2$ where a and b are legs of a right triangle and c is the hypotenuse.   (36)

quadrantal values   Quadrantal values are values which occur at the boundaries of the quadrants.   (130)

quadrants   The two axes separate the plane into four regions called quadrants.   (34)

quadric surfaces   Second-degree equations which contain three variables describe surfaces called quadric surfaces.   (285)

radian   A radian is the measure of a central angle whose sides intercept an arc which has length one unit.   (165)

range   The range is the set of all second elements.   (65)

rational function   A rational function is the quotient of two polynomial functions. It has the form $y = \frac{P(x)}{Q(x)}$, where P and Q are polynomials and $Q(x) \ne 0$.   (321)

rational number line   The rational number line is the correspondence established between the rational numbers and a subset of the points on a line.   (4)

Rational Zero theorem   Suppose that $P(x) = a_n x^n + a_{n-1} x^{n-1} + \ldots + a_1 x + a_0$ is a polynomial with integer coefficients. If $\frac{p}{q}$ is a rational zero of P, and $\frac{p}{q} \ne 0$, then p is a factor of a_0 and q is a factor of a_n providing p and q are relatively prime.   (313)

real part   The real part of the complex number, $a + bi$ is a.   (56)

reflection   Two distant points P and P' are symmetric with respect to a point Q, or P' is the reflection of P in Q, if Q is the midpoint of $\overline{PP'}$ Point Q is symmetric with respect to itself.   (99)

reflexive property   If a is an element of F, then $a = a$.   (12)

relation   A pairing of elements of a set with elements of the same or a second set is called a mathematical relation.   (65)

roots of a polynomial equation   The roots of

a polynomial equation are those values of x for which $P(x) = 0$. Such a value also is called a zero of the polynomial. (296)

rose A rose is a curve with equation of the form $r = a \cos n\theta$ or $r = a \sin n\theta$, $n \in \mathbb{N}$. (377)

scalar component The norm of a vector projection on a line is called the scalar component of that vector on the line. (214)

scalar multiplication Scalar multiplication kf of a function produces a multiplication of the ordinates of f.

$$(kf)(x) = k \cdot f(x). \quad (117)$$

secant function The secant function is defined as follows. (137)

$$\left\{ (x, y) \mid y = \sec x = \frac{1}{\cos x} \right\}$$

second order determinant The symbol $\begin{vmatrix} a & b \\ c & d \end{vmatrix}$ in which a, b, c, and d denote numbers is called a second order determinant. (251) $\begin{vmatrix} a & b \\ c & d \end{vmatrix} = ad - bc$

second derivative The derivative of the derived function of f written as f'' is called the second derivative. (469)

sequence A sequence is a function with domain $\mathbb{N}$. Any sequence maybe defined by a formula or by listing ordered pairs of the sequence. (389)

series When an infinite number of addends are given in order, the expression is called a series. (414) $\sum\limits_{n=1}^{\infty} a_n$, or $a_1 + a_2 + \ldots$

slope The slope of the line is the ratio of the change in the ordinates of the points to the corresponding change in the abscissas. (39) $m = \dfrac{y_2 - y_1}{x_2 - x_1}$

slope-intercept form Suppose the slope of a line is m and its y-intercept is $(0, b)$. The slope-intercept form of the equation of the line is $y = mx + b$. (43)

solution theorem If a and b are elements of F, then there is a unique element $x = b + (-a)$, in F such that $x + a = b$. (15)

sphere The locus of all points in space at a given distance from a given point is a sphere. (261)

Spiral of Archimedes The Spiral of Archimedes has an equation of the form $r = a\theta$. (381)

standard position An angle with its vertex at the origin and its initial side along the positive x-axis is said to be in standard position. (165)

stationary values Stationary values are points at which the function is neither increasing nor decreasing. If $f'(x) = 0$, then $f(a)$ is a stationary value of f at $x = a$. (465)

step function A step function is a discontinuous function which "jumps" from one level to another. (73)

symmetric form If the parameter, t, is eliminated from parametric equation of a line the resulting set of equalities is said to be in symmetric form. (254)

symmetric property If a and b are elements of F and $a = b$, then $b = a$. (12)

symmetry Two distant points P and P' are symmetric with respect to a line ℓ if it is the perpendicular bisector of $\overleftrightarrow{PP'}$. If $P = P'$, the point is symmetric with respect to ℓ if P is on ℓ. (97)

terminal side The terminal side of an angle is the final position of a ray used to generate the angle by rotation. (165)

terms The addends $a_n x^n$, $a_{n-1} x^{n-1}$, $a_{n-2} x^{n-2}$, $\ldots a_1 x$, a_0 are the terms of the polynomial. (295)

traces Sections of quadric surfaces formed by planes which are parallel to the coordinate axis are called the traces of the surface in the coordinate planes. (285)

transitive property If $a, b,$ and c are elements of F with $a = b$ and $b = c$, then $a = c$. (12)

translation If a function $y = f(x)$ has the variable x replaced by $(x - h)$, then the result is a translation $|h|$ units to the right if $h > 0$ or $|h|$ units to the left is $h < 0$. (110)

transverse axis A transverse axis is a line segment that has its endpoints at the vertices. (278)

Trapezoid Rule The trapezoid rule is a method to obtain approximations for some number n of small intervals.

$$\int_a^b f(x) \, dx = \frac{1}{2} h \left[f(x_0) + 2f(x_1) + 2f(x_2) + \ldots + 2f(x_{n-1}) + f(x_n) \right] \cdot \quad (500)$$

trichotomy property If a and b are elements of F, then exactly one of the following is true. (17)

$$a < b, a = b, b < a$$

trigonometric form Complex numbers written in terms of trigonometric functions are said to be in trigonometric form. (183)

$$a + bi = r \cos \theta + (r \sin \theta) i$$

trigonometric functions (1) For any angle with measure α, point $P(x, y)$ on its terminal side, and $r = \sqrt{x^2 + y^2}$, the trigonometric functions of α are as follows.

$$\sin \alpha = \frac{y}{r} \quad \cos \alpha = \frac{x}{r} \quad \tan \alpha = \frac{y}{x}$$

$$\csc \alpha = \frac{r}{y} \quad \sec \alpha = \frac{r}{x} \quad \cot \alpha = \frac{x}{y}$$

(165) (2) For an acute angle A in right triangle ABC, the trigonometric functions are as follows. (171)

$$\sin A = \frac{\text{side opposite}}{\text{hypotenuse}} \quad \cos A = \frac{\text{side adjacent}}{\text{hypotenuse}}$$

$$\tan A = \frac{\text{side opposite}}{\text{side adjacent}} \quad \cot A = \frac{\text{side adjacent}}{\text{side opposite}}$$

$$\sec A = \frac{\text{hypotenuse}}{\text{side adjacent}} \quad \csc A = \frac{\text{hypotenuse}}{\text{side opposite}}$$

unit circle A circle with center at the origin and a radius of 1 unit is called a unit circle. (127)

unit vector A unit vector is defined for each direction and has a length of 1 unit. (199)

upper bound A real number u such that no zero of a function f is greater than u is called an upper bound for the zeros of f. (312)

vector A vector is a quantity which possesses both magnitude and direction. (198)

vector space A vector space is a mathematical system that consists of a nonempty set of ordered pairs, a nonempty set of scalars, an equivalence relation, and two binary operations, addition and scalar multiplication. (208)

vertex The point of a conic that is nearest the focus and the directrix is called the vertex. (271)

vertical unit vector The vertical unit vector is $\vec{j} = \begin{pmatrix} 0 \\ 1 \end{pmatrix}$ for two-dimensional vectors. (217)

x-axis The horizontal line is usually called the x-axis. (33)

x-intercept The x-intercept is the point, $(a, 0)$, where the line intersects the x-axis. (103)

y-axis The vertical line is usually called the y-axis. (33)

y-intercept The y-intercept is the point, $(0, b)$, where the line intersects the y-axis. (42, 103)

zero vectors Zero vector or null vector has any direction and has length zero. (199)

zero polynomial A zero polynomial has no degree. (295)

Selected Answers

CHAPTER 1 THE REAL NUMBER LINE

Page 6 Exploratory Exercises 1. Draw a line l and label 0 and 1. Draw a second line m intersecting l at 0. Mark off 5 congruent intervals on m and label the endpoints of the intervals A, B, C, D, E. Now draw a line k through E on m and 1 on l. Construct a line through B parallel to k. The point at which this line intersects l corresponds to $\frac{2}{5}$.

For Problems **5–8**, use the method of Example 2. The values for m and n are given for each case, **5.** $m = 2, n = 2$ **7.** $m = 7, n = 3$ **9.** Use the method of Example 2 with $m = 2$ and $n = 6$. Or, use $m = 3$ and $n = 4$.

Page 6 Written Exercises 1. . . . cut off congruent segments on any transversal. **7.** Begin by drawing a line intersecting the axis at the origin. Mark off on the line, n congruent intervals. Then draw a line from the nth point to 1. Find the mth interval on the line of intersection and draw a line parallel to the line through the nth point and 1. **13.** Example 2: Given a right triangle ABC, draw the altitude, h, from the right angle C to the hypotenuse $\overline{AB}$. Label the intersection D. Two right triangles are formed. $\triangle ADC$ has sides of $h, m,$ and b. $\triangle BDC$ has sides of $h, n,$ and a where $m + n = c$. Using the Pythagorean Theorem, we have the following equations.

$$a^2 + b^2 = c^2$$
$$m^2 + h^2 = b^2$$
$$n^2 + h^2 = a^2$$

By substitution, $m^2 + h^2 + n^2 + h^2 = c^2$. But $c^2 = (m + n)^2 = m^2 + 2mn + n^2$. By substitution, $m^2 + h^2 + n^2 + h^2 = m^2 + 2mn + n^2$ Solve for h.

$$2h^2 = 2\,mn$$
$$h = \sqrt{mn}$$

Page 7 Challenge Exercises 1. yes **3.** yes

Page 9 Exploratory Exercises 1. The point x is 3 units from the origin. **3.** The point x is 2 units from the point -3. **5.** $|x + 2| < 3$ **7.** $|x| \leq 5$

Page 9 Written Exercises 1. The points x and y are d units apart. **3.** The point x is less than 1 unit from -3. **5.** The point x is equidistant from 2 and -4. **7.** $|x - 5| \geq 3$ **9.** $|2d + 3| > 4$ **11.** 9, -9 **13.** 2, -2 **15.** $x < -5$ or $x > -1$

Page 10 Challenge Exercises 1. False; $x = 1, y = -2$ **3.** If $x \geq 0$ and $y \geq 0$, then $xy = |xy| = |x| \cdot |y|$. If $x < 0$ and $y < 0$, then $xy > 0$ so $|xy| = xy = (-x) \cdot (-y) = |x| \cdot |y|$. If $x \geq 0$ and $y < 0$, then $xy \leq 0$ and $|xy| = x(-y) = |x| \cdot |y|$. If $x < 0$ and $y \geq 0$, then $xy \leq 0$ and $|xy| = (-x)y = |x| \cdot |y|$. **5.** If $a > b$, then $a - b = |a - b|$ and $|b - a| = |-(a - b)| = |a - b|$. If $b > a$, then $|a - b| = |-(b - a)| = |b - a|$.

Page 13 Exploratory Exercises 1. Commutativity for Addition **3.** Uniqueness of Addition **5.** Symmetric Property of Equality Answers will vary for Problems **7–12**. Answers should be similar to the answers given. **7.** $(1 + 3) + 4 = 1 + (3 + 4)$ **9.** $5 \cdot 6 = 6 \cdot 5$ **11.** If $8 = 4 + 4$ and $4 + 4 = 3 + 5$, then $8 = 3 + 5$. **13.** Since subtraction is defined as addition of the opposite (or additive inverse), then $x - y = x + (-y)$. Thus, the addition rules apply. Also division implies $\frac{x}{y} = x \cdot \left(\frac{1}{y}\right)$. Thus, the multiplication rules apply.

Page 13 Written Exercises 1. Additive Inverse **3.** Multiplicative Inverse **5.** Distributive Property Answers will vary for Problems **7–12**.

15. Assume $1'$ is any Multiplicative Identity in F.

a.	$1 \cdot 1' = 1'$	M_3
b.	$1 \cdot 1' = 1$	M_3
c.	$1 = 1 \cdot 1'$	E_2
d.	$1 = 1'$	E_3

Page 16 Exploratory Exercises 1. If a and b are elements of F and $a \neq 0$, then there is a unique element $x = b\left(\frac{1}{a}\right)$ in F such that $x \cdot a = b$. **3.** Commutativity for Multiplication **5.** Distributive Property **7.** M_2 and M_5 **9.** $M_2, M_3, M_4,$ and M_5

Page 16 Written Exercises For Problems **1–10**,

proofs will vary. The solutions are given for 1, 3, and 5. **1.** -3 **3.** 5 **5.** no solution

7. 1. $x \cdot a = b, a \neq 0$ Hypothesis

   2. $x \cdot a \cdot \dfrac{1}{a} = b \cdot \dfrac{1}{a}$ Uniqueness

   3. $x \cdot \left(a \cdot \dfrac{1}{a}\right) = b \cdot \dfrac{1}{a}$ M_2

   4. $x = b \cdot \dfrac{1}{a}$ M_4, M_3

   5. $x = \dfrac{b}{a}$ Definition of Division

9. 1. $a + -a = 0$ A_4
   2. $b + -b = 0$ A_4
   3. $a + (-a) + b + (-b) = 0$ A_3
   4. $(a + b) + (-a) + (-b) = 0$ A_2, A_5
   5. $(a + b) + -(a + b) = 0$ A_4
   6. $-(a + b) = (-a) + (-b)$ Uniqueness

Page 17 Challenge Exercises
A. Prove: $a(-b) = -ab$
   1. $a[b + (-b)] = ab + a(-b)$ D
   2. $b + (-b) = 0$ A_4
   3. $a[b + (-b)] = a \cdot 0 = 0$ Uniqueness
   4. $ab + a(-b) = 0$ E_3
   5. $a(-b) = -(ab)$ Uniqueness

Page 21 Exploratory Exercises 1. $x > y; y < x$

3. $5 \leq x \leq 20; 5 \leq x$ and $x \leq 20$ **5.** $\left\langle \dfrac{1}{2}, \rightarrow \right\rangle$

7. $\langle -2, 8 \rangle$ **9.** $4, -4$

Page 22 Written Exercises 1. $-3 \leq x \leq 3$; $-3 \leq x$ and $x \leq 3$ **3.** $x \leq 6; 6 \geq x$ **5.** $[-2,$ $\rightarrow \rangle$ **7.** $\left\langle -\dfrac{6}{5}, \rightarrow \right\rangle$ **9.** $\langle \leftarrow, -5] \cup [-1, \rightarrow \rangle$ **11.** $\langle \leftarrow, 0 \rangle \cup \langle 0, \rightarrow \rangle$ **13.** $\langle -1, 3 - \sqrt{3} \rangle \cup \langle 3 + \sqrt{3},$ $\rightarrow \rangle$ **15.** $\left\langle \leftarrow, \dfrac{1}{4} \right\rangle \cup \langle 2, \rightarrow \rangle$ **17.** If $|x - a| < b$ then $x - a < b$ and if $x - a > -b$ then $x < b + a$. Thus, if $x > -b + a$ then $-b + a < x < b + a$.

Page 22 Challenge Exercises 1. If P_z is between P_x and P_y, then $|x - z| + |z - y| = |x - y|$. If P_x is between P_y and P_z, then $|z - y| = |x - z| + |x - y|$. So $|x - z| + |z - y| = |x - z| + |z - x| + |x - y| > |x - y|$. Similarly if P_y is between P_x and P_z, $|x - z| + |z - y| = |x - y| + |y - z| + |z - y| > |x - y|$. **3.** If $x > 0$ and $y > 0$, then $x + y > 0$ and $|x + y| = x + y = |x| + |y|$. If $x < 0$ and $y < 0$, then $-(x + y) = (-x) + (-y)$ and $|x + y| = |x| + |y|$. If $x > 0$ and $y < 0$, then $x + y < x + (-y)$ and $|x + y| < x + -y = |x| + |y|$. The last argument applies to the case where $x < 0$ and $y > 0$.

Page 24 Written Exercises 1. $\{[2.2, 2.3], [2.23, 2.24], [2.236, 2.237], [2.2360, 2.2361], [2.23606, 2.23607]\}$ **3.** $\{[2.6, 2.7], [2.64, 2.65], [2.645, 2.646], [2.6457, 2.6458], [2.64575, 2.64576]\}$ **5.** $\{[5.0, 5.1], [5.09, 5.10], [5.099, 5.100], [5.0990, 5.0991], [5.09901, 5.09902]\}$ **7.** Answers will vary. **9.** $\dfrac{15}{11}$

Page 25 Challenge Exercise 1. No, it can be proved to be unique. The case in the section specifies uniqueness but other alternatives do not specify this property.

Page 26 Excursion Exercises 1. Case 1: For every x, either $x^2 \geq 3$ or $x^2 < 3$, so $x \in R$ or $x \in L$. **Case 2:** $1 \in L, 2 \in R$, so $L \neq 0$ and $R \neq 0$. **Case 3:** If $a \in L$ and $b \in R$ then $a^2 < 3 \leq b^2$ for the case that $a > 0$. If $a < 0$, then $a < 0 < 3 \leq b^2$. In either case $a < b$.

Page 27 Chapter Review 1. Draw line l intersecting the number line at 0. Mark off 5 congruent segments on l starting at 0. Number their endpoints 1, 2, 3, 4, 5. Draw line m through 5 on l and 1 on the number line. Construct a line parallel to m through 4 on l. This line intersects the number line at $\dfrac{4}{5}$. **3.** Use the method of Exercise 1 on $[-5, -4]$ to find $[-4.5, -4.4]$. Repeat the procedure to find -4.47. **5.** Construct a right triangle with the altitude from the right angle indicated so that it intersects the hypotenuse forming two segments of length $m = \dfrac{1}{2}$ and $n = \dfrac{17}{2}$. **7.** Point x is 4 units from the origin. **9.** The point x is d units from the point $-y$. **11.** $|x| = 5$ **13.** $3, -3$ **15.** $3, -\dfrac{11}{3}$ **17.** Prove if $a, b, c \in F$ and $c + a = c + b$, then $a = b$.

   1. $c + a = c + b$ Hypothesis
   2. $-c + c + a = -c + c + b$ Uniqueness of +
   3. $(-c + c) + a = (-c + c) + b$ A_2
   4. $a = b$ A_4, A_3

19. Assume $\dfrac{1}{a}$ and b are inverses of a.

   1. $(b \cdot a) \cdot \dfrac{1}{a} = 1 \cdot \dfrac{1}{a}$ M_4

   2. $1 \cdot \dfrac{1}{a} = \dfrac{1}{a}$ M_3

3. $(b \cdot a) \cdot \dfrac{1}{a} = b \left(a \cdot \dfrac{1}{a} \right)$ M_2

4. $b \left(a \cdot \dfrac{1}{a} \right) = b \cdot 1$ M_4

5. $b \cdot 1 = b$ M_3

6. $\dfrac{1}{a} = b$ E_3, E_2

23. -7 **25.** $ad + cb$ **27.** $[-3, 3]$

31. $\{[3.8, 3.9], [3.87, 3.88], [3.872, 3.873]\}$

CHAPTER 2 THE PLANE

Page 35 Exploratory Exercises 1. I, III; (0, 0)
3. All; points of the form (0, y) **5.** II, IV; none
7. $\{(1, A), (1, B), (1, C), (2, A), (2, B), (2, C), (3, A),$
$(3, B), (3, C), (4, A), (4, B), (4, C)\}$ **9.** $\{(\pi, -4),$
$(\pi, -3), (\pi, 0), (\pi, 15), (e, -4), (e, -3), (e, 0), (e, 15), (i,$
$-4), (i, -3), (i, 0), (i, 15)\}$

Page 35 Written Exercises 1. $x = 5$, $y = 1$
3. $x = -4$, $y = 4$ or -4 **5.** $x = 4$, $y = 3$ **7.**
$(h, k + 1)$ **9.** (2, 5) **11.** $\{(a, d), (a, b), (a, c)\}$
13. $M \times N = \{(a, a), (a, c), (b, a), (b, c)\}$; $N \times$
$M = \{(a, a), (a, b), (c, a), (c, b)\}$; no **15.** $\{(-1, 0),$
$(-1, 1), (-1, 2), (0, 0), (0, 1), (0, 2), (1, 0), (1, 1),$
$(1, 2)\}$ **17.** (4, -5) **19.** $(p + 2, 3 - q)$ **21.**
$(-3, -2)$ **23.** $(-p - 2, q - 3)$ **25.** $45°$

Page 38 Exploratory Exercises 1. 8 **3.** $3\sqrt{5}$
5. $\sqrt{58}$ **7.** $\left(\dfrac{13}{4}, 5 \right)$ **9.** $\left(\dfrac{5}{2}, -\dfrac{11}{2} \right)$ **11.** $\left(\dfrac{5}{2}, 4 \right)$
13. (1, -4)

Page 38 Written Exercises 1. 3 **3.** $|a - b|$
5. $k\sqrt{5}$ **7.** $\left(\dfrac{3}{5}h, \dfrac{2}{5}m \right)$ **9.** (0.7, 8.3) **11.** $\left(\dfrac{1}{2}h, \right.$
$\left. \dfrac{1}{2}m \right)$ **13.** (-0.3, 8.3) **15.** $AB = \sqrt{58}$, $BC =$
$\sqrt{58}$, $CA = \sqrt{116}$, $(AB)^2 + (BC)^2 = (CA)^2$ **17.** The
midpoint of $\overline{AB}$ is (1, 3), the midpoint of $\overline{AC}$ is
(2, 1). The segment joining them has length $\sqrt{5}$
and $BC = 2\sqrt{5}$. **19.** The midpoint of diagonal
$\overline{AC}$ is (1, -1), the midpoint of $\overline{BD}$ is (1, -1). Thus,
the diagonals bisect each other. **21.** Each point
is 5 units from (2, 3). **23.** $(-3 + 2\sqrt{3}, 4)$ and
$(-3, -2\sqrt{3}, 4)$ **25.** -8 or 0 **27.** The distance
between (2, 5) and the center is $\sqrt{17}$. Since
$\sqrt{17} > 4$, the point is outside the circle.

Page 41 Exploratory Exercises 1. $\dfrac{3}{2}$ **3.** 9
5. 0 **7.** The slope between each pair of points
is 1 so the points are collinear. **9.** The slope between each pair of points is 2.

Page 41 Written Exercises 1. $-\dfrac{2b}{7a}$, $a \neq 0$
3. a, $a \neq 1$ **5.** 2, $m \neq 3$ **7.** 8 **9.** 2
13. 59 **15.** The slope of the median is $\dfrac{1}{2}$, the
slope of the base is -2. **17.** -3 and $\dfrac{1}{3}$ **19.** $135°$
21. It falls to the right.

Page 46 Exploratory Exercises 1. $y - 7 = \dfrac{2}{5}(x -$
$1)$ **3.** $y - 4 = 2(x - 10)$ **5.** $x - y + 4 = 0$
7. $x - 8 = 0$ **9.** $y + 5 = 0$

Page 46 Written Exercises 1. $x + 4y + 31 = 0$
3. $rx - 2y - 2r - 6 = 0$ **5.** $7x - 2y - 31 = 0$
7. $3x + 5y - 14 = 0$ **9.** $3bx + 4y - b = 0$ **11.**
$5x + 16y + 47 = 0$ **13.** $\dfrac{x}{a} + \dfrac{y}{b} = 1$, a and $b \neq 0$
15. $(x - y + 3)(x + y - 3) = 0$

17. $(3x - y - 1)(x - 2) = 0$

19. $4x + 7y - 48 = 0$

Page 48 Exploratory Exercises 1. parallel
3. perpendicular **5.** neither

Page 49 Written Exercises 1. $3x - 4y + 39 = 0$
3. $ax + by - a^2 - b^2 = 0$ **5.** $x + 5y - 25 = 0$
7. $k = 4$; $k = -\dfrac{49}{4}$ **9.** $x + y - 6 = 0$ **11.** $ax +$
$4by - 5a^2 - 16b^2 = 0$ **13.** The slope of $\overline{AB}$ is $\dfrac{4}{5}$;
The slope of $\overline{CD}$ is $-\dfrac{5}{4}$. So $\overline{AB} \perp \overline{CD}$ and (3, 11) is
the midpoint of each segment. **15.** $\overline{AC}$ and $\overline{BD}$
have the same midpoint, (1, 1). The slope of $\overline{AC}$

is $-\frac{3}{2}$ and the slope of $\overline{BD}$ is $\frac{2}{3}$ so the diagonals are perpendicular. **17.** $4x + 3y - 22; x + 4y + 1 = 0$

Page 52 Exploratory Exercises 1. $A = 1, B = 1,$ $C = -5, \sqrt{A^2 + B^2} = \sqrt{2}$ **3.** $A = -2, B = 3,$ $C = -5, \sqrt{A^2 + B^2} = \sqrt{13}$ **5.** $A = 1, B = -1,$ $C = -7, \sqrt{A^2 + B^2} = \sqrt{2}$ **7.** $A = 15, B = 8,$ $C = -34, \sqrt{A^2 + B^2} = 17$ **9.** $A = 12, B = -5,$ $C = -20, \sqrt{A^2 + B^2} = 13$

Page 52 Written Exercises 1. $\frac{2\sqrt{10}}{5}$ **3.** $\frac{12\sqrt{10}}{5}$ **5.** 0 **7.** $\frac{12\sqrt{5}}{5}, 12$ **9.** $\frac{19\sqrt{5}}{5}, 57$

Page 54 Exploratory Exercises 1. $(1, 0)$ **3.** $(8, 9)$ **5.** $\left(\frac{a}{2}, \frac{b}{2}\right)$

Page 54 Written Exercises Proofs will vary. **1.** Choose axes as in the figure. The diagonals, $\overline{PR}$ and $\overline{QS}$ have slope -1 and 1 which are negative reciprocals. Therefore, the diagonals are perpendicular.

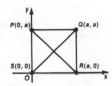

Page 54 Challenge Exercises Proofs will vary. **1.** The sum of the squares of the lengths of the sides equals $2(a^2 + b^2 + c^2 - ac)$. The sum of the squares of the lengths of the medians equals $\frac{3}{2}(a^2 + b^2 + c^2 - ac)$. The ratios of these measures is $\frac{3}{4}$.

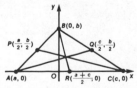

Page 55 Exploratory Exercises 1. It is a sphere with the given point as center and the given distance as length of its radius. **3.** It is the perpendicular bisector of the segment with the given points as endpoints.

Page 55 Written Exercises 1. $5x - 3y + 4 = 0$ **3.** $x + 2 = 0$ **5.** $x = \frac{p}{2} + 1$ **7.** $y^2 - 12x + 36 = 0$ **9.** $xy - 9x - 7y + 47 = 0$

11.

Page 58 Exploratory Exercises 1. $13 + i$ **3.** $2 + 0i$ **5.** $-7 + 0i$

Page 58 Written Exercises 1. $0 - i$ **3.** $-3 + 0i$ **5.** $1 + 27i$ **7.** $\frac{24}{61} + \frac{20}{61}i$ **9.** $2 - i$ **11.** $1 - 2i$ **13.** $x = 2, y = 1$ **15.** $6 - 3i$ **17.** $9 + 5i$ **19.** $-8 + 10i$ **21.** $\sqrt{34}, -\frac{5}{3}$ **23.** $\sqrt{17},$ $-\frac{1}{4}$ **25.** $[(a + bi) + (c + di)] + (e + fi) = [(a + c) + e] + [(b + d) + f]i = [a + (c + e)] + [b + (d + f)]i = (a + bi) + [(c + di) + (e + fi)]$ **27.** Let $a + bi$ and $c + di$ be complex numbers where a, b, c, and d are real numbers. Since the real numbers are closed under addition, $a + c$ and $b + d$ are unique real numbers. Thus, $(a + c) + (b + d)i$ is a unique complex number.

Page 60 Chapter Review 1. $x = -7, y = -6$ **3.** $\{(3, 1), (3, 2), (3, 3), (5, 1), (5, 2), (5, 3)\}$ **5.** $\left(\frac{1}{3}, \frac{7}{3}\right)$ **7.** 0 or 5 **9.** It falls to the right. **11.** $4x - 3y + 2 = 0$ **13.** $3x - 5y + 23 = 0$ **15.** 7 **17.** P and Q are the midpoints of $\overline{AB}$ and $\overline{CD}$. The slopes of $\overline{PQ}$ and $\overline{AD}$ equal 0. Therefore, $\overline{PQ} \parallel \overline{AD}$.

$$PQ = \left| \frac{a + c}{2} - \frac{-a - c}{2} \right| = |a + c|$$

$$AD + BC = |2a + 2c| = 2|a + c|$$

Therefore $QP = \frac{1}{2}(AD + BC)$.

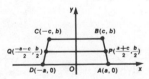

19. $x^2 - 4x + y^2 + 10y + 26 = 0$ **21.** $6 - 2i$ **23.** $13, -\frac{5}{12}$

Chapter 3 FUNCTIONS

Page 67 Exploratory Exercises 1. {(1, a), (1, b), (1, c), (2, a), (2, b), (2, c)} **3.** yes **5.** Answers will vary {(1, a), (2, c)} **7.** {x|x ≥ 0}, {y|y ≥ 0}

Page 67 Written Exercises 1. {x|x ∈ ℛ} {y|y ∈ ℛ} **3.** {x|x ∈ ℛ} $\left\{y|y \geq -\frac{1}{4}\right\}$ **5.** {x|−2 ≤ x ≤ 2}, {y| − 2 ≤ y ≤ 2}

7. a. **9.** b.

Page 68 Challenge Exercise D(U) = {x|x ≤ −1 or x > 2}, R(U) = {y|y ≥ 0 but y ≠ 1}

Page 71 Exploratory Exercises 1. 6 **3.** −6 **5.** 2 **7.** $\frac{24}{x^2}$ − 2 **9.** The numbers are equal.

Page 71 Written Exercises 1. −2 **3.** −2 or 0 **5.** −3 or 3 **7.** D(f) = R(f) = ℛ; D(g) = {x|x ≠ −1}, R(g) = {y|y ≠ −2} The functions are the same except for x = − 1, g is undefined.

9. {y|−3 ≤ y ≤ 3} **11.** $\frac{1}{2}$ and 5 **13.** 3 **15.** 3 **17.** 3(x + h) − 1 **19.** x² + 3x **21.** yes **23.** no **25.** yes

Page 72 Challenge Exercises 1. If (a, b) ∈ f and (a, c) ∈ f, then b = $\frac{3}{a - 2}$ and c = $\frac{3}{a - 2}$, a ≠ 2. Thus, b = c **3.** D(g) = ℛ; R(g) = $\left\{y|0 < y \leq \frac{1}{3}\right\}$

Page 75 Exploratory Exercises 1. I **3.** C **5.** L **7.** L **9.** N

Page 75 Written Exercises

3.  **7.**

11. −4, −1, 0, 1, 0 **13.** $-\frac{4}{5}$ **15.** x ≥ −2 **17.** $\frac{10}{3}$ or −2 **19.** −1 or −3

Page 76 Challenge Exercises 1. f(s − 1) = 3(s − 1) + 2 = 3s − 1 **3.** π, 3π, 5π

Page 77 Exploratory Exercises 1. {(1, 0), (2, −1)} **3.** {(1, −1), (2, −12)} **5.** (1, −2), (2, 7)} **7.** $\left\{(1, -1), \left(2, -\frac{3}{4}\right)\right\}$

Page 77 Written Exercises 1. 5x −2 **3.** 6x² − 7x −3 **5.** x + 4 **7.** $\frac{3x + 1}{2x - 3}$ if x ≠ $\frac{3}{2}$ **9.** x + $\frac{1}{x}$ if x ≠ 0. **11.** 1 **13.** x − $\frac{1}{x}$, if x ≠ 0 **15.** x²

17. **19.**

27. f(x) = $-\frac{3}{2}x + \frac{19}{2}$

Page 78 Challenge Exercise By definition, −f = −1f. Since f = 0, f + (−f) = f + (−1f) = 0 + (−1·0) = 0

Page 80 Exploratory Exercises 1. f∘g = {(1, −1)}; g∘f = {(2, 5), (−3, 3)} **3.** (f∘g)(x) = $\frac{1}{x}$, if x ≠ 0; (g∘f)(x) = $\frac{1}{x}$, if x ≠ 0 **5.** f∘g = {(2, 2), (3, 0), (−2, √5)}; g∘f' = {(1, −1), (4, 4), (9, 0)} **7.** 1 **9.** 0

Page 80 Written Exercises 1. 2(x + 1)² **3.** 3√t² − 1 **5.** (f∘g)(x) = √x³, {x|x ≥ 0}, {y|y ≥ 0}; (g∘f)(x) = (√x)³, {x|x ≥ 0}, {y|y ≥ 0} **7.** (f∘g)(u) = u, D − R = ℛ; (g∘f)(u) = u, D = R = ℛ **9.** (f∘g)(t) = √1 − 3t², $\left\{t| -\frac{\sqrt{3}}{3} \leq t \leq \frac{\sqrt{3}}{3}\right\}$, {y|0 ≤ y ≤1|}; (g∘f)(t) = 1 − 3t, {t|t ≥ 0}, {y|y ≤ 1} **11.** f(r) − √r, g(r) = r² − 1, f∘g(r) = √r² − 1 **13.** f(x) = x², g(x) = $\frac{x + 2}{x}$, h(x) = x − 1, f∘g∘h(x) = $\left(\frac{x + 1}{x - 1}\right)^2$ **15.** h(x) = $\frac{3}{2}x$, g(x) = $\frac{x^2}{x + 1}$, f(x) = x + 1, f∘g∘h(x) = $\frac{3(x + 1)^2}{2(x + 2)}$

Page 81 Challenge Exercises 1. The sections of the graph of g in Quadrants III and IV are reflected in the x-axis by $f \circ g$. **3.** $(f \circ g)x = acx + ad + b$, slope of ac; $(q \circ f)x = acx + bc + d$.

Page 85 Exploratory Exercises 1. $f^{-1}(x) = \dfrac{3x - 5}{2}$ **3.** $g^{-1}(x) = \sqrt[3]{x + 6}$ **5.** $h^{-1}(x) = \{(1, 7), (3, 2), (-1, -3)\}$

Page 86 Written Exercises 1. $f^{-1}(x) = \dfrac{1 + x}{1 - x}$, $D = \{x \mid x \neq 1\}$ **3.** $f^{-1}(x) = \sqrt{x - 2}$, $D = \{x \mid x \geq 2\}$ **5.** $g^{-1}(t) = \sqrt{1 - t^2}$, $D = \{0 \leq t \leq 1\}$ **7.** $j^{-1}(x) = \sqrt{\dfrac{1 - x}{x}}$, $D = \{x \mid 0 < x \leq 1\}$ **9.** $m^{-1}(x) = (x - 5)^2$, $D = \{x \mid x \geq 5\}$

11.

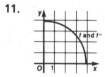

15.

23. $f^{-1}(x) = \dfrac{x - 1}{x} = g(x)$ **25.** $h = g$

Page 87 Challenge Exercises 1. Let f be a 1-1 function, and suppose that $(a, c), (b, c) \in f^{-1}$. Then $(c, a), (c, b) \in f$. Since f is a function $a = b$. Hence, f^{-1} is also a 1-1 function. **3.** Let $f(x) = ax + b$, $a \neq 0$. Then $f^{-1}(x) = \dfrac{1}{a}x - \dfrac{b}{a}$ which is a linear function.

Page 90 Exploratory Exercises 1. decreasing **3.** combination **5.** nondecreasing

Page 91 Written Exercises 1. nondecreasing **3.** combination **5.** increasing **7.** decreasing on $\langle \leftarrow, 1 \rangle$; increasing on $\langle 1, \rightarrow \rangle$ **9.** greater than or equal to **11.** greater than or equal to **13.** Suppose $x_1 < x_2 \leq 0$. Then $(x_1 - x_2) < 0$ and $(x_1 + x_2) < 0$. Therefore $(x_1 - x_2)(x_1 + x_2) = x_1^2 - x_2^2 > 0$ or $x_1^2 > x_2^2$. Thus, $y = x^2$ is decreasing for $x \leq 0$. **15.** Suppose $x_1 < x_2$. Then $x_2^3 - x_1^3 = (x_2 - x_1)(x_2^2 + x_2 x_1 + x_1^2)$ and $x_2 - x_1 \geq 0$. If either $0 \leq x_1 < x_2$ or $x_1 < x_2 \leq 0$ then $x_1 x_2 \geq 0$. This implies that $x_2^2 + x_2 x_1^2 + x_1^2 \geq 0$. If $x_1 < 0 \leq x_2$, then $x_1 x_2 \leq 0$. This implies that $x_2^2 + x_2 x_1 + x_1^2 > x_2^2 + 2x_2 x_1 + x_1^2 = (x_2 - x_1)^2 > 0$. Therefore, $x_2^3 - x_1^3 > 0$ and $x_2^3 > x_1^3$ **17.** Let $f(x) = x$ and $g(x) = -1$. Both f and g are nondecreasing functions. $(f \cdot g)(x) = x(-1) = -x$ which is nonincreasing.

Page 90 Challenge Exercises 1. If $0 < b$ then $f(a) \leq f(b)$ and $g(a) \leq g(b)$. So $f(a) = g(a) \leq f(a) + g(b) \leq f(b) + g(b)$. Therefore, $(f + g)(a) \leq (f + g)(b)$. **3.** If f is strictly monotonic, it is 1-1 by the theorem for strictly monotonic functions. Hence, it has an inverse function.

Page 92 Chapter Review 1. S is a parabola with vertex at $(0, 4)$. The graph opens upward. **3.** $R(S) = [4, \rightarrow)$ **5.** $\dfrac{4}{3}$ **7.** undefined **9.** -4 **11.** $-\dfrac{256}{63}$ **15.** 1.5 **17.** N **19.** C **23.** $\{(0, 0), (-1, 6), (2, 0)\}$ **25.** $\{(0, 2), (-1, 1), (2, -1)\}$ **27.** $\left\{(0, 0), \left(-1, \dfrac{3}{2}\right)\right\}$ **29.** $f \circ g = \{(2, -1), (-1, 2), (1, 2) (0, 2)\}$, $D(f \circ g) = \{2, -1, 1, 0\}$ $R(f \circ g) = \{-1, 2\}$; $g \circ f \{(0, 1), (1, 3),(3, 1)\}$, $D(g \circ f) = \{0, 1, 3\}$, $R(g \circ f) = \{1, 3\}$ **31.** $\{(2, 1), (3, -1), (1, 0)\}$ **33.** increasing **35.** f is decreasing on $\left\langle \leftarrow, \dfrac{3}{2} \right\rangle$ and increasing on $\left\langle \dfrac{3}{2}, \rightarrow \right\rangle$. On the interval $[0, 0.5]$, f has the maximum value 2 and minimum $\dfrac{3}{4}$.

CHAPTER 4 GRAPHING TECHNIQUES

Page 102 Exploratory Exercises 1. (a) $(0, 0)$ (b) $(0, 0)$ (c) $(0, 0)$ (d) $(0, 0)$ (e) $(6, -4)$ **3.** (a) $(-2, -5)$ (b) $(2, 5)$ (c) $(2, -5)$ (d) $(5, -2)$ (e) $(8, 9)$ **5.** (a) $(2, 0)$ (b) $(-2, 0)$ (c) $(-2, 0)$ (d) $(0, 2)$ (e) $(4, -4)$

Page 102 Written Exercises 1. c **3.** e **5.** e **7.** b **9.** e **11.** a **13.** a, b, c, d **15.** e **17.** b **19.** c **21.** even: 7, 8, 10, 13, 17, 20; odd: 1, 4, 6, 10, 12, 13, 19 **23.** The results are the same.

Page 105 Exploratory Exercises 1. Symmetric with respect to the x-axis, y-axis, and origin; $(-1, 0)$, $(1, 0)$; $x \in [-1, 1]$ no excluded regions. **3.** None of these symmetries; $\left(-\dfrac{1}{2}, 0\right)$, $(0, -1)$; $x \neq 1$

Page 105 Written Exercises 5. $\left(\dfrac{\sqrt{6}}{2} - 1, 0\right)$, $\left(-\dfrac{\sqrt{6}}{2} - 1, 0\right)$; $(0, -1)$ **7.** no x-intercept; $(0, 39)$ **9.** $x > 4$ or $x < -4$; $y > 1$ or $y < -1$

Page 109 Exploratory Exercises 1. The horizontal asymptote is $y = 0$, the vertical asymptotes are $x = 1$ and $x = -2$. **3.** The horizontal asymptote is $y = \dfrac{1}{2}$. The vertical asymptotes are $x = -\dfrac{1}{2}$ and $x = -2$. **5.** $y = \dfrac{3}{2}x$ **7.** $y = 3x^2$

Page 110 Written Exercises

1.

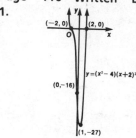

5.

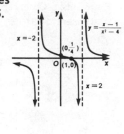

7.

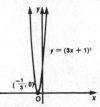

9.

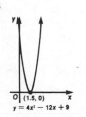

Page 112 Exploratory Exercises 1. $P'(7, 5)$; $Q'(-4, 3)$ **3.** $P'(a - h, b - k)$; $Q'(c - h, d - k)$ **5.** $P'(-h, -k)$; $Q'(a - h, a - k)$ **7.** $P'(-3, 1)$; $Q'(-2, -5)$ **9.** $P'(-2, 1)$; $Q'(-1, 2)$

Page 112 Written Exercises

3.

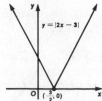

5.

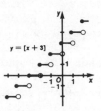

9.

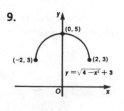

11.

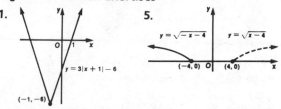

15. $x' = x - 5, y' = y - 10$

Page 115 Exploratory Exercises 1. $P'\left(\dfrac{5 + 2\sqrt{3}}{2}, \dfrac{-5\sqrt{3} + 2}{2}\right)$ **3.** $P'\left(\dfrac{-2\sqrt{3} - 1}{2}, \dfrac{2 - \sqrt{3}}{2}\right)$

Page 115 Written Exercises 1. $P'\left(1 - \dfrac{5\sqrt{3}}{2}, -\sqrt{3}\right.$

$\left. -\dfrac{5}{2}\right)$ **3.** $P'\left(\dfrac{5\sqrt{3}}{2} + 6, -\dfrac{5}{2} + 6\sqrt{3}\right)$ **9.** $P'\left(\dfrac{3}{2} + \dfrac{5\sqrt{3}}{2},\right.$

$\left.\dfrac{-3\sqrt{3}}{2} + \dfrac{5}{2}\right)$ **11.** $(0, 0) \to (0, 0)$; $(5, 0) \to \left(\dfrac{5\sqrt{2}}{2}, \dfrac{5\sqrt{2}}{2}\right)$;

$(5, 5) \to (0, 5\sqrt{2})$; $(0, 5) \to \left(\dfrac{-5\sqrt{2}}{2}, \dfrac{5\sqrt{2}}{2}\right)$

Page 115 Challenge Exercise $x' = x \cos\theta + y \sin\theta$; $y' = x \sin\theta + y \cos\theta$

Page 118 Exploratory Exercises 1. $k > 1$ **3.** $g = f$ **5.** Points of the graph of g are closer to the x-axis than corresponding points of the graph of f, with such points of g and f on the same side of the x-axis. **7.** The points $(x, f(x))$ and $(x, g(x))$ are on opposite sides of the x-axis and $|f(x)| < |g(x)|$.

Page 118 Written Exercises

1.

5.

Page 118 Challenge Exercises 1. It changes the slope to km while the intercepts are unchanged.

Page 120 Exploratory Exercises 1. infinite discontinuity at $x = 0$. **3.** continuous **5.** continuous **7.** no; The function f has a jump discontinuity at a. **9.** The function g is continuous at a if and only if $g(a) = b$.

Page 120 Written Exercises 1. point discontinuity at $x = 0$. **3.** point discontinuity at $x = 1$ **5.** continuous **7.** jump discontinuity at every integer x **9.** continuous **11.** $g(-\sqrt{5}) = 2\sqrt{5}$

Page 122 Chapter Review 1. b **3.** a, b, c **5.** Symmetric with respect to $y = x$; intercepts: $(-1, 0)$ and $(0, 1)$; asymptotes: $x = 1, y = 1$ **7.** Symmetric with respect to y-axis; $(0, 1)$; no asymptotes. The function is excluded in $y < 1$. **9.** The function is not symmetric with respect to any of these; $(0, 0)$, $\left(-\dfrac{1}{3}, 0\right)$ $(2, 0)$; none **11.** $P'(4, -4)$; $Q'(7, -12)$ **13.** $P'(-2, 8)$; $Q'(-3, 4)$; $x' = x - 5$; $y' = y + 7$ **17.** $(\sqrt{2}, 3\sqrt{2})$ **21.** continuous **23.** jump discontinuity at $x = 0$

CHAPTER 5 CIRCULAR FUNCTIONS

Page 128 Exploratory Exercises 1. $(0, -1)$ **3.** $(0, -1)$ **5.** $\pi, -\pi$ **7.** I **9.** IV **11.** III

Page 128 Written Exercises 1. I **3.** III **5.** II **7.** $(x, -y)$ **9.** $(-x, y)$ **11.** (y, x) **13.** If $\pi \rightarrow (-1, 0)$, then $0 \rightarrow (1, 0)$ and $\frac{\pi}{2} \rightarrow (0, 1)$. Since $\frac{\pi}{4}$ is equidistant from 0 and $\frac{\pi}{2}$, $x = y$. Thus $x = y = \frac{\sqrt{2}}{2}, \frac{\pi}{4} \rightarrow \left(\frac{\sqrt{2}}{2}, \frac{\sqrt{2}}{2}\right)$. **15.** $f(x) = f(x + k)$ and $g(x) = g(x + k)$. By definition of addition of functions $(f + g)(x) = f(x) + g(x) = f(x + k) + g(x + k) = (f + g)(x + k)$. Hence, $f + g$ has period k.

Page 131 Exploratory Exercises 1. 0 **3.** 1 **5.** 0 **7.** $\frac{4}{3}$

Page 131 Written Exercises 1. $\frac{\sqrt{7}}{4}$ **3.** $-\frac{\sqrt{3}}{4}$ **5.** $-\frac{12}{13}$ **7.** $\frac{3\sqrt{7}}{7}$ **9.** 0 **11.** $\frac{1}{2}, \frac{\sqrt{3}}{2}, \frac{\sqrt{3}}{3}$ **13.** $\frac{\sqrt{3}}{2}$ **15.** $\frac{\sqrt{2}}{2}, \frac{\sqrt{2}}{2}, 1$ **17.** $\frac{\sqrt{2}}{2}$ **19.** $-\frac{1}{2}$ **21.** 1

Page 137 Exploratory Exercises 1. $y = 3 \sin \frac{\pi}{2} x$ **3.** $y = \pm\frac{1}{3} \cos 2x$ **5.** $y = \pm \tan \frac{1}{2} x$

Page 137 Written Exercises
1. amplitude $= 2$; period $= 2\pi$ **3.** Period $= 3$.
5. Maximum value $= 5$; minimum value $= -1$
7. Period $= 6$; phase shift $= -\frac{1}{2}$; amplitude $= 3$.

9.
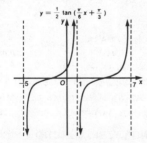
$$y = \tfrac{1}{2} \tan \left(\tfrac{\pi}{6} x + \tfrac{\pi}{3}\right)$$

Page 139 Exploratory Exercises 1. $(2k + 1)\frac{\pi}{2}$ **3.** $k\pi$ **5.** $(2k + 1)\frac{\pi}{4}$ **7.** $2\pi(k - 1)$ **9.** $k\pi$

Page 140 Written Exercises
1.

5. $|\sin x| \le 1$. Therefore, $\frac{1}{|\sin x|} \ge 1$. By definition, $|\csc x| = \frac{1}{|\sin x|} = \frac{1}{|\sin x|} \ge 1$. Therefore, $|\sin x| \le |\csc x|$.

7. If $\sin^2 x + \cos^2 x = 1$, $\sin^2 x \ne 0$ then $\frac{\cos^2 x}{\sin^2 x} = \frac{1}{\sin^2 x} + \cot^2 x = \csc^2 x$.

Page 141 Exploratory Exercises 1. 1 **3.** $2 \sin x$ **5.** 2 **7.** $\pm\sqrt{1 - \cos^2 x}$ **9.** $\pm\sqrt{\csc^2 x - 1}$

Page 142 Written Exercises For Problems **1–15**, proofs will vary.

1. $\sin x \sec x = \sin x \dfrac{1}{\cos x}$
$\qquad = \tan x$

3. $\cos^2 x - \sin^2 x = (1 - \sin^2 x) - \sin^2 x$
$\qquad = 1 - 2 \sin^2 x$

5. $\cos^4 x - \sin^4 x = (\cos^2 x - \sin^2 x)(\cos^2 x + \sin^2 x)$
$\qquad = \cos^2 x - \sin^2 x$

7. $\tan B + \cot B = \dfrac{\sin B}{\cos B} + \dfrac{\cos B}{\sin B}$
$\qquad = \dfrac{\sin^2 B + \cos^2 B}{\cos B \sin B}$
$\qquad = \dfrac{1}{\cos B} \dfrac{1}{\sin B}$
$\qquad = \sec B \csc B$

9. $\dfrac{\sec x}{\cos x} - \dfrac{\tan x}{\cot x} = \dfrac{1}{\cos^2 x} - \dfrac{\sin^2 x}{\cos^2 x}$
$\qquad = \dfrac{1 - \sin^2 x}{\cos^2 x}$
$\qquad = 1$

Page 146 Exploratory Exercises 1. $\dfrac{\sqrt{2} - \sqrt{6}}{4}$ **3.** $-\sqrt{3}$ **5.** $\sqrt{2}$ **7.** $\dfrac{1}{2}$ **9.** $\dfrac{\sqrt{2} + \sqrt{6}}{4}$

Page 147 Written Exercises 1. $\cos x$ **3.** $\tan x$ **5.** $-\tan x$ **7.** $\dfrac{24}{25}$ **9.** $\dfrac{-24}{7}$
11. $\sin(x + y) + \sin(x - y)$
$\quad = \sin x \cos y + \sin y \cos x + \sin x \cos y - \cos x \sin y$
$\quad = 2 \sin x \cos y$
15. $\sin\left(\dfrac{\pi}{6} + x\right) = \sin\dfrac{\pi}{6} \cos x + \cos\dfrac{\pi}{6} \sin x$.

Since $\sin \frac{\pi}{6} = \cos \frac{\pi}{3}$, $\cos \frac{\pi}{6} = \sin \frac{\pi}{3}$, $\sin \left(\frac{\pi}{6} + x\right) =$

$\cos \frac{\pi}{3} \cos x + \sin \frac{\pi}{3} \sin x = \cos \left(\frac{\pi}{3} - x\right)$ **17.** $\sqrt{3}$

$\sin 3x + \cos 3x = 2\left(\frac{\sqrt{3}}{2} \sin 3x + \frac{1}{2} \cos 3x\right)$. Since

$\cos \frac{\pi}{6} = \frac{\sqrt{3}}{2}$, $\sin \frac{\pi}{6} = \frac{1}{2}$, $\sqrt{3} \sin 3x + \cos 3x =$

$2\left(\sin 3x \cos \frac{\pi}{6} + \cos 3x \sin \frac{\pi}{6}\right) = 2 \sin \left(3x + \frac{\pi}{6}\right)$

Page 149 Exploratory Exercises 1. $\frac{1}{2}\sqrt{2 - \sqrt{2}}$

3. $3 - 2\sqrt{2}$ **5.** $-\frac{1}{2}\sqrt{2 - \sqrt{3}}$ **7.** $\frac{1}{2}\sqrt{2 + \sqrt{2}}$
9. $\sqrt{2} + 1$

Page 149 Written Exercises 1. $\frac{24}{25}$ **3.** $\frac{24}{7}$

5. $\frac{3\sqrt{10}}{10}$

7. $\sec 2\theta = \dfrac{1}{\cos 2\theta}$

$\qquad = \dfrac{1}{2\cos^2\theta - 1}$

$\qquad = \dfrac{\dfrac{1}{\cos^2\theta}}{2 - \dfrac{1}{\cos^2\theta}}$

$\qquad = \dfrac{\sec^2\theta}{2 - \sec^2\theta}$

9. $\cot 2\theta = \dfrac{1}{\tan 2\theta}$

$\qquad = \dfrac{1 - \tan^2\theta}{2\tan\theta}$

$\qquad = \dfrac{\dfrac{1}{\tan^2\theta} - 1}{\dfrac{2}{\tan\theta}}$

$\qquad = \dfrac{\cot^2\theta - 1}{2\cot\theta}$

Page 151 Exploratory Exercises 1. $\frac{\pi}{4}, \frac{\pi}{12}$ **3.** 2
$\sin \frac{3\pi}{4} \cos \left(-\frac{\pi}{2}\right)$

Page 151 Written Exercises 1. $2 \sin 3x \cos x$
3. $2 \cos \frac{\pi}{4} \sin \frac{\pi}{12}$ **5.** $2 \cos \frac{7x}{2} \sin \frac{x}{2}$ **7.** $\sin 6x +$
$\sin 2x$ **9.** $\frac{1}{2}(\sin 8x - \sin 2x)$ **11.** $\frac{1}{2}\left[\sin \frac{\pi}{2} - \right.$
$\left. \sin\left(\frac{\pi}{6} + 2x\right)\right]$ **13.** $\frac{1}{2} - \frac{1}{2} \cos 2x$

15. $\dfrac{\cos 5x + \cos 3x}{\sin 5x - \sin 3x} = \dfrac{2 \cos 4x \cos x}{2 \cos 4x \sin x}$
$\qquad\qquad\qquad\quad = \cot x$

Page 155 Exploratory Exercises 1. $\frac{\pi}{3} + 2n\pi$,
$\frac{2\pi}{3} + 2n\pi$ **3.** $\frac{\pi}{4}$ **5.** π

Page 155 Written Exercises 1. $\frac{\pi}{3} + n\pi$

3. $\frac{\pi}{6} + 2n\pi, \frac{11\pi}{6} + 2n\pi$ **5.** $\pm$ Arccos $\frac{1}{3}$
$+ 2n\pi$ **7.** $\frac{5\pi}{6}$ **9.** $\frac{4}{5}$ **11.** $\pm\frac{2\sqrt{3}}{3}$ **13.** $\frac{3}{5}$

17. Let $x_1 = $ Arctan $\frac{1}{2}$ and $x_2 = $ Arctan $\frac{1}{3}$. Then,

$\tan x_1 = \frac{1}{2}$ and $\tan x_2 = \frac{1}{3}$. So, $\tan (x_1 + x_2) =$

$\dfrac{\frac{1}{2} + \frac{1}{3}}{1 - \frac{1}{2} \cdot \frac{1}{3}} = 1$ or $x_1 + x_2 = \frac{\pi}{4}$. Thus, Arctan $\frac{1}{2} +$

Arctan $\frac{1}{3} = \frac{\pi}{4}$.

Page 157 Exploratory Exercises 1. $\frac{\pi}{6}, \frac{5\pi}{6}$

3. $\frac{2\pi}{3}, \frac{4\pi}{3}$ **5.** $\frac{\pi}{3}, \frac{4\pi}{3}$

Page 157 Written Exercises 1. $\pm\frac{\pi}{3} + 2n\pi$

3. $\pm\frac{\pi}{6} + n\pi$ **5.** Arcsin $\frac{3}{4} + 2n\pi, (2n + 1)\pi -$
Arcsin $\frac{3}{4}$ **7.** $0, \pi$ **9.** $\pm\frac{\pi}{6}$ **11.** Arcos $\left(\dfrac{1 - \sqrt{17}}{4}\right)$
13. $\frac{3\pi}{8}, \frac{7\pi}{8}, \frac{11\pi}{8}, \frac{15\pi}{8}$ **15.** $\frac{\pi}{2}, \frac{3\pi}{2}$ **17.** $0, \pi$

Page 160 Chapter Review 1. Quadrant I
3. Quadrant III **5.** $(-x, -y)$ **7.** $\pm\frac{\sqrt{133}}{13}$ **9.** -1
11. Period $= \frac{\pi}{3}$; amplitude, not applicable; phase
shift $= \frac{\pi}{18}$; point symmetric. **13.** $\sqrt{2}$ **15.** $2 \sec x$
17. $-\cos x$ **19.** $2 \sin \theta \csc 2 \theta = \dfrac{2 \sin \theta}{2 \sin \cos \theta} =$
$\dfrac{1}{\cos \theta} = \sec \theta$ **21.** $2 \sin 4t \cos t$ **23.** $\frac{13}{12}$
25. $0, \frac{\pi}{2}, \frac{2\pi}{3}$

CHAPTER 6 TRIGONOMETRIC FUNCTIONS

Page 168 Exploratory Exercises 1. $18°$ **3.**
$-216°$ **5.** $\left(\dfrac{360}{\pi}\right)°$ **7.** $\frac{\pi}{5}$ **9.** $\frac{8\pi}{9}$ **11.** $\frac{1}{2}$

Page 168 Written Exercises 1. $\frac{3}{5}, \frac{-4}{5}, \frac{-3}{4}$
3. $\frac{-\sqrt{2}}{2}, \frac{\sqrt{2}}{2}, -1$ **5.** $\frac{\pi}{4}, 45°$ **7.** $\frac{5\pi}{3}$ 300° **9.** sin $\theta°$
11. $-\cot \theta°$ **13.** sec $\theta°$ **15.** $\frac{1}{4}(\sqrt{6} + \sqrt{2})$

17. $2 - \sqrt{3}$ **19.** $\frac{1}{2}\sqrt{2 - \sqrt{2}}$ **21.** $2 - \sqrt{3}$

23. $\frac{1}{2}(1 + \sqrt{3})$ **25.** NC **27.** C **29.** C

Page 171 Exploratory Exercises 1. 0.9511
3. 3.340 **5.** 1.114 **7.** 0.9408 **9.** 3.130

Page 171 Written Exercises 1. 22°30′
3. 38°13′ **5.** 14°35′ **9.** −0.3352 **11.** −1.069
13. 153°35′ **15.** 194°13′

Page 173 Exploratory Exercises 1. sin $A = \frac{a}{c}$
3. $a = b \tan A$ **5.** 4 **7.** 1 **9.** 4

Page 173 Written Exercises 1. $m\angle B = 66°50'$;
$a = 10.7$; $b = 24.9$ **3.** $m\angle A = 11°52'$; $m\angle B = 78°8'$; $b = 0.600$ **5.** $m\angle A = 22°22'$; $a = 27.57$; $b = 67.00$ **7.** $m\angle B = 52°45'$; $a = 8.36$; $c = 13.82$ **9.** no; Triangle 1: leg 3, leg 4; Triangle 2: leg 3, hypotenuse, 4 **11.** yes; $c = 5.66$, $m\angle A = m\angle B = 45°$ **13.** no; Triangle 1: $a = 2\sqrt{3}$, $b = 2$, $c = 4$; Triangle 2: $a = 3\sqrt{3}$, $b = 3$, $c = 6$ (any triangle with sides in proportion $b\sqrt{3}$: b : 2b) **15.** 187 m **17.** 143 ft, 174 ft **19.** 225 m

Page 177 Exploratory Exercises 1. yes **3.** no
5. yes

Page 177 Written Exercises 1. $m\angle C = 115°$, $a = 18$, $c = 27$ **3.** $m\angle B = 111°$, $a = 1.6$, $c = 3.9$ **5.** $m\angle A = 60°$, $m\angle B = 49°$, $c = 74$ **7.** $m\angle A = 84°$, $m\angle B = 58°$, $m\angle C = 38°$ **9.** $m\angle B = 72°$, $m\angle C = 46°$, $c = 0.42$ or $m\angle B = 108°$, $m\angle C = 10°$, $c = 0.1$ **11.** no solution **13.** 53°, 53°, 74° **15.** 97°

Page 180 Exploratory Exercises 1. 54 **3.** 65
5. 22 **7.** 0.52 **9.** 6.5

Page 181 Written Exercises 1. $\frac{49\pi}{6}$ **3.** $\frac{968\pi}{15}$
5. $\frac{75}{4}(5\pi - 3)$ **7.** $\frac{16}{3}(4\pi - 3\sqrt{3})$ **9.** $(144\pi - 216\sqrt{3})$ cm² **11.** 302.6 m² **13.** 110 square units **15.** $\frac{1000\pi}{3}$ km²

Page 181 Excursion Exercises 1. 6
3. 58.8

Page 182 Exploratory Exercises 1. $\frac{5\pi}{2}$ **3.** $\frac{5\pi}{2}$
5. $\frac{27}{\pi}$

Page 183 Written Exercises 1. 6πin./min **3.** 4πcm/s **5.** 40πm/min **7.** 2 rad/s **9.** 22 rad/s **11.** 37.7 rad/s

Page 185 Exploratory Exercises 1. cos 0 + i sin 0 **3.** $\cos \frac{2\pi}{3} + i \sin \frac{2\pi}{3}$ **5.** −12

Page 186 Written Exercises 1. $6i$ **3.** $-\frac{3}{2} + \frac{\sqrt{3}}{4} i$ **5.** $\sqrt{3} + i$ **7.** $3 + 3\sqrt{3}\, i$ **9.** 16 **11.** $-\frac{\sqrt{3}}{4} + \frac{1}{4} i$ **13.** $3\sqrt{6}\, i$ **15.** $r(\cos \theta + i \sin \theta)$. $\frac{1}{r}(\cos \theta - i \sin \theta) = r \cdot \frac{1}{r}(\cos \theta + i \sin \theta)\, [\cos(-\theta) + i \sin(-\theta)] = 1 \cdot \cos 0 + i \sin 0 = 1$ **17.** $\frac{1}{3}\left(\cos \frac{5\pi}{6} - i \sin \frac{5\pi}{6}\right)$

Page 189 Exploratory Exercises 1. π and $\frac{5\pi}{3}$
3. $\pi, \frac{3\pi}{2}, 2\pi$ (or 0)

Page 189 Written Exercises 1. $-2 - 2i$ **3.** $-8 - 8\sqrt{3}\, i$ **5.** $2^{2/3}\left(\cos \frac{\pi}{9} - i \sin \frac{\pi}{9}\right)$, $2^{2/3}\left(\cos \frac{13\pi}{9} - i \sin \frac{13\pi}{9}\right)$, $2^{2/3}\left(\cos \frac{7\pi}{9} - i \sin \frac{7\pi}{9}\right)$ **7.** 1, $-\frac{1}{2} \pm \frac{\sqrt{3}}{2} i$ **9.** ± 2, $\pm 1 + \frac{\sqrt{3}}{2} i$, $\pm 1 - \frac{\sqrt{3}}{2} i$ **11.** $2^{5/4}\left(\cos \frac{3\pi}{8} + i \sin \frac{3\pi}{8}\right)$, $2^{5/4}\left(\cos \frac{11\pi}{8} - i \sin \frac{11\pi}{8}\right)$ **13.** $2^{3/4}\left(\cos \frac{3\pi}{8} - i \sin \frac{3\pi}{8}\right)$, $2^{3/4}\left(\cos \frac{11\pi}{8} - i \sin \frac{11\pi}{8}\right)$ **15.** cos $3\theta = 4 \cos^3\theta - 3 \cos \theta$, sin $3\theta = -4 \sin^3 \theta + 3 \sin \theta$

Page 191 Chapter Review 1. 300° **3.** $\left(\frac{450}{\pi}\right)°$
5. $\frac{3\pi}{4}$ **7.** 0.6911 **9.** 37°45′ **13.** 11.70 **15.** no solution **17.** 107 **19.** 45 rev/min **21.** $-128 + 128\sqrt{3}\, i$

CHAPTER 7   VECTORS IN THE PLANE

Page 200 Exploratory Exercises 1. $\begin{pmatrix} 3 \\ 5 \end{pmatrix}$ **3.**
$\begin{pmatrix} 3 \\ -6 \end{pmatrix}$ **5.** $\begin{pmatrix} 2 \\ -4 \end{pmatrix}$ **7.** $\begin{pmatrix} -2 \\ -4 \end{pmatrix}$ **9.** $\begin{pmatrix} 4 \\ 0 \end{pmatrix}$ **11.** $\begin{pmatrix} -x \\ -y \end{pmatrix}$

Page 201 Written Exercises 1. $(5, 7)$ **3.** $(2, 2)$
5. $(-4, 2)$ **7.** $(3 + a, -4 + b)$ **9.** $(-6, 3)$ **11.**
$(-3, -1)$ **13.** $(-8, 1)$ **15.** $\begin{pmatrix} -1 \\ 3 \end{pmatrix}$ **17.** $\begin{pmatrix} -2 \\ -6 \end{pmatrix}$
19. $\begin{pmatrix} b_1 - a_1 \\ b_2 - a_2 \end{pmatrix}$ **21.** neither **23.** $-\overrightarrow{PQ}$ **25.** $\overrightarrow{PQ}$
27. $(-3, 3)$ **29.** $(-3, -6)$

Page 204 Exploratory Exercises 1. $\overline{w}$ **3.**
$-\overline{v}$ **5.** $2\overline{w}$ **7.** $2\overline{w}$ **9.** $2\overline{w}$ **11.** $\overline{0}$
13. $\overline{u}$ **15.** $\overline{u}$ **17.** $\overline{q} = -\overline{p}$
If two vectors are added tail to head and the sum is
$\overline{0}$, the vectors are opposites.

Page 204 Written Exercises
9. 3 **11.** $-\frac{2}{3}$ **13.** $\begin{pmatrix} 2 \\ -5 \end{pmatrix}$ **15.** $\begin{pmatrix} -5 \\ -2 \end{pmatrix}$ **17.** $\overline{0}$
19. $\begin{pmatrix} 2 \\ -6 \end{pmatrix}$ **21.** $\begin{pmatrix} 7a \\ 7b \end{pmatrix}$ **23.** $\begin{pmatrix} 0 \\ 0 \end{pmatrix}$ **25.** $\begin{pmatrix} ac \\ bc \end{pmatrix}$ **27.**
If $ABCD$ is a parallelogram, then $\overrightarrow{AB}$ and $\overrightarrow{CD}$ are on
parallel lines and have equal length. Since they have
opposite directions, $\overrightarrow{AB} = -\overrightarrow{CD}$ or $\overrightarrow{AB} + \overrightarrow{CD} = \overline{0}$. If $\overrightarrow{AB}$
$+ \overrightarrow{CD} = \overline{0}$, then $\overrightarrow{AB} = -\overrightarrow{CD}$ so $\overrightarrow{AB}$ and $\overrightarrow{CD}$ lie on
parallel lines and have equal length. Therefore,
$ABCD$ is a parallelogram.

Page 205 Challenge Exercises
1. $\overrightarrow{RQ} = \overrightarrow{RM} + \overrightarrow{MN} + \overrightarrow{NQ}$
$\overrightarrow{PS} = \overrightarrow{PM} + \overrightarrow{MN} + \overrightarrow{NS}$
$\overrightarrow{RQ} + \overrightarrow{PS} = 2\,\overrightarrow{MN}$ since $\overrightarrow{NQ} = -\overrightarrow{NS}$ and $\overrightarrow{RM} = -\overrightarrow{PM}$. So $4\overrightarrow{MN} = \overrightarrow{PQ} + \overrightarrow{RQ} + \overrightarrow{PS} + \overrightarrow{RS}$.

Page 207 Exploratory Exercises 1. $\begin{pmatrix} 5 \\ 2 \end{pmatrix}, \begin{pmatrix} 3 \\ 4 \end{pmatrix}, \begin{pmatrix} 5 \\ 2 \end{pmatrix}$
3. $\begin{pmatrix} 13 \\ 1 \end{pmatrix}, \begin{pmatrix} -1 \\ -9 \end{pmatrix}, \begin{pmatrix} 3 \\ -2 \end{pmatrix}$ **5.** $\begin{pmatrix} 1 \\ 13 \end{pmatrix}, \begin{pmatrix} 7 \\ 5 \end{pmatrix}, \begin{pmatrix} a \\ 13a \end{pmatrix}$ **7.**
$r = -3, s = 5$ **9.** $r = -2, s = 13$

Page 207 Written Exercises 1. $\begin{pmatrix} 1 \\ 3 \end{pmatrix}$ **3.** $\begin{pmatrix} -7 \\ 7 \end{pmatrix}$
5. $\begin{pmatrix} -3 \\ -9 \end{pmatrix}$ **7.** $r = 3, s = 5$ **9.** $r = \frac{2}{3}, s = \frac{-4}{5}$ **11.**
$r = 0, s = 0$ **13.** $r = 3, s = 2$

Page 210 Exploratory Exercises 1. AV$_4$ Additive
Inverse **3. AV$_5$** Commutativity **5. DV$_1$** Distributive Property

Page 210 Written Exercises
1. Prove: $\overline{v} + (-\overline{v}) = (-\overline{v}) + \overline{v} = \overline{0}$

1.	$\overline{v} + (-\overline{v}) = 1 \cdot \overline{v} + (-1)\overline{v}$	SV$_3$, SMV$_4$
2.	$\qquad\qquad = [1 + (-1)]\overline{v}$	DV$_2$
3.	$\qquad\qquad = 0 \cdot \overline{v}$	Additive inverse
4.	$\qquad\qquad = \overline{0}$	SMV$_5$
5.	$\overline{v} + (-\overline{v}) = (-\overline{v}) + \overline{v} = \overline{0}$	AV$_5$

5. Prove: $1\overline{v} = \overline{v}$.

1.	$1 \cdot \overline{v} = 1 \cdot \begin{pmatrix} a \\ b \end{pmatrix}$	Def. of vector
2.	$= \begin{pmatrix} 1 \cdot a \\ 1 \cdot b \end{pmatrix}$	Def. of scalar multiplication
3.	$= \begin{pmatrix} a \\ b \end{pmatrix}$	Multiplication identity of $\mathcal{R}$
4.	$= \overline{v}$	Def. of vector

Page 210 Challenge Exercise Assume $\overline{v} = \begin{pmatrix} a \\ b \end{pmatrix}$
and $\overline{w} = \begin{pmatrix} r \\ s \end{pmatrix}$ such that $-\overline{v} \neq \overline{w}$ and $\overline{v} + \overline{w} =$
$\overline{w} + \overline{v} = \overline{0}$. Then $\overline{v} + \overline{w} = \begin{pmatrix} a + r \\ b + s \end{pmatrix} = \begin{pmatrix} 0 \\ 0 \end{pmatrix}$. Thus
$a + r = 0$ and $b + s = 0$ by vector addition. Therefore, $r = -a$ and $s = -b$. So $\overline{w} = \begin{pmatrix} r \\ s \end{pmatrix} = \begin{pmatrix} -a \\ -b \end{pmatrix} = -\overline{v}$
which contradicts the assumption. So $\overline{v}$ has a unique
addition inverse.

Page 212 Exploratory Exercises 1. 2 **3.** 2
5. 1 **7.** $\frac{3}{2}$ **9.** 1

Page 212 Written Exercises 1. 5 **3.** $\sqrt{r^2 + s^2}$
5. $\sqrt{82}$ **7.** $\sqrt{(3 + r)^2 + (4 + s)^2}$
9. $\sqrt{(-2 - r)^2 (5 - s)^2}$ **11.** $\sqrt{29}$ **13.** yes
15. yes **17.** yes **19.** no **21.** yes **23.** Let
$\overline{v} = \begin{pmatrix} a \\ b \end{pmatrix}$, then $\|\overline{v}\| = \sqrt{a^2 + b^2}$. If $\|\overline{v}\| = 0$, $\sqrt{a^2 + b^2}$
$= 0$. But $\sqrt{a^2 + b^2} = 0$ if and only if $a = 0$ and $b =$
0. Thus, $\overline{v} = \overline{0}$. If $\overline{v} = \overline{0}$, $\overline{v} = \begin{pmatrix} 0 \\ 0 \end{pmatrix}$ and $a = 0$ and
$b = 0$. Thus, $\sqrt{a^2 + b^2} = 0$ and $\|\overline{v}\| = 0$. **25.** Let
$\overline{v} = \begin{pmatrix} 1 \\ 0 \end{pmatrix}$ and $\overline{u} = \begin{pmatrix} 0 \\ 1 \end{pmatrix}$. Then $\|\overline{v}\| = 1$ and $\|\overline{u}\| = 1$.
Although $\|\overline{v}\| = \|\overline{u}\|$, $\overline{v} \neq \overline{u}$. The statement is disproved.

Page 215 Exploratory Exercises 1. $\overline{v}_x = \begin{pmatrix} 3 \\ 0 \end{pmatrix}$,
$\overline{v}_y = \begin{pmatrix} 0 \\ 4 \end{pmatrix}$ **3.** $\overline{v}_x = \begin{pmatrix} -3 \\ 0 \end{pmatrix}$, $\overline{v}_y = \begin{pmatrix} 0 \\ 2 \end{pmatrix}$ **5.**
$\overline{AB}_x = \begin{pmatrix} 3 \\ 0 \end{pmatrix}$, $\overline{AB}_y = \begin{pmatrix} 0 \\ 4 \end{pmatrix}$ **7.** $\overline{AB}_x = \begin{pmatrix} 5 \\ 0 \end{pmatrix}$,

$\overline{AB}_y = \begin{pmatrix} 0 \\ -11 \end{pmatrix}$

Page 216 Written Exercises 1. $\overline{F}_x = \begin{pmatrix} 30\sqrt{3} \\ 0 \end{pmatrix}$,

$\overline{F}_y = \begin{pmatrix} 0 \\ 30 \end{pmatrix}$ **3.** $\overline{F}_x = \begin{pmatrix} 10\sqrt{2} \\ 0 \end{pmatrix}$, $\overline{F}_y = \begin{pmatrix} 0 \\ 10\sqrt{2} \end{pmatrix}$ **5.**

$\overline{u}_x = \begin{pmatrix} 9\sqrt{3} \\ 0 \end{pmatrix}$, $\overline{u}_y = \begin{pmatrix} 0 \\ 9 \end{pmatrix}$ **7.** 262 km at 110° **9.**

334.3 mph at 189°, 55 mph west, 329.74 mph south

Page 217 Challenge Exercises 1. $\|\overline{v}_2\| = 309$ lb; $\|\overline{v}_3\| = 82.8$ lb **3.** The magnitude of the vector perpendicular to the ramp holding the object is $\|\overline{F}\| \sin y$ and of that parallel to the ramp is $\|\overline{F}\| \cos y$. The magnitude of the vector perpendicular to the ramp tending to make the object move is $\|\overline{w}\| \cos x$ and of that parallel to the ramp is $\|\overline{w}\| \sin x$. So, $\|\overline{F}\| \cos y = \|\overline{w}\| \sin x$. Hence, $\|\overline{F}\| = \dfrac{\|\overline{w}\| \sin x}{\cos y}$.

Page 220 Exploratory Exercises 1. no **3.** yes **5.** yes

Page 220 Written Exercises 1. $3\vec{i} - 7\vec{j}$ **3.** $-3\vec{i} - \vec{j}$ **5.** $\vec{i} + \vec{j}$ **7.** $(3a + b)\vec{i} + (-7a + 5b)\vec{j}$ **9.** $r = \dfrac{28}{13}$, $s = \dfrac{3}{13}$ **11.** $\begin{pmatrix} \frac{\sqrt{2}}{2} \\ \frac{\sqrt{2}}{2} \end{pmatrix}$ The slope is 1. **13.**

$\begin{pmatrix} -\frac{3}{\sqrt{34}} \\ \frac{5}{\sqrt{34}} \end{pmatrix}$ The slope is $-\dfrac{5}{3}$. **15.** $\begin{pmatrix} \frac{1}{\sqrt{2}} \\ \frac{1}{\sqrt{2}} \end{pmatrix}$ The slope

is 1. **17.** $r = -8$, $s = 29$ **19.** $\begin{pmatrix} \frac{3}{\sqrt{10}} \\ -\frac{1}{\sqrt{10}} \end{pmatrix}$

Page 224 Exploratory Exercises 1. $|r| + |s| = 1$ **3.** $s > 0$ **5.** $r > 0$ **7.** V is located at $\dfrac{2}{3}$ the distance from U to X. **9.** V is located at $\dfrac{1}{3}$ the distance from U to W.

Page 224 Written Exercises 1. $r = 6$, $s = \dfrac{19}{2}$; $\overline{v} = 6\overline{u} + \dfrac{19}{2}\overline{w}$ **3.** $r = -7$, $s = 20$; $\overline{v} = -7\overline{u} + 20\overline{w}$ **5.** $r = 0$, $s = 0$; $\overline{v} = 0 \cdot \overline{u} + 0 \cdot \overline{w}$ **7.** yes

13. $\begin{cases} x = -5r + 3; \ \overline{v} = r\begin{pmatrix} -2 \\ 1 \end{pmatrix} + (1 - r)\begin{pmatrix} 3 \\ -4 \end{pmatrix} \\ y = 5r - 4 \end{cases}$

15. $\begin{cases} x = 5 - 5r; \ \overline{v} = r\begin{pmatrix} 0 \\ 10 \end{pmatrix} + (1 - r)\begin{pmatrix} 5 \\ 0 \end{pmatrix} \\ y = 10r \end{cases}$

17. If V is the point of trisection of $\overline{UW}$, $\overline{v} = \overline{u} + \dfrac{2}{3}(\overline{w} - \overline{u}) = \overline{u} + \dfrac{2}{3}\overline{w} - \dfrac{2}{3}\overline{u} = \dfrac{1}{3}\overline{u} + \dfrac{2}{3}\overline{w}$.

Page 225 Challenge Exercises 1. Suppose $\overrightarrow{OX}$ terminates on $\overrightarrow{PQ}$, then $\overrightarrow{PQ} = k\overrightarrow{BX}$. Since $\overrightarrow{PX} = \overrightarrow{OX} - \overrightarrow{OP}$, $\overrightarrow{OQ} - \overrightarrow{OP} = \overrightarrow{PQ} = k\overrightarrow{PX} = k(\overrightarrow{OX} - \overrightarrow{OP})$. Thus, $\overrightarrow{OQ} - \overrightarrow{OP} = k(\overrightarrow{OX}) - k(\overrightarrow{OP})$ or $\dfrac{1}{k}\overrightarrow{OQ} - \left(\dfrac{1}{k} - 1\right)\overrightarrow{OP} = \overrightarrow{OX}$. Let $r = \dfrac{1}{k}$, then $r\overrightarrow{OQ} + (1 - r)\overrightarrow{OP} = \overrightarrow{OX}$. Let $s = 1 - r$, then $r\overrightarrow{OQ} + s\overrightarrow{OP} = \overrightarrow{OX}$ and $r + s = 1$. Now suppose $r\overrightarrow{OQ} + (1 - r)\overrightarrow{OP} = \overrightarrow{OX}$. Then $r\overrightarrow{OQ} - \overrightarrow{OP} - r\overrightarrow{OP} = \overrightarrow{OX}$ or $r(\overrightarrow{OQ} - \overrightarrow{OP}) = \overrightarrow{OX} - \overrightarrow{OP}$ or $r(\overrightarrow{PQ}) = \overrightarrow{PX}$. Thus, $\overrightarrow{PX}$ is a scalar multiple of $\overrightarrow{PQ}$ and X must be on the line $\overleftrightarrow{PQ}$.

Page 229 Exploratory Exercises 1. 4 **3.** -8 **5.** 8 **7.** 2

Page 229 Written Exercises 1. $2\sqrt{39}$ **3.** not orthogonal **5.** orthogonal **7.** 145.5°

Page 230 Challenge Exercises 1. $\|\overline{v} - \overline{u}\|^2 = (\sqrt{(a - c)^2 + (b - d)^2})^2 = a^2 - 2ac + c^2 + b^2 - 2bd + d^2 = \|\overline{v}\|^2 - 2\overline{v} \cdot \overline{u} + \|\overline{u}\|^2$. When $\overline{v} \cdot \overline{u} = 0$, $\overline{v}$ and $\overline{u}$ are orthogonal and $\|\overline{v} - \overline{u}\|^2 = \|\overline{v}\|^2 + \|\overline{u}\|^2$. Likewise, when $\|\overline{v} + \overline{u}\|^2 = \|\overline{v}\|^2 + \|\overline{u}\|^2$ then $\overline{v} \cdot \overline{u} = 0$, and $\overline{v}$ and $\overline{u}$ are orthogonal. **3.** $\overline{v} \cdot \overline{v} = a^2 + b^2$. Then $(\overline{v} \cdot \overline{v})^{1/2} = \sqrt{a^2 + b^2} = \|\overline{v}\|$.

Page 232 Written Exercises
1.

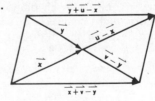

Let the diagonals of the figure be $\overline{u}$ and $\overline{v}$. So, $\overline{y} = k\overline{v}$ and $\overline{x} = k'\overline{u}$. Since the figure is a parallelogram, $\overline{x} + \overline{v} - \overline{y} = \overline{y} + \overline{u} - \overline{x}$. Therefore, $2\overline{x} - 2\overline{y} = \overline{u} - \overline{v}$ and $\overline{x} - \overline{y} = \frac{1}{2}\overline{u} - \frac{1}{2}\overline{v}$. But $\overline{x} - \overline{y} = k'\overline{u} - k\overline{v}$. So $k'\overline{u} - k\overline{v} = \frac{1}{2}\overline{u} - \frac{1}{2}\overline{v}$, or $(k' - \frac{1}{2})\overline{u} = (k - \frac{1}{2})\overline{v}$. Since $\overline{u} \neq \overline{0}$ and $\overline{v} \neq \overline{0}$ and $\overline{u}$ and $\overline{v}$ are not collinear, $k' - \frac{1}{2} = 0$, $k - \frac{1}{2} = 0$, and $k = k' = \frac{1}{2}$. So $\overline{y} = \frac{1}{2}\overline{v}$ and $\overline{x} = \frac{1}{2}\overline{u}$.

Page 232 Challenge Exercises 1. Follows directly from the proofs of written Problems **1** and **5.**

Page 233 Chapter Review 1. neither **3.** $-\overline{PQ}$ **5.** A few examples are $\overline{AB} = \overline{DC}, \overline{AD} = \overline{BC}, \overline{BE} = \overline{ED}, \overline{AE} = \overline{EC},$

9. -1 **11.** $\begin{pmatrix} 4 \\ 4 \end{pmatrix}, \begin{pmatrix} -2 \\ 0 \end{pmatrix}, \begin{pmatrix} 2 \\ 2 \end{pmatrix}$ **13.** $r = -2, s = 7$ **15.** $\sqrt{13}$ **17.** $\sqrt{13}$ **19.** $\sqrt{13} + \sqrt{26}$ **21.** yes **23.** yes **25.** $\begin{pmatrix} 1 \\ 0 \end{pmatrix}$ and $\begin{pmatrix} 0 \\ -18 \end{pmatrix}$ **27.** a

29. $\frac{\sqrt{3}}{2}\vec{i} + \frac{1}{2}\vec{j}$ **31.** $4\vec{i} + 2\vec{j}$ **33.** F

CHAPTER 8 SPACE

Page 240 Exploratory Exercises 1. $\{(1, 2, 5), (1, 2, 6), (3, 2, 5), (3, 2, 6)\}$ **3.** $\{(a, a, b), (a, a, c), (a, c, b), (a, c, c), (b, a, b), (b, a, c), (b, c, b), (b, c, c)\}$ **5.** $\{((1, 2), 5), ((1, 2), 9), ((1, 3), 5), ((1, 3), 5), ((1, 3), 9)\}$ **7.** xy – plane **9.** xz – plane

Page 241 Written Exercises 1. It is a plane parallel to the yz-plane and intersecting the x-axis at $(4, 0, 0)$. **3.** It is a plane parallel to the xz-plane and containing $(0, -2, 0)$. **5.** $(3, -4, -8)$

Page 242 Exploratory Exercises 1. 5;3 **3.** 17;8 **5.** $7; \left(\frac{5}{2}, -4, 2\right)$ **7.** $\sqrt{41}; \left(4, \frac{1}{2}, -1\right)$

Page 243 Written Exercises 1. $\sqrt{34}$; 5 **3.** $n\sqrt{113}$; $8n$ where $n \geq 0$ **5.** $2\sqrt{10}$; 2 **7.** $4n\sqrt{13}$; $15n$ where $n \geq 0$ **9.** 6 **11.** $\sqrt{269}$ **13.** $\left(3\sqrt{3}, -\frac{1}{2}, -2\right)$ **15.** $\left(\frac{a+b}{2}, \frac{d}{2}, \frac{c}{2}\right)$ **17.** $(4, -3, 1)$ **19.** $AB = \sqrt{105} = AC, BC = \sqrt{254}$ **21.** The coordinates of the midpoint of each diagonal are $(5, 1, 1)$. No, the figure might be a skew quadrilateral. **23.** The coordinates of the midpoint of each diagonal are $\left(\frac{7}{4}, -\frac{3}{2}, \frac{7}{12}\right)$.

Page 246 Exploratory Exercises 1. 3, 3, 5 **3.** 3, -2, $-\frac{3}{5}$ **5.** $\begin{pmatrix} -6 \\ 4 \\ -4 \end{pmatrix}$ **7.** $\begin{pmatrix} -5 \\ 3 \\ 2 \end{pmatrix}$ **9.** $\begin{pmatrix} -10 \\ 5 \\ 20 \end{pmatrix}$

Page 246 Written Exercises 1. 5, -2, 1 **3.** $-1, -3, -2$ **5.** Let $\vec{u} = \begin{pmatrix} a_1 \\ b_1 \\ c_1 \end{pmatrix}$ and $\vec{v} = \begin{pmatrix} a_2 \\ b_2 \\ c_2 \end{pmatrix}$ and $\vec{w} = \begin{pmatrix} a_3 \\ b_3 \\ c_3 \end{pmatrix}$. Since $\vec{u} = \vec{v}, a_1 = a_2, b_1 = b_2, c_1 = c_2$. Since

$\vec{v} = \vec{w}, a_2 = a_3, b_2 = b_3, c_2 = c_3$. Therefore, $a_1 = a_3, b_1 = b_3$, and $c_1 = c_3$. Thus $\vec{u} = \vec{w}$.

Page 249 Exploratory Exercises 1. $\sqrt{6}; \frac{1}{\sqrt{6}}, \frac{1}{\sqrt{6}}, \frac{2}{\sqrt{6}}$ **3.** 13; $-\frac{3}{13}, \frac{4}{13}, \frac{12}{13}$ **5.** $\pm\frac{4}{9}$ **7.** 20

Page 249 Written Exercises 1. 7; $-\frac{6}{7}, \frac{2}{7}, -\frac{3}{7}$ **3.** $9; \frac{2}{3}, -\frac{1}{3}, \frac{2}{3}$ **5.** $\pm\frac{7\sqrt{3}}{15}$ **7.** $\pm\frac{\sqrt{15}}{5}$ **9.** $(-10, 4, -22)$ **11.** 16 **13.** -64 **15.** $\frac{131}{189}$ **17.** 17

Page 253 Exploratory Exercises 1. 10 **3.** 36 **5.** $\begin{pmatrix} 5 \\ 3 \\ -7 \end{pmatrix}$

Page 253 Written Exercises 1. Pa **3.** N **5.** Pe **7.** $a = -\frac{3}{2}, b = \frac{5}{2}$ **9.** $\begin{pmatrix} 2 \\ -34 \\ 8 \end{pmatrix}$

Page 256 Exploratory Exercises 1. $\vec{v} = \begin{pmatrix} -3 \\ 1 \\ 4 \end{pmatrix}$; $P(1, 4, 2)$ **3.** $\vec{v} = \begin{pmatrix} 3 \\ 4 \\ -3 \end{pmatrix}$; $P(2, -1, 4)$ **5.** $x = 4 + 2t, y = 1 + 4t, z = 2 - 3t; \frac{x-4}{2} = \frac{y-1}{4} = \frac{z-2}{-3}$

Page 256 Written Exercises 1. $x = 7 + 2t, y = 1 + t, z = -1 + 2t; \frac{x-7}{2} = \frac{y-1}{1} = \frac{z+1}{2}$ **3.** $x = -1 - 2t, y = 2, z = \sqrt{3} + t; \frac{x+1}{-2} = \frac{z-\sqrt{3}}{1}, y = 2$ **5.** $\frac{x-4}{2} = \frac{y-6}{-1} = \frac{z+1}{10}$ **7.** $\vec{v} = \begin{pmatrix} 2 \\ 0 \\ -1 \end{pmatrix} + t\begin{pmatrix} 3 \\ 1 \\ -1 \end{pmatrix}$ **9.** The line is perpendicular to the x-axis. **11.** The line is parallel to the z-axis.

Page 259 Exploratory Exercises 1. 3, -4, and 12; $\cos\alpha = \pm\frac{3}{13}, \cos\beta = \mp\frac{4}{13}, \cos\gamma = \pm\frac{12}{13}$ **3.** 2, -2, and 1; $\cos\alpha = \pm\frac{2}{3}, \cos\beta = \mp\frac{2}{3}, \cos\gamma = \pm\frac{1}{3}$

Page 260 Written Exercises 1. $2x - 5y + z - 4 = 0$ **3.** $4x + y - 3z - 7 = 0$ **5.** $11x + 8y - 2z - 41 = 0$ **7.** $x - 9y + 5z + 11 = 0$ **9.** $\frac{5}{13}$ **11.** $\frac{2}{9}$ **13.** $\frac{10}{27}$

Page 260 Challenge Exercises 3. $x = t$, $y = 1 + t$, $z = -7 + 3t$

Page 262 Exploratory Exercises 1. $(x - 7)^2 + (y + 1)^2 + (z - 2)^2 = 9$ **3.** $(x - 3)^2 + (y - 5)^2 + (z + 1)^2 = 4$ **5.** $y^2 + z^2 = 16$

Page 262 Written Exercises 1. $(x - 11)^2 + (y + 2)^2 + (z - 7)^2 = 25$ **3.** $x^2 + y^2 = 4$ **5.** $y^2 + z^2 = 1$ **7.** $x + 3y - 5z + 13 = 0$ **9.** $(x + 3)^2 + (y - 9)^2 + (z - 4)^2 = 16$ **11.** $x^2 + y^2 = 144$ **13.** $3x - 2y + 2z + 7 = 0$ **15.** $2x - 3y + 6z - 3 = 0$ **17.** $x - 4y + 8z + 20 = 0$ or $x - 4y + 8z - 34 = 0$

Page 264 Chapter Review 1. yz-plane **3.** It is a line in the xy-plane and parallel to the y-axis.
5. $5\sqrt{3}$ **7.** Let $\vec{v} = \begin{pmatrix} v_1 \\ v_2 \\ v_3 \end{pmatrix}$. Then $k\vec{v} = \begin{pmatrix} kv_1 \\ kv_2 \\ kv_3 \end{pmatrix} = \vec{0}$. That is, $kv_1 = kv_2 = kv_3 = 0$. If $k \neq 0$, then $v_1 = v_2 = v_3 = 0$ and $\vec{v} = \vec{0}$. If $v_1 \neq 0$, $v_2 \neq 0$, and $v_3 \neq 0$, then $k = 0$. **9.** $\sqrt{29}$; $\frac{2}{\sqrt{29}}$, $\frac{3}{\sqrt{29}}$, $\frac{4}{\sqrt{29}}$ **11.** $\sqrt{70}$; $-\frac{5}{\sqrt{70}}$, $-\frac{3}{\sqrt{70}}$, $\frac{6}{\sqrt{70}}$ **13.** -75 **15.** Pe **17.** $\begin{pmatrix} -2 \\ -20 \\ 14 \end{pmatrix}$ **19.** $\frac{x - 4}{4} = \frac{y - 5}{-2} = \frac{z - 3}{3}$

CHAPTER 9 SECOND-DEGREE RELATIONS

Page 270 Exploratory Exercises 1. $(2, 1)$; 4 **3.** $(0, -1)$; 3 **5.** $(x - 3)^2 + (y + 7)^2 = 9$ **7.** $(x - 3)^2 + (y - 5)^2 = 4$ **9.** $(x + 1)^2 + y^2 = 25$

Page 270 Written Exercises 1. $(x - a)^2 + (y - 2a)^2 = a^2$ **3.** $(x - 7)^2 + (y + a)^2 = 2$ **5.** $x^2 + (y - 5)^2 = 13$ **7.** $(3, -2)$; 4 **9.** $(a, -2a)$; a

Page 271 Challenge Exercises 1. $x + 2y + 3 = 0$

Page 273 Exploratory Exercises 1. $(0, 0)$; $x = -2$ **3.** $(-4, 2)$; $y = 3$ **5.** $(2, 1)$; $y = 1$ **7.** $y^2 = 8x$ **9.** $(x + 3)^2 = -8(y - 5)$

Page 273 Written Exercises
1.

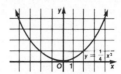

3.

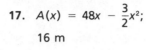

9. $x^2 + 14x - 4y + 65 = 0$ or $(x + 7) = 4(y - 4)$ **11.** $y^2 = -8x$

17. $A(x) = 48x - \frac{3}{2}x^2$; 16 m

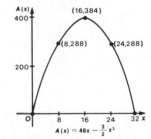

Page 274 Challenge Exercise The equation of the parabola is $y^2 = 4px$. Let the points (p, a) and $(p, -a)$ be the endpoints of the latus rectum. Thus, $a^2 = 4p^2$ and $a = |2p|$. So, the length of the latus rectum is $2a$ or $|4p|$.

Page 276 Exploratory Exercises 1. $\frac{(x - 4)^2}{25} + \frac{(y - 3)^2}{9} = 1$ **3.** $\frac{(x + 5)^2}{36} + \frac{(y + 9)^2}{4} = 1$ **5.** $C(0, 3)$; $V_1(-6, 3)$ and $V_2(6, 3)$ **7.** $\frac{4}{5}$ **9.** $\frac{3}{5}$

Page 276 Written Exercises
5. $\frac{(x - 3)^2}{9} + \frac{(y - 2)^2}{25} = 1$ **7.** $\frac{(x - 1)^2}{16} + \frac{(y - 1)^2}{15} = 1$ **9.** $\frac{x^2}{25} + \frac{y^2}{16} = 1$ **11.** 151.533 million km

Page 277 Challenge Exercises 1. Find $|2y|$ where $x = c$. Solve for y in $\frac{c^2}{a^2} + \frac{y^2}{b^2} = 1$. Then $y = \pm\frac{b^2}{a}$ and $|2y| = \frac{2b^2}{a}$

Page 280 Exploratory Exercises 1. $\frac{(x - 4)^2}{9} - \frac{(y - 7)^2}{4} = 1$ **3.** $x^2 - y^2 = 1$ **5.** $C(1, 3)$; $V_1(6, 3)$ and $V_2(-4, 3)$ **7.** $\frac{13}{5}$ **9.** $\frac{17}{8}$

Page 280 Written Exercises

5. For $\frac{x^2}{4} - \frac{y^2}{9} = 1$, the asymptotes are $y = \pm\frac{3}{2}x$ since $b = 3$, $a = 2$. For $\frac{y^2}{9} - \frac{x^2}{4}$, the asymptotes also are $y = \pm\frac{3}{2}$ since $a = 3$, $b = 2$. **7.** $\frac{y^2}{36} - \frac{x^2}{28} = 1$ **9.** $\frac{4}{25}\left(y - \frac{3}{2}\right)^2 - \frac{16}{25}(x - 1)^2 = 1$ **11.** $\frac{(y - 2)^2}{16} - \frac{(x - 4)^2}{9} = 1$ **13.** $\frac{(x - 5)^2}{9} - \frac{(y - 1)^2}{16} = 1$ **15.** $\frac{y^2}{16} - \frac{x^2}{9} = 1$

Page 283 Exploratory Exercises 1. circle **3.** parabola **5.** line **7.** point **9.** 5 **11.** undefined

Page 283 Written Exercises 1. circle **3.** parabola **5.** hyperbola **7.** $A' + C' = (A\cos^2\theta + B\sin\theta\cos\theta + C\sin^2\theta) + (A\sin^2\theta - B\sin\theta\cos\theta + C\cos^2\theta) = A(\cos^2\theta + \sin^2\theta) + C(\sin^2\theta + \cos^2\theta) = A + C$ **9.** parabola **11.** parabola **13.** $\frac{x'^2}{1} + \frac{y'^2}{2} = 1$; hyperbola

Page 286 Exploratory Exercises 1. ellipse **3.** ellipse **5.** hyperbola

Page 286 Written Exercises
1.
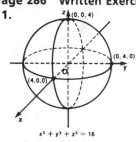

3.
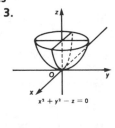

9. $4x^2 + 4y^2 = 3|z|$

Page 289 Chapter Review 1. $(x + 3)^2 + (y - 5)^2 = 9$ **3.** $(0, 0)$; $3\sqrt{3}$ **5.** $\left(-\frac{3}{2}, -\frac{1}{2}\right)$; $\frac{\sqrt{58}}{2}$ **7.** $(7, 3)$; $y = 1$ **9.** $(y - 1)^2 = -8(x - 2)$ **15.** $\frac{x^2}{4} + \frac{4y^2}{7} = 1$ **17.** $\frac{(x - 2)^2}{25} + \frac{(y + 1)^2}{16} = 1$ **23.** $\frac{y^2}{4} - \frac{(x - 1)^2}{9} = 1$ **25.** $\frac{(x - 4)^2}{4} - \frac{(y + 2)^2}{5} = 1$ **27.** circle **29.** ellipse **31.** parabola **33.** hyperbola

CHAPTER 10 POLYNOMIAL FUNCTIONS

Page 297 Exploratory Exercises 1. polynomial, degree 2, leading coefficient 3, constant term 0 **3.** polynomial, degree 3, leading coefficient 0.25, constant term 0 **5.** polynomial, degree l, leading coefficient $\sqrt{5}$, constant term $-\sqrt{2}$

Page 297 Written Exercises 1. $P(0) = -5$, $P(1) = -2$, $P(-1) = -8$, $P(2) = 1$, L **3.** $P(0) = -7$, $P(1) = -5$, $P(-1) = -9$, $P(2) = 9$ **5.** $P(0) = 2$, $P(1) = 0$, $P(-1) = 4$, $P(2) = 124$ **7.** $P(0) = 0$, $P(1) = 2i - 2$, $P(-1) = 2$, $P(2) = 6i - 4$, Q

Page 300 Exploratory Exercises 1. odd **3.** even **5.** neither

Page 300 Written Exercises
1. $x(x - 1)(x + 1)$ **5.** $(x - 1)^2(x + 1)$

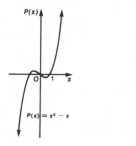

Page 304 Exploratory Exercises 1. 15 **3.** 311 **5.** 31

Page 304 Written Exercises 1. $x^2 + 4x + 5 + \frac{15}{x - 2}$ **3.** $3x^3 - 9x^2 + 33x - 104 + \frac{311}{x + 3}$ **5.** $2x^2 + 5x - 12 + \frac{31}{x + 2}$ **7.** $x^6 - x^5 + x^4 - x^3 + x^2 - x + 1 + \frac{-141}{x + 1}$

Page 305 Challenge Exercises 1. $k = 2$ **2.** $k = 2$

Page 307 Exploratory Exercises 1. $a = 0$ **3.** $-1, 5$ **5.** $P(x) = (x - 3)(x + 2)(x - 1)(x + 1)$ or $x^4 - x^3 - 7x^2 + x + 6$ P is not unique since any factor may be repeated. For example, $P(x) = (x - 3)^2(x + 2)^3(x - 1)^4(x + 1)$

Page 307 Written Exercises 1. $(x + 1)(x - 3)(x - 2)$ **3.** $(x + 1)\left(x - \frac{1 + 3i}{2}\right)\left(x - \frac{1 - 3i}{2}\right)$

Page 307 Challenge Exercises 1. $(x - 2)^2(x + 1)^2(x - i)(x + i)$

Page 309 Exploratory Exercises 1. 5 **3.** 5 **5.** 5

Page 310 Written Exercises
1. $(x - 1)^3(x - \sqrt{2})$ $(x + \sqrt{2})$ 1, $\sqrt{2}$, and $-\sqrt{2}$ are zeros. 1 has multiplicity three and $\sqrt{2}$ and $-\sqrt{2}$ have multiplicity one. **3.** $(x - 1)^3(x + 3)^2$ 1 has multiplicity three and -3 has multiplicity two.

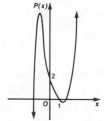

$P(x) = x^5 - 3x^4 + x^3 + 5x^3 - 6x + 2$

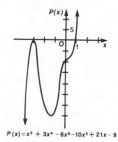

$P(x) = x^5 + 3x^4 - 6x^3 - 10x^3 + 21x - 9$

9. $(x - 1)(x + 1)(x - \sqrt{2})(x + \sqrt{2})$ or $(x^2 - 1)(x^2 - 2)$ **11.** $x^3(x^2 - 4x + 1)$

$P(x) = (x^2 - 1)(x^2 - 2)$

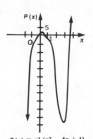

$P(x) = x^3(x^2 - 4x + 1)$

Page 312 Exploratory Exercises 1. 3 **3.** 3 **5.** 3

Page 312 Written Exercises
1. Zeros between -2 and -1, 2 and 3, and 3 and 4. The greatest integer lower bound is -2 and the least integer upper bound is 4.

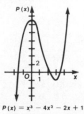

$P(x) = x^3 - 4x^2 - 2x + 13$

3. Zeros between -4 and -3, 4 and 5, and at $x = -1$. The greatest integer lower bound is -4 and the least integer upper bound is 5.

5. Zeros between -2 and -1 and at $x = 3$. The greatest integer lower bound is -2 and the least integer upper bound is 3.
7. Zero between -3 and -2

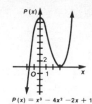

$P(x) = x^3 - 4x^2 - 2x + 15$

Page 312 Challenge Exercises 1. $k < 3$ and $k > 20$ **3.** If a function f is continuous on the interval $[a, b]$ and t is a real number such that $f(b) < t < f(a)$, then there exists at least one real number c such that $a < c < b$ and $f(c) = t$. yes; no, unless $t = f(a) = f(b)$

Page 315 Exploratory Exercises 1. $(x - 3)(x + 2)(x - 1)$ **3.** $(3x - 2)(6x - 1)(x - 2)$ **5.** $x(x + 1)(x^2 - 2x - 2)$

Page 315 Written Exercises 1. $\dfrac{2}{3}$, $2 \pm \sqrt{3}$
3. $1, 3, \dfrac{-1 \pm i\sqrt{3}}{2}$ **5.** $-\dfrac{1}{3}, \dfrac{-1 + i\sqrt{15}}{4}$ **7.** $\dfrac{1}{2}$
9. 1 and 3

Page 318 Exploratory Exercises 1. $-i$ **3.** $3i$
5. $\dfrac{1}{2} - \dfrac{\sqrt{3}}{2}i$ **7.** $\sqrt{5} - 3i\sqrt{2}$ **9.** $5 + 4i$

Page 318 Written Exercises 1. $z_2 = -2i$, $z_3 = 2$ **3.** $z_2 = 3 + i$, $z_3 = 4$ **5.** $z_3 = -2i$, $z_4 = -3i$
7. $z_2 = 1 - 3i$, $z_3 = \dfrac{9 + \sqrt{113}}{4}$, $z_4 = \dfrac{9 - \sqrt{113}}{4}$ **9.** $x^3 - 11x + 20$ **11.** $x^4 + 29x^2 + 100$ **13.** $12x^4 - 89x^3 + 240x^2 - 223x + 66$ **15.** $2x^3 - 11x^2 + 17x - 6$

Page 318 Challenge Exercises 1. $P\left(\dfrac{1}{z}\right) = \left(\dfrac{1}{z}\right)^3 + k\left(\dfrac{1}{z}\right)^2 + k\left(\dfrac{1}{z}\right) + 1 = \dfrac{1}{z^3}(1 + kz + kz^2 + z^3) = \dfrac{1}{z^3}(P(z))$ Since $P(z) = 0$, $\dfrac{1}{z^3}(P(z)) = 0$. Therefore, $P\left(\dfrac{1}{z}\right) = 0$

Page 321 Exploratory Exercises 1. $\pm 1, \pm 3$ **3.** $\pm 1, \pm 11$ **5.** $\pm 1, \pm 3, \pm\dfrac{1}{2}, \pm\dfrac{3}{2}$

Page 321 Written Exercises 1. 1.67, -0.84 $\pm 1.05i$ **3.** 2.13, 0.44 $\pm 2.23i$ **5.** -0.10, -7.34, 1.44 **7.** -1.38, 0.94 $\pm 0.46i$ **9.** -0.73, 2.73, $1 \pm i$

Page 324   Written Exercises

1. 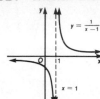 **3.**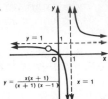

9. 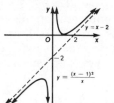 **11.**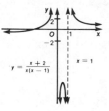

Page 325   Chapter Review   1. 0, 9 **3.** $\frac{3}{2}$, −1
5. $x(x^2 + 1)$ **7.** $P(x) = (x^2 − 1)(x − 2)(x + 3)$ $P(x) = 1 − x^4$ **9.** $P(x) = (x + 3)(3x^2 − 11x + 34) − 104$

15. $(x − 1)(x + 1)^2(x + 2)(x − 2)$. Zeros are −1 multiplicity two; 1, 2, −2 each multiplicity one.

17. $(x − 3)(x + 3)(x + 2)^3$. Zeros are −2 multiplicity three; 3, −3 each multiplicity one.

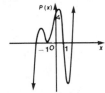

$P(x) = x^5 + x^4 − 5x^3 − 5x^2 + 4x + 4$

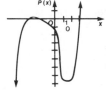

$P(x) = x^5 + 6x^4 + 3x^3 − 46x^2 − 108x − 72$

23. $1 < k < 8$ **25.** $4, 6, \frac{1}{4}, −\frac{1}{4}$ **27.** $−i, 2i, −2i$
29. $4x^3 − 17x^2 + 40x − 9$ **31.** 0.27, −2.24, 3.73, 2.24

CHAPTER 11   TRANSCENDENTAL FUNCTIONS

Page 334   Exploratory Exercises   1. $\frac{2}{5}$ **3.** $\frac{1}{9}$
$\sqrt[3]{3}$ **5.** $\frac{1}{4}$ **7.** 3.5 **9.** 0.4 **11.** 5792.6

Page 335   Written Exercises   1. $8 − 3\sqrt[3]{3}$ **3.**
$\frac{\sqrt[5]{2}}{2a^2b}$ **5.** $\frac{51}{16}$ **7.** 1.9 **9.** −2.3 **11.** 5.0 **13.** 5.8 **15.** 3.6 **17.** 2.1

Page 335   Challenge Exercises

1.  **3.**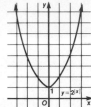

Page 338   Exploratory Exercises   1. 3.3201 **3.** 221.41 **5.** 2.36 **7.** 4.946

Page 338   Written Exercises   1. $a^4 + 4a^3b + 6a^2b^2 + 4ab^3 + a^4$ **3.** $a^5 − 5a^4b + 10a^3b^2 − 10a^2b^3 + 5ab^4 − b^5$ **5.** 0.00000028 and 0.000000025 For Problems **7** and **9**, accurate answers are given. **7.** 7.389 **9.** 1096.633

Page 339   Challenge Exercises   1. The least upper bound is e.

Page 339   Excursion Exercises   1. The expressions are equivalent. **3.** $i = (−1)^{1/2}$ and $e^{i\pi} = −1$ So, $i = (e^{i\pi/2}$ or $e^{\pi/2\ i}$. Hence $i^i = (e^{\pi/2\ i})^i$ or $e^{−\pi/2}$.

Page 343   Exploratory Exercises   1. $b = \log_a c$
3. $\log_5 \frac{1}{125} = −3$ **5.** $\log_3 t = \sqrt{2}$ **7.** $\log_{0.01} 0.000001 = 3$ **9.** 2.0643 **11.** 1.6778 **13.** −2.7001 **15.** 8.1800 **17.** 166.8174

Page 343   Written Exercises   1. $\frac{1}{8}$ **3.** 0 **5.** $\frac{2}{5}$
7. 8 **9.** 1 **11.** $b \neq 0$ **13.** a **15.** 8 **17.** 4
19. 15 **21.** $2t$ **23.** $\frac{1}{\log_{10}e}$ **25.** $\frac{\log_5 3.8}{\log_5 e}$
33. Let $\log_a 1 = x$. **37.** 1.7604 **39.** 3.7377
So $a^x = 1$ **41.** 0.4655
and $x = 0$

Page 344   Challenge Exercises

1.
$y = \ln|x|$

3.
$y = x \ln x$
(e, e)

Page 346   Exploratory Exercises   1. 2 **3.** −1.322 **5.** ± 0.55342 **7.** 141.8

Page 347   Written Exercises   1. $x < 2.3219$

3. ±0.5997 **5.** 93.89 **7.** ±1.6651 **9.** 5
11. 127 **13.** 0.4336 **15.** −7.6377 **17.** 0.2861

Page 347 Challenge Exercises 1. No, it is not defined for $x \leq 0$. **3.** No, it is not defined for $x \leq 0$. **5.** Yes, it is true because $\log_{10} 10^x = x$.

Page 350 Written Exercises 1. 2000, 2,048,000 **3.** 1.44 oz **5.** a. 25, 172 b. 2010 **7.** $774.40 **9.** 7.7 years **11.** $4274.15

Page 353 Chapter Review 1. 36 **3.** $\dfrac{a^2 - ab + b^2}{ab(a + b)}$
5. 100 **7.** 2.8 **9.** 2.6 **11.** 14.8797 **13.** 18.119
15. 1.7712 **17.** 3.00 **19.** 1.001 **21.** $\dfrac{1}{32}$
23. −2 **25.** −2 **27.** 9 **29.** $\dfrac{1}{\ln 10}$ **31.** $\dfrac{1}{\log_2 e}$
33. 1.5518088 **35.** 2.05745 **39.** 1.26
41. 152.41 **43.** 0.2215 **45.** 0.22149031
47. 11.6 days **49.** $672.06 **51.** 4.4%

CHAPTER 12   POLAR COORDINATES

Page 361 Written Exercises 1. (−3, 160°)
3. $\left(1.5, \dfrac{5\pi}{2}\right)$

5–8.   **9–12.**

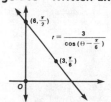

17. (8.27, Arctan (−4.01)) or (8.27, −76°)
Page 361 Challenge Exercise $(r, \theta) = ((-1)^1 r, \theta + 1 \cdot \pi) = ((-1)^2 r, \theta + 2\pi) = ((-1)^k r, \theta + k\pi$

Page 365 Exploratory Exercises 1. 4 **3.** $\sqrt{61}$ **5.** 5.66

Page 365 Written Exercises 1. $x^2 + y^2 = 3y$; circle **3.** $x^2 + y^2 = 3\sqrt{x^2 + y^2} - x$ **5.** $xy = 2$; hyperbola **7.** $x^2 + y^2 = x^2 y$ **9.** $y = x^3$ **11.** $(x^2 + y^2)^2 = 2y(3x^2 - y^2)$ **13.** $r = \sqrt{10}$ **15.** $r = -3 \sin \theta$ **17.** $r = \dfrac{3 \cos \theta}{\sin^2 \theta}$

Page 369 Exploratory Exercises 1. pole; $\theta = -\dfrac{\pi}{4}$ **3.** (−3, 0); $r \cos \theta = -3$ **5.** $-\dfrac{\pi}{6}$; (6, π), $\left(2\sqrt{3}, \dfrac{3\pi}{2}\right)$; $r \cos\left(\theta - \dfrac{4\pi}{3}\right) = 3$ **7.** (10, 0), (10

$\tan 2\theta, \dfrac{\pi}{2}\Big)$; $r \cos(\theta - 70°) = 3.42$

Page 369 Written Exercises
1.   **3.**

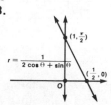

5. $r = 6 \sin \theta$ **7.** $r = 10 \sin \theta$ **9.** $r = -2\sqrt{2} \sin \theta$ **11.** $r = -8.4 \cos\left(\theta - \dfrac{7\pi}{6}\right)$ **13.** $1 = r^2 + 4 - 4r \cos\left(\theta - \dfrac{3\pi}{4}\right)$ **15.** $16 = r^2 + 23.04 - 9.6 r \cos(\theta - 210°)$ **17.** $2 = r^2 + 12 + 4\sqrt{3}\, r \cos\left(\theta + \dfrac{\pi}{4}\right)$ **19.** $r = 3\sqrt{2} \cos\left(\theta - \dfrac{\pi}{4}\right)$ **21.** $9 = r^2 + 25 - 10r \cos\left(\theta + \dfrac{\pi}{6}\right)$

Page 370 Challenge Exercises 1. $3x + y - 5 = 0$; $3r \cos \theta + 4r \sin \theta = 5$; 1 **3.** $r(a \cos \theta + b \sin \theta) = c$ in rectangular form is $ax + by = c$ which represents a line if a and b are not both zero.

Page 376 Exploratory Exercises 1. Symmetric about $\theta = \dfrac{\pi}{2}$; Intercepts: $\left(0, \arcsin -\dfrac{1}{3}\right)$ or pole; $(1, 0)$, $\left(4, \dfrac{\pi}{2}\right)$, $(-1, \pi)$, $\left(-2; \dfrac{3\pi}{2}\right)$; Extent: $-2 \leq r \leq 4$; Tangents: $\theta = \arcsin -\dfrac{1}{3}$ and $\theta = \pi + \arcsin \dfrac{1}{3}$ **3.** Symmetric about $\theta = \dfrac{\pi}{2}$; Intercepts: pole, $(2, 0)$, $\left(4, \dfrac{\pi}{2}\right)$, $(2, \pi)$, $\left(0, \dfrac{3\pi}{2}\right)$; Extent: $0 \leq r \leq 4$; Tangent: $\theta = \dfrac{3\pi}{2}$ **5.** Symmetric about the polar axis; Intercepts: $\left(0, \dfrac{1}{2}\right)$, $\left(1, \dfrac{\pi}{2}\right)$, $\left(1, \dfrac{3\pi}{2}\right)$; Extent: $r \geq \dfrac{1}{2}$; Tangents: none

Page 376 Written Exercises
1.   **3.**

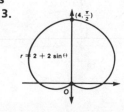

9.

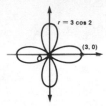

$r = 3 \cos 2$

(3, 0)

11. $(-2\sqrt{2}, 0)$, $\left(2\sqrt{2}, \dfrac{\pi}{2}\right)$, $(2\sqrt{2}, \pi)$, $\left(-2\sqrt{2}, \dfrac{3\pi}{2}\right)$, pole

13.

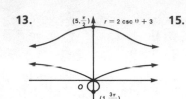

$\left(5, \dfrac{\pi}{2}\right)$ $r = 2 \csc \theta + 3$

$\left(1, \dfrac{3\pi}{2}\right)$

15.

$r^2 = \dfrac{4}{\theta}$

Page 377 Challenge Exercises 1. $r = \sin 2\theta$ **3.** $r = 1$ **5.** Since $P(r, \pi - \theta)$ implies $P(-r, -\theta)$, II holds. **7.** There is no property in this section dealing with symmetry with respect to the line $y = x$ in rectangular coordinates.

Page 381 Exploratory Exercises 1. Symmetric about the polar axis, $\theta = \dfrac{\pi}{2}$, and the pole; Intercept: (0, 0); Extent: $|r| \le 3$; Tangents: $\theta = 0$, $\dfrac{\pi}{2}, -\dfrac{3\pi}{2}$ **3.** Symmetric about $\theta = \dfrac{\pi}{2}$; Intercept: the pole, $\left(-4, \dfrac{\pi}{2}\right)$; Extent: $|r| \le 4$; Tangents: polar axis, $\theta = \dfrac{\pi}{3}, \dfrac{2\pi}{3}, \pi, \dfrac{4\pi}{3}, \dfrac{5\pi}{3}$ **5.** Symmetric about $\theta = \dfrac{\pi}{2}$; Intercepts: the pole, (4, 0); Extent: $|r| \le 4$; Tangents: $\theta = \dfrac{\pi}{10}, \dfrac{3\pi}{10}, \dfrac{\pi}{2}, \dfrac{7\pi}{10}, \dfrac{9\pi}{10}, \dfrac{11\pi}{10}$, $\dfrac{13\pi}{10}, \dfrac{3\pi}{2}, \dfrac{17\pi}{10}, \dfrac{19\pi}{10}$ **7.** n **9.** rotate $\dfrac{\pi}{2} - \theta$

Page 381 Written Exercises
1. Symmetric about the polar axis; Extent: $|r| \le 6$; Intercepts: (6, 0), $\left(3, \dfrac{\pi}{2}\right)$, $\left(3, \dfrac{3\pi}{2}\right)$, the pole; Tangent: the polar axis. It is a cardioid.

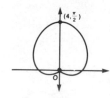

$r = 3(1 + \cos \theta)$

(6, 0)

3. Symmetric about $\theta = \dfrac{\pi}{2}$; Extent: $|r| \le 4$; Intercepts: (2, 0), $\left(4, \dfrac{\pi}{2}\right)$, (2, π), the pole; Tangent: $\theta = \dfrac{3\pi}{2}$; It is a cardioid.

$\left(4, \dfrac{\pi}{2}\right)$

Page 383 Chapter Review In Problems **1–6** answers will vary. **9.** (4 cos 22°), (4 sin 22°) or (3.7, 1.5) **11.** 7.8 **13.** $\sqrt{x^2 + y^2} = \left(\arctan \dfrac{y}{x}\right)$, spiral **15.** $r \cos \theta + r \sin \theta = 2$ **17.** $r = -1 + \csc \theta$ **19.** $r \sin \theta = -2$ **25.** $r = 8 \sin \theta$ **27.** $0.25 = r^2 + 0.36 + 1.2 \cos \left(\theta - \dfrac{\pi}{3}\right)$ **29.** $r = \cos\left(\theta - \dfrac{\pi}{4}\right)$

39. It is a limaçon.; Symmetric about the polar axis; Intercepts: the pole, $\left(1, \dfrac{\pi}{2}\right)$, (3, π), $\left(1, \dfrac{3\pi}{2}\right)$; Extent: $-1 \le r \le 3$; Tangents $\theta = \dfrac{\pi}{3}, -\dfrac{\pi}{3}$

41. It is a spiral.; Intercepts: the pole, $\left(\dfrac{n\pi}{2}, \dfrac{n\pi}{2}\right)$, $(n\pi, n\pi)$ where n is a natural number.; Extent: $r \ge 0$; Tangents: $\theta = 0$

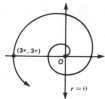

$(3\pi, 3\pi)$

$r = \theta$

CHAPTER 13 SEQUENCES AND SERIES

Page 397 Written Exercises 1. $a = 1$; $d = 2$; 7, 9, 11; 19 **3.** $a = -9$; $d = 7$; 12, 19, 26; 54 **5.** $a = 5$; $d = -6$; $-13, -19, -25$; -49 **7.** 2, -1 **9.** 10, 13 **11.** 35 **13.** $17\sqrt{2}$ **15.**

$$S_{11} = 1 + 3 + 5 + \cdots + 21$$
$$S_{11} = 21 + 19 + 17 + \cdots + 1$$

$$\overline{\phantom{2S_{11} = 22 + 22 + 22}}$$
$$2S_{11} = 22 + 22 + 22 + \cdots + 22$$
$$2S_{11} = 11\,(22)$$
$$S_{11} = 121$$

Page 397 Challenge Exercises 1. 21, 28, 36 **3.** 210 **5.** 15 **7.** 8

Page 399 Exploratory Exercises 1. $r = 2$; 9.6, 19.2, 38.4 **3.** $r = 2$; $\frac{8}{3}, \frac{16}{3}, \frac{32}{3}$ **5.** $a_n = 3(2)^{n-1}$

7. $a_n = 9\left(\frac{2}{3}\right)^{n-1}$

Page 399 Written Exercises 1. $r = \frac{3}{2}$; $\frac{27}{8}, \frac{81}{16}$, $\frac{243}{32}$; $a_n = \left(\frac{3}{2}\right)^{n-1}$ **3.** $r = \frac{1}{3}$; $\frac{5}{9}, \frac{5}{27}, \frac{5}{81}$; $a_n = 5(3)^{2-n}$ **5.** 32, 16 **7.** $5\sqrt{3}$, 15 **9.** 2^{n-1} **11.** 2^{3-n} **13.** 3^{3-n} **15.** 1; 3; 81 **17.** $a_1 = 6$; $a_2 = -3$; $\frac{3}{8}$ **19.** $a = \frac{1}{3}$; $r = 3$; 27 **21.** $a = 6$; $r = \pm 2$; 96 **23.** $a = 50$; $r = 2$; 800 **25.** 115 **27.** 152.0875 **29.** $\{100(1.15)^n\}$ **31.** $a = 1$; $r = 2$; 255 **33.** $a = \frac{1}{2}$; $r = \frac{1}{2}$; $\frac{1023}{1024}$ **35.** $a = 2$; $r = -\frac{1}{3}$; $\frac{244}{81}$ **37.** 4

Page 401 Challenge Exercises 1. $a_0 = 1$; $r = 1.05$; $a_2 = 1.1025$; $a_3 = 1.157625$; $a_4 = 1.2155062$; $a_5 = 1.2762816$; $a_{10} = 1.6288946$ **3.** The return of the payments (S) is $100(1.05)^{40} + 100(1.05)^{39} + \cdots + 100(1.05) = 105[1 + \cdots + 1.05^{38} + 1.05^{39}] = 105\left[\frac{1 - 1.05^{40}}{1 - 1.05}\right] \approx 105(121) \approx$ 12,700.

Page 404 Exploratory Exercises 1. $\frac{n + 1}{n + 2}$

3. $n^2 + 3n + 2$ **5.** $\frac{1}{2}$ **7.** 2

Page 404 Written Exercises

1. Let $P(n)$ be $1 + 2 + 4 + 8 + \cdots + 2^{n-1} = 2^n - 1$ for every $n \in$ N.
   a. $1 = 2^1 - 1$. Therefore $P(1)$ is true.
   b. For some $k \in$ N, assume that $P(k)$ is true.
   $$1 + 2 + 4 + \cdots + 2^{k-1} = 2^k - 1$$
   $$1 + 2 + 4 + \cdots + 2^{k-1} + 2^k = 2^k - 1 - 2^k$$
   $$= 2^1 \cdot 2^k - 1$$
   $$= 2^{k+1} - 1$$
   Therefore $P(k + 1)$ is true whenever $P(k)$ is true. So $P(n)$ is true for every $n \in$ N.
3. Let $P(n)$ be $1 + 3 + 5 + \cdots + (2n - 1) = n^2 + 3$ for every $n \in$ N.
   a. $2 \cdot 1 - 1 = 1$ but $1^2 + 3 = 4$ Therefore, $P(1)$ is not true. Since $P(n)$ is not true for 1, it is not true for every $n \in$ N.

Page 404 Challenge Exercises

1. Let $P(n)$ be $(\cos \theta + i \sin \theta)^n = \cos n\theta + i \sin n\theta$ for every $n \in$ N.
   a. $(\cos \theta + i \sin \theta)^1 = \cos 1 \cdot \theta + i \sin 1 \cdot \theta$ So $P(1)$ is true.
   b. Assume $P(k)$ is true for $\sin k \in$ N. $(\cos \theta + i \sin \theta)^k = \cos k\theta + i \sin k\theta$ Then $(\cos \theta + i \sin \theta)^{k+1} = (\cos \theta + i \sin \theta)^k(\cos \theta + i \sin \theta)$
   $= (\cos k\theta + i \sin k\theta)(\cos \theta + i \sin \theta)$
   $= (\cos k\theta \cos \theta) + i(\sin k\theta \cos \theta$
   $\quad + \cos k\theta \sin \theta) - (\sin k\theta \sin \theta)$
   $= \cos (k\theta + \theta) + i \sin (k\theta + \theta)$
   $= \cos(k + 1)\theta + i \sin (k + 1)\theta$
   Thus $P(k + 1)$ is true when $P(k)$ is true. So $P(n)$ is true for $n \in$ N.

Page 407 Exploratory Exercises 1. 4 **3.** 5 **5.** no terms **7.** $n > 8$ **9.** $n > \frac{2}{5h}$

Page 407 Written Exercises 1. $a_n \in \left\langle \frac{1}{2}, \frac{5}{6} \right\rangle$ if $n > 10$; $a_n \in \left\langle \frac{1}{2}, \frac{5}{6} \right\rangle$ if $n \leq 10$ **3.** $a_n \in \langle 2.98, 3.02 \rangle$ if $n \geq 51$; $a_n \in \langle 2.98, 3.02 \rangle$ if $n < 51$ **5.** $n > -\frac{1}{h}$ **7.** $n > \frac{-23 - 14h}{49h}$ **9.** 5 **11.** 10

Page 407 Challenge Exercises 1. $a_1 = 3$, $a_2 = 2.25$, $a_3 = 2.\overline{1}$, $a_4 = 2.0625$. The limit is 2. $n > 10^3$

Page 411 Exploratory Exercises 1. $-\frac{2}{5}$ **3.** $\frac{1}{2}$ **5.** 1

Page 411 Written Exercises 1. Given $\epsilon > 0$, let M be any natural number such that $M > \frac{1}{\epsilon}$. Then from $n > M > \frac{1}{\epsilon}$, $\epsilon > \frac{1}{n}$. Since $\frac{1}{n} > 0 > -\epsilon$, for all n, it follows that for all $n > M$, $-\epsilon < \frac{1}{n} < \epsilon$. Thus, $\left\{\frac{1}{n}\right\} \to 0$ **3.** $n > 3998$ **5.** $n > \frac{2}{5\epsilon}$ **7.** $M = 1$ if $\epsilon > \frac{1}{2}$ **9.** L_1 does not exist. **11.** $\frac{1}{2}$ **13.** $\frac{1}{2}$

Page 411 Challenge Exercises 1. 2, 1.75, 1.73214, 1.7320505

Page 415 Exploratory Exercises 1. $r = \frac{1}{3}$; 1, $1.\overline{3}$, $1.\overline{4}$, $1.48\overline{148}$; yes, 1.5 **3.** $r = \frac{1}{4}$; 4, 5, 5.25,

5.3125; yes, $\frac{16}{3}$ **5.** $r = -5$; 1, -4, 21, -104; no, the series diverges. **7.** $r = 1$; 1, 2, 3, 4; no the series diverges

Page 415 Written Exercises 1. $\frac{1}{3}$ **3.** Since r would be -8, then $|r| > 1$ and there is no sum. **5.** $13\frac{1}{3}m$ **7.** $\frac{12}{11}$ **9.** $\frac{1}{7}$

Page 416 Challenge Exercises 1. $\frac{1}{2}, \frac{2}{3}, \frac{3}{4}, \frac{4}{5}$ **3.** 1

Page 417 Chapter Review 1. $1, \frac{1}{4}, \frac{1}{9}, \frac{1}{16}$ **3.** $4n$ **5.** $10 + 11 + 12 + 13 + 14 = 60$ **7.** $a = 5$; $d = 4$; 17, 21, 25 **9.** $a = -n$; $d = n$; $2n, 3n, 4n$ **11.** 315 **13.** $r = \frac{1}{2}$; $\frac{1}{2}, \frac{1}{4}, \frac{1}{8}$; 2^{3-n} **15.** $r = t$; t^{n-3} **17.** $\frac{121}{81}$ **19.** 41.5625 **25.** $n < \frac{2h}{5-h}$ **27.** 0 **29.** $\frac{3}{2}$

CHAPTER 14 LIMITS OF FUNCTIONS

Page 425 Exploratory Exercises 1. $f(x) \in \langle 4.8, 5.2 \rangle$ **3.** $1.99\overline{6} < x < 2.00\overline{3}$ **5. a.** $x \in \langle 0.5, 0.7 \rangle$; $f(x) \in \langle 0.8, 1.2 \rangle$ **b.** $0.5 < x < 0.7$; $0.8 < f(x) < 1.2$ **c.** $|x - 0.6| < 0.1$; $|f(x) - 1| < 0.2$

Page 425 Written Exercises 1. $f(x) \in \langle -0.19, 0.21 \rangle$ **3.** $f(x) \in \langle 6 - 2a, 6 + 2a \rangle$, $a > 0$ **5.** $x \in \langle 0.9\overline{6}, 1.0\overline{3} \rangle$ **7.** $x \in \left\langle \frac{-3 + \sqrt{48.6}}{2}, \frac{-3 + \sqrt{49.2}}{2} \right\rangle \cup \left\langle \frac{-3 - \sqrt{48.6}}{2}, \frac{-3 - \sqrt{49.4}}{2} \right\rangle$ **9. a.** $x \in \langle 2.5, 35 \rangle$, $f(x) \in \langle 5.9, 6.1 \rangle$ **b.** $2.5 < x < 3.5$; $5.9 < f(x) < 6.1$ **c.** $|x - 3| < 0.5$; $|f(x) - 6| < 0.1$

Page 426 Challenge Exercises 1. $12.96 < d < 14.96$

Page 429 Exploratory Exercises 1. 2; 0.1; 0.01, 0.001 **3.** 4; 0.05, 0.005, 0.0005 **5.** $-\frac{1}{2}$; 0.1, 0.01, 0.001

Page 429 Written Exercises 1. $1, \frac{1}{30}, \frac{1}{300}$ **3.** 0.01 **5.** 0.03 **7.** Given $\epsilon > 0$, choose $\delta = \epsilon$. Then $0 < |x - 3| < \delta$. So $|x + 3 - 6| < \epsilon$ and $\left| \frac{x^2 - 9}{x - 3} - 6 \right| < \epsilon$ for $x \neq 3$ **9.** The limit does not exist because given any real number M, a value of x sufficiently close to 0 can be found such that $\left| \frac{1}{x} \right| > M$. **11.** $\frac{2}{3}$ **13.** 3

Page 433 Exploratory Exercises 1. 1; Theorems 2f, 2c, 2b, 1 **3.** -6; Theorems 2d, 2a, 2c, 1 **5.** 12, Theorems 2f, 2a, 2c, 3a, 2b, 1

Page 433 Written Exercises 1. $\frac{3}{4}$ **3.** $\frac{4}{27}$ **5.** $\frac{1}{2}$ **7.** $\delta = \frac{1}{3600}$ **9.** $\lim_{c} [f(x) - g(x)] = \lim_{c} f(x) - \lim_{c} g(x)$ **11.** $\lim_{c} \frac{1}{g(x)} = \frac{1}{\lim_{c} g(x)}$ **13.** $\lim_{c} [f(x)]^n = [\lim_{c} f(x)]^n$

Page 434 Exploratory Exercises 1. The function is discontinuous at $x = 0$. **3.** The function is discontinuous at $-1 < x < 6$.

Page 435 Written Exercises Answers will vary for Problems **1–4.** Typical answers are given. **1.** $f(x) = 1$ **3.** $f(x) = \frac{1}{x - 3}$ **5.** $f(x) = \frac{1}{\sin \frac{x}{2}}$ **7.** Let $a \in D(f)$. The value of the function at a is given by $f(a) = c$. Given $\epsilon > 0$, choose $\delta = \epsilon$. Then $0 < |x - a| < \delta$ implies $|f(x) - f(a)| < \epsilon$. Since $|f(x) - f(a)| = |c - c| = 0$ for every $x \in D(f)$.

Page 436 Written Exercises 1. $\frac{1}{2}$ is a zero, $\frac{5}{8}$ is an approximate zero. **3.** $\frac{-3}{4}$ is a zero. **5.** $\frac{1}{4}$ is a zero. **7.** $\frac{9}{8}$

Page 437 Exploratory Exercises 1. 1 **3.** 1 **5.** -1

Page 438 Written Exercises 1. Given $\epsilon > 0$, chose $N = \frac{5}{3\epsilon}$ Then $x > N$ implies $x > \frac{5}{3\epsilon} > 0$ So that $0 < \frac{5}{3x} < \epsilon$ Hence $\left| \frac{5}{3x} \right| < \epsilon$. So, $\left| \frac{5}{3x} + \frac{2}{3} - \frac{2}{3} \right| < \epsilon$. Thus, $\left| \frac{2x + 5}{3x} - \frac{2}{3} \right| < \epsilon$. **3.** $\frac{4}{3}$ **5.** $\frac{2}{3}$ **7.** A limit does not exist.

Page 441 Written Exercises 3. 0 **5.** 0 **7.** 0

Page 442 Chapter Review 1. $|f(x) - 5| < 0.15$

or $f(x) \in \langle 4.85, 5.15 \rangle$ **3.** 0.002 **5.** 4 **7.** 31 **9.** $x = 3$ **11.** A zero is $-\frac{3}{4}$. **13.** $\frac{5}{7}$ **15.** 3

CHAPTER 15 RATES OF CHANGE

Page 449 Written Exercises 1. 45 ft/s **3.** $(40 + 10h)$ ft/s **5.** 81 ft/s **7.** As $h \to 0$, $(40 + 10h)$ ft/s $\to 40$ ft/s. **9.** If $t = 2$, $v = 40$ If $t = 3$, $v = 60$ If $t = 4$, $v = 80$ **11.** 4.4 s **13.** 15 in./s **15.** 12.3 in./s **17.** 18 in./s

Page 450 Challenge Exercises 3. 106 ft at $2\frac{1}{2}$ s, $v = 0$, $\left(2\frac{1}{2}, 106\right)$

Page 453 Exploratory Exercises

1. $\dfrac{(1 + h)^2 - 1^2}{h} = 2 + h$

3. $\dfrac{2(4 + h) + 1 - (2 \cdot 4 + 1)}{h} = 2$

5. $\dfrac{4(2 + h)^2 - 4(2)^2}{h} = 16 + 4h$

Page 453 Written Exercises 1. 2 **3.** 2 **5.** 16 **7.** 8 **9.** 2π cm/cm **11.** 12 mm³/mm

Page 453 Challenge Exercises 1. 24π cm²/cm

Page 456 Exploratory Exercises 1. $6x^5$ **3.** x **5.** $3ax^2$ **7.** 5 **9.** $2x + 2$

Page 456 Written Exercises 1. $2x + 6$ **3.** $-20x^4 + 18x^8$ **5.** $4x^3 - 18x^2 + 18x$ **7.** $6x^2 + 10x - 18$ **9.** $f'(0) = 1$, $f'\left(\frac{1}{2}\right) = 0$, $f'(1) = -1$, $f'(-10) = 21$ **11.** $2x$ **13.** $x = -3$ or $x = 2$ **15.** $-3 < x < 2$ **17.** $f(r) = \pi r^2$, $f'(r) = 2\pi r$

Page 457 Challenge Exercises No, the derivative of a product (quotient) is not the product (quotient) of the derivative. Let $f(x) = x^5$, $g(x) = x^2$, $h(x) = x^3$. Then $f(x) = g(x) \cdot h(x)$ and $g(x) = \dfrac{f(x)}{h(x)}$. But, $f'(x) = 5x^4$, $g'(x) = 2x$, $h'(x) = 3x^2$ So $g'(x) \cdot h'(x) = 2x \cdot 3x^2 = 6x^3 \ne f'(x)$ Also, $\dfrac{f'(x)}{h'(x)} = \dfrac{5x^4}{3x^2} = \dfrac{5}{3}x^2 \ne g'(x)$.

Page 459 Exploratory Exercises 1. 6 **3.** 8 **5.** 12

Page 459 Written Exercises 1. -8, $8x + y + 6 = 0$ **3.** 10, $10x - y - 8 = 0$ **5.** 0, $y = 5$ **7.** The tangent is $x - y - 1 = 0$ at $x = 2$. The x-intercept is $P(1, 0)$ and the y-intercept is $0(0, -1)$. The midpoint of $\overline{PQ}$ is $\left(\dfrac{1 + 0}{2}, \dfrac{0 - 1}{2}\right)$ or $\left(\dfrac{1}{2}, -\dfrac{1}{2}\right)$. **9.** If $f'(x) = 2x$ then $2x = 4$ has one solution, $x = 2$. The tangent with slope x is $4x - y + 1 = 0$. **11.** The tangent at $x = 1$ is $y = 3x - 2$. It meets the curve again at $(-2, -8)$.

Page 462 Exploratory Exercises 1. $\frac{3}{2}x^{1/2}$ **3.** $\frac{1}{2}x^{-1/2}$ **5.** $-6x^{-4}$ **7.** $\frac{1}{2}x^{-1/2}$ **9.** $\frac{2}{3}x^{-1/3}$

Page 462 Written Exercises 1. $-4x^{-5}$ **3.** $-6x^{-4}$ **5.** $-\frac{4}{3}x^{-3}$ **7.** $-\frac{4}{5}x^{-5}$ **9.** $-2x^{-2}$ **11.** $2x^2 - \frac{1}{4}x^{-2}$; $4x + \frac{1}{2}x^{-3}$ **13.** $8x^{3/4} - 6x^{-2/3}$; $6x^{-1/4} + 4x^{-5/3}$ **15.** $x^4 - 2 + x^{-4}$; $4x^3 - 4x^{-5}$ **17.** $2 - 3x^{-1} + 4x^{-3}$; $3x^{-2} - 12x^{-4}$ **19.** $2x + 2 + 2x^{-3}$ **21.** $f(x) = x^{1/2}(x^2 - x^{-2})$

$= x^{5/2} - x^{-3/2}$

$f'(x) = \dfrac{5}{2}x^{3/2} + \dfrac{3}{2}x^{-5/2}$

$= \dfrac{x^{5/2}}{2x^{5/2}}(5x^{3/2} + 3x^{-5/2})$

$= \dfrac{5x^4 + 3}{2x^{5/2}}$

27. $y = -2$ **29.** $f(x) = x^3 - 6x^2 + 12x + 1$ So $f'(x) = 3x^2 - 12x + 12 = 3(x^2 - 4x + 4) = 3(x - 2)^2 \ge 0$ for all $x \in \mathcal{R}$. Thus $f'(x)$ is never negative. $(2, 9)$ **31.** $f(x) = 8x^{1/2}$ so $f'(x) = 4x^{-1/2}$. If $x = 4$, $f'(x) = 2$ and $y = 16$. The tangent at $x = 4$ is $y - 16 = 2(x - 4)$ or $y = 2x + 8$. The tangent crosses the y-axis at $(0, 8)$.

Page 464 Exploratory Exercises 1. (1) increasing **3.** (2) decreasing **5.** (1) increasing

Page 465 Written Exercises 1. (1) $x > 0$ (2) $x < 0$ **3.** (1) $x < \frac{1}{2}$ (2) $x > \frac{1}{2}$ **5.** (1) $|x| > 1$ (2) $-1 < x < 1$ **7.** (1) $x < -1$ or $x > 3$ (2) $-1 < x < 3$ **9.** (1) $x > 3$ or $-3 < x < 0$ (2) $x < -3$ or $0 < x < 3$ **11.** (1) $x < -\frac{4}{3}$ or $x > 2$ (2) $-\frac{4}{3} < x < 2$

Page 465 Challenge Exercises 1. $f'(x) = 3x^2 +$

$1 > 0$ for all $x \in \mathcal{R}$, So the function is increasing for all $x \in \mathcal{R}$; $y = 4x + 4$; $(2, 12)$

Page 468 Exploratory Exercises 1. $(0, 0)$ **3.** $\left(\frac{1}{2}, \frac{1}{4}\right)$ **5.** $(1, -2)$ and $(-1, 2)$ **7.** $f(0)$ is an absolute minimum value. **9.** $f\left(\frac{1}{2}\right)$ is an absolute maximum value. **11.** $f(-1)$ is a relative maximum value and $f(1)$ is a relative minimum value.

Page 468 Written Exercises 1. $f(1)$ relative maximum value; $f(2)$, relative minimum value. **3.** $f(-3)$ and $f(3)$, relative minimums; $f(0)$, relative maximum. **5.** $f(-1)$, relative maximum; $f(1)$, relative minimum. **7.** $f(-2)$ relative maximum, and $f(2)$, relative minimum. **9.** $f(0)$, minimum and $f(-4) = f(4)$, maximums, for $x \in [-4, 4]$. **11.** $f(-3)$, minimum, and $f(3)$, maximum, for $x \in [-3, 3]$.

Page 470 Written Exercises

1.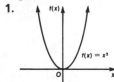

3.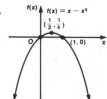

9.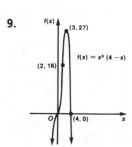

Page 471 Written Exercises 1. 45,000 m²
3. Let x = the height of the box.
Then $6 - 2x$ = the length of each side of the box.
$V = (6 - 2x)^2 x$ or $[2(3 - x)]^2x$ or $4x(3 - x)^2$.
16 cm³

5. The maximum height of 20 units is reached at 2 s. **9.** $t = 30$, $v = 654.5$ mph

Page 472 Challenge Exercise $\frac{20\sqrt{3}}{3}$ in. and $\frac{20\sqrt{6}}{3}$ in.

Page 473 Chapter Review 1. 110
3. $\lim\limits_{h \to 0} \dfrac{f(3 + h) - f(3)}{h} = \lim\limits_{h \to 0} \dfrac{20(3 + h)^2 - 20(3)^2}{h} =$ $\lim\limits_{h \to 0} \dfrac{20(9 + 6h + h^2)}{h} = \lim\limits_{h \to 0} 120 + 20h = 120$
5. 12 **7.** $2x^5$ **9.** $6x^2 - 4, 2$ **11.** $y = 10x - 16$
13. At $(3, -1)$ the equation of the tangent is $y = 9x - 27$. At $(-1, -4)$ the equation of the tangent is $y = 9x + 5$. **15.** $\frac{1}{3}x^{-2/3}$ **17.** $-3x^{-4}$ **19.** $-\frac{1}{3}x^{-4/3}$ **21.** 2 **23.** $(1, 0)$ **25. (a)** $x \in \mathcal{R}$ **(b)** $f(x)$ is decreasing for no x. **27.** $f(-2)$ is a relative maximum value and $f(2)$ is a relative minimum value. **31.** 28 cm²

CHAPTER 16 INTEGRALS

Page 480 Written Exercises 1. $42 < S < 68$
3. $45 < S < 55$ Divide $\overline{OA}$ into a greater number of congruent parts. **5.** $2025 < S < 3025$ **7.** $\left(\dfrac{b - a}{2}\right)\left[f(a) + f\left(\dfrac{a + b}{2}\right)\right] < S < \left(\dfrac{b - a}{2}\right)$ $\left[f\left(\dfrac{a + b}{2}\right) + f(b)\right]$ **9.** Their difference decreases.

Page 484 Written Exercises 1. $\frac{9}{2}$ **3.** 9 **5.** $\frac{81}{4}$
7. $\frac{1}{2}\left(b^2 - a^2\right)$ **9.** $\frac{1}{4}\left(b^4 - a^4\right)$

Page 486 Exploratory Exercises 1. $\displaystyle\int_0^1 x\, dx$
3. $\displaystyle\int_0^1 x^2\, dx$ **5.** $\displaystyle\int_a^b x^2\, dx$

Page 487 Written Exercises 1. The height is multiplied by 4. **3.** The area of the region is multiplied by 4. **5.** 64 **7.** $\frac{14}{3}$

9.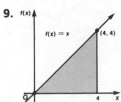

11.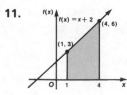

13. The area bounded by the y-axis, the line $x = 3$, the x-axis, and the curve of $y = \sqrt{9 - x^2}$ which is a semicircle. **15.** The area bounded by the y-axis, the line $x = 1$, the x-axis, and the curve of $y = x^2(1 - x)$. **17.** The areas are the same but on opposite sides of the x-axis. The integrals have different signs. **19.** $\int_{2}^{8} \frac{1}{x}\, dx$

Page 489 Exploratory Exercises 1. $\int_{0}^{2} x^2\, dx$ **3.** $\int_{0}^{9} \sqrt{x}\, dx$ **5.** $\int_{0}^{2} (2x - x^2)\, dx$

Page 489 Written Exercises

1.

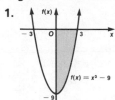

$f(x) = x^2 - 9$

3.

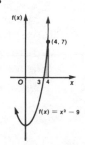

$(4, 7)$

$f(x) = x^2 - 9$

5. The value of $\int_{-2}^{2} (x^4 - 2x^2 - 8)\,dx$ is twice the value of $\int_{0}^{2} (x^4 - 2x^2 - 8)\,dx$.; $-29.8\overline{6}$ **7.** $\int_{-2}^{2} x^3\, dx = 0$ **9.** Each curve is symmetric with respect to the midpoint of the x-axis in the interval.

Page 495 Written Exercises 1. $x^3 + 2x^2 + 7x + C$ **3.** $2x^3 - x + C$ **5.** $x - \frac{x^2}{2} + C$ **7.** $\frac{x^4}{4} - \frac{x^3}{3} - x^2 + C$ **9.** $\frac{x^3}{3} - 2x - x^{-1} + C$ **11.** $\frac{x^3}{3} + 2x - x^{-1} + C$ **13.** $3x^{4/3} - \frac{3}{2}x^{2/3} + C$ **15.** $\frac{8}{7}x^{7/4} + \frac{4}{3}x^{3/4} + C$ **17.** $x^2 - 6$ **19.** $2x^3$ **21.** $x = 2x^{1/2} + 1$

Page 495 Challenge Exercises 1. $2x^{1/2} + 2x + \frac{2}{3}x^{3/2} + C$ or $2\sqrt{x} + 2x + \frac{2x\sqrt{x}}{3} + C$

Page 496 Written Exercises 1. $f(x) = 2x^2 + 1$ **3.** $x^3 - 5x^2 + 6$ **5.** $3x^2 - x^3 + 6$ **9.** $v = -10t + 15$ **11.** $v = \frac{t^3}{3} + t^2$, 18 m/s

Page 498 Exploratory Exercises 1. 4 **3.** $\frac{1}{3}$ **5.** $2\frac{2}{3}$

Page 498 Written Exercises 1. 5 **3.** 2 **5.** 21 **7.** -3 **9.** $345\frac{2}{3}$ **11.** $\frac{p^2}{2} + \frac{4p\sqrt{p}}{3} + p$ **13.** -496 **15.** 0 or $\frac{3}{2}$ **17.** 9 **19.** $\frac{16}{3}$

Page 499 Challenge Exercises 1. 128

Page 501 Written Exercises 1. 0.6956 **3.** 0.8802 **5.** 6.75; 6.$\overline{6}$

Page 503 Exploratory Exercises 1. $\int_{0}^{4} 3\,dx = 12$ **3.** $\int_{0}^{4} 2x\, dx = 16$ **5.** $4\frac{1}{3}$ **7.** $1\frac{1}{3}$ **9.** $\frac{1}{20}$

Page 504 Written Exercises 1. $\int_{0}^{4} (4 - x)\,dx = 8$ **3.** $\int_{1}^{3} 3x^2\,dx = 26$ **5.** $\int_{0}^{9} \sqrt{x}\, dx = 18$ **7.** $\int_{0}^{2} (2x - x^2)\,dx = 1\frac{1}{3}$ **9.** This area is unbounded. **17.** $4\frac{1}{2}$ **19.** $A(0, -5)$; $B(1, 0)$; $C(5, 0)$; 13

Page 507 Chapter Review 1. 1 **3.** 8 **5.** $14\frac{2}{3}$ **7.** $x^3 - 4x^2 + 5x + C$ **9.** $\frac{x^2}{2} - x + C$ **11.** $F(x) = 4x^2 - 3x + 3$ **13.** $x^3 - \frac{1}{x^2} + C$ **15.** $2x^2 - \frac{8}{3}x^{3/2} + x + C$ **17.** $y = 2x^2 + 4x^{-1} + 1$ **19.** 3 **21.** $-2 + \sqrt{5}$ **23.** 15

$y = 2x + 4$

$(2, 8)$

$(-1, 2)$

25. $4\frac{1}{2}$

27. 36 **29.** $21\frac{1}{3}$

List of Symbols

$f(x)$	f of x or the value of function f at x	$\vec{v}$ or $\overline{AB}$	a vector or directed line segment
$f'(x)$	f prime of x or the derivative of f at x	$\|\vec{v}\|$	magnitude of the vector v
$f''(x)$	*the second derivative of $f(x)$*	$\vec{a} \cdot \vec{b}$	inner product or dot product of vectors a and b
$f \circ g$ or $f(g(x))$	composite of functions f and g	$\vec{a} \times \vec{b}$	cross product of vectors a and b
$\lim\limits_{x \to a}$	the limit as x approaches a	∞	infinity
		i	$\sqrt{-1}$
$\triangle ABC$	triangle ABC	$a + bi$	complex number
$\overset{\frown}{RTS}$	arc RTS	e	base of natural logarithms; ≈ 2.718
$\angle ABC$	angle ABC		
$m \angle ABC$	measure of angle ABC	$n!$	n factorial
AB	measure of line segment AB	$\ln x$	logarithm of x to the base e; natural logarithm
$\overline{AB}$	line segment AB		
$|n|$	the absolute value of n	$\log_a x$	logarithm of x to the base a
x^n	the nth power of x	$\log x$	logarithm of x to the base 10
$\sqrt{x}$	the square root of x	$\dfrac{dy}{dx}$	the derivative of y with respect to x
$\sqrt[n]{x}$ or $x^{\frac{1}{n}}$	the nth root of x		
$[x]$	greatest integer not greater than x	$\int$	integral
		Σ	sigma (summation)
A^{-1}	inverse of A	$\langle a, b \rangle$	open interval a, b
$\begin{pmatrix} a \\ b \end{pmatrix}$	vector with components a and b	$[a, b]$	closed interval a, b
		$\to$	maps to
		$\in$	is an element of

Greek Alphabet

Letters		Name	Letters		Name	Letters		Name
A	α	Alpha	I	ι	Iota	P	ρ	Rho
B	β	Beta	K	κ	Kappa	Σ	σ	Sigma
Γ	γ	Gamma	Λ	λ	Lambda	T	τ	Tau
Δ	δ	Delta	M	μ	Mu	Υ	υ	Upsilon
E	ϵ	Epsilon	N	ν	Nu	Φ	ϕ	Phi
Z	ζ	Zeta	Ξ	ξ	Xi	X	χ	Chi
H	η	Eta	O	o	Omicron	Ψ	ψ	Psi
Θ	θ	Theta	Π	π	Pi	Ω	ω	Omega

Index